BARRY G. KING, Ph. D.

Environmental Control Administration,
U.S. Public Health Service, Cincinnati, Ohio;
Formerly Associate Professor of Physiology,
Ohio State University School of Medicine;
Lecturer in Physiology, University of Maryland;
Assistant Professor of Physiology, College of
Physicians and Surgeons, Columbia University

MARY JANE SHOWERS, R.N., Ph. D.

Professor of Anatomy, Hahnemann Medical
College and Hospital, Philadelphia

197 ILLUSTRATIONS BY LUCILLE CASSELL INNES

1969

HUMAN ANATOMY AND PHYSIOLOGY

SIXTH EDITION / 312 ILLUSTRATIONS, 69 IN COLOR

W. B. SAUNDERS COMPANY • Philadelphia • London • Toronto

W. B. Saunders Company: West Washington Square
Philadelphia, Pa.   19105

12 Dyott Street
London W.C.1

1835 Yonge Street
Toronto 7, Ontario

Human Anatomy and Physiology

PREFACE

The preface of the fifth edition states that the objective of this text is to help the student acquire requisite knowledge of normal development, structures, and functions of man. The authors continue in this objective in the preparation of the sixth edition. "Requisite knowledge," however, needs redefining according to the present time. Our concern for health and social problems, combined with technical advances in overcoming the stresses acting within our customary environment as well as within space, aquatic, and other exotic environments, has focused attention on the life sciences and behavioral sciences. For many years it has been recognized that anatomy and physiology are essential to professional training in medicine, nursing, and agriculture. It is now apparent that their usefulness has extended to many other fields within the behavioral, social, and health sciences, to law, physical education, physical therapy, medical and dental technology, and to several other paramedical specialties. This text is designed to provide a foundation for the undergraduate college and university student and to serve as a point of departure for advanced studies in specialized areas in a number of fields of endeavor.

The revision has involved rewriting most of the material, rearrangement of the sections, forming new combinations within the sections, and introduction of new material. Unit One is concerned with fundamental definitions, organization of the body as a whole, the internal environment, physiological processes, and cell structure, function and specialization. The following five sections are organized on the basis of the functions and correlative structural adaptations subserved by the various systems of the body. Thus Unit Two is concerned with integration and control of the body; Unit Three is on biomechanics; Unit Four deals with exchange and transport; Unit Five describes metabolism, and Unit Six traces reproduction and growth of the individual.

In revising the text, major emphasis has been placed upon improving the teaching value of the presentations, expanding discussions of physiological function, and introducing the student to cellular and molecular biology, including selected aspects of genetics.

Extensive revision and rearrangement have been made in the method of presentation of material on the cranial nerves and special senses; the bones of the axial and appendicular skeleton; the skeletal muscles and their associated articulations and axes of motion, and on the vascular circuits. The data pertinent to the particular part, structure, or circuit are given in the figure description of the illustration associated with it. This arrangement is designed to provide a simultaneous visual aid to assist the student in relating the text to the structure. The proximity of the illustrations to the text enables the student visually to verify the parts, relations, and dimensions as described in the text. The discussions of kidney function (formation of urine), digestion, metabolism, muscular contraction, and respiration are examples of more comprehensive discussions of physiological function. New material on acid-base balance, pH, and enzymes has been added. Sections on cellular and molecular biology have been introduced because of the advances and greatly increased interest in these fields, and because of their teaching value in understanding complex biological systems.

In spite of the extended coverage of the material in this sixth edition the length of the book is less than that of earlier editions. This is partly due to arrangement and partly to elimination, insofar as possible, of all except substantive matter in presenting a subject. Summaries at the ends of the chapters have been deleted since the method of presentation of the material has rendered them unnecessary.

Of the 312 illustrations 100 have been modified or corrected, and 49 new drawings have been added.

As in prior editions, the questions at the end of each chapter have been formulated to encourage students to develop a concept of relevancy of the information acquired as their instruction progresses. These questions are not designed to evaluate the student's acquisition of information; indeed many questions are constructed so that there is no one "correct" answer. Thus, discussions can be adjusted to reveal understanding and to provide for a continuous integration of the concepts presented throughout the book.

BARRY GRIFFITH KING
MARY JANE C. SHOWERS

ACKNOWLEDGMENTS

The authors are indebted to our associates in physiology and anatomy, who, though use of this text and sensitivity to student comments and needs, have advised us of needed corrections and have made constructive suggestions for its improvement. Grateful acknowledgment is due Dr. Charles A. Hoffman for his comprehensive and detailed review of the earlier edition. We wish to thank Dr. Edward B. Steen for his helpful comments and Dr. George F. Piltz for review and suggestions about portions of the manuscript. Miss Majorie Stodgell has sedulously given her efforts to maintain artistic continuity in the additions made to original illustrations drawn by Mrs. Lucille Cassell Innes. We are indebted to our publishers, W. B. Saunders Company, for the careful attention that they gave to the difficult and demanding task of arranging the format to follow the authors' presentation on cranial nerves and special senses, skeletal support and muscular movements, and vascular circuits of the human body.

BARRY GRIFFITH KING
MARY JANE C. SHOWERS

CONTENTS

UNIT 5 METABOLISM

UNIT 6 REPRODUCTION OF THE HUMAN BEING

HUMAN ANATOMY
AND PHYSIOLOGY

UNIT 1

THE BODY AS AN INTEGRATED WHOLE

1. THE BODY AS A WHOLE   2. THE CELL AND ITS ENVIRONMENT   3. CELL STRUCTURE AND FUNCTION   4. CELLULAR SPECIALIZATION

Unit One introduces the sciences of anatomy and physiology. It is intended to provide a general, if somewhat elementary, overall account of the structure and functions of the body. This is necessary because the interrelations of the parts and systems of the body are so close that understanding of any one function or system requires some knowledge of all systems. The introductory material is presented to provide this knowledge so that, in the discussion of a single part or system, the necessary references to other functions or systems will have meaning.

Since the body as a whole is an aggregation of cells, the structure of the cell, its chemical composition, its physical nature and its method of division or reproduction are described in detail.

Considerable emphasis has been placed on the discussion of basic principles and mechanisms of physiological functioning of body cells, tissues, and systems. These sections are intended to provide an introduction to the fundamentals early in the study of anatomy and physiology. They are also intended to serve a more important function as a source of reference for the student as he continues in his studies. By repeated reference and review, the student can learn to recognize the involvement of these fundamentals in physiological processes and can develop a degree of *understanding* that could not be obtained by other means.

The cellular specializations which involve epithelial and connective tissues are discussed in this unit because they are widely distributed throughout the body and form important building materials in all parts.

THE BODY AS A WHOLE

CHAPTER ONE

ANATOMY AND PHYSIOLOGY— DEFINITIONS AND SUBDIVISIONS

In contrast with art, which implies *doing*, science implies *understanding*. In the early days of science *physiologia*, from which the term *physiology* is derived, was the science concerned with "the nature of all things." As detailed knowledge and understanding of physiologia or natural philosophy increased, an increasing number of scientific disciplines became recognized. Biology is the broad field of science encompassing the knowledge of *living* things. The science of anatomy, which teaches an understanding of the architecture of the body as a whole and the structure and relation of its parts, is a biological science. Physiology is also a biological science. It is concerned with an understanding of the mechanisms by which the body performs its various functions or, more simply, how it works. Because of the recognition and increasing emphasis on the importance of the cell as a unit of biological structure and function, cell biology or cell physiology and molecular biology have become distinct scientific disciplines. The sciences and their subdivisions with which we will be principally concerned in this text include:

Gross or *macroscopic* anatomy—the study of structures that can be distinguished with the unaided eye.

Microscopic anatomy or *histology*—the study of minute structure, composition, and function of tissues.

Embryology—the study of development of the embryo, which, in the case of man, involves the period of development from origin to the end of the second month.

Human physiology—a branch of mamma-

5

lian physiology concerned with an understanding of the mechanisms by which the human body performs its functions.

Biophysics — the study of the physical composition and structure of living materials and the physical principles, such as the laws of mechanics, radiation, and thermodynamics.

Cell biology — the study of the structure, life activities, and physical and chemical mechanisms of the function of the cell.

Molecular biology — the study of the configuration of molecules and intramolecular constituents of the cellular system.

Knowledge developed by these and other scientific disciplines will be brought together to contribute to an understanding of structure and function. The student should have had preliminary courses in the biological sciences and elementary physics and chemistry.

PLAN OF THE HUMAN BODY*

Man's body shows bilateral symmetry; that is, in general form, the two sides of the body are the mirror images of each other.

In describing the body, precise terms are used to denote position and describe the location of parts. These are shown in Figures 1.1 and 1.2. Some of the more important descriptive terms are listed in Table 1.1. In defining the terms it is assumed in the case of man that he is in the *anatomic position*, that is, standing erect, with the arms at the sides and the palms of the hands turned forward.

Cavities. Internal body structure in the vertebrate is characterized by two body cavities (Fig. 1.3).

The *dorsal* cavity, which contains the brain and spinal cord, is divided into the *cranial* cavity, formed by the bones of the

---

*The student is encouraged to refer frequently to the transparencies following page 18, in addition to other figures referred to in his study of body parts, their locations and anatomic relations.

skull, and the *vertebral* cavity, formed by the vertebrae.

The *ventral* cavity of man is divided into the thoracic and abdominopelvic cavities by the diaphragm (Figs. 1.3, 1.4). The *thoracic* cavity is subdivided into the pericardial cavity, which contains the heart, and the pleural cavities, which contain the lungs. Trachea, bronchi, esophagus, thymus gland, blood and lymph vessels lie between these subdivisions in the thoracic cavity. The *abdominopelvic* cavity has two portions which are continuous — an upper abdominal part and a lower pelvic portion. The abdominal portion contains the liver, gallbladder, stomach, spleen, pancreas, and small and large intestines. The pelvic portion contains the bladder, rectum, and sigmoid colon. In the female the pelvic portion has, in addition, the ovaries, uterine tubes, and uterus; in the male, the prostate gland, seminal vesicles, and a part of the ductus deferens. The organs contained in any of the ventral body cavities are called *viscera*.

Organization of the Body. The cell is both the structural and the functional unit of the body. In spite of great variations in appearance and consistency, all parts of the body are aggregates of many of these units. During the early stages of the development of the embryo the cells look alike. They are known as undifferentiated or embryonal cells. Soon, however, they begin to show changes in structure; this process is called *differentiation*. As the structural changes occur, groups of cells become specialized in function; that is, they perform chiefly one type of physiologic activity. Such differentiation and *specialization* of groups of cells result in the formation of the tissues of the body. A *tissue* may be defined as an organization of like cells, performing a special bodily function, bound together with intercellular substance and bathed by extracellular, i.e., *interstitial*, fluid.

There are four primary tissues. *Epithelial* tissue forms the covering of the body, the lining of its parts and the secreting portions of glands. *Connective* tissue forms the supporting framework of the body and binds the parts together; vascular and lymphatic tissue, which arises from the same

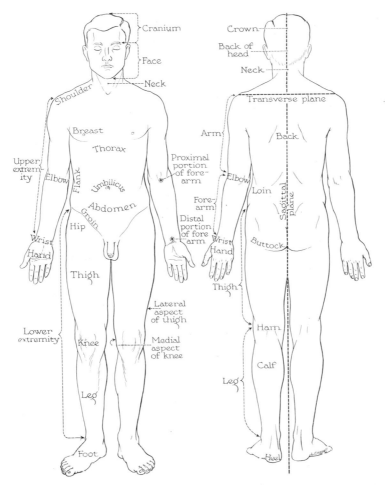

Figure 1.1 Human figure in anatomical position; planes of reference; parts of the body.

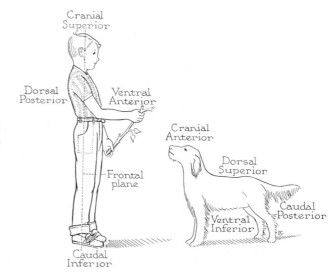

Figure 1.2 Terminology of quadruped and man compared. Frontal plane is shown.

TABLE 1.1 DESCRIPTIVE TERMS USED IN ANATOMY

Terms	Name	Explanation	
Plane or section	Sagittal	Vertical plane or section, dividing body into right and left portions	
	Midsagittal	Vertical at midline; dividing body into right and left halves	
	Frontal or Coronal	Vertical, but at right angles to sagittal sections, dividing body into anterior (front) and posterior (back) portions	
	Transverse	Horizontal, hence at right angles to both sagittal and frontal sections, dividing body into upper and lower portions	
Surface or relative position	Anterior or Ventral	*Man* Front of body, hence on or nearest abdominal surface	*Quadrupeds* Anterior—head end Ventral—abdominal or lower surface
	Posterior or Dorsal	Back of body	Posterior—tail end Dorsal—back
	Superior Inferior	Upper or higher Lower	
Relative position or direction	Cranial (Craniad) or Cephalic (Cephalad)	Nearest or toward the head	
	Caudal (Caudad)	Away from the head	
	Medial (Mesad)	Middle or nearest the midsagittal plane	
	Lateral (Laterally)	Side or farthest from midsagittal plane	
	Proximal (Proximally)	Near the source or attachment	
	Distal (Distally)	Away from source or attachment	
	Afferent	In relation to nerves or blood vessels—conducting toward structure or organ	
	Efferent	Conducting away from structure or organ	

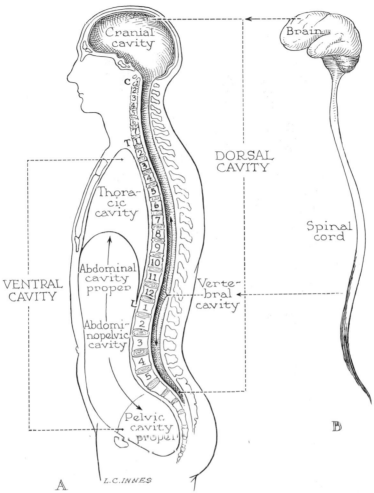

Figure 1.3 Body cavities as seen in a midsagittal section of head and trunk. *A*, Diagram of midsagittal section of head and trunk, showing vertebral column and body cavities. *B*, Organs of the dorsal cavity.

more primitive parent material as connective tissue, performs the functions of transporting substances throughout the body and providing the immediate environment of the cell. *Muscular* tissue is specialized for the performance of work by its ability to shorten or contract. *Nervous* tissue, because of its specialized properties of irritability and conductivity, may carry electrochemical impulses to all parts of the body, thus coordinating its functions.

Two or more tissues grouped together, which perform a highly specialized function, form an *organ*. The stomach, the heart, and the lungs are organs. On examining the stomach, for example, we find that it is made up of all the types of tissues; it is covered and lined with epithelial tissue; connective and muscular tissues form the stomach walls; and nervous tissue is distributed throughout its structure. The stomach carries out early stages of digestion and passes the ingested materials along to the small intestine. Thus the organ, a combination of tissues, performs specialized functions not accomplished by the separate tissues.

Groups of organs that act together to perform highly complex but specialized functions are called *systems*. Thus the en-

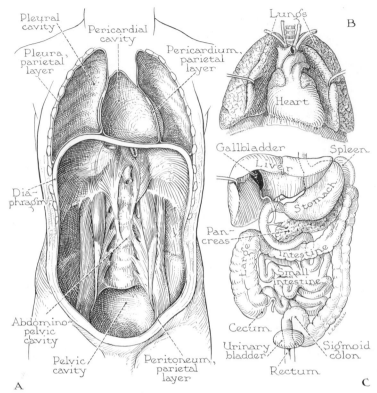

Figure 1.4 *A*, Front view of the trunk, showing subdivisions of the ventral cavity. *B*, Organs of the thoracic cavity. *C*, Organs of the abdominopelvic cavity.

tire process of digestion is carried out through the coordinated activity of the organs of the digestive system. Nine body systems are commonly recognized: the skeletal, muscular, circulatory, respiratory, digestive, excretory, endocrine, reproductive, and nervous systems. A brief description of each follows. In succeeding chapters we shall study the cell, the tissues, and then again in detail the different systems in which each organ will be considered.

SOME CHARACTERISTICS OF BODY SYSTEMS AND FUNCTIONS

The systems of the body can be grouped according to the general class of function they serve. These are integration and control, biomechanics, exchange and transport, metabolism, and reproduction.

INTEGRATION AND CONTROL

The nervous system and the endocrine system share in the control of all the activities of the body tissues. For the most part, the nervous system controls the more rapid responses of the body to changes in the outside world or external environment. The endocrine system, on the other hand, more frequently controls the slower changes or adaptations of the body to its environment.

The Nervous System. The function of the nervous system is to coordinate activities of the body. It provides for the mechanism through which the body responds to the outside world in avoiding injury, obtaining food, and performing many other more complex acts. The control of responses and behavior may be voluntary or may be below the level of consciousness, i.e., without voluntary effort or awareness that a reaction has been initiated, as in reflex movement and visceral response.

The brain, spinal cord, nerves, and ganglia constitute the nervous system. The nervous system in the process of its formation develops from a tube. Knowledge of this factor in development is of importance in visualizing the architecture of the brain and spinal cord as enclosing a continuous cavity. In the brain the parts of this cavity are called ventricles; in the spinal cord, where it is relatively small, the cavity is called the central canal.

The brain and the spinal cord — that is, the structures contained in the dorsal body cavity (Fig. 1.3) — constitute the *central* nervous system. Those parts of the nervous system lying outside the dorsal body cavity constitute the *peripheral* nervous system.

The brain is made up of the *cerebrum*, which includes the cerebral hemispheres (endbrain); the *diencephalon* (interbrain); the *midbrain*; and the *cerebellum*, the *pons*, and the *medulla oblongata* (hindbrain). The cerebral hemispheres contain the higher centers, including those concerned with sensations, associative memory, and other forms of consciousness. Other parts of the forebrain mediate complex reflexes or activities which are not directly concerned with consciousness. The midbrain contains principally the tracts, or nerve pathways, between the forebrain and parts of the hindbrain and the spinal cord, and important cell relay stations, i.e., nuclei or "centers." The cerebellum is an elaborate integrating system, especially for muscular activity. The pons, or bridge, is chiefly made up of pathways between the halves of the cerebellum. The medulla oblongata contains all the nerve pathways which connect the spinal cord to the higher parts of the nervous system; it includes important nerve centers, such as the "center" for breathing.

SENSE ORGANS. Man receives his information concerning the outside world through his sense organs, which are specialized endings of the sensory division of the peripheral nerves. The eyes, the ears, and the membranes of the nose contain such specialized endings. They give information concerning objects in the outside world which are at a distance from the body. The skin contains receptors for touch, temperature, and pain, which give information about objects in contact with the body.

The sensory receptors respond to a variety of conditions, but the basic factor in all the conditions is a sudden change in the environment. This sudden change, which constitutes a *stimulus*, excites the sensory receptors. If a piece of ice is suddenly placed against the skin, it causes a sudden change in environment of the body and the sensation of cold results. If an object passes in front of the eyes, the changes in the intensity of the light stimulate the nerve endings in the eye. Blows or electric shocks may constitute stimuli.

In addition to the receptors which give information as to the outside world, there are receptors which give information as to conditions or activity within the body. We are aware of the position of an arm or a leg without looking at it. This information is supplied by the *proprioceptors*, which are nerve endings that register muscle tension and sense of position. The proprioceptors in the muscles not only supply information as to the condition of the muscles, but through numerous connections aid in controlling the energy and extent of muscular activity. Proprioceptors in the inner ear aid in maintenance of balance.

The body acts upon a great part of the information received by the receptors. Stimulation of a sensory nerve may bring about activity of muscles or glands, since there are physiologic connections between the sensory nerves and motor nerves (the nerves capable of causing movement or activity).

A response to a stimulus may be either voluntary or reflex. Most harmful stimuli, unless they are expected, cause reflex responses. The harmful stimuli, which are so intense that they may cause injury, bring about a rapid reaction because they travel over a direct and relatively uncomplicated pathway. In the reflex (involuntary) response the nerve impulse resulting from the stimulus travels over a series of connecting neurons from a receiving structure (receptor), into the central nervous system and out to a responding structure (effector). This pathway, which forms the physical basis of the reflex, is called a *reflex arc*.

THE AUTONOMIC NERVOUS SYSTEM. Though skeletal muscle is under control of the central nervous system and its peripheral nerves, all other functions of body tissues are controlled by the autonomic nervous system. We are not generally conscious of such activities as the heart beat, the contraction of the smooth muscles of the blood vessels and digestive tract, or the secretion of glands, all of which are under autonomic control. These activities are regulated for the most part by two sets of nerves to a single structure, one set causing increased activity, the other causing decreased activity (inhibition). The performance of the structure is a result of the combined effect of both these influences.

The Endocrine System. The endocrine system is composed of the glands of internal secretion. These are the hypophysis, the thyroid, the parathyroids, and the suprarenals, together with the islet cells of the pancreas and parts of the stomach, duodenum, ovaries, and testes (Fig. 9.1, p. 135). The secretions of the endocrine or ductless glands are taken up directly by the blood stream, in contrast to the exocrine glands, which empty their secretions into ducts.

BIOMECHANICS

The biomechanical functions can be described in broad terms as involving movement of the body and its parts and maintenance of body posture. The musculoskeletal system's functions involve the skeleton and the voluntary muscles. Activities of muscles which are not under voluntary control serve other systems of the body.

The Skeletal System. The skeletal system serves as the bony framework for attachment of voluntary muscles and for support and protection of the more delicate organs. It is composed of bones held together by ligaments.

The Muscular System. There are three types of muscle: the quick-acting *voluntary* or *skeletal muscles*, the more slowly acting *smooth muscle* of the blood vessels and the viscera, and the *cardiac* or *heart muscle*.

The *skeletal muscle* tissue forms the organs of the muscular system. These muscles are, with few exceptions, attached to two or more bones. They are capable of various degrees of shortening or contraction. Contractions of the muscles attached to the bones of the thigh and leg act across the knee joint. When several of these muscle groups shorten just enough to cause tension — that is, *muscle tone* — they keep the knee in a fixed position and aid in maintaining a standing posture. When the muscle groups which act to bend the leg and those which act to straighten the leg contract alternately, and shorten to a greater extent than when merely maintaining posture, they cause movement of the body.

The skeletal muscles are under voluntary control. This does not mean that all the coordinated activities of the muscle groups used in making a movement must be consciously directed. It is more probable that, once the voluntary movement is started, the degree of the contractions and finely coordinated activity of the many muscles involved is controlled to a large extent through nerve endings in the key muscles.

Muscle groups that cause opposite effects when acting across a joint are said to act antagonistically. Thus the muscles which shorten when bending the arm are *antagonistic* to those which shorten when straightening the arm. Muscles which contract together to carry out a certain movement are said to be *synergistic*.

The architecture of a skeletal muscle is such that some of the fibers making up a single muscle may contract while other fibers are at rest. This results in an economy of energy for contractions just sufficiently strong to maintain posture.

Smooth muscle tissue forms parts of other systems, such as the digestive and circulatory systems. The smooth muscle in the walls of the blood vessels is important in altering the size of the vessel. In the viscera the extent of the contraction of the muscle alters the capacity of the organ. Thus the muscles of the stomach, by relaxing, may increase its capacity to accommodate the food taken at a meal. Contraction of the muscles diminishes its size and empties the stomach during digestion.

Heart muscle tissue forms an organ; together with smooth muscle it makes up a major part of the circulatory system. Heart muscle is responsible for pumping blood through the blood vessels. The architecture of cardiac muscle is such that all fibers act together, in contrast to the fibers of skeletal muscle, which may act independently of one another.

EXCHANGE AND TRANSPORT

Exchange and transport of materials within the body and between the body and the outside world are accomplished through the integrated activities of the respiratory, circulatory, and urinary systems. Together they maintain the internal environment of the cells and body tissues within the limits necessary for survival and for physiologic functions. These systems control the acidity, i.e., the hydrogen ion concentration of the blood and other body fluids, as well as such other critical factors as water balance and electrolytes or salt balance, and heat exchange.

The Circulatory System. The function of the circulatory system is to provide for the transport of gases, nutrient materials, and other essential substances to the tissues and the subsequent transport of waste products from the cells to the appropriate sites for their excretion. The circulatory system includes the heart, the blood vessels, and the lymphatics.

The heart pumps blood through an elastic system of blood vessels. The blood vessels form a continuous closed system made up of three main divisions. The *arterial* system carries blood away from the heart to a vast network of minute vessels, the *capillaries*. From the capillaries the blood is collected and returned to the heart by the *venous* system.

The blood in the arteries carries oxygen from the lungs to all the tissues of the body. Nutrient material is also distributed throughout the body by the circulation. Waste products are collected from all the body tissues and carried to the excretory organs.

There is, however, a "middleman" in any exchange between the blood stream and the tissues. Some of the fluid portion of the blood, the plasma, passes through the capillary walls to form the *tissue fluid*. Oxygen, nutrient and other materials pass through the thin-walled capillary system into the tissue fluid which bathes all the cells of the body. These substances pass from the tissue fluid into the cells, while waste products pass in the opposite direction. A circulation of the fluid is achieved as it is returned to the blood stream through a system of lymphatic vessels.

Great variations in the blood supply in any part of the body may be brought about by the nervous system and other systems of the body acting upon the heart and blood vessels. The heart beat can be increased to pump more blood, or the same amount of blood at a higher pressure. The blood supply to any part of the body may be altered by an increase or decrease in the size of the blood vessels in that area. Changes in the caliber of the vessels are brought about by the action of the nervous system and by chemical means.

The Respiratory System. The functions performed by the respiratory system provide for absorption of oxygen and elimination of carbon dioxide from the body. Two processes are involved. One is called external respiration, i.e., ventilation of the lungs or breathing, and the exchange of gases between the lungs and the blood. The other process, internal respiration, involves exchanges between the cells and the body fluids. Accessory functions of the respiratory system are talking, sneezing, and coughing.

The respiratory system comprises the nose, pharynx, larynx, trachea, bronchi, and lungs. The first five structures form the air passages connecting the lungs with the outside air. The muscles of respiration, chiefly the diaphragm, enlarge the chest cavity by their contractions so that fresh air flows into the air spaces of the lungs. Oxygen then passes through the air sacs or alveoli of the lungs into the capillary blood vessels of the lungs. At the same time carbon dioxide passes from the capillaries into the air spaces. Relaxation of the inspiratory muscles diminishes the size of the chest, and the air is expired.

The Urinary System. The function of the urinary system is the selective excretion of water, salts, products of catabolism, and foreign substances. The kidneys, ureters, and urethra comprise the system.

The kidney filters the fluid portion of the blood into a system of small tubes. The waste products and products foreign to the body, which are dissolved in water, are carried to the bladder and excreted as urine. Many substances, important to the body economy, are reabsorbed through the tubules together with sufficient water to maintain the concentration of the body fluids at a relatively constant level.

Additional excretory functions are carried out by organs in other systems. Water is lost from the lungs and the skin. Carbon dioxide is dispelled through the lungs. Bacteria, cast-off cells from the lining of the digestive tract, some secretions and indigestible parts of the diet are eliminated through the intestines as feces.

METABOLISM

Metabolism includes the complex functions involved in the release and utilization of chemical energy by the body. The original source of this energy is the radiant energy of the sun which is stored in plants during the process of photosynthesis. Metabolic processes transform the chemical energy into work and heat. The two principal processes involved are *catabolism* and *anabolism*. Catabolism is the breakdown of nutrients and endogenous material (cells and tissues). Anabolism is the synthesis of complex constituents of cells from simpler compounds for various uses, including building materials for growth and repair of the body, for storage of nutrients, and for elaboration of biological substances such as enzymes, hormones, and vitamins.

The Digestive System. The digestive system prepares nutrient materials for the metabolic functions carried out by the cells. It consists of the mouth, pharynx, esophagus, stomach, and the small and large intestines. Accessory structures are the teeth, hard and soft palate, and the salivary glands associated with the mouth. Three pairs of salivary glands pour their secretions through ducts into the mouth. The liver, gallbladder, and pancreas are accessory structures associated with the small intestine.

Food entering the body is acted upon mechanically and chemically in the digestive system in such a way that it is reduced to a state in which the body may draw upon it for energy and for material for growth and repair of the tissues.

The stomach acts primarily as a storage reservoir for food. The early stages of digestion are brought about by chemical and mechanical action in the stomach. By far the greater part of absorption takes place in the small intestine. The mechanical movements not only aid in the division of the food, but control the rate at which food passes through the digestive tract. If the passage occurs too rapidly, there is not sufficient time for absorption of the foodstuffs.

REPRODUCTION

The term reproduction is used to describe the functions that provide for continuation of the species. It also has another meaning, i.e., the increase in the number of cells of the body.

The Reproductive System. The functions of the system are perpetuation of the species and production of cells for growth and repair of the organism.

The reproductive system in the female is composed of the ovaries, uterine tubes, uterus, vagina, and the external genitalia. In the male the organs are the testis, epididymis, ductus deferens, seminal vesicle, and ejaculatory duct, which are all paired structures, and the prostate gland, penis, and urethra.

QUESTIONS FOR DISCUSSION

1. Describe the location of the following parts of the body with respect to plane,

and give their position and direction in relation to two or more prominent body structures: ear, elbow, palm of hand, heel.

2. What are the names of the cavities of the body and what are the organs they contain? Relate the organs to the system and general function.

3. Discuss the statement, "The cell is the structural and functional unit of the body."

4. What systems participate in exchange and transport? What systems participate in the elimination of waste products?

5. Trace a molecule of oxygen from the time it is taken into the body until the time it is utilized.

THE CELL AND ITS ENVIRONMENT

CHAPTER TWO

The internal environment of man lies between the outermost layer of the skin and membranes that constitute the external covering of the body, and the interface between the lumen of the digestive tract and its mucous membranes, which are essentially the inner cover of the tissues and body fluids. All the living material of the human body is contained within this space. Differences exist in the chemical composition of the fluids within the different compartments of the internal environment, e.g., the circulatory systems, the extracellular spaces, and the space within the cell. However, free cells, e.g., blood cells, and aggregates of cells forming tissues can survive and function only if their physical-chemical environment is maintained within physiologic limits. Constancy within the cells is maintained by continuous exchange between the cells and the fluids of the extracellular compartments of the internal environment.

In this chapter, we will consider some of the chemical and physical characteristics of the internal environment and some pertinent physiochemical processes before we take up our studies of the structure, organization, and functions of cells.

MEDIA FOR EXCHANGE AND METABOLIC PROCESSES

Water. Water is the most abundant component of the body, comprising 60 to 70 per cent of the weight of adult man. Water contained within the cell accounts for about 50 per cent of body weight, and extracellular water about 20 per cent of body weight. In addition to being the principal constituent of the internal environment, water is of first importance in all physiologic reactions because of its unusual physical and chemical properties. It plays an essential role in the biological processes that provide for exchange and distribution of materials in cells and tissues. It is a solvent for many organic and inorganic substances. Water requires more heat per unit weight to increase its temperature 1 degree (specific heat) than any other common substance. This means that it can absorb more heat per unit weight with less change in its own temperature. It acts as a temperature stabilizer of the internal environment. A prominent scientist has recently said that it appears that all chemical reactions of importance to life occur in aqueous solutions.

Solutions. Solutions may be classified as either homogeneous solutions, which are considered to have only one phase, or heterogeneous solutions, which have a *continuous phase* in which particles are dispersed. The particles constitute the *dispersed phase*. In a homogeneous solution water or another solvent is considered as a continuous phase even though molecules of the solute are dispersed among the water molecules. Examples of this type of solution in the body are sodium chloride or glucose dissolved in water. Suspensions, emulsions, and colloids are heterogeneous types of solutions. In suspensions insoluble solid particles are dispersed in a liquid. Emulsions consist of two liquids in which the suspended substance will not dissolve in the continuous phase. For example, an emulsion may consist of fat droplets suspended in water or water droplets suspended in oil. Colloidal solutions are characterized by the particle size in the dispersed phase. Colloid particles, which may be solid or liquid, range in size from 1/10 micron to 1 micron.* In contrast to coarser particles in suspensions and emulsions which can be seen by the light micro-scope or the unaided eye, colloid particles are visible only under the electron microscope. Protoplasm, which is the name given to "living substance," is a multiphasic aqueous solution containing dissolved substances, colloids, and suspended particles. There is considerable variability in protoplasm with respect to nature and composition from one location to another, and from time to time even within a cell. This variability within a cell and between different cells is within physiologic limits. Plasma, the fluid portion of blood, contains many organic and inorganic substances in solution and may contain suspended particles such as fat droplets following a meal with high fat content. Other extracellular fluids and secretions may be homogeneous or polyphasic solutions.

Chemical Constituents of Protoplasm. Although there are differences in the nature and quantity of chemical substances in different cells, tissues, and body fluids, approximate values may be given for the chemical elements of the body (Table 2.1).

TABLE 2.1 ELEMENTS COMPOSING THE HUMAN BODY

Element	Per cent
Oxygen	65.00
Carbon	18.00
Hydrogen	10.00
Nitrogen	3.00
Calcium	2.00
Phosphorus	1.00
Potassium	0.35
Sulfur	0.25
Chlorine	0.15
Sodium	0.15
Magnesium	0.05
Iron	0.004
Other elements	0.046

Examination of the table shows that 99 per cent of the body is composed of six common elements: oxygen, carbon, hydrogen, nitrogen, calcium, and phosphorus. Very small amounts of fluorine, iodine, copper, manganese, vanadium, zinc, molybdenum, nickel, cobalt, cad-

*Micron $(\mu) = \frac{1}{1000}$ of a millimeter.

mium, aluminum, lithium, and barium are also found in living forms.

The compounds which make up protoplasm are both organic and inorganic. The inorganic substances are water and inorganic salts. The organic constituents are the proteins, carbohydrates, and fats.

The inorganic salts in the body are composed chiefly of the chlorides, carbonates, phosphates, and sulfates of the metals sodium, potassium, calcium, and magnesium. Familiar examples are sodium chloride, sodium bicarbonate, and calcium carbonate. These salts do not exist in molecular form but are chemically dissociated and ionized; e.g., NaCl would be present in the body fluids as Na^+ and Cl^-. Such substances which ionize in water and are capable of conducting electricity are called *electrolytes*.

The positive ions are called *cations*, because in an electric field they travel toward the cathode or negative pole; the negatively charged ions, which are repelled by like or negative electrical charges, move toward the anode, or positive pole, and hence are called *anions*. The principal cations are H^+ and the *basic ions* Na^+, K^+, NH_4^+, Ca^{++}, and Mg^{++}. The principal anions are OH^- and the *acidic ions* Cl^-, HCO_3^-, HPO_4^{--}, SO_4^{--} and the organic acidic ion, proteinate, P^-. Na^+ is the chief extracellular cation; K^+ and Mg^{++} are the chief intracellular cations. The predominant extracellular anions are Cl^- and HCO_3^-, while phosphates, sulfates, and proteins constitute the principal intracellular anions. The carbonate-bicarbonate (H_2CO_3 and $NaHCO_3$) system and the phosphate system (Na_2HPO_4 and NaH_2PO_4) are of major importance in influencing the H^+ concentration of the internal environment; i.e., they act as *buffers*.

The organic constituents—proteins, carbohydrates, and lipids—comprise approximately 10 to 30 per cent of protoplasm. Proteins form the framework of protoplasm and are the substances that give the cell its characteristic structure. Most proteins and their constituents, the amino acids, are chemically dissociated and bear electric charges. They carry both positive and negative charges at a certain H^+ concentration; this is called their isoelectric point, since at this point the charges are balanced or neutralize one another. The isoelectric point is different for different proteins. The charge they carry in biological solutions depends upon the H^+ and the salts and amino acids present. They can act as acids or bases; such substances are called *ampholytes*. The proteins and amino acids probably act as buffers within the cell. The protein hemoglobin participates in the buffer system of the blood.

Hydrogen Ion Concentration. The acidity of the internal environment is important for chemical reactions within the cell and for maintenance of physiologic function and survival. This acidity depends upon the concentration of free hydrogen ions (H^+) in solution.

Chemical dissociation of the water molecule, H_2O, results in the presence of free H^+ and free OH^- ions. Since the concentrations of H^+ and OH^- ions are equal, water is considered to be neutral, i.e., neither acid nor alkaline. In describing the acidity or alkalinity of a solution, we refer to the H^+ concentration and disregard the OH^- concentration. In water the H^+ concentration is 0.0000001 gram H^+ per liter, or in terms of normality, 0.0000001 N. This method of expression is cumbersome. Therefore it is customary to express hydrogen ion concentration as the negative logarithm of the hydrogen ion concentration. Thus,

$$\log \text{ of } 0.0000001 = -7, \text{ and}$$
$$\text{negative log} = -(-7) = 7$$

This negative logarithm of concentration is called *pH*.

$$pH = -\log (H^+)$$

The limits of the pH scale range from concentration of 1N (H^+) to 1N (OH^-); pH 7.0, the H^+ concentration of water, is the midpoint in the scale and denotes neutrality. A pH less than 7.0 indicates that the H^+ concentration is greater than that of water and the solution is acid. Solutions on the alkaline side of neutrality have a pH of more than 7.0.

Extracellular fluid has a pH fairly close

to neutrality, i.e., about 7.4, with a range of about 7.35 to 7.5. There are few precise, reliable measurements of intracellular pH. Some cells with such extreme values as pH 4.5 and pH 8.0 have been reported. It is believed that most cells have a pH of 7.0 or somewhat less. Differences in pH among different areas of the cell would be expected to result from the different chemical reactions taking place at different locations and different times.

The acids in the internal environment are weak acids. Weak acids dissociate less readily than strong acids and so yield lower concentrations free of H^+ in solution. Salts of weak acids "mop up" free hydrogen ions and so limit the concentration of H^+ in the cellular and extracellular fluids. This process is called buffering. Buffering is responsible for keeping the pH of the extracellular and intracellular fluids relatively constant.

Physiochemical Processes. The ceaseless chemical activity of the cell requires continuous entrance of nutrients or raw materials and the elimination of waste products. The quantities of some substances within the cell remain remarkably constant, but this does not mean that the same particles of that substance remain indefinitely in the cell. Rather, small amounts of the substance are continually entering the cell while at the same time identical substances are leaving it — a condition called *dynamic equilibrium*. Further, material is being distributed throughout the cell or is being transported along special routes within cells. Physical processes are responsible for the distribution and exchange of molecules and their dissociated ions between cells and the body fluids, and within the cells themselves. Distribution can occur alone in a continuous gas or liquid medium. Exchange and distribution occur in systems in which membranes are interposed between fluid or gaseous compartments and alter the free distribution process. The biological processes which we will consider are *filtration, diffusion, osmosis*, modified diffusion involving *passive or active transport*, and *phagocytosis* and *pinocytosis*, in which cells ingest solid particles or liquids directly into the cell. The first three will be con-

sidered as physical processes *per se*, and then, together with modified diffusion and ingestion, they will be considered from the viewpoint of biology.

Filtration is a process which depends upon mechanical pressure to produce the movement of materials across a barrier. It is essentially the same process as straining a broth or jelly. The substances that are passed through the barrier or filter depend upon the size of the particles and the fineness of the filter. Filtration may be defined as the passage of water and dissolved substances across a membrane because of differences in mechanical pressure on the two sides of the membrane (Fig. 2.1, *A*). Hydrostatic pressure, or the effects of gravity on the column of water, provides the mechanical force. In the body, filtration takes place through the walls of the capillaries (Fig. 2.1, *B*). The cells of the capillary walls form the membrane. Some of the fluid portion of the blood and substances in solution such as electrolytes, glucose, and urea pass through the membrane. Red blood cells and colloids are held back. The energy, *filtration pressure*, is exerted through the blood pressure produced by the pumping of the heart.

Diffusion may be described as the tendency of substances to distribute themselves uniformly throughout a space. This process depends upon the fact that molecules of gases, liquids, and solids are never at rest. They are in continuous thermal

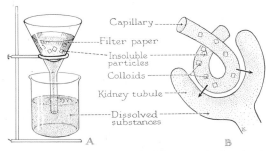

Figure 2.1 Filtration. *A*, Water and dissolved substances pass through the filter paper into the beaker. *B*, Water and dissolved substances in the blood pass from the capillaries into the kidney tubule. Colloids of the blood which do not pass through the capillary wall correspond to insoluble substances in the funnel.

motion so that the molecules of one substance move into spaces between the molecules of other substances. If at one point there is a high concentration of molecules of a substance and at another point their concentration is low or zero, this can be described as a *concentration gradient*, i.e., a continuous or an abrupt change in concentration of molecules (or ions). In simple diffusion the molecules or ions move *with the gradient* — that is, from the point of high concentration to points of lower concentration. Concentration gradients may also be called *pressure gradients* since at any given temperature and volume the pressure exerted by molecules of gas or liquid depends upon their concentration.

Gases diffuse rapidly from a point of higher pressure to points of lower pressure until they are uniformly distributed in the area in which they are enclosed. In a mixture of gases each gas acts independently, exerts its own partial pressure, and distributes itself evenly throughout space. If a bottle of ammonia and one of perfume are opened in a room, both their odors may be detected at distant points. Figure 2.2, *A*, shows diffusion of perfume molecules. Separating two gases by means of living membranes such as are found in the capillaries or in the *alveoli* (air sacs) of the lungs (Fig. 2.2, *B*) does not interfere with diffusion. The carbon dioxide diffuses from the site of high pressure, in the lung capillaries, to the point of low pressure in the alveoli. Since the oxygen pressure is greater in these air sacs than in the capillaries, the oxygen diffuses from the alveoli into the blood.

When a small amount of a substance is dissolved to make a dilute solution, its active particles (i.e., the molecules, or if the substance is an electrolyte, the ions) exert the same pressure as they would if they were in a gaseous form at the same temperature and the same volume.* The intensity of the bombardment by the particles of dissolved substance — first of the surrounding liquid, and then of the restraining walls of the container — is dependent upon their concentration. Diffusion in liquids is, however, a much slower process than in gas because of the greater density of the medium in which the distribution of particles is taking place. For example, if a crystal of copper sulfate is placed in a glass and covered with water, it will take months before the solution attains a uniform blue color, if extreme care is taken to avoid stirring and temperature changes. Dilute mixtures of solutes (dissolved substances) behave in the same manner as mixtures of gases; the active particles of each substance act independently and become uniformly distributed throughout the water (the solvent).

If two solutions of different strengths are separated by a membrane which will pass both water and the dissolved substance, the solute will pass from the side of higher concentration into the side of lower concentration, while the solvent will pass in the opposite direction until the solutions are of the same concentration on each side of the membrane. If we depart momentarily from the standard custom of referring to the more concentrated solution as the one containing more of the dissolved substance, we can recognize more readily that water is behaving like a gas or solute, in that it passes from the area of *higher concentration of water molecules*, until the water molecules are uniformly distributed on the two sides of the membrane. Membranes which pass both the solvent and the solute are said to be *permeable membranes* with respect to those substances. If they allow some substances to pass through but hold

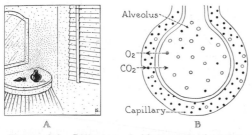

Figure 2.2 Diffusion. *A*, Molecules of perfume spread throughout enclosure. *B*, Diffusion in air sac of lung. Carbon dioxide, represented as black dots, passes from capillary into alveolus. Oxygen molecules, shown as circles, pass from air sac into blood capillary.

*One gram molecule, i.e., the molecular weight in grams, of a gas occupies a volume of 22.4 liters at 0° C. and 760 mm. (sea level) pressure.

back other molecules or ions, they are called *semipermeable membranes.* If solutions contain both substances that will pass through a membrane and other active particles which, for example, are too large to pass through it, a modified diffusion known as *dialysis* takes place. The method of dialysis can be used to separate larger molecules to which the membrane is impermeable from diffusible salts.

Osmosis is a process involving the movement of water molecules across a membrane from a less concentrated to a more concentrated solution. Thus osmosis takes place both through membranes that permit passage of all solutes and through selectively permeable membranes that permit dialysis of diffusible solutes, but hold back other molecules.

In osmosis, water molecules pass through membranes in both directions, but their final distributions on the two sides of a membrane when an equilibrium is established will depend upon the pressures exerted by the active particles in the two solutions (Fig. 2.3). A simple, though perhaps inadequate, picture of the process of the passage of water across a membrane from the less concentrated to the more concentrated solution may be gained from the following illustration. Because of their constant motion, the molecules of the two solutions would be constantly hitting the membrane separating them. Now, the

number of water molecules striking any given area per unit of time would determine the exchange of water between the two solutions. In the more concentrated solution, however, particles of the dissolved substance would occupy a greater total area of the membrane in contact with the solution and would prevent molecules from striking and passing through the membrane at those points. In the dilute solution, greater numbers of water molecules would strike and pass through the membrane in a unit of time. As a result of the differences in the number of molecules in contact with the two sides of the membrane, more water will pass from the dilute to the more concentrated solution (see Fig. 2.3). If the membrane permits the solutes to pass, the conditions on the two sides of the membrane will finally be alike, the water uniformly distributed and the rate of exchange of water in both directions across the membrane will be equal. When the membrane holds back some of the solute particles, however, the molecules which are held back continue to occupy areas of the membrane, so that water enters the solution of greater concentration faster than it leaves it, and its volume increases. If the container is open, the fluid level rises and a difference in hydrostatic pressure results. At some point the hydrostatic pressure becomes sufficiently great to force the water out at the same rate it enters the solution containing the impermeable solute. The development of hydrostatic pressure demonstrates the force of the process of osmosis. Osmotic pressure will be maintained only by solutes held back by a membrane which allows the water molecules to pass. Both the non-electrolyte and electrolyte particles to which the membrane is impermeable contribute to this pressure. It is the total number rather than the kind of molecules and ions that determines osmotic pressure.

Osmotic pressure may be demonstrated and measured by an *osmometer.* We can construct an osmometer by covering a thistle tube with a membrane impermeable to sugar molecules, introduce a sugar solution into the tube and immerse the membrane end of the tube in a container of pure water. If we mark the original

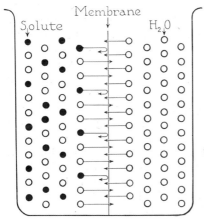

Figure 2.3 Osmosis. Black dots represent molecules of dissolved substances; circles indicate the water molecules.

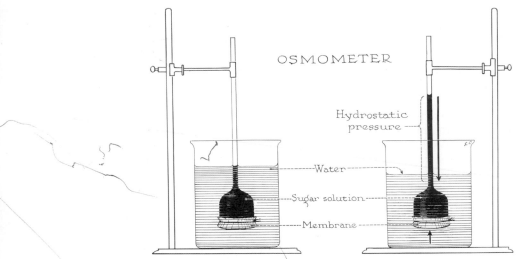

OSMOMETER

Hydrostatic
pressure

Water

Sugar solution

Membrane

Figure 2.4 Osmotic pressure. More water molecules strike and pass through the semipermeable membrane from the side in contact with pure water than from the side in contact with the sugar solution. Since more water is entering than leaving the thistle tube through the membrane, the height of the column of the sugar solution increases.

height of the column of sugar solution in the tube, we can note the rise in its level (see Fig. 2.4). After allowing time for a dynamic equilibrium to be established, i.e., an equal transfer rate of water in two directions across the membrane, no further increase in level occurs. The difference between the levels of the solutions indicates the hydrostatic pressure that is required to balance the force of the water molecules entering the sugar solution. This closely approximates the osmotic pressure of the more concentrated solution.

OSMOTIC EFFECTS OF SOLUTIONS ON BODY CELLS

Red blood cells may be used to demonstrate osmosis (Fig. 2.5). In the blood, the cells and plasma are in osmotic equilibrium. If we should separate the red blood cells from the plasma and place them in distilled water or a salt solution that is dilute as compared to plasma, the cells will swell until the osmotic pressure becomes so great that the cell bursts. This destruction of red blood cells is called *hemolysis*. Solutions and plasma in which hemolysis occurs show a red tinge, which becomes

deeper as greater numbers of cells are destroyed and greater amounts of hemoglobin are released. Should we alter the procedure and substitute a concentrated solution for the plasma, water will pass out of the cell and it will be shriveled or *crenated*.

The osmotic pressure of the contents of the red cell can be determined by finding the most dilute solution that will cause only slight hemolysis and the most concentrated solution at which no hemolysis occurs; the osmotic pressure midway between the two solutions will be approximately equal to that of the red blood cells. This method also tests the fragility of the cell membrane, i.e., its resistance to rupture from osmotic pressure. A more accurate measurement of the red cell osmotic pressure, then, would be to observe the effects of a graded series of solutions and determine the values at which changes in the volume of the cell occur (see Fig. 2.5).

All body cells are susceptible to the osmotic effects shown by the red cells. In consequence, great care is taken in the selection of solutions for medical use and for laboratory research in order to avoid subjecting body tissues to chemical insult. A solution that is in osmotic equilibrium with cells and tissues is said to be *isotonic* or

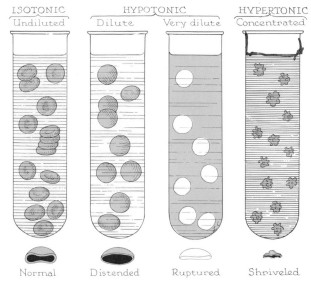

Figure 2.5 Osmosis. In whole blood, or isotonic solution, the red cells are typical biconcave discs. In hypotonic solutions, or in plasma in which the salt concentration has been reduced, water enters the cells and distends them so that they appear rounded. In very dilute solutions (water or diluted plasma) the cell envelope ruptures and the contents escape. In concentrated salt solution (hypertonic), water passes out of the cells and they become shriveled.

isosmotic. Unless otherwise described, the terms isotonic and isosmotic are commonly used to mean that the solution has the same osmotic pressure as normal human blood plasma; if the solution is isosmotic for cells of a cold-blooded species such as frogs or for plant cells, this should be specifically stated. The terms hypotonic and hypertonic are used to describe solutions that are more dilute or more concentrated, i.e., whose osmotic pressure is lower or higher than that of plasma.

Statement of Concentrations of Biological Solutions. Solutions are commonly described in terms of per cent, i.e., weight or volume of the solute per 100 cc. of solvent. This does not give us the biological information we require when, for example, we wish to inject the solution, use it in the artificial kidney for diffusion of waste products from the blood, bathe exposed tissues to prevent drying, or for other clinical or laboratory purposes. If we are to know how these solutions will act, we must know the concentration (a) in terms of osmotic pressure or (b) in terms of chemical combining power (gram-equivalent weights).

(a) Descriptions of concentration and osmotic pressure in terms of *molarity* and *milliosmols:*

1. *Molar Solutions.* A solution containing the molecular weight of a solute, expressed in grams, dissolved in one liter of water is known

1

$$\text{molar concentration} = \frac{\text{wt. in gm. per 100 cc.} \times 10}{\text{molecular wt.}}$$

Examples:

PER CENT SOLUTION	GRAMS/L.	MOL. WT.	MOLARITY
5.4% glucose	5.4 gm. (per 100 cc.) × 10 ÷ 180		= 0.30
0.9% NaCl	0.9 gm. (per 100 cc.) × 10 ÷ 58.5		= 0.15

as a molar solution. To convert per cent concentration to molar concentration, multiply the number of grams per 100 cc. times 10 to obtain the number of grams per liter, and divide this value by the molecular weight. The general formula, then, is shown at the bottom of page 23.

2. *Osmols and Milliosmols.* When speaking of the osmotic pressure of a solution, the concentration of osmotically active particles is given in *osmols.* Where the solute is a nonelectrolyte, a one molar solution is identical with a one osmolar solution since the osmotically active particles are molecules. If the solute is an electrolyte, both ions act independently as osmotically active particles, so that a gram molecular weight of solute per liter of water makes a two osmolar solution. Thus a gram-molecular weight of NaCl makes a two osmolar solution. A smaller unit, the *milliosmol,* or $1/1000$ of an osmol, is customarily employed in referring to body fluids or solutions. The general formulae are shown in 2 at the bottom of this page.

3. *Osmotic Pressure of Isotonic Solutions.* The purpose of describing a solution in terms of pressure is so that it can be readily related to the osmotic pressure of the body fluids. We may consider that a mol of a gas or nonelectrolyte, or a half mol of an electrolyte, when contained within the volume of one liter, will exert a pressure which is 22.4 times greater than the pressure of the atmosphere (see footnote, p. 20). A milliosmol is, thus, a unit of osmotic pressure equivalent to 0.0224 atmosphere. The solutes in a liter of blood plasma exert a pressure of approximately 6.72 atmospheres. The blood plasma, then, is an approximate 300 mOsm. solution (6.72 atmos. ÷ 0.0224 = 300 mOsm.). Reference to example 2 below shows that 5.4 per cent glucose and 0.9 per cent NaCl are 300 mOsm., and hence are isotonic solutions.

In a solution containing a mixture of ions, the osmotic pressure exerted by each ion may be obtained by dividing the quantity of the ion in grams per liter by the *atomic weight* (since the ions are the active particles). Adding the result for each ion and multiplying by 1000 will give the total milliosmols per liter.

(b) Description of concentration in terms of *chemical combining power:*

A *gram-equivalent* weight of a chemically reactive unit will react with or displace one gram of hydrogen or one equivalent of other substance. For monovalent ions, i.e., those carrying a single electrical charge, an *equivalent* is equal to its atomic weight. For example, Na^+, K^+, and Cl^- are monovalent ions; the atomic weight of Na^+ is 23, so 23 grams is its gram-equivalent weight. For divalent cations like Ca^{++} and Mg^{++}, the gram-equivalent weight is given by dividing the atomic weight by 2, i.e., by the valence. For trivalent ions the atomic weight is divided by 3. The term milliequivalent, which is one thousandth of a gram-equivalent weight, is used for describing the concentration of solutes in biological solutions. To convert concentrations given in milligrams per 100 cc., i.e., milligrams per cent, to milliequivalents, multiply the weight in milligrams by 10 to obtain milligrams per liter, divide this value by the atomic weight and multiply by the valence. The general formula is shown in 3 at the top of the following page.

Thus, plasma sodium may combine with 143 equivalents or ions of chloride or other monovalent substance, while the divalent calcium of the plasma may combine with 5 equivalents or ions of Cl or replace 5 hydrogen ions.

2

milliosmolar conc. = nonelectrolyte molar conc. × 1000
milliosmolar conc. = electrolyte molar conc. × 2 × 1000

Examples:		MILLIOSMOLS/L. MILLIOSMOLAR CONC.
% SOLUTION	MOLARITY	
5.4% glucose	0.30 M × 1000	= 300 (mOsm.) = 300
0.9% NaCl	0.15 M × 2 × 1000	= 300 (mOsm.) = 300

3 milliequivalents per liter (mEq./L) $= \dfrac{\text{mg. per 100 cc.} \times 10}{\text{atomic wt.}} \times$ functional valence.

Examples:

(i) The Na^+ in plasma is given as 330 mg. per 100 cc. Convert this to mEq./L.
(ii) The Ca^{++} in plasma is given as 10 mg. per 100 cc. Convert to mEq./L.

	CONC. MG. PER 100 CC.			ATOMIC WT.	FUNCTIONAL VALENCE	mEq./L.
(i)	330	× 10 =	3300 ÷	23	× 1 =	143
(ii)	10	× 10 =	100 ÷	40	× 2 =	5

FACTORS INFLUENCING CELL PERMEABILITY

The rates of exchange of materials are of major importance in biological systems. Materials are constantly being used up and waste products are being formed. The rates of exchange must be adequate to provide for the constancy or *steady state* condition necessary for maintaining the internal environment within physiologic limits. These rates depend upon the nature of substances and the characteristics of the membranes separating various compartments or areas.

Forces Influencing the Movement of Molecules and Ions. The force and velocity of movement of ions or molecules through any medium represents a balance between accelerating and decelerating forces. Some of these forces are:

Accelerating forces:
1. Thermal agitation or kinetic energy of particles and their dissociated components.
2. Attraction between unlike electrical charges.
3. Repulsion of like electrical charges in the same region.

Decelerating forces:
1. Viscous resistance to movement.
2. Repulsion between like charges.
3. Attraction of unlike charges in the same region.

At any one time, and in any one cell system, all of the forces are acting to a greater or lesser extent. Movement of substances within the fluids of the body is rapid, and concentration and electrochemical gradients are quickly reduced. The biological membranes limit the velocity and degree of movement. Their permeability, or the ease with which a substance can penetrate a membrane, is a principal factor in determining the rates of exchange. The chemical activities within the cell and the rates of exchange of materials and waste products maintain significantly large concentration and electrochemical gradients on opposite sides of a membrane. Although the characteristics and mechanisms that determine membrane permeability are incompletely understood we know that the movement of particles may be influenced by their size, electrical charge, and solubility. We also know that the permeability of a membrane changes when a cell changes from a resting to an active state or is injured. Transport across living membranes may be either active or passive.

Passive Transport. In passive transport no energy is expended by the cell for transfer of the material; substances move with the gradients from a higher concentration or electrochemical potential to a lower concentration or electrical potential.

We have learned that water moves freely in and out through living membranes. Osmosis is the movement of water from a solution of lower concentration of a solute to a higher concentration of solute. The energy for transport is provided by the kinetic energy associated with water molecules at body temperature. Oxygen and carbon dioxide also move quite freely across membranes.

The rate of diffusion through a membrane is increased with increasing concentration of the solute up to a certain point. It is postulated that the solubility or other chemical characteristic of some solutes causes them to combine with some substance in the membrane—a *carrier system*. The carrier may pick up a molecule or ion, transport it through the membrane, release it, and return for another. This process is referred to as *facilitated diffusion*. Above a certain concentration of solute the capacity of such a transport system would be exceeded and no further increase in rate could be attained. It is known that the rate of transport of some molecules is influenced by the presence of other solutes. Such influences on the rate of transport of some substances may be due to the fact that solutes may compete in utilizing the same carrier system.

We can also think of a permeable or selectively permeable membrane as having minute pores large enough to admit water and some of the smaller molecules. This would permit exchange by bulk flow of water and some of the contained solutes through the pores, as through the holes in a sieve. It would also permit thermal diffusion of smaller molecules through the water filling the pores of the membrane. It has been suggested that some of these pores may be electrically neutral, i.e., noncharged. Others may have a positive or negative charge depending upon whether the majority of ions are cations or anions.

Electrical charges on solutes also influence the rate of transport. Uncharged particles pass through a biological membrane more rapidly than charged particles. There are two factors to consider in the rate of movement of ionized particles. One is the distribution of ions on the membrane, the other the electrical potential across it. Both anions and cations are slowed down; this would imply that both positive and negative charges are distributed along the membrane so that like charges are repelled and particles with unlike charges attracted. The second factor

is that there is an electrical gradient across the membrane, i.e., a large voltage difference between the outside and inside of the cell. Positive charges predominate on the exterior surface of the membrane, and negative ions are distributed along the interior surface of the membrane. The interior of a cell is electrically negative to the outside. This favors the rate of entry of cations into the cell over the rate of entry of anions.

If the membrane is permeable to the electrolytes in solution the positive and negative ions on each side of the solution will be equal. If, on the other hand, there are anions (such as protein) which are held back by the cell membrane, electrical forces create a situation in which the concentration of the permeable cation is greater on the same side of the membrane as the nondiffusible anion, while the concentration of the permeable anion is greater on the opposite side of the cell membrane. The electrical charge of the cations inside the cell balances both the permeable and impermeable anions; outside, the permeable cations and anions balance. This type of distribution in which the product of the permeable anions, times the cations inside the cell, equals the product of the permeable anions, times the cations outside the cell, is known as the Donnan equilibrium. This may be expressed as:

$$
\begin{Bmatrix} Na^+ \times Cl^- \\ \text{in protein-free} \\ \text{solution} \end{Bmatrix}_{\text{Outside cell}} = \begin{Bmatrix} Na^+ \times Cl^- \\ \text{in solution with } P^- \\ \text{(protein ion)} \end{Bmatrix}_{\text{Inside cell}}
$$

or by the ratios:

$$
\frac{(Cl^-) \text{ protein-free}}{(Cl^-) \text{ protein}} = \frac{(Na^+) \text{ protein}}{(Na^+) \text{ protein-free}}
$$

The distribution by passive transport of permeable electrolyte and nonelectrolyte substances is known as *diffusion permeability*; that involving both permeable and nonpermeable substances is known as *osmotic permeability*.

Active Transport. Some substances may not be distributed equally inside and outside the cell even though the membrane is quite permeable to them. Although they pass through the cell membrane in both directions, they may accumulate in higher concentration on one side than on the other. For example, the principal cation inside the cell is potassium while the principal cation outside is sodium. Where such an inequality exists there must be a movement of ions against the concentration and electrochemical gradients. This activity of biological membranes is known as *active transport* or *metabolically-linked transport*. Increasing the concentration of any given constituent of a solution requires work, just as work is necessary to compress a gas so that a greater number of molecules are contained in a given volume. The energy for the performance of this work is supplied by the cell. The energy requirement is not inconsiderable — it may amount to over a quarter of the total energy being released by the cell.

The mechanism of exchange from the lesser to the greater concentration has been likened to a pump. For example, as Na^+ enters a cell by passive transport a *sodium pump* (active transport) returns it to the outside of the membrane where the concentration is higher. Simultaneously as K^+ leaves the cell by passive transport it is returned by the K^+ pump.

Phagocytosis and Pinocytosis. Solid particles can be taken directly into the cell by the process of *phagocytosis*. Fluid material can be assimilated by the process of *pinocytosis*. There are two principal theories concerning this type of activity of membranes of cells capable of ameboid-like movement. According to one theory, a portion of the membrane of an advancing pseudopodium (false foot or flowing of protoplasm) remains adherent to the protoplasmic gel and becomes wrinkled. As it encounters a solid or liquid particle the membrane becomes weakened at the point of contact due to an electrochemical effect induced by the particle. The membrane is drawn or invaginated into the cell, forming a channel. Sections of this channel containing the ingested materials break off to form vacuoles or *pinosomes*. According to another theory, there is first a physical reaction involving attachment of a particle to the outer surface of the membrane. The attachment is not a vital process; i.e., it

does not require a living membrane. Following this attachment there is engulfment of the particle, then separation of pinosomes.

Various substances can be ingested by phagocytosis and pinocytosis. These include protein or other molecules and particulate matter too large to traverse a cell membrane by other means — fat, hormones, antibodies, cell debris, bacteria, colloidal particles, and other materials. Vacuoles and waste materials may also be eliminated from the cell directly through the membrane — a type of reversal of the ingestion and engulfment processes. There are substances which, when present in the fluid surrounding the cell, may induce an extended period of pinocytosis. These substances include acid proteins (a protein at a pH below its isoelectric point) and some inorganic cations.

Although these are active processes, they cannot be considered as active transport. The transfer is not made against concentration and electrical gradients.

CATALYSIS OF CHEMICAL REACTIONS IN THE BODY

We have referred to catabolic and anabolic processes in the body, chemical activity within cells, and utilization of nutrients and waste products without any mention of the mechanisms involved. These mechanisms will be discussed in some detail in later sections of the text. In anticipation of studies in this field it is appropriate to consider the general classes of chemical reactions and the catalysts which hasten the speed of reaction. This information will be helpful in the discussion of the cell in Chapter 3.

Enzymes and Metabolic Processes. Enzymes are the catalysts of chemical reactions in biological systems. They speed up reactions and make them go. The common pattern of action is for an enzyme to become loosely attached to nonprotein material to form a somewhat unstable enzyme-coenzyme, or it may become firmly attached to a nonprotein prosthetic group. The coenzyme may exist free in solution within the cell and become associated with the enzyme at the instant the reaction is taking place. Compounds containing protein and prosthetic groups, as in the case of the stable enzyme-prosthetic group, are called *conjugated* proteins. The enzyme-coenzyme combination forms a compound with the *substrate*, i.e., the material in the chemical reaction being catalyzed by the enzyme. The breakdown or cleavage of the substrate material can take place only at one or more *reactive sites* on the enzyme molecule. The reaction yields the end products of the cleavage of the substrate and the enzyme in its original form, since as a catalyst it does not enter the reaction. The state of the enzyme-coenzyme compound depends upon the stability or degree of dissociation of the compound. The reaction may be summarized as shown at the bottom of the page.

The speed of the reactions is influenced by temperature, pH, the enzyme concentration, and the concentration of the substrate. The reactions either yield energy (*exerogonic reactions*) or require energy (*enderogonic reactions*). In the cell and the body as a whole, the energy for all the work and activities performed (e.g., enderogonic reactions, active transport, electrical phenomena, movement) is provided by exerogonic reactions. There are *high energy* compounds that yield a large amount of free energy when changed rapidly from one chemical state to another through catalytic action of enzymes.

Enzymes catalyze four general classes of reactions: hydrolysis, oxidation and reduction, transference, and addition and removal reactions. The enzyme nomenclature describes the type of reaction, to which is added the suffix *ase*. Thus the *general* classifications are *hydrolases, oxidoreductases, transferases,* and *desmolases.* Successive subclassifications are based upon the general or specific name of the substrate and frequently include the type of reaction. For example a *hexokinase* catalyzes a hexose in (carbohydrate) catabolism; *transphorylases* transfer phosphate groups from one molecule to another.

Hydrolases catalyze the reaction of a molecule of substrate with a molecule (or molecules) of water, splitting the substance into two or more parts. Examples of these reactions include hydrolysis of proteins to amino acids. Oxidoreductases generally catalyze dehydrogenations or de-electronations. The reducing agent (*reductant*) loses electrons, which in turn are transferred to the oxidizing agent (*oxidant*). Thus the reducing agent is oxidized and the oxidizing agent reduced. Transferases catalyze reactions involving the direct *transfer* of a chemical group of a substrate to become part of another molecule, such as in the direct transfer of a glucose molecule to phosphate in the breakdown of glycogen, and the direct transfer of an amino group ($-NH_2$) from one amino acid to a keto acid forming another amino and keto acid in protein metabolism. An example is the conversion of protein (the amino acid, alanine) plus a keto acid to carbohydrate (pyruvic acid) and another amino acid. The desmolases catalyze reactions involving first freeing a chemical group from a substrate or taking up a group from a free state and adding it to the substrate. This type of reaction proceeds without hydrolysis, oxidation, reduction, or *direct* transfer. An example

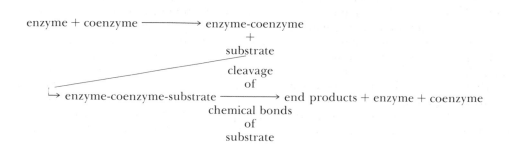

enzyme + coenzyme ⟶ enzyme-coenzyme
\+
substrate
cleavage
of
⟶ enzyme-coenzyme-substrate ⟶ end products + enzyme + coenzyme
chemical bonds
of
substrate

is the catalysis of the reversible reaction between CO_2 and H_2O ($CO_2 + H_2O \rightleftarrows H_2CO_3$) by carbonic anhydrase. Later you will learn about the importance of this reaction in the carriage and elimination of CO_2 in the blood stream, and for control of the hydrogen ion concentration (acidity) in the body fluids.

QUESTIONS FOR DISCUSSION

1. A semipermeable artificial membrane is interposed between two solutions. One solution contains NaCl. The other solution contains glucose and KCl. The membrane is permeable to all the ions and molecules except glucose. Describe the exchange processes that will occur. What difference would it make if the membrane was that of an intact, viable erythrocyte?

2. Are enzymes essential for most of the chemical reactions in which they serve as biological catalysts? What is their principal influence as catalysts on reactions occurring within the body?

3. Discuss the role of water in physiologic exchange processes.

4. Define and discuss briefly: pH, gradient, milliosmol, milliequivalent, pinocytosis.

5. Name the type of enzyme associated with each of the following reactions: breakdown of glucose to carbon dioxide and water; splitting of a protein into amino acids; splitting of fats to glycerol and fatty acid; splitting of starch into sugar; transfer of a glucose molecule to phosphate in the breakdown of glycogen.

CELL STRUCTURE AND FUNCTION

CHAPTER THREE

Recent advances in development and combined use of physical and chemical methods have introduced a new era in the study of cells and their activities. The electron microscope and other devices with high resolving power have provided powerful tools in the study of cell structure. Separation of cellular elements by ultracentrifugation followed by biochemical study have increased our knowledge of the composition and functions of organelles, i.e., little organs, and of inclusions of the cell. Radioisotope techniques using tagged identifiable elements have provided information on exchange processes. Studies on normal living cells and on cells subjected to microsurgery (micromanipulation) have also contributed important advances.

We can consider cells from two viewpoints—as the basic unit of structure and function within the body and as an organism containing complex biological systems performing functions essential for preservation and reproduction. Thus, while cells within the body are grouped in such a way as to subserve various requirements of the body as a whole, they also perform functions which are self-serving and just as comprehensive as those seen in independent self-sustained unicellular organisms such as the ameba.

ORGANIZATION OF THE CELL

Typical cells in man are small masses of protoplasm containing a nucleus and other structures surrounded by a plasma membrane. Such cells consist of two principal compartments or systems—the cytoplasm with its organelles, inclusions, and cell membrane, and the nucleus with its nuclear membrane or envelope, nuclear sap or nucleoplasm, and its inclusions and bodies. In turn the cytoplasm itself has two major types of organization or systems. There is the *cytoplasmic matrix*, i.e., a *ground cytoplasm* that surrounds and supports the development of various organizational units of the cell. Outside the matrix there is the *cytoplasmic vascular system*, which is a system of intracellular membranes that are connected at various points. These structures are subject to change and are thought to be continually breaking down and re-forming. The nuclear sap is comparable to the ground substance of the cytoplasm. Table 3.1 is presented as a guide to discussion of some details of structure and function of the cell. Reference to Figures 3.1, 3.2, 3.3, and 18.12 also will assist in developing a concept of the various cellular structures.

Membranes of the Cell. The true plasma membrane or outermost surface of the cell can be seen only with the aid of an electron microscope. Theories as to its structure have been developed principally by relating information from chemical and physical chemical studies. It appears to be a two-unit membrane formed by a double layer of lipid molecules between two layers of protein molecules; there is a lipid-aqueous interface between the lipid molecules and the pro-

tein molecules. The lipid layer and the two protein layers are each approximately 25 Å (angstrom units)* thick. The membrane is believed to have water-filled pores. Other membranes of the cell include those of the nucleus, the endoplasmic reticulum, the Golgi apparatus, and the lysosome. It is postulated that all the membrane systems within the cell are derived from the cell membrane.

Endoplasmic Reticulum. The endoplasmic reticulum, ER, is part of the cytoplasmic vacuolar system. It is a system of canals bounded by two membranes that form networks throughout the cytoplasm. The canals connect with *cisterna*, or small reservoirs. The network appears to be connected to the nuclear membrane and to the Golgi complex. It provides for a continuous communication system throughout the cell. The walls of the system are semipermeable membranes capable of active

---

*Å (angstrom unit) $= \dfrac{1}{10,000}$ micron.

TABLE 3.1 CELL STRUCTURE AND FUNCTION

Structure	Function
Nucleus	Controls cellular activities and reproduction of like cells
Nucleoplasm	Constitutes the environmental medium of the inclusions within the nucleus
Chromatin substance	Carrier of genes, i.e., units of heredity, in dispersed form in "resting" cell
Chromosomes	Condensed chromatin substance; carrier of genes during cell division
Nucleoli	Produce cytoplasmic ribosomes (see below); provide plans or templates for synthesis of ribosomal RNA
Nuclear membrane	Controls interchange of materials between nucleus and cytoplasm
Cytoplasm, cytoplasmic structures	Metabolism, transport, and reproduction
Cytoplasm	Constitutes the internal environment or milieu
Mitochondria	"Powerhouse" releasing energy to carry out work of the cell
Ribosomes	Protein synthesis
Endoplasmic reticulum (granular)	Transfer and delivery system of ribosomes
Golgi complex	Assembly site for various secretions
Lysosomes	Packaging and storing intracellular digestive enzymes
Centrioles	Participate in cell division and are apparently associated with development of cilia, hair cells in the ear, and light-receptive cells in the eye

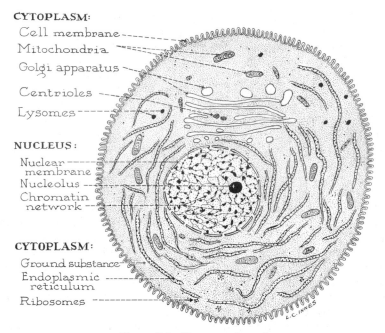

CYTOPLASM:
Cell membrane
Mitochondria
Golgi apparatus
Centrioles
Lysomes

NUCLEUS:
Nuclear membrane
Nucleolus
Chromatin network

CYTOPLASM:
Ground substance
Endoplasmic reticulum
Ribosomes

L.C. INNES

Figure 3.1 Diagram of a cell.

transport. They separate the chemical environment of the matrix from that of the ER. Material which is exchanged between the two environments may be used in synthesis or stored. The membranes contain enzymes which are presumably involved in lipid metabolism. There are two principal types of ER. In *granular endoplasmic reticulum*, great numbers of ribosomes are attached to the canals and cisternas. This type is particularly prominent in cells that manufacture proteins for export. The other type, *agranular endoplasmic reticulum*, appears to serve principally as a communication system; it is believed to provide pathways for the rapid spread of excitation in muscle tissues which enables more or less simultaneous contraction of the muscle fibrils.

The Golgi Complex. After a long period of controversy, it is now believed that the Golgi complex is a definite structural unit of the vacuolar system. Its function appears to be the assembly and concentration of a variety of substances. These may include secretions such as enzymes, hormones, and other materials elaborated in other parts of the cell or present in the cytoplasm. The locations of these complexes are different in different types of cells.

Lysosomes. Lysosomes are included in the vacuolar system in that they are surrounded by a membrane separating their contents from the cytoplasmic matrix. They contain a large number of hydrolytic enzymes. They are very stable structures in living cells. Injury resulting in rupture of the membrane would release enzymes capable of digesting the cell. Lysosomes may serve as storage units; they may be associated with vacuoles formed by phagocytosis or pinocytosis and aid in the digestion of the ingested material; or they may participate in digestion of cellular debris contained in vacuoles, and in elimination of the nondigestible components from the cell.

Mitochondria. These organelles, which are very numerous, are distributed in the cytoplasmic matrix. Some may be mobile and others may be fixed in one location. They may be seen in many forms and sizes depending upon the state of their activity. The mitochondrion is frequently represented as a cocoon or sausage-shaped structure with an inner and an outer membrane. The inner membrane forms a succession of folds that reach part of the way across the inner compartment or *mitochondrial matrix*. The two membranes are semipermeable.

Mitochondria have been called the "powerhouses of the cell." Their function is to free energy stored in foodstuffs and transform it into a usable form for providing chemical energy for all cell activities. They provide the chemical energy for active transport, synthesis and all enderogonic chemical reactions, mobility and contraction of muscle, and transmission of nerve impulses.

When glucose enters the cell it is broken down in the cytoplasm to pyruvic acid. In the presence of oxygen, the breakdown of one molecule of glucose yields eight molecules of *adenosine triphosphate*, ATP. The further breakdown of pyruvic acid releases by far the greater amount of the chemical energy of formation of glucose and yields 30 molecules of ATP. The succession of changes that occur in the mitochondria is called the Krebs or citric acid cycle, the details of which may be found in biochemistry texts.

ATP can be written as adenosine, A, combined with three phosphates, P. The phosphates are joined by chemical bonds which yield high energy when broken; a conventional sign is used to indicate the high energy bonds: $A \sim P \sim P \sim P$. ATP is a relatively unstable compound. The breaking of one of the high energy bonds supplies the initial energy required for the metabolism of glucose.

$$A \sim P \sim P \sim P \rightarrow A \sim P \sim P + P + energy.$$

Thus, through enzymatic action, P is split off, a large amount of energy is freed, and ATP is changed to ADP, *adenosine diphosphate*.

If a continuous supply of ATP were not provided, ATP would soon be used up, no chemical energy would be available, all cell functions would cease, and the cell would die. The activities within the "powerhouse" provide for the formation of ATP in sufficient quantities to meet the needs of the cell. All that a mitochondrion needs is P and energy. As stated previously, the breakdown of pyruvic acid to

CO_2 and H_2O provides a large amount of energy, enough to form 30 molecules of ATP from ADP, thus

$$A \sim P \sim P + P + energy \rightarrow A \sim P \sim P \sim P$$

Some of the ATP is retained in the mitochondria for reactions there, but most of it passes out into the cytoplasmic matrix and supports other activities of the cell.

Ribosomes. The ribosomes are fine granules attached to the outer membranes of the endoplasmic reticulum. During growth of the cell they may also be seen in the ground substance. Ribosomes are comprised of ribonucleic acid and protein. These organelles are the "factories" for the production of protein for growth and repair. The pattern, or mRNA, for each protein synthesized will be discussed later.

Nucleus. In the *interphase*, i.e., the "resting" stage between cell divisions, the nucleus is surrounded by the nuclear membrane. This membrane has the same general structure as the plasma membrane except that it is believed to have somewhat larger pores. It appears to have connections with the endoplasmic reticulum. The nucleus is usually a globular or oval body lying near the center of the cell. Within the nucleus is the nuclear sap, a fine network of chromatin fibers, relatively large chromatin flakes, chromocenters, which appear as coarse granules (sometimes called false nucleoli), and the nucleolus. The chromatin material of the interphase forms into chromosomes during the early stage of cell division. The nucleolus, which is concerned with the formation of ribosomes, lies within the nuclear sap. It does not appear to have a surrounding membrane.

The nucleus is considered to be the control center of the cell, directing cellular activities and reproduction of like cells. The principal constituents of the nucleus are DNA and RNA; it also contains basic proteins, lipids, inorganic salts, and enzymes. The enzymes catalyze anaerobic metabolic reactions, formation of high energy phosphate, and the synthesis of some proteins and coenzymes. The nucleolus contains relatively large amounts of RNA. Chemical tests indicate a lack of

DNA in the nucleolus during its "resting" phase.

DNA and RNA. Two components of protein, deoxyribonucleic acid (DNA) and ribonucleic acid (RNA), warrant special emphasis because of their fundamental roles in cell physiology. DNA is responsible for transmission of hereditary characteristics by its presence in chromosomes and is in control of the syntheses occurring within the cell. The DNA molecule is reproduced during cell division so that in the new cell there is an exact copy of the DNA molecule of the old cell. In this way hereditary characteristics are passed along from one cell generation to another. RNA is intimately concerned with synthesis that takes place in the cells. All RNA molecules are formed in the nucleus. Messenger RNA (mRNA), under control of DNA, forms a somewhat unstable blueprint or pattern that is followed in the synthesis of new protein. It migrates from the nucleus into the cytoplasm where it becomes attached to a ribosome. The ribosomal RNA (rRNA) forms a template from a restricted region of DNA for synthesis of the protein to be formed. Transfer RNA (tRNA), which is in soluble form in the cytoplasm, picks up amino acids and conveys them to the rRNA for the formation of a specific protein.

DNA and RNA are nucleic acids as their name implies. They are made up of building blocks called *nucleotides*. Nucleotides, in turn, are molecules formed from the combination of a pentose (a sugar molecule with five carbon atoms) plus phosphoric acid plus a base. The sugar molecule in RNA is *ribose*; in ribose a hydroxyl group (OH) is attached to one of the carbon atoms. In the sugar molecule in DNA a hydrogen atom is attached to a carbon atom. It is for this reason that it is called deoxyribonucleic acid, that is, "ribonucleic acid without oxygen." Three bases occur in the nucleotides forming both DNA and RNA. These are *adenine*, *guanine*, and *cytosine*. A fourth base in DNA is *thymine*; a fourth base in RNA is *uracil*.

WATSON-CRICK MODEL OF THE DNA MOLECULE. In 1953 two eminent scientists proposed a model of the molecular structure of DNA which helps to explain

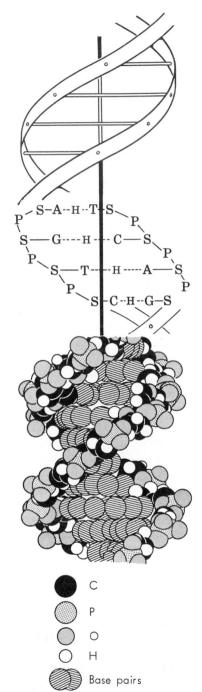

Figure 3.2 Three different ways of representing the DNA helix. *Upper:* as a spiral staircase. *Middle:* as an arrangement of organic molecules and hydrogen bonds:(A) adenine, (C) cystine, (G) guanine, (H) hydrogen, (P) phosphate, (S) sugar, and (T) thymine. *Lower:* as an arrangement of atoms and base pairs: (C) carbon, (H) hydrogen, (O) oxygen, (P) phosphorus, and base pairs as shown. (From Swanson: The Cell, Prentice-Hall, Inc., 1960.)

its suitability for control of protein synthesis and for transmission of hereditary characteristics. DNA is represented as two helical chains joined together by crossbars. Such a double helix can be visualized by thinking of a ladder with flexible uprights. If the uprights were held firmly at the bottom so that they could not move, and the ladder twisted at the top, a double helix would be formed with the sides joined by crossbars or rungs. The uprights or spirals are formed by the phosphate and deoxyribose portions of the nucleotides. The crossbars are formed by a hydrogen bond linking the base of the nucleotide molecule on one side with the base of the nucleotide molecule on the other side. The linkage of bases follows a pattern in which one of the purine bases (i.e., adenine or guanine) is always linked to a pyrimidine base (cytosine or thymine) on the other side. The structures of the molecules are such that adenine (A) and thymine (T) can be linked together by a hydrogen bond, and cytosine (C) and guanine (G) can also be linked. Thus the possible combinations are A−T, C−G, and, reversing the order of the linkages, T−A and G−C. The sequence of successive runs ensures that the bases of one chain will always complete the linkage with the opposite bases of the same pair.

CELL DIVISION

Cell division provides for an increase in the number of cells for reproduction and for growth and repair of the body. Body or somatic cells divide by the process of *mitosis* in which each cell receives the same number of chromosomes as there were in the parent cell. In man there are normally forty-six chromosomes; duplicates of each chromosome appear in each daughter cell. *Gametes* or sex cells (ovum and spermatozoon) divide by the process of *meiosis*. In meiosis the number of chromosomes are halved so that when fertilization of an ovum occurs twenty-three chromosomes are contributed by the male sex cell and twenty-three by the female sex cell.

Mitosis. In mitosis we will discuss changes that occur in the chromatin material and the chromosomes, and those associated with the other mitotic apparatus and nuclear envelope. The phases of mitosis are shown diagrammatically in Figure 3.3. Interphase is the phase or stage between divisions. Prophase, metaphase, anaphase, and telophase are convenient but arbitrary terms used to describe the progressive processes of cell division.

INTERPHASE (Fig. 3.3, *A*). During the resting phase DNA and RNA are being rapidly synthesized in the nucleus.

PROPHASE (Fig. 3.3, *B*, *C*, *I*). Each chromosome appears as two coiled threadlike segments of chromatin, called *chromatids*, lying within the nucleus. The two longitudinal halves or chromatids are joined at a central constriction, the *centromere*. The region of the centromere is associated with movement and orientation of the chromosome with respect to the poles or centers of activity of the cell. Filamentous *chromonemata* spiral through the chromatids. Particles of DNA protein form enlargements or *chromomeres* on the chromonemata. The chromosomes shorten and thicken through most of the prophase. The chromosomes move away from the center of the cell to lie near the nuclear envelope. In the meantime the two cylinders of the *centriole*, located at right angles to one another, duplicate themselves and start to migrate toward opposite poles of the nucleus. Fibers radiate from each centriole, and their extensions, a bundle of filaments, meet at the equator midway between the two poles, thus forming the spindle.

METAPHASE (Fig. 3.3, *D*). The nuclear envelope disintegrates and disappears. The centromere of each chromosome becomes attached to the spindle fibers and moves toward the center or equator of the cell. The chromosomes become distributed radially around the spindle; this can be seen when viewing them through or near the pole (as if the cell were tilted around its equator). The longitudinal chromatids or halves are now more apparent in the structure of the chromosome. If we now view the cell from the side through the plane of the equator, the halves appear to be aligned with it, forming the *equatorial plate*. The constriction in the region of the

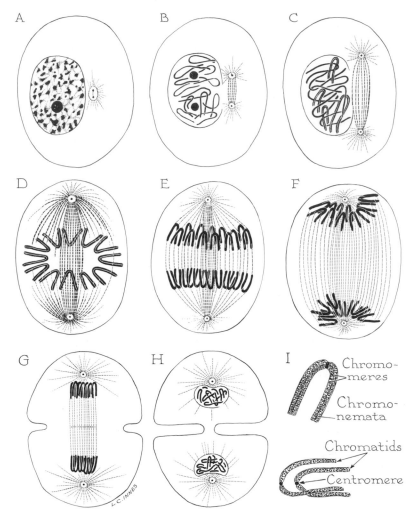

Figure 3.3 Diagram showing various phases of mitosis. *A,* Interphase cell. *B, C,* Prophase. *D,* Metaphase. *E, F,* Anaphase. *G, H,* Telophase. *I,* Chromosomes.

centromere is now more marked, and each chromatid can be seen to be connected by chromosomal fibers of the spindle to opposite poles of the cell.

ANAPHASE (Fig. 3.3, *E, F*). The longitudinal separation of the chromatids, beginning at the centromere, precedes migration of the halves of the chromosome to opposite poles.

TELOPHASE (Fig. 3.3, *G, H*). The telophase begins at the end of the migration of the chromatids, which, following their separation, are called daughter chromosomes. A nuclear membrane forms around

the group of daughter chromosomes at each pole. These chromosomes become less compact, reversing the processes of formation which occurred in the prophase. The spindle fibers disappear, constriction of the cytoplasm occurs at the equator, and its final separation gives rise to two daughter cells.

Meiosis (Fig. 3.4). Meiosis is derived from a Greek word meaning diminution. It involves two cell divisions of the gametes or sex cells during which the chromosomes divide only once. Both somatic and sex or germ cells originate from a succession of

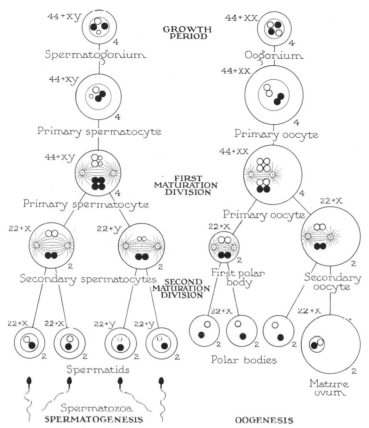

Figure 3.4 Diagram showing gametogenesis. Chromosome number in human sex cells is shown above and to the left of the cells. Chromosome number used in the diagram is below and to the right of the cells. The circles represent sex chromosomes. Large circles are X chromosomes, small circles are Y chromosomes.

divisions of a fertilized ovum. Those developing into germ cells after repeated divisions produce *gonocytes* which become gonial cells. The male gonial cells are called *spermatogonia* and those of the female *oogonia*. At puberty both oogonia and spermatogonia pass through changes that prepare them to take part in the reproduction process. At this stage of development the cells are known as *spermatocytes* and *oocytes*. The spermatocytes and the oocytes then undergo two meiotic divisions. The entire process, from the mitotic division of gonial cells through the meiotic divisions, is *gametogenesis.*

After a spermatogonium (singular of spermatogonia) or an oogonium has divided for the last time, it increases in size and becomes a *primary spermatocyte* or

primary oocyte. Insofar as the chromosomes are concerned, the first meiotic divisions of the primary spermatocyte and primary oocyte accomplish the same purpose. However, since there are some differences in other respects, the meiotic divisions of the spermatocytes and oocytes are described separately.

SPERMATOGENESIS (Fig. 3.4). In the primary spermatocyte the spindle appears, and chromosomes are formed as in the usual mitotic process, but in the equatorial plane the chromosomes come together in pairs in a process known as synapsis. At the same time the chromosomes split lengthwise, so that in cross section each pair presents a figure composed of four parts, called a *tetrad.* The arrangement of the chromosomes on the spindle is such that the whole chromosome lies parallel with the equator. When the cell divides, the chromosome with the split through the center moves as a unit into the new cell. As a result two new cells are formed, the *secondary spermatocytes*, each containing twenty-three whole chromosomes. This is known as the "reduction division" because the chromosome number is reduced from forty-six to twenty-three. The second maturation division may begin without an intervening resting period. When the spindle is formed, the chromosomes, already showing two parts and now referred to as *dyads*, are arranged on the spindle so that the dyad lies at right angles to the equator. When the cell divides, the halves of the dyads separate and twenty-three new daughter chromosomes pass into each new cell. The division of the two secondary spermatocytes results in four spermatids in each of which there are twenty-three chromosomes. This is called the "equation division."

The spermatids are tranformed into motile cells called spermatozoa. The *spermatozoon* consists of an oval head, a middle piece, and a thin, tapering, motile organ, the tail (Fig. 3.5). Four spermatozoa result from the maturation of one spermatogonium. The cytoplasm of the spermatid is concentrated in the acrosome of the head and tail. Chromatin of the twenty-three chromosomes forms most of the head of the sperm. The midpiece of the spermatozoon contains mitochondria, centrosome, and the proximal portion of the axial filament.

OOGENESIS (Fig. 3.4). The female sex cells, oogonia, increase greatly in size during the growth period and become the primary oocytes, ready for the first maturation division. During the prophases, the spindle is formed and the chromosomes come together in pairs, forming the tetrads, and, as described in spermatogenesis, twenty-three whole chromosomes pass into each new cell. However, the spindle forms near the periphery of the cell instead of in the center, so that, as division of the cytoplasm occurs at the equator, one large cell, the secondary oocyte, is formed and one small cell, the polar body. In the second maturation

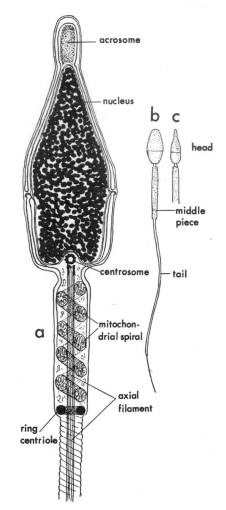

Figure 3.5 Mammalian spermatozoa. *A*, Semi-diagrammatic drawing after electron micrograph by Fawcett. *B*, Front view. *C*, Side view. (From Balinsky: Introduction to Embryology. 1965.)

division the twenty-three chromosomes of the secondary oocyte, now known as dyads, come into position on the spindle. Each dyad, representing one chromosome already split into daughter chromosomes, takes a position at right angles to the equator, so that as the cytoplasm divides, the halves of the twenty-three dyads (or twenty-three daughter chromosomes) pass into each new cell. Again the result is one large cell and one small cell. The large cell is the ovum, and the small cell is the second polar body. While the secondary oocyte is dividing, the first polar body may divide in regular mitotic fashion into two polar bodies. The result of the two maturation divisions is one large cell, the ovum, and three small, nonfunctional cells, the polar bodies.

THE GENETIC CODE

In our earlier discussion of DNA and RNA we mentioned that DNA is responsible for the transmission of hereditary characteristics by its presence in the chromosomes and is in control of the syntheses occurring within the cells. The chromosome is made up of protein and DNA. The protein may serve as a structural support for masses of DNA molecules or for a combination of DNA and protein. The *gene* is a subdivision or segment of a DNA molecule. We have seen that in the model of the DNA molecule there are four possible combinations of the bases forming the crossbars of the double helix, and that the bases attached to one strand of the helix, i.e., attached to one "upright," may be arranged in innumerable ways. For example, three successive bases on one strand may be adenine, adenine, adenine. The next three might be thymine, cytosine, guanine, and so on in any possible sequence. It has been established that each segment of the DNA molecule, that is, each gene, is coded by three of these nucleotide bases.

Now, if the DNA is to transmit hereditary characteristics, each new cell will have to receive the exact duplicate of the parent cell. The DNA in successive generations of cells must be matched in kind and in amount. Further, the protein synthesized by the daughter cells must follow the same patterns as those of their parent cell. Three processes are necessary if these requirements are to be met: *duplication, transcription,* and *translation.*

First DNA must duplicate itself. To do this the DNA molecule must be uncoiled, "unzipped," or separated at the H bonds between the two bases, and each half or single strand reconstructed so that it is an exact duplicate of the original double helix. The first step in duplication can be visualized as uncoiling the double helix—untwisting the flexible uprights. This would be followed by unzipping the two halves. The rungs would then be reformed following the plan of the four possible linkages of bases, i.e., A−T, C−G, T−A, and C−G, as previously described.

Transcriptions of the code form patterns for the synthesis of proteins. Here again the double helix becomes unzipped, and sections of a strand of the DNA molecule serve as patterns for the formation of RNA molecules. The sequence of bases in the RNA pattern are determined by the sequence of bases in the DNA template; e.g., a pyrimidine nucleotide will "match" or be compatible for joining a purine nucleotide as shown in the Watson-Crick model. However, only three of the nucleotide bases are present in both DNA and RNA; uracil is the fourth base in RNA. Thus the compatible pairs of nucleotides in the development of the RNA transcript are shown as follows:

DNA nucleotide	RNA nucleotide
adenine (A)	uracil (U)
thymine (T)	adenine (A)
guanine (G)	cytosine (C)
cytosine (C)	guanine (G)

After the transcripts are made the two original strands of the DNA molecule rejoin.

The transcription process translates the DNA code into the RNA language. For example AAT in the DNA code would be translated as UUT in the RNA code. RNA then forms a template for protein synthesis. Since there are four nucleotides, there are four letters in the DNA and RNA codes. Three nucleotides, constituting a gene, can form sixty-four combinations of letters, i.e., 4^3 code "words." This number is more than enough to code the twenty amino acids. In the synthesis of proteins, sections of the DNA molecule which have been transcribed contain a large number of genes in various orders. The ribosomal RNA pattern controlled by the section of DNA is to be followed at the ribosome protein factory in linking amino acids to form polypeptides and proteins. Thus transcription and translation provide for production of proteins patterned after the DNA code of the parent cell.

QUESTIONS FOR DISCUSSION

1. Describe the intracellular fluid (cytoplasm) as a heterogeneous solution.

2. Write the RNA transcription of segments of DNA coded CAT, GCA, AAT, and TAG.

3. Discuss the similarities and differences in the reproduction of somatic cells and of body cells.

4. Discuss the role of the nucleolus in the transmission of hereditary characteristics.

5. Discuss methods that you might use if you were going to conduct research on the composition, structure, and functions of cells.

CELLULAR SPECIALIZATION

CHAPTER FOUR

EPITHELIAL TISSUES

CELLULAR MOTION

CELLULAR SECRETION AND GLANDS

CONNECTIVE TISSUES
    Osseous Tissue
    Cartilage
    Connective Tissues Proper

SKIN

Epithelial and connective tissues are intimately associated throughout all parts of the body as important architectural materials. Their fundamental position in cellular specialization makes it appropriate to consider the relationships of these two tissues at this time.

EPITHELIAL TISSUES

Epithelial tissue has come to mean all the cellular membranes that cover and line the surfaces of the body. Embryologic studies have indicated that groups of cells have grown away from the covering or lining membranes to form *glands*. Thus epithelial membranes are formed during development of the individual to provide protection, selective absorption, and secretion. The *endothelial* cells which line the vascular channels (arteries, veins, lymphatics, capillaries) and heart are epithelial in form and function. So are the *mesothelial* cells which line the ventral body cavities and cover the viscera. When subjected to stim-ulation from a malignant tumor both en-dothelial and mesothelial cells may behave more like the primitive connective tissue from which they are derived.

The epithelial membranes consist entirely of cells with no capillaries (Figs. 4.1 to 4.6). Thus they are dependent upon the underlying connective tissue for support and nourishment. Between the epithelial and connective tissues is a thin layer of nonliving *basement lamina* (membrane).

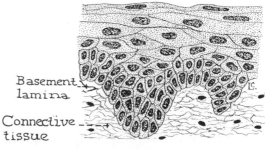

Basement lamina

Connective tissue

Figure 4.1 Stratified squamous epithelium of the esophagus.

This permeable lamina also serves an adhesive function in anchoring the epithelial membrane to the connective tissue and appears to be synthesized by both tissues. It contains mucopolysaccharides which have the capacity to exchange ions and thus control transport of materials between connective and epithelial tissue.

Adherence of the cells of the epithelial membrane may be provided by three structures illustrated in Figure 4.2. The *tight junction* (zonula occludens), *intermediate junction* (zonula adherens), and *desmosome* (macula adherens) occur close to the free surfaces of the cells. These supporting mechanisms are seen in other tissues and represent modifications and approximations of the adjacent cell membranes with the reinforcement of a delicate fibrillar cytoplasmic *cell web*, as in the desmosome, or without such reinforcement.

The shapes of the epithelial cells provide a means for their classification; some examples are indicated in the outline below.

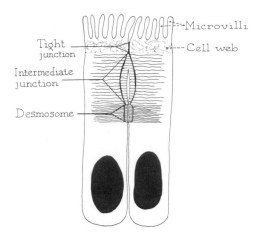

Figure 4.2 Diagram of two columnar cells showing types of cellular adherence.

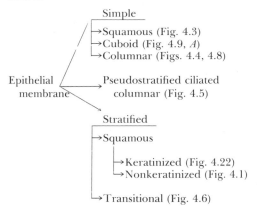

The kind and extent of protective surface vary in different areas of the body as does the amount of selective absorption or secretion required in the function of the area. *Microvilli* (Fig. 4.2) are most commonly found on the absorptive surfaces of the digestive system. All epithelial membranes retain cells that are capable of mitosis for repair of injury or replacement of normally worn out cells. *Simple epithelium* is one cell layer in thickness. The thin *squamous* cells are very well adapted to filtration and dialysis (Fig. 4.3). The *columnar* cells are often found as secreting

units for *mucus*. This sulfate-containing glycoprotein provides a nonfrictional, protective material in the respiratory, digestive, and urogenital passageways. The epithelial membranes of these systems comprise the mucous membranes of the body. Mesothelial cells and their loose connective tissue form moist, nonfrictional *serous membranes* of pleura, pericardium, and peritoneum within the ventral body cavities. Epithelial membranes which cover the exterior of the body cannot remain alive because they are subject to continual dehydration. A waterproof albuminoid keratin is formed in the outer layers of the skin (p. 51), and this protects the living cells in deeper regions of the membrane.

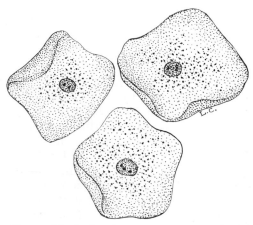

Figure 4.3 Isolated cells of squamous epithelium.

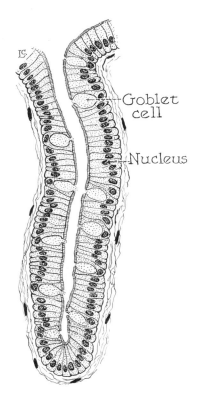

Figure 4.4 Simple columnar epithelium of the intestine.

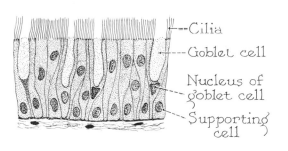

Figure 4.5 Pseudostratified ciliated columnar epithelium of the trachea.

Figure 4.6 Transitional epithelium from the urinary bladder.

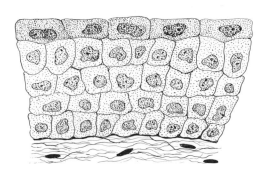

CELLULAR MOTION

A large percentage of vital phenomena in cells and tissues transpire without visible signs. Movement within or involving the entire cell and cellular aggregates is convincing evidence of life. This is most apparent in muscular tissue (see p. 12). Cellular motion may occur as *cytoplasmic streaming* or *cyclosis*. This is important in the nutrition and maintenance of cells with long processes, such as axons of nerve cells. In *ameboid movement* the cytoplasmic streaming and possible contraction of the cytoplasm displace the shape of the cell into the projections of pseudopodia. Ameboid motion is common among several cell types found in connective tissue, and especially in the white blood cells. In this manner connective tissues are able to defend the body against infection and to effect healing of an injured area. Fixed tissue cells which have been *explanted* into tissue cultures acquire ameboid motion by *dedifferentiation* as they free themselves from the original explant of nerve, muscle, or skin to move about within the culture. Ameboid motion is a mechanism by which embryonic cells are differentiated into germ layers and ultimately into tissues and organs.

Cellular motion may be carried out by especially adapted organelles such as *cilia* and *flagella* of epithelial cells or *myofibrils* of muscle cells. The structure of cilia is shown in Figures 4.7, 4.8. Enclosed in the cell membrane over the extension of cytoplasm are eleven filaments running upward from the basal body and basal plate. Projecting downward into the cytoplasm are two rootlets. The basal body is similar to the centriole of the centrosome. A protein (similar to myosin) which reacts in the presence of ATP has been found in ciliated cells. Effective ciliary beat depends upon the underlying cytoplasm. Waves of ciliary contraction occur as indicated in Figure 4.8. The frequency of the wave is believed to depend upon a *pacemaker* cilium which initiates intraciliary excitation and which is then followed by interciliary conduction. Within the single cilium

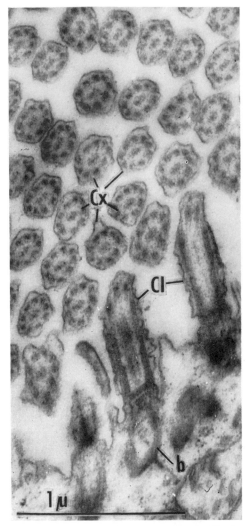

Figure 4.7 Electron micrograph of cilia from the gill of a clam (Mya). *Cx,* Cilia in cross section, and *Cl,* in longitudinal section. At lower right, junction of a cilium, with its basal body, *b,* in longitudinal section. (Courtesy of D. Fawcett.)

the central fibril appears to conduct impulses from the basal body for contraction of fibrils 1, 2, 9, 3, 8 causing the cilium to bend forward. Relaxation of fibrils 1, 2, 9, 3, 8 accompanied by shortening of fibrils 4, 7, 5, 6 produces the recovery of the original position of the cilium. Ciliary activity is important in moving materials in the respiratory, reproductive, and nervous systems.

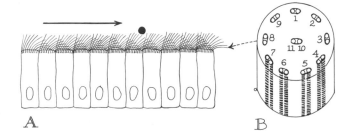

Figure 4.8 Cilia moving a particle.

CELLULAR SECRETION AND GLANDS

Secretion is a common cellular function. It occurs among different types of tissue cells but is highly characteristic of epithelial cells in the specialized arrangements known as glands. Secretion implies that molecules are absorbed by the cell by means of the various transport mechanisms (p. 25), transformed into a product of different chemical structure, and eliminated by the cell into an *exocrine* (body cavity) environment or *endocrine* (into circulation) environment. When cellular secretion is continuous, as in the parathyroid and adrenal glands (p. 134), the absorption of raw materials, intracellular synthesis, and elimination of secretion occur simultaneously. Rhythmic secretory

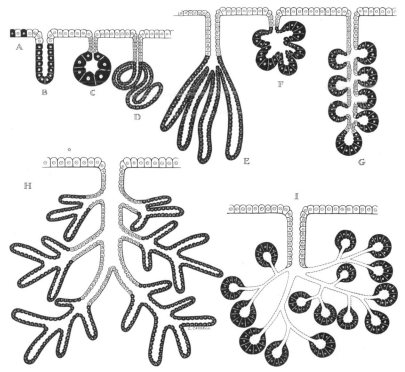

Figure 4.9 Diagrams of various types of glands, shown as invaginations from the epithelium sheet. Shaded portions represent secreting cells. *A*, Surface cells differentiated as unicellular glands. *B*, Simple tubular gland. *C*, Simple acinus or alveolar gland, formed from a group of glandular cells. *D*, Simple coiled tubular; and *E*, Simple branched tubular glands. *F*, *G*, Simple branched alveolar glands. As complexity increases, each tubule or acinus has its own duct, and all ducts communicate with a common duct that leads to a single outlet. *H*, Compound tubular gland. *I*, Compound tubulo-alveolar gland.

activity implies a timed sequence from absorption of raw materials to the elimination of the secretory product. This is apparent in the goblet cells (Figs. 4.4, 4.5), salivary glands (p. 350), and pancreas (p. 147). Protein secretion, as followed in the pancreatic acinar cells (Fig. 18.19), proceeds through five stages. In the ribosomal stage (1) proteins are synthesized within three minutes on the surface of the endoplasmic reticulum by the interaction of mRNA and the aminoacyl-transfer RNA complex. The newly synthesized enzymes (2) migrate through the endoplasmic reticulum. Upon reaching the Golgi zone dilute enzymatic proteins (3) are concentrated into *zymogen* granules. The zymogen granules (4) are further concentrated in their movement toward the apex of the cell. The enzymes (5) are diluted and mixed with other secretions as they move through the gland. Carbohydrate macromolecules of secretion follow a similar sequence except that their site of synthesis appears to be in the Golgi apparatus.

Unicellular glands such as goblet cells (Figs. 4.4, 4.5) and mucus-producing cells of the intestine are abundantly present in mucous membranes. In the multicellular exocrine glands a communicating duct system maintains a connection to the surface environment. The secretory units shown in black in Figure 4.9 may assume a *tubular* shape (Fig. 4.9, *B, D, E, H*) or *acinous* shape (Fig. 4.9, *C, F, G, I*). In *simple glands* the duct system is unbranched (Fig. 4.9, *B* to *G*). *Compound glands* have complex branching of their duct system (Fig. 4.9, *H, I*). Cellular aggregates of endocrine glands are irregular cords in proximity to blood vessels since they possess no duct system for elimination of their secretory products.

CONNECTIVE TISSUES

Connective tissues differentiate from *mesenchyme* (Fig. 4.10), an embryonic tissue developed from the middle germinal layer, the mesoderm. The wide variety of developmental potential of mesenchyme is partially reflected in the major types of

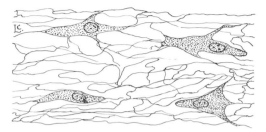

Figure 4.10   Embryonic connective tissue.

connective tissue. The following types are recognized by the character of the *ground substance* or matrix:

1. Osseous tissue — solid matrix;
2. Cartilage — semisolid matrix;
3. Connective tissues proper — gelatinous to fibrous matrix;
4. Blood, hemopoietic organs and tissues — liquid matrix (refer to Chapter 14).

Osseous Tissue.   Bone tissue, like cartilage, is a dense form of connective tissue consisting of cells distributed through the intercellular material (Fig. 4.11). The matrix is rendered hard by the deposition of lime salts, mainly calcium phosphate and calcium carbonate. The bone cells lie in spaces in the matrix called lacunae, as in cartilage. Fine projections of the cell body grow out into channels in the matrix. These canals are called *canaliculi.* They radiate from the lacunae and penetrate the hard matrix in all directions, connecting with canaliculi of other lacunae, thus forming a continuous system of communicating cavities. Bone tissue is formed in layers or lamellae. A *lamella* is composed of bone cells and the matrix which these cells have deposited. Bone may be

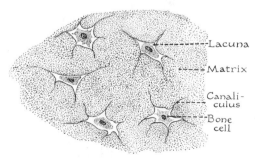

Figure 4.11   Decalcified bone; connections of canaliculi are not evident.

divided into two types, depending on the arrangement of the lamellae: porous or spongy, and hard or compact. In spongy or cancellated bone the lamellae are arranged to form an interlacing lattice-work with large spaces. In compact bone the lamellae are arranged in layers to form solid masses. The organization consists of a large number of haversian systems (Fig. 4.12). A *haversian system* consists of a central canal around which concentric lamellae of bone have been deposited. This canal contains blood and lymph vessels. The haversian systems are held together by the ground or interstitial lamellae.

Cartilage. Cartilage, commonly known as "gristle," has a firm, tough, resilient texture. It is composed of cells and the intercellular substance, which contains the glycoprotein, chondromucoid. The space in the matrix occupied by a cartilage cell is called a lacuna. The cells may be irregular in shape, but usually appear round or oval and tend to be arranged in groups of two, three, four and sometimes more cells (Fig. 4.13). Except on bare surfaces in joint cavities, cartilage is always covered by a sheath of dense connective tissue, the perichondrium. The fibroblasts of the perichondrium transform into young cartilage cells, deposit matrix, and become mature cartilage cells.

In the parts of the embryo where cartilage will develop, the mesenchymal cells accumulate in dense masses. Closely crowded together, they soon lose their processes and become rounded; the spaces between them decrease, and compact cellular precartilage is formed. As development proceeds, matrix forms in abundance between the cells, and they become widely separated. Cartilage grows externally through the activity of the perichondrium and internally by mitotic division of cartilage cells and increase in the matrix. Cartilage contains no blood vessels of its own, and, since the cells lie in isolated lacunae, the lymph from the blood vessels of the perichondrium must pass through the matrix to reach the cells. According to the texture of the intercellular substance, three types of cartilage are distinguished: hyaline or glassy cartilage, fibrous cartilage, and elastic cartilage.

Hyaline cartilage (Fig. 4.13) is the simplest and most widespread. It has the blue-white color of skimmed milk. The matrix is homogeneous, but, when stained, the portion surrounding the cartilage cell is often more deeply stained than elsewhere and is for this reason referred to as the capsule of the cell. Hyaline cartilage covers the surfaces of bones within joints, forms the rib cartilages, the cartilage of the nose, and ring cartilages of the trachea and bronchi; in the embryo it constitutes most of the temporary skeleton.

Fibrous cartilage contains large numbers of collagenous fibers arranged in parallel rows in the matrix (Fig. 4.14). This type is found in the discs between the bodies of the vertebrae, between the two pubic bones in the pelvis, and in the articular discs in many joints.

Elastic cartilage has a network of yellow

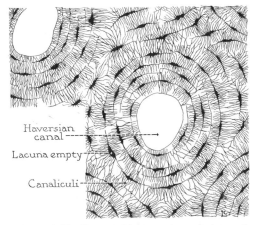

Figure 4.12 Compact bone as seen in haversian systems.

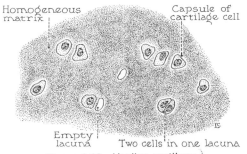

Figure 4.13 Hyaline cartilage.

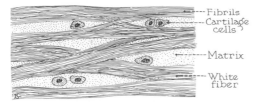

Figure 4.14 White fibrous cartilage.

fibers through the matrix (Fig. 4.15). It forms the cartilages of the external ear, auditory tube, epiglottis, and some small cartilages of the larynx.

Connective Tissues Proper. Connective tissues proper perform a number of important functions in the body. Mechanical support provided by fibrous elements of these tissues is adapted to a wide range of local structural requirements. The basement laminae of epithelial membranes, capillaries, individual muscle fibers, and gland cells are supported by delicate *reticular* fibers. Coarse, tough *collagenous* fibers are present in ligaments and capsules where great tensile strength is needed. *Elastic* fibers are abundant in the heart and other organs where distention and recoil are a part of normal function. *Loose connective* tissues are present between surfaces such as skin and muscle, where the mobility of the parts is a prominent feature. All metabolic substances must pass from blood through layers of connective tissue ground substance to reach other tissue cells. Two major mucopolysaccharides are present in ground substance, hyaluronic acid and chondroitin-sulfuric acid. The polyelectrolyte properties of these chemicals vary the viscosity and the amount of water and organic salts held in this compartment of the body (see also p. 318). About half the circulating body proteins are loosely held within connective tissue matrix. These proteins coupled with the stored lipids in *adipose* connective tissue comprise an important source of nutrition for the body. Cellular, fibrous, and ground substance components of connective tissues all participate in protection of the body against infection and in the repair of injured tissues.

Cellular elements found in connective tissues proper differentiate from mesenchymal cells:

The *fibroblasts* are the common connective tissue cells. They are flattened cells with large oval nuclei and a large amount of cytoplasm that sends out a number of long, tapering processes. It is now widely accepted that fibroblasts secrete tropocollagen into ground substance. Extracellular condensation of tropocollagen yields freely branching reticular fibers which have an affinity for silver stains, *argyrophilia* (Fig. 4.21). Growth in diameter (Fig. 4.16) yields the typical collagenous fibers. Elastic fibers with a different composition of amino acids are also similarly formed by secretion of the fibroblasts.

The *histiocytes*, or macrophages, may be as numerous as the fibroblasts, and are similar in structure although larger. They are phagocytic; that is, they are able to ingest many types of particles: cell fragments, debris, bacteria, and dye granules.

Mast cells are frequently found in association with the blood vessels in the connective tissue. Their large granules stain easily with most aniline dyes. These cells are thought to elaborate the anticoagulant, heparin (see p. 265).

Plasma cells are prominent in the connective tissues near the gastrointestinal tract. They are usually flattened, spheroidal cells with a dark-staining, eccentric nucleus. It is believed that the plasma cells are closely related to the transition forms

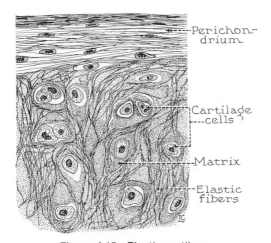

Figure 4.15 Elastic cartilage.

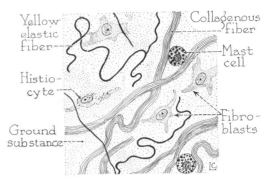

Figure 4.17 Fibroelastic tissue of the superficial fascia.

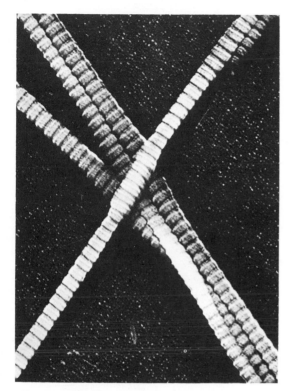

Figure 4.16 Shadowed electron micrograph of collagen fibrils from human skin, showing the characteristic cross banding at intervals of 640 A along their length. (Courtesy of J. Gross and F. O. Schmitt, in Bloom and Fawcett, A Textbook of Histology, 0th Ed., 1960.)

of reticular cells and lymphocytes (Fig. 4.21) and that they produce antibody chemicals for the protection of the body against disease.

Eosinophils (see p. 261) migrate from blood vessels by ameboid motion into loose connective tissues. These cells are conspicuous in inflammatory and allergic reaction.

Although classification of connective tissues proper is difficult, some differences are apparent because of the comparative presence of cells, fibrous elements, and ground substance. The *loose connective tissues* (Fig. 4.17) are common in the fascia around muscle, subcutaneous tissue, supporting blood vessels, nerves, and epithelial membranes. *Dense irregular connective tissue* (Fig. 4.22) is found in the skin and supporting capsules of joints. *Dense regular connective tissue* (Fig. 4.18)

is characteristic of tendons, ligaments, and the cornea of the eye.

Adipose connective tissue is shown in Figures 4.19 and 4.20. Some of the mesenchymal cells give rise to lipoblasts, which are the forerunners of the fat cells. A lipoblast deposits within its cytoplasm droplets of fat, which increase in number and coalesce to form a globule. As the fat globule enlarges, it distends the cell and pushes the nucleus to a peripheral position. In this way adipose tissue stores neutral fat, which serves as a nutritional reserve. The fat deposit in the subcutaneous tissue cushions and protects parts exposed to pressure; and, as it is a poor conductor of heat, it minimizes heat loss through the skin. Organs such as the eyes, kidneys, palms of the hands, and soles of the feet receive support and protection from the adipose tissue accumulated in relation to them. The distribution of fat is different in the child and adult and also in men and women. The action of the endocrine and nervous systems is important in maintaining the dynamic exchange of circulating and stored lipids.

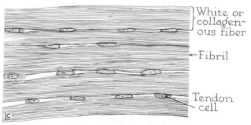

Figure 4.18 White fibrous tissue from a tendon.

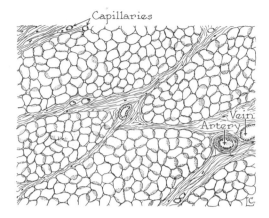

Figure 4.19 Adipose tissue under low magnification. Lobules of fat cells are separated from one another by partitions of fibrous connective tissue.

Figure 4.20 Adipose tissue under high magnification; a few fat cells.

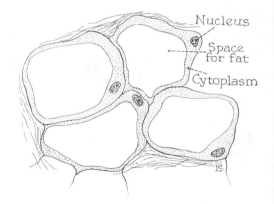

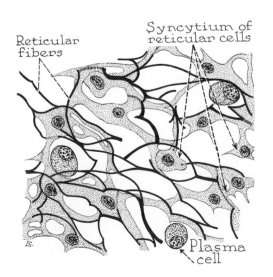

Figure 4.21 Recticular tissue of a lymph gland.

Reticular tissue is similar to fibroelastic tissue, but much more delicate, and is thought to be more primitive in form, since it exhibits less differentiation from embryonic connective tissue. It consists of primitive reticular cells with a network of fine, nonelastic fibers. The cells are stellate or spindle-shaped and adhere closely to the fibers of the reticulum. As in the mesenchyme, the cell processes are in contact and appear to form a syncytium; that is, cell membranes delimiting one cell from another are not easily distinguished, and the cytoplasm is shared in common by the nuclei (Fig. 4.21). It forms the supporting framework of lymph glands, liver, spleen, bone marrow, lungs, and kidneys.

Reticuloendothelium is a term used to designate groups of cells scattered throughout the tissues of the body which have the ability to engulf and store or destroy foreign particles. These cells differ in shape and appearance, and they have accordingly been given different names in the various organs and tissues in which they are found. They include the macrophages or histiocytes of the fibroelastic tissues, the reticular cells of the spleen, lymph glands and bone marrow, Kupffer's cells of the liver sinusoids, "dust" cells in the lung, and the lining cells of sinuses of the adrenal glands and the hypophysis. Antibody chemicals are thought to be produced in the metabolism of macrophages, and plasma cells elaborated by connective tissues. These antibodies aid in the neutralization and destruction of foreign proteins, particularly those of bacterial origin. As a result of some stimulus, particularly an inflammatory one, histiocytes, reticular cells, or any of the stationary cells may become detached and actively motile.

SKIN

The skin or integument is composed principally of epithelial and connective tissues. It consists of two layers: an outer, the epidermis, and an inner, the derma or corium (Fig. 4.22).

The *epidermis* is composed of stratified squamous epithelium. The superficial portion forms the stratum corneum. Here the cells are horny in nature and devoid of nuclei, and the outermost layers are being shed constantly. The deep portion is the stratum germinativum, or germinating layer, in which mitosis of cells replaces those shed from the surface. The basal layer of the stratum germinativum contains melanocytes, which produce the brown pigment of the skin. The *corium* or *derma* is composed of connective tissue and contains many blood vessels and nerve endings. In most of the skin of the body

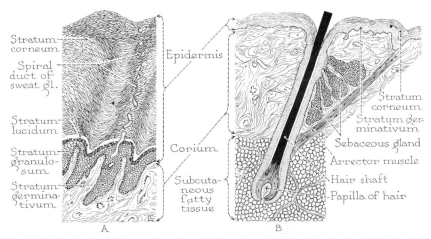

Figure 4.22 *A*, Section of skin from sole of foot. *B*, Section of scalp, showing hair follicle with sebaceous gland (semidiagrammatic).

the upper surface of the derma is thrown into conelike elevations called papillae which appear as ridges on the surface of the skin, especially on the palms and the soles. The papillae contain capillary loops and, in many cases, special nerve endings for the sense of touch. The deep surface of the derma fuses with the subcutaneous tissue so that there is no sharp boundary between them, and the fibers of one layer extend over into the other layer.

The accessory organs of the skin are the nails, hair, sebaceous glands, and sweat glands:

The *nails* are the keratinized or hardened stratum corneum overlying the dorsal surface of the terminal bone of the fingers and toes. The nail bed is composed of stratum germinativum and derma of the skin.

Hair is distributed over almost the entire body. The parts of the hair are the root, or portion below the surface, and the shaft, or portion extending above the surface. The root is embedded in a pitlike depression called the hair follicle, which widens out at its lower end to enclose a small vascular papilla. This papilla is homologous with the other dermal papillae and projects upward into the root, providing nutrition for the growth of the hair. Hair grows as a result of division of the cells of the root. The hair follicle is placed obliquely in the skin, and a small muscle, called the *arrector muscle*, is fastened to its side, causing the hair to stand up in cold or fright and giving the appearance of gooseflesh to the skin.

The *sebaceous glands* secrete sebum or oil. They are of the simple, branched alveolar type, and their ducts usually empty into hair follicles, although some open directly on the surface of the skin. The alveoli of the gland are filled with cells. The cells in the center become infiltrated with fat droplets and then degenerate to yield the oily secretion as a result of their own destruction. Sebum anoints the hair and keeps it from drying and becoming brittle. On the surface of the skin the oil forms a protective film which limits the absorption and evaporation of water from the surface.

The *sweat glands* are simple, coiled tubular glands. The secreting portion of the gland is coiled into a ball and lies in the deep part of the corium. A network of capillaries surrounds the coil. The cells are supplied with nerve fibers from the thoracolumbar division of the autonomic nervous system. Sweat, the product of these cells, passes upward through the duct that opens on the surface of the skin. The amount of sweat secreted varies greatly with changes in environmental temperature, exercise, emotional stress, and other factors. Sweat is a weak solution of sodium chloride in water, with traces of other salts and urea.

The various functions of the skin are described in different sections of this book. They are discussed briefly here.

1. Protection: The skin covers the body and protects the deeper tissues from injury and drying. Ordinarily, bacteria cannot penetrate the epidermis.
2. Regulation of body temperature: The skin serves a major role in maintaining a constant body temperature in warm-blooded animals. It forms a large radiating surface for heat exchange. The rate of heat exchange between the body and the environment will be influenced by the difference in their temperatures, the circulation of blood through the superficial vessels, the evaporation of sweat from the body's surface, and the movement of the layer of air which makes up "a private environment" immediately surrounding the skin. A more extensive discussion of this function is given in Chapter 19.
3. Excretion: The excretory function of the skin (sweat glands) is slight and is confined mainly to the elimination of water, together with some salts and small quantities of urea.
4. Absorption: The absorbing power of the skin is extremely limited; only a few substances can pass this barrier. Examples of such substances are ointments and lotions containing methyl salicylate or compounds of mercury.
5. A sense organ: The skin is an important organ of sensation because it contains the receptors for touch, pain, heat, and cold. Through these

receptors in the outermost layer of the body we receive information of changes in the immediate environment. Not only do we become aware of external conditions, but stimulation of these receptors initiates reflexes that are important in adaptation to the environment. These sensory organs in the skin and their mechanisms are discussed more fully in Chapters 5 and 8.

QUESTIONS FOR DISCUSSION

1. List types of epithelium found in the respiratory tract; in the digestive tract.

Discuss the relationship between the types of epithelium and the function of the parts in which they are found.

2. Discuss how the types of connective tissue are related to the function of the part of the body to which they belong.

3. Discuss the influence of at least two of the functions of the skin on organs or systems of the body.

4. How do glands develop? How are they related to epithelial tissues? To connective tissues? To skin? Explain secretion in terms of transport mechanisms and cell organelles.

5. In what manner is cellular motion concerned with physiologic processes in the body?

UNIT 2

INTEGRATION AND CONTROL OF THE BODY

5. TISSUES OF THE NERVOUS SYSTEM 6. THE SPINAL CORD AND SPINAL NERVES 7. THE BRAIN 8. CRANIAL NERVES; SPECIAL SENSES AND VEGETATIVE FUNCTIONS 9. ENDOCRINE MECHANISMS

It is mainly through the agency of the nervous system and endocrine system that tissues, organs, and systems of the body function as a smoothly running unit. The nervous system acts as an integrating mechanism by which activities of the body are rapidly adjusted in response to stimuli received from the internal and external environment. The high degree of specialization in the properties of irritability and conductivity make nerve tissue admirably suited for the performance of this function. The endocrine system complements these rapid adjustments by the slower and more prolonged responses in tissues and organs. Such changes are brought about by hormones secreted by endocrine glands into circulation and hence into the cellular environment.

TISSUES OF THE NERVOUS SYSTEM

CHAPTER FIVE

THE NERVOUS SYSTEM AS A COORDINATING MECHANISM

The nervous system constitutes the link between the external environment and the many physiological and psychological mechanisms which bring about man's continuous adjustment to the outside world. Sudden environmental changes stimulate advantageously located sensory receptors (Fig. 5.2) of the peripheral nervous system. The impulses that result travel afferently over sensory nerves through simple or complex connections within the centers of the brain and spinal cord, and are efferently directed through peripheral motor nerves to effector organs that bring about a response (Fig. 5.2). Besides providing for receiving informa-tion and for acting upon it in a coordinated manner, the central nervous system "records" and "relates" both stimulus and response, so that man builds up a background of experience that may be used in determining his future reactions. The nervous system also plays a leading role in integrating adjustments to changes in the internal environment with the result that the total response, made up of many separate responses, is coordinated rather than chaotic.

NON-NEURONAL CELLS AND NEURONS (Figs. 5.1-5.4)

Nervous tissue consists of *neurons*, or nerve cells, which are the irritable and con-

57

ducting units, and the non-neuronal *neuroglial cells*, which play the passive role of making up the supporting framework.

Neuroglial Cells. These are the non-nervous interstitial cells of nervous tissue. Similar to the connective tissues in other areas of the body, these cells give mechanical support and protection and appear to carry out nutritive functions. *Ependymal* cells line the spaces of the ventricles of the brain and the central canal of the spinal cord (Fig. 6.2). Three types of neuroglial cells can be identified as central glia. The largest glial cells, *astrocytes*, are found close to neuronal cell bodies, blood vessels, and coverings of the brain and spinal cord (Fig. 5.1). With fewer cytoplasmic processes, the *oligodendrocytes* are located along the axons and dendrites as well as the cell body of the neurone. *Microglial* cells are the smallest and the most variable in form of the central glia. This last type of neuroglia may become phagocytic. (See reticulo-endothelium, page 51.)

Peripheral glia include the *neurilemmal (Schwann) cells* and *satellite cells* upon the neurons outside the central nervous system (Fig. 5.2).

Neurons: The neuron is composed of a cell body and one or more processes. The cell body or *perikaryon* has a prominent spherical nucleus in a central position in most cells. The conspicuous nucleolus con-taining a large quantity of ribonucleic acid is easily seen in the diffuse pale-staining background of deoxyribonucleic acid of the nucleus. A small condensation of DNA may appear as a *nucleolar satellite* in neurons as well as in other cells of female animals. The cytoplasm is crowded with mitochondria, Golgi substance, endoplasmic reticulum, ribosomes, fibrils, and microvesicles. Aggregates of parallel fragments of endoplasmic reticulum whose surfaces are covered by ribosomes are characteristically stained by aniline dyes. These particles appear as the *Nissl bodies* shown in Figure 5.2. The Nissl bodies are sites of active protein synthesis within the cell. Their dissolution or chromatolysis indicates injury to the cell or its processes. The slender interlacing *neurofibrils* in Figure 5.3 are collections of spirally organized protein neurofilaments or tubules 100 Å in diameter. These tubules extend into the neuronal processes. Pigment granules of melanin and lipochrome are frequently found in neurons and may be altered in aging or pathologic processes. Specific shapes are characteristic of neurons in certain parts of the nervous system (Fig. 5.4). Some neurons have been modified so that their principal function is the secretion of hormonal substances or *neurohumors*.

The cytoplasmic processes provide for a

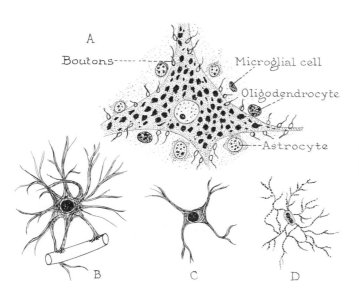

Figure 5.1 *A,* Pyramidal cell of cerebral cortex with axosomatic synapses and Nissl granules. *B,* Astrocyte. *C,* Oligodendrocyte. *D,* Microglial cell.

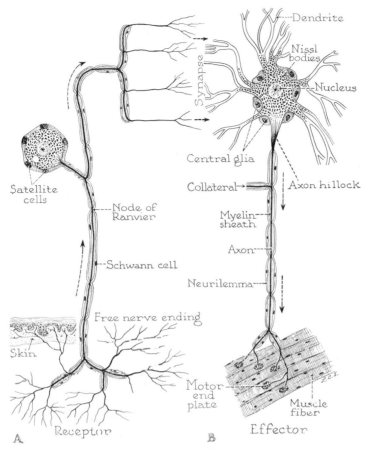

Figure 5.2 Diagram of two types of neurons. *A*, Sensory or afferent neuron. *B*, Motor or efferent neuron.

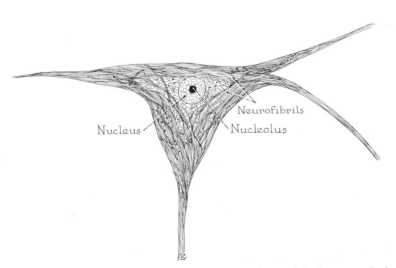

Figure 5.3 Neurofibrils in a cell from the anterior gray column of the human spinal cord.

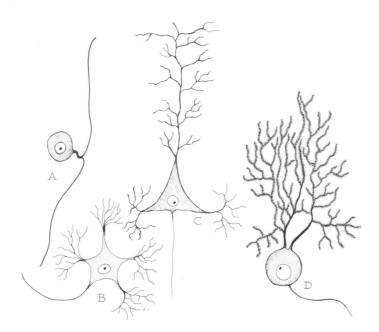

Figure 5.4 *A*, Pseudounipolar neuron from dorsal root ganglion of spinal cord. *B*, Multipolar neuron from anterior column of spinal cord. *C*, Pyramidal neuron of cerebral cortex, and *D*, Purkinje neuron of cerebellar cortex.

receptive zone and a zone of origin and transmission of the nerve impulse. *Dendritic* or receiving processes are usually short, profusely branched, close to the perikaryon and contain Nissl substance (Fig. 5.2, *B*). Dendrites may also lie close to a peripheral structure for sensory reception (Fig. 5.2, *A*). The usually single, non-branched process containing no Nissl substance is the transmitting process or *axon*. The *axon hillock* is the site of origin of the nerve impulse in the motor neuron (Fig. 5.2, *B*). Most of the neurons in the brain and spinal cord are *multipolar* with numerous branched processes (Figs. 5.2, *B*, 5.3, 5.4). The *pseudounipolar* cell shown in Figure 5.2, *A* is typical of sensory neurons in *ganglia* outside the brain and spinal cord. True *bipolar* cells are found in the special sensory areas of the eye, ear, and nose.

The cell membrane (or plasmalemma) and nuclear membrane of the neurons is triple layered and 75 to 100 Å thick. Plasmalemma is the site of transmission of the nerve impulse. A constant renewal of cytoplasm occurs in the interior of the perikaryon and its processes. The flow of cytoplasm through the processes proceeds at a rate of 1 mm. a day and provides for the viability of the cell at far distant points where the physiologic demands of transmission of the nerve impulse remain high.

The circumference of the axons or transmitting processes is covered by neuroglial cells (Figs. 5.1, 5.2). The oligodendrocytes in the brain and spinal cord and Schwann cells of the peripheral neurons provide successive layers of their plasma membrane as a *myelin sheath* for protection of the neuronal process (Fig. 5.5). Numerous layers of myelin give a heavy insulation of lipid material to the *myelinated* fibers. A few layers of myelin or a single glial membrane is found on the *nonmyelinated* fibers (Fig. 5.5). Adjacent Schwann and oligodendroglial cells of the heavily myelinated fibers are separated by the scant space of the *node of Ranvier*. Conduction of the nerve impulse along the plasmalemma jumps rapidly from one node of Ranvier to the next at a rate faster than that found for nonmyelinated fibers. The small amount of cytoplasm, the nucleus, and external cell membrane of the Schwann cells and oligodendrocytes provide a continuous neurilemma as the outermost covering of axons. Functional regeneration of injured nerve processes depends upon the neurilemma.

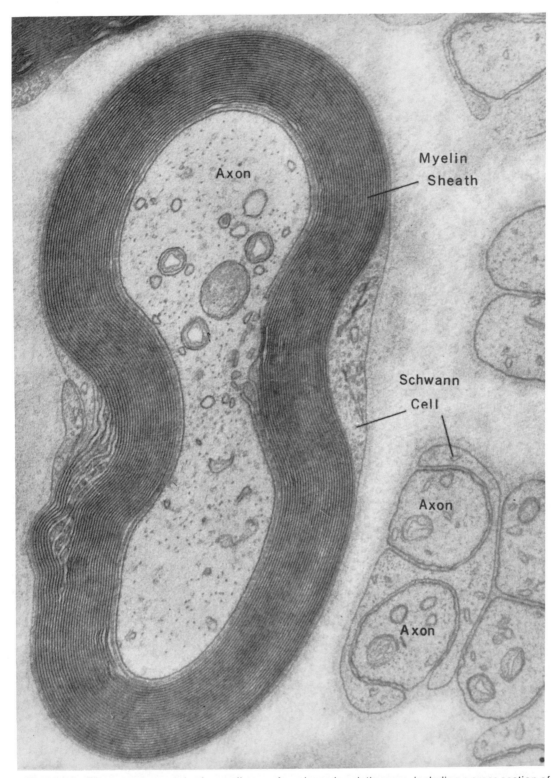

Figure 5.5 Electron micrograph of a small area of a guinea pig sciatic nerve, including a cross section of a myelinated nerve (at the left) and several unmyelinated axons (at the right) partially enveloped by a Schwann cell process. × 50,000. (Courtesy of H. Webster, in Bloom and Fawcett, A Textbook of Histology, 9th Ed., 1968.)

SYNAPSES

The connections between neurons are *synapses*. They are selective routing mechanisms for the nerve impulse where a power step-up or step-down and delay in time can occur. As the axon reaches its point of termination it divides into numerous *telodendria* whose ends are tiny *boutons* (Fig. 5.1, *A*). The form of the synapses may vary considerably as the connections occur from axon to dendrite, axon to perikaryon, axon to axon, and possibly from dendrite to dendrite. The numerical potential of synaptic contact on a particular neuron varies from 2000 on spinal cord cells to 100,000 on cells in the brain. Only a few of these numbers belong to any one synapsing neuron. The physiologic significance of these synaptic contacts is discussed on pages 83 to 85.

In the fine structure of mammalian synapses the expanded termination or bouton approximates a part of the postsynaptic neuron (Fig. 5.6). The cytoplasm and plasmalemma at pre- and postsynaptic sites are thickened and a synaptic cleft of 200 Å can be observed. Mitochondria and a large number of *synaptic vesicles* are found in the presynaptic ending. Synaptic activity involves the release of a chemical mediator from the packets of presynaptic vesicles into the synaptic cleft. The nature of the mediator activity upon the postsynaptic membrane may be such as to cause excitation and result in an excitatory postsynaptic potential (EPSP). Other mediator activity may cause inhibition by the generation of an inhibitory postsynaptic potential (IPSP). Acetylcholine and norepinephrine have been found in synaptic vesicles and are known to generate EPSP's. Serotonin (5-hydroxytryptamine) and substance "P" are thought to act as excitatory

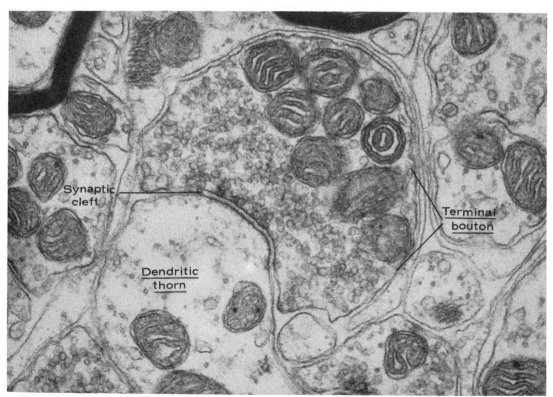

Figure 5.6 Tip of a dendritic thorn, capped by a terminal bouton from the ventral horn of the spinal cord in a rat. The typical features of synapses—mitochondria, clustered vesicles, and the cleft—are well shown. The terminal is enclosed within a thin astrocytic process. × about 60,000. (Courtesy of S. L. Palay, in Bloom and Fawcett, A Textbook of Histology, 9th. Ed., 1968.)

transmitter substances. An inhibitory transmitter substance has not been identified with certainty in mammals.

PERIPHERAL NEURONAL ENDINGS

Neuroeffectors. *Neuroeffector junctions* are specialized terminations of axons of efferent neurons in muscle tissue or glands. In skeletal muscle a single neuron supplies a number of muscle fibers, each fiber ending in a *motor end plate* (Fig. 5.2, *B*). The terminal branches of the axon are expanded and contain numerous mitochondria and synaptic vesicles. The motor end plate is in effect a neuromuscular synapse. Expanded axonal endings occur in smooth muscle, cardiac muscle, and glands. Their fine structure is not fully understood but may be similar to that of the motor end plate, although simpler.

Receptors. While all cells retain a potential for response to general internal stimulation, only certain cells become particularly sensitive to external stimulating forces. These external forces may be changing light wave lengths, alterations in temperature that cause a cell to gain or lose heat, mechanical forces, and chemicals in solution. The specialized cells which respond to variations in external environment are *receptors*. Once the receptor cells are adequately stimulated they will initiate a nerve impulse (p. 69). That is, the receptor will perform transduction of various forms of physical or chemical energy into *generator potentials* (p. 67). Several ways in which receptors may be classified (by location, type of stimulus to which they respond, structural characteristics, and sensation) are summarized in Table 5.1.

A few of the cutaneous receptors are illustrated in Figures 5.2 and 5.7. The simplest type of receptor is the free sensory nerve ending. It consists of a dendritic process which has lost its covering. These endings abound in the hairy areas of the skin, the cornea of the eye, and are also found around the joint capsules and in deeper visceral structures of the body (Table 5.1). Encapsulated nerve endings such as Meissner's corpuscles and the end bulbs of Krause and Ruffini are located in the dermal papillae of hairless skin. The Pacinian corpuscle occurs in the hypodermis, joint capsules, and numerous visceral sites (Table 5.1). Muscle spindles and Golgi organs are discussed and illustrated on pages 188 and 191, Figure 11.1. The receptors associated with special senses will be dealt with in Chapter 8.

ARTIFICIAL AND PHYSIOLOGICAL STIMULATION OF NERVE AND MUSCLE

Special characteristics of nerve and muscle enable man to perceive external and many internal environmental changes and respond to them. The characteristics shared by nerve and muscle are irritability (excitability) and conductivity; muscle has, in addition, the capability to contract. (See page 194.) Environmental changes affecting man are natural stimuli capable of acting upon the sensory end organs described in the previous chapter, and on the specialized receptors. (See Chapter 8.) Natural stimuli may be simulated by artificial means so that their characteristics can be readily measured and controlled. Artificial stimuli are employed in many kinds of physiological experiments on nerve and muscle. Electrical stimulation is frequently used. Temperature changes, chemical agents, light, sound, and mechanical deformation are other types of stimuli used in experimental studies.

A stimulus, to be effective in bringing about a response in excitable tissue, must have certain characteristics: (1) it must be of sufficient strength, (2) the rate of change in environmental conditions of the cell caused by the stimulus must be sufficiently rapid, and (3) the stimulus must be applied for a certain minimum duration. For example, if you were to touch an electric wire and receive a shock of 4 or 5 milliamperes (ma.) of either direct or alternating current, you would not only feel it, but the muscles of your hand and arm would contract violently. If the intensity of the stimu-

TABLE 5.1 CLASSIFICATION OF RECEPTORS

Stimulus Quality	Receptor	Sensation	Type
Nociceptor, mechanoreceptor, thermoreceptor	Naked nerve endings	Pain, touch, temperature	General cutaneous receptors — Exteroceptors
Mechanoreceptor	Meissner's corpuscles	2-Point touch	
Thermoreceptor	Ruffini's end bulb	Warmth	
Thermoreceptor	Krause's end bulb	Cold	
Mechanoreceptor	Pacinian corpuscle	Pressure	
Photoreceptor	Rods and cones	Vision	Special distance receptors — Exteroceptors
Mechanoreceptor	Organ of Corti	Audition	
Chemoreceptor	Olfactory mucosa	Smell	
Chemoreceptor	Taste buds	Taste	Special visceral receptors — Interoceptors
Chemoreceptor Thermoreceptor	Cell groups in hypothalamus	Osmotic pressure, blood temperature, and glucose concentration	General visceral receptors — Interoceptors
Chemoreceptor	Carotid and aortic bodies	Oxygen pressure	
Mechanoreceptor	Walls of vena cava and atria	Central venous pressure	
Mechanoreceptor	Walls of aorta and carotid sinus	Central arterial pressure	
Mechanoreceptor	Free endings in lung	Inflation of lungs	
Mechanoreceptors	Free endings and Pacinian corpuscles in gastrointestinal tract	Stretch, torsion, and pain	
Mechanoreceptor	Golgi tendon organ	Muscle stretch	General receptors — Proprioceptors
Mechanoreceptor	Muscle spindle	Muscle stretch	
Mechanoreceptor	Pacinian corpuscle	Pressure	
Mechanoreceptor	Semicircular canals	Angular acceleration	Special receptors — Proprioceptors
Mechanoreceptor	Utricle (saccule)	Up and down acceleration	

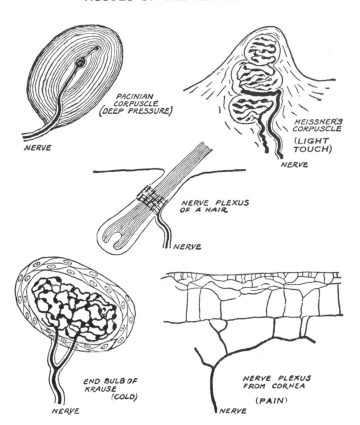

PACINIAN
CORPUSCLE
(DEEP PRESSURE)

NERVE

MEISSNER'S
CORPUSCLE

(LIGHT
TOUCH)

NERVE

NERVE PLEXUS
OF A HAIR

NERVE

END BULB OF
KRAUSE
(COLD)

NERVE

NERVE PLEXUS
FROM CORNEA

(PAIN)

NERVE

Figure 5.7 Receptors and the sensations they arouse. (From Starling: Human Physiology. London, J. & A. Churchill, Ltd.)

lus were reduced below 1 ma., you would not feel it, nor would your muscles contract. Now suppose you were to start with a very low direct current and increase it very gradually. You could tolerate a much higher current, say 5 or 10 ma., without sensation or muscle contraction, provided the electrical contact were good enough to avoid fluctuations in current. You would not respond because the rate of change was insufficient. The lack of response in this case is due to the process of *accommodation*. If, again, you were treated for a muscular pain by high frequency diathermy current, there would be no muscle response to this stimulus because the electrical fluctuations are so rapid that exposure to each pulse of current is less than the minimum duration required for stimulation.

When the energy of an applied stimulus is too low to bring about a muscle contrac-

tion or initiation of a nerve impulse, the stimulus is said to be *subthreshold* or *subliminal*; if the energy is just sufficient to excite the tissue, the stimulus is said to be *threshold* or *liminal*. Stimuli above threshold level may be *maximal* or *supramaximal*.

The imposed changes or stimuli may occur once or may be applied in rapid succession. Under certain conditions, when the intervals between stimuli are sufficiently brief, the energies of subliminal stimuli may be additive, and thus bring about a response. This phenomenon is called *summation of subliminal stimuli*.

When we use the term "threshold" stimuli, we are referring to the energy which is just sufficient to elicit a response *when the tissue is normally excitable*. Immediately after a tissue responds, it loses its excitability to such a degree that no stimulus, regardless of intensity, can excite it. The tissue is then said to be in a refractory state, and the duration of this interval is called the *absolute refractory period*. For a short time after this, when the tissue has partially recovered its excitability, it is said to be in the *relative refractory period*. At this time, stimuli of an intensity greater than that at normal threshold level are required to bring about a response.

Electrical current from domestic and industrial installations, and chemical substances form part of our environment and may act as harmful stimuli when accidental contact is made with them directly. Nervous activity may also be initiated in the higher centers of the central nervous system and result in responses which appear to be quite unrelated to changes occurring in the environment at the time.

CELL MEMBRANE POTENTIALS

Membrane Potentials of Living Cells. The studies of electrophysiologic phenomena have advanced rapidly in recent years as the result of the development of specialized electronic equipment for quantitative electrical measurement and recording. A particularly important advance has been the development of glass capillary microelectrodes of submicroscopic dimensions, which can be inserted into a single cell without interfering with its function. This enables investigators to study the electrochemical conditions within the cell at rest and during activity.

The semipermeable cell membranes separate interstitial fluid from the fluid within the cell. The interstitial and intracellular fluids differ in composition because the membrane permits the passage of some ions while holding back others. Cell membranes, by separating the charged ions, maintain different electrical conditions inside and outside the cell. Thus a voltage difference exists across living cell membranes. This voltage difference is known as the *membrane potential*, i.e., the electrical potential (voltage) difference between the inside and the outside of the cell membrane.

Resting and Injury Potentials. Special methods are used for measuring the electrical characteristics of living cells. If an electrode is placed in the interstitial fluid that bathes living cells and an ultramicroelectrode is brought into contact with the surface membrane of a resting cell, there will be no voltage difference between the two. When one electrode is placed outside the cell and the tip of the microelectrode is pushed through the cell membrane, the voltage difference across the nerve or muscle cell membrane will amount to 70 to 90 millivolts (mV.), the interior of the cell being negative, i.e., -70 to -90 mV., and the exterior zero. This is known as the *resting potential*, the degree of electrification of the resting cell membrane. If the cell membrane is injured so that the cell contents can escape, the surface of the injured cell becomes electrically negative to the surfaces of uninjured cells; this is called the *injury potential*. Thus it may be concluded that the electrical potentials are dependent upon the effectiveness of the cell membrane in separating the interstitial fluid from the intracellular cytoplasm.

The membrane potentials are determined (a) by the distribution of ions along the cell membrane, (b) by the concentration of cations and anions inside and outside the cell, and (c) by the permeability of the cell membrane for these substances. The cell membrane is highly permeable to the K^+ and the Cl^- ions, but only slightly permeable to Na^+, and relatively impermeable to organic anions, A^-.* Thus the potassium ions (K^+) can pass freely in and out of the cell, but relatively few sodium ions (Na^+) can do so.

The membrane of a resting cell is said to be polarized, having ions of opposite sign distributed on its two sides (Fig. 5.8). This resting potential represents a state of dynamic equilibrium. (See page 19.) The intercellular and extracellular fluids are almost equally electroconductive, with Na^+ and Cl^- accounting for more than 90 per cent of the ion concentration outside the cell and only about 10 per cent of the ion concentration within the cell. The K^+ con-

---

*Organic anions are sometimes indicated by the general symbol A^-.

Figure 5.8 Diagram of polarized plasma-lemma of an axon.

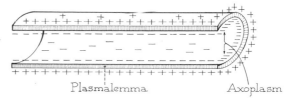

Plasmalemma   Axoplasm

centration is 30 times or more higher inside than outside the cell. In spite of the low permeability of the membrane for sodium, there is a relatively slow leakage of the ions of that metal into the cell (Fig. 5.9). The sodium ions are, however, forced out of the cell, as fast as they enter, by the so-called sodium pump; Na^+ outflow through the membrane, which maintains the ratio of internal to external concentrations of the resting cell, is effected by active transport at low energy cost. (See page 26.) Concurrently, there is an outward leak of K^+, resulting from its high concentration within the cell. This outward movement is counteracted to some degree by the positive electric charge of the Na^+ outside the cell. The K^+ ions that do leave the cell add to the net positive charge on the outside of the membrane. Since the anions A^- are left behind and Cl^- may enter the cell, and since the outflow of K^+ is not balanced by the inflow of Na^+, the inside of the membrane acquires a net negative charge. There is a movement of K^+ into the cell as well as out of the cell. The negative A^- concentration favors the influx of K^+ ions, but this attractive force is partially counteracted by the high concentration of K^+ in the intracellular fluid itself.

Action Potentials. The cells of nerve, muscle and glandular tissue have the special characteristic of excitability. Excitation is a process by which the ionic permeability of the membrane, i.e., its potential, is altered as the result of a stimulus imposed by a change in the cell environment.

The potential difference across a membrane and membrane permeability are closely interdependent. The difference in potential is determined by the relative permeability of a membrane for Na^+ and K^+. In turn, permeability is regulated by the voltage difference across the membrane.

The mechanisms by which the various forms of stimulus energy, light, heat, particular molecules (of chemical agents), or mechanical deformation may bring about changes in the permeability of a membrane are not known. While physiologists have not been able to unravel the detailed events by which the electrical disturbances or various degrees of depolarization of the membrane are brought about, the consequences of such disturbances, called the action potentials, have been studied in considerable detail. Various types of action potentials have been observed in excitable (irritable) cells. These are:

1. *Pacemaker potentials*, from intrinsic spontaneity
2. *Transduced potentials*, from external events
   (a) *Receptor* or *generator potentials*
   (b) *Synaptic potentials*
3. *Internal response potentials*, from immediately preceding activity within the cell
   (a) *Local potentials*
   (b) *Spike potentials*

PACEMAKER POTENTIALS. Electrophysiologic changes have also been recorded in single cells in the absence of environmental changes, under normal steady state conditions. This spontaneous activity has been observed in central neurons, sensory receptors such as the eye, and the pacemaker of the heart. The intracellular changes are observed as a nonpropagated, subthreshold, varying potential of the cell body and adjacent membrane. These spontaneous changes of state may occur at one locus or at several different loci within the cell. These pacemaker potentials sometimes give rise to local potentials that may be observed to extend to the neighboring areas of the dendrites.

TRANSDUCED POTENTIALS. These are changes in membrane potential brought about by influences outside the cell. These

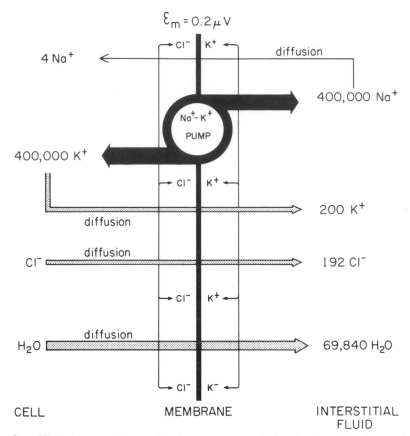

Figure 5.9 Simplified scheme of ion and water movements during the first jiffy of operation of a Na^+–K^+ pump in a hypothetical cell. Cell membrane is assumed to contain a one-for-one Na^+–K^+ exchange pump and to be 50 times more permeable to K^+ and Cl^- than to Na^+. Cell is assumed to have a large initial volume, and ionic compositions of interstitial and intracellular fluid are assumed to be the same except that the latter also contains K^+A^- at a low concentration. Width of arrow indicates size of flux. As shown, exchange of 400,000 Na^+ for 400,000 K^+ by the pump in a jiffy results in net movement of 399,800 K^+ into the cell and 399,996 Na^+ and 192 Cl^- out of the cell. The net efflux of $200 + 192 - 4 = 388$ ions requires a net efflux of 69,840 H_2O molecules to maintain osmotic balance. Four K^+ and Cl^- have separated, charging the membrane capacity (fine line branches from K^+ and Cl^- efflux lines and generated a transmembrane potential of 0.2 microvolts which maintains the Cl^- concentration difference, a 192 Cl^- deficit inside the cell. Operation of pump gradually reduces cell volume and increases ε_m; $[Cl^-]_i$ decreases and $[A^-]_i$ increases. In steady state, all net fluxes are zero and cell volume has decreased until $[A^-]_i$ is approximately equal to $[Cl^-]_o$. Na^+–K^+ pumping rate and membrane permeabilities in real cells are such that hours would be required to achieve steady state condition. Final cell diameter = 10 μ; $P_K = P_{Cl} = 4.5 \times 10^{-6}$ cm. per second; $P_{Na}/P_K = 1/50$ active flux = 10 pMol per cm.^{2}-sec.; 1 jiffy = 20 milliseconds; $C = 10^{-6}$ F. per cm.^{2}. Fluxes calculated on basis of steady state membrane area. (Woodbury, J. W., from Ruch and Patton, ed.: Physiology and Biophysics. 19th Ed. 1965.)

are the mechanisms that mediate responses to stimuli from the external and the internal environments of body acting directly upon the sensory receptor neurons. They are also responsible for changes that occur at postsynaptic membranes, the areas of dendrite or cell body membrane that are contiguous with the terminal process on the axon of the immediately preceding neuron in the nerve pathway and at motor end places. (See page 63.)

The transduced potentials are graded potential changes. The magnitude of the potential change across the membrane is dependent upon the magnitude and, in some receptors, the rate of change of stimulus energy. The changes in permeability due to stimuli or activation from outside the cell may be in the direction of either increased or decreased permeability. The nonspecific increased permeability first to Na^+ then to K^+, which results in depolarization of the membrane, is associated with a decrease in the electrical potential across the membrane. Specific changes in permeability which permit an increased flow of the small K^+ and Cl^- ions, are associated with increased membrane potential. Nonspecific increased permeability up to the point of depolarization of the membrane increases the irritability locally and makes the membrane more responsive to other stimuli. The first stimulus is therefore a *potentiating* or a *facilitating* stimulus in respect to concurrent or immediately succeeding stimuli. Thus a succession of stimuli may be additive in their effect on permeability of the membrane and on excitability of the cell.

INTERNAL RESPONSE POTENTIALS. The changes accompanying the increased permeability of the membrane may affect the electrochemical condition of the cell body and dendrites locally. The responses of most parts of the cell membrane to stimulation do not develop into nerve impulses directly, but rather help to initiate a nerve impulse at the initial segment of the axon. The local electrical disturbances are conducted with decrement, i.e., the electrical change in the condition of the membrane of the cell body and dendrites decreases as its distance from the point of excitation increases. The electrical disturbance at any one point also decreases with time after its initiation.

Successive changes in permeability of the cell membrane may occur relatively rapidly. Each cycle of depolarization following restoration of the increased electrical resistance of the membrane may initiate a succession of local action potentials. The summed effect may reach a critical value and initiate a nerve impulse or a volley of nerve impulses.

NATURE OF EXCITATION AND PROPAGATION OF THE NERVE IMPULSE

Development and Propagation of Spike Potential. The first steps in initiation of a propagated or spike potential are the decrease in cell membrane permeability, and the development of local action potentials. As the permeability of the membrane increases Na^+ ions leak through at an increased rate and tend to neutralize a portion of the excess negative charge inside the cell. The initial inflow of sodium ions makes it easier for other Na^+ to follow, since membrane permeability increases as the potential across the membrane decreases. When the level of a threshold potential difference is reached, the Na^+ ions enter in such quantity that the internal cell potential changes from negative to positive, reaches a critical value for excitation, and initiates a nerve impulse at the initial segment of the axon. The electrical disturbance, which gives the appearance of a spike when recorded graphically, has the characteristic of regenerating itself from point to point, maintaining its amplitude and speed as it is propagated along the entire length of the axon. The spike changes the permeability and potential of the axon membrane immediately ahead of it and sets up conditions for Na^+ to flow into the axon (Fig. 5.10; see electrotonic invasion, alteration). This propagation of an impulse without decrement is the principal characteristic setting these apart from other action potentials.

The analogy that considers the combination of factors that control the permeability of the Na^+ and K^+ as "sodium gates" and "potassium gates" provides a useful concept in visualizing the sequence of events in the development and propagation of the spike potential. Following this analogy, we may say that the sodium gates, which opened during the rise of the spike potential, close as it falls, and the potas-

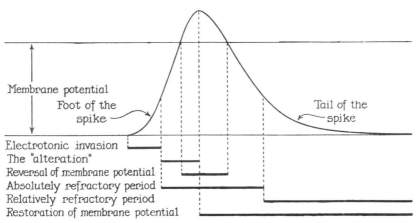

Figure 5.10 The spike potential, really, is not a single simple event. This diagram relates spike potential to membrane potential, and to a number of the events that take place in association with conduction of a nerve impulse. As impulse approaches a given region of nerve, that region is progressively depolarized by electrotonic extension of impulse. When a critical level of depolarization is reached, "alteration" or nerve impulse proper occupies region, and lasts until spike potential reaches it peak. Phase of repolarization then begins. Region is absolutely refractory from onset of alteration until a major restoration of membrane potential has taken place; it is then relatively refractory during "tail" of spike potential. Since spike potential may exceed in voltage membrane potential, it is assumed that membrane potential may reverse during passage of an impulse. (David P. C. Lloyd in Fulton: Textbook of Physiology. 17th ed. 1956.)

sium gates open briefly (Fig. 5.10; see reversal and restoration of membrane potential). The rapid outflow of K^+ polarizes the membrane, restoring electrical negativity to the interior of the cell. The neuron is unresponsive or refractory for a few milliseconds after the initial level of membrane potential has been restored. During this period it is difficult to displace the voltage and initiate another impulse (relative refractory period). The original condition of permeability and electrification of the membrane is, however, quickly restored, and the axon made ready to initiate and propagate succeeding nerve impulses.

The nerve cell is capable of repeated "firing." The periods during which the sodium gates and the potassium gates are open are so brief that relatively few particles are involved, and the composition of the intracellular fluid is scarcely affected. Even if the K^+ store within the cell were not replenished, there would be enough to provide for tens of thousands of impulses. Further, the cellular enzyme system associated with the operation of the sodium pump is capable of maintaining

without difficulty the level of excitability for triggering new spike potentials.

The consequences of the nerve impulse for the succeeding links in the chain of neurons will be considered under synaptic transmission and transmission at effector end plates in a subsequent chapter.

Conduction in Single Fibers and Nerves; All-or-None Law. In discussion of action potentials of the nerve cell, it was noted that all action potentials except the nerve impulse or spike potential were graded responses. The degree of depolarization was said to depend upon the stimulus energy, the magnitude of the electrical disturbance to decrease with increasing distance from the point of stimulation, and the restoration of the initial polarization to proceed rapidly after the last stimulus. The spike potential, however, is conducted without decrement, at an amplitude and velocity that depend only on the physiological condition of the tissue. Restated in a different way, a nerve impulse initiated at a point on a fiber is conducted along the length of the fiber by maximum response at every point along its course for the given physiological conditions. This response is called the *all-or-none law*. The law applies equally to individual muscle fibers: they respond to stimuli by contracting either maximally or not at all. Intact nerves and muscles, however, contain many fibers and are capable of graded response under both natural and experimental conditions. This behavior does not conflict with the all-or-none law; it results from the number of individual fibers in the organ that are being stimulated and are responding at any one time.

Velocity of Nerve Impulses. The velocity of a nerve impulse is quite independent of the strength of the stimulus and is determined only by the size, type and physiological condition of the nerve fiber. The type or group showing the highest velocities includes the larger myelinated nerve fibers. All the motor nerve fibers and the larger sensory fibers belong in this class. The rates of conduction of impulses in these myelinated nerve fibers of the central nervous system vary between 5 and 120 meters per second, depending upon the diameter of the fiber. If we record spike potentials from a nerve trunk at successive points farther and farther from the point of stimulation, the deflection will show first a series of small elevations, and finally separate waves of lesser amplitude than the original spike. The separation of disturbances conducted at different rates increases as the distance from the point of stimulation becomes greater. This is similar to the situation which occurs in distance races in a track meet; the runners start in a group, but because of their different speeds we soon see a succession of individuals rather than a compact group. It has been determined that the smaller the diameter of the fiber within the central myelinated group, the slower the rate of conduction of the impulse. Myelinated nerve fibers of the autonomic system may conduct at rates between 3 and 15 meters per second. Unmyelinated nerve fibers have conduction rates of 0.6 to 2 meters per second.

Significance of Refractory Period. If a nerve fiber is subjected to continued stimulation by repeating effective electrical stimuli at a very rapid rate, it responds by a rapidly interrupted stream of impulses that are comparable to a stream of machine-gun bullets rather than to the continuous flow of a stream of water. We know, however, that if the rate of stimulation is continually increased, a point will be reached where one stimulus will fall at the time the fiber is in a refractory state from the preceding stimuli, and the rate at which the nerve impulses are initiated will no longer show an increase.

While the refractory period of a nerve fiber sets the limit at which it can respond to repeated stimulation, the rates of discharge of normal physiological stimuli in the body are well below this value. This means that the fiber can respond to successive physiological stimuli normally occurring in the body, and still have a margin of safety in its ability to respond at a higher rate.

During the relative refractory period of altered physiological conditions, the magnitude of the nerve impulse is diminished and its rate of conduction slowed. This decrease in the rate of conduction prevents the possibility of interference caused by a second impulse "catching up" to a previously initiated impulse and encountering nerve tissue left in an absolute refractory state by it.

Metabolism of Nervous Tissue. Resting nerve tissue consumes oxygen and gives off carbon dioxide. If placed in a solution containing either carbohydrate or fat, the quantity of the substance decreases, indicating that it is used by the nerve tissue. The prime source of energy for the brain is glucose; peripheral nerves utilize noncarbohydrate and carbohydrate substances. Both respiratory quotients and heat production have been measured for nerve by means of delicate instruments.

Activity increases both oxygen consumption and heat production. Coincident with the passage of the nerve impulse there is a small and rapid heat production, followed by two further periods of heat liberation during the recovery phase. The first of these periods occurs during the relative refractory period and the second after the nerve has regained normal excitability.

Nerve fibers appear remarkably resistant to fatigue because of their property of rapid recovery. However, it has been demonstrated that prolonged activity diminishes the irritability of nerve fibers, decreases the action potentials, rate of oxygen consumption and heat liberation, and prolongs the refractory period.

The Embden-Meyerhof glycolytic pathway is the principal course of carbohydrate metabolism in nervous tissue. Phospholipids represent the majority of lipids in nervous tissue, accounting for about half of the dry weight of this tissue. The biosynthesis and degradation of lipids is closely related to a number of hereditary diseases of the nervous system. Amino acid metabolism is carefully controlled in nervous tissue. The presence of a second group of neurologic disorders is related to disturbed amino acid metabolism secondary to enzyme deficiency. Thiamin (B_1) and cobalamin (B_{12}) vitamin deficiencies also contribute to the presence of neurologic symptoms.

CHARACTERISTICS OF RECEPTORS

A particular sensory terminal may have a low threshold for a given type of stimulus, that is, a change in the environment (Table 5.1). The less complicated free sensory endings may be sensitive to or *overlap* several types of stimulation. A particular hair follicle may have fifteen terminal nerve branches. Clusters of Meissner's tactile corpuscles occur in groups of three to ten. The nerve fibers of touch and pressure endings range from one to twenty microns in size, and their conduction rates range from six to one hundred meters per second. A similar range exists for pain. Every cutaneous sensation has particular attributes of time, space, and intensity. *Wetness* may be cold and pressure without moisture. *Texture* may suggest uniform, smooth tactile stimulation or rough, interrupted tactile stimulation.

It is possible to divide receptors into classes according to response to stimulation. *On receptors* are activated when a stimulus is applied. *Off receptors* cease their activity when a stimulus is applied. *On-off receptors* react to the onset of a stimulus and to the cessation of the stimulus. *Spontaneously discharging receptors* continue to fire at a steady rate. The first three types of receptors cease to produce impulses after a time and are considered to be *adapted*. Touch receptors adapt very rapidly as you will note when you consider that you are not usually aware of the contacts of your clothing. Pressure receptors around joints adapt very slowly and you are generally able to describe where arms and legs are in space without tactile or visual clues. These responses of receptors emphasize that their activation depends upon a change in the environment. When the sensory input to the brain and spinal cord is reduced to a very low level serious disturbance of brain function can occur.

The brain and spinal cord interpret the changes of the environment principally on the basis of the *frequency code* of action potentials from receptors. The intensity or amplitude of the stimulus is coded by the frequency of discharge of the propagated nerve impulse. Associated with the frequency code arising from the receptor potentials are the other characteristics of the receptors: overlapping sensory fields, variable responses to stimulation level, and different rates of conduction and adaptation. These have formed a pattern of nervous activity for an *integration* of the characteristics of the stimulus, *localization*, and *sensory discrimination* to occur in particular areas of the brain. Highly intense stimulation may give rise to pain irrespective of the type of receptor involved.

QUESTIONS FOR DISCUSSION

1. The study of nervous tissue introduces many new structural features. Make a complete, concise statement about each one of the following: neuron, axon, dendrite, Nissl bodies, neurofibrils, myelin sheath, nodes of Ranvier, neurilemma, receptor, effector, afferent neuron, efferent neuron, internuncial neuron, synapse, ganglion, motor end plates, and neuroglia.

2. State the characteristics of an ade-

quate stimulus and describe one or more external environmental changes in terms of these characteristics.

3. Discuss the effect of a succession of subminimal stimuli on the cell membrane potential and level of excitability of a neuron.

4. Discuss the electrical disturbances that can take place in the different parts of a single neuron.

THE SPINAL CORD AND SPINAL NERVES

CHAPTER SIX

GENERAL ORGANIZATION OF THE SPINAL CORD

The spinal cord serves as a reflex center and as a pathway for conducting and integrating afferent nerve impulses as they pass centrally from receptors and peripheral nerves toward the brain, or efferent impulses as they pass from the central nervous system toward the effector organs.

When we speak of a "center" in the nervous system, we are referring to an area where two, several, or a great many neurons have synapses that provide for integrated responses. In serving as a reflex center, the cord provides the connections and performs the functions necessary to carry out a series of events beginning with stimulation of a sensory receptor and terminating with an effector response. The cord provides for two general classes of reflex mechanisms (Fig. 6.6), the *circumscribed*, which involves the same or adjacent segments, and the *diffuse*, which involves a number of segments and brings about widespread integrated action. The intrasegmental activity may be so limited as to involve only two neurons. Here, the afferent neuron process lies in the dorsal root, and the efferent neuron process in the ventral root of the same spinal nerve. A slightly less limited response may involve both right and left sides of a single segment of the cord, i.e., a section corresponding to one vertebra and associated with a single pair of spinal nerves. Spinal reflexes resulting from natural rather than experimentally applied stimuli more generally involve several levels or segments of the cord. The diffuse mechanism involves one or more connector neurons known as *interneurons*. Under some conditions, particularly strong stimulation may result in a spread of nervous activity throughout all segments of the cord.

The conducting and integrating functions of the cord become evident when more than two neurons are involved. Because of the multitude of interconnections of the neurons within the cord, an almost infinite variety of responses is possible. Further study will show, however, that in spite of the number and complexity of interconnections, there is an orderly arrangement of fibers that conduct between the various levels of the spinal cord and between the cord and the brain. It is more difficult to recognize the orderly arrangement of cell bodies and synapses within the cord. Evidence for the existence of orderly arrangement and knowledge of detailed architecture is provided by precise methods of physiological and neurologic experimentation and clinical neurologic observation.

STRUCTURE

General Structure. The spinal cord occupies the upper two thirds of the vertebral canal. It is composed of thirty-one segments of nervous tissue, each bearing a pair of spinal nerves. It extends from the foramen magnum, where it is continuous with the medulla oblongata, to the level of the body of the second lumbar vertebrae. The lower end tapers off to the conus medullaris and filum terminale. Until the third month of fetal life the cord extends the entire length of the canal, but thereafter, because of the more rapid linear growth of the vertebral column, the spinal cord has the appearance of having been drawn upward within the canal. The disparity between the length of the spinal cord and vertebral canal increases the distance between the attachment of the various nerve roots and the intervertebral foramina (Fig. 10.25) through which the several nerves leave the vertebral canal.

Therefore the nerve roots arising from the lumbar and sacral regions pass for some distance in the canal before making their exit. This bundle of nerve roots is descriptively called the *cauda equina* (Fig. 6.1).

White and Gray Matter. Examination of a cross section (Fig. 6.2) shows the spinal cord divided into right and left halves by the anterior median fissure and posterior median septum. A striking feature of the central portion of the section is an area of gray matter which follows the general form of the letter **H**. This gray matter is made up of neuron cell bodies and their processes, which are largely unmyelinated fibers, held together by neuroglia. This central gray core is surrounded by white matter made up of cross sections of longitudinal columns of nerve fibers, most of which are myelinated, embedded in a network of neuroglia.

The two projections of "**H**" extending dorsally are called the *posterior columns* of the gray matter. In some microscopic sections, central processes of the spinal root ganglia cells may be seen entering the posterior column; the posterior root or afferent fibers branch, giving off rami which run in bundles or tracts to other levels of the cord or to the brain, or synapse with interneurons, or with ventral horn cells in the gray matter at the same level. The *anterior columns*, which form the ventral or forward projections of the **H**, contain the ventral horn cells, whose axons constitute the ventral root fibers of the spinal nerve which innervate the skeletal muscles. Some microscopic sections show these anterior root fibers passing out from the anterior columns. The *lateral columns* of gray matter, which are most prominent in the thoracic region of the cord, contain the cell bodies of the axons which, as preganglionic fibers, pass to the sympathetic ganglia; they form part of the motor innervation of the visceral organs (p. 127). The band of gray matter forming the horizontal bar of the **H** is the *central gray* or *gray commissure*. It encloses a small opening, the central canal, and is lined by ependymal cells.

The anterior and posterior columns of gray matter divide the white matter of the cord into *anterior, lateral, and posterior*

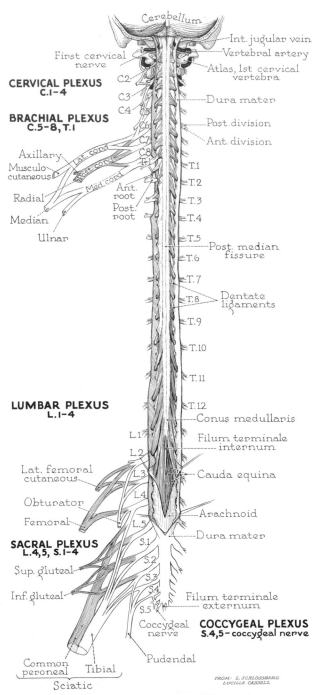

Figure 6.1 The spinal cord and spinal nerves. The dura mater has been opened to the spinal cord and nerve roots. The plexuses are represented diagrammatically. Only the main branches are shown.

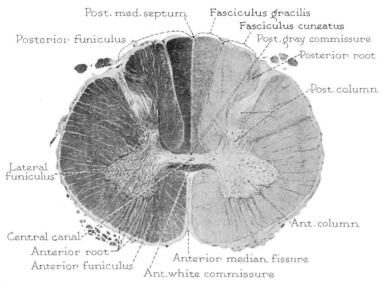

Figure 6.2 Cross section of the spinal cord from the lower cervical region. (From Sobotta and McMurrich.)

portions or funiculi. These funiculi make up the ascending and descending fiber tracts; most of the fibers in these tracts are myelinated. The ascending tracts conduct sensory or afferent impulses to the brain; the descending tracts conduct motor or efferent impulses from the brain to cells of the anterior and lateral columns.

The size and shape of the cord and the proportion of gray and white matter vary in different regions (Fig. 6.3). These variations are more easily understood if they are thought of in terms of both structure and function. As might be expected, the funiculi of the afferent pathways increase in size from caudal to cranial portions of the cord, since new afferent fibers are joining these tracts. The arrangement of the fibers is orderly; the details of the arrangement depend upon the course taken by the fibers. For example, if we consider the posterior funiculi, we find that the afferent fibers from the lower extremities are displaced medially as they pass up the cord by the afferent fibers that enter at successively higher levels. The medial funiculi of the posterior white columns contain afferent fibers associated with receptors in the lower extremities, while the more lateral portions of the posterior funiculi contain fibers associated with the

receptors of the trunk and upper extremities.

The overall gradual decrease in the diameter of the cord from the upper to the lower ends is determined, not only by

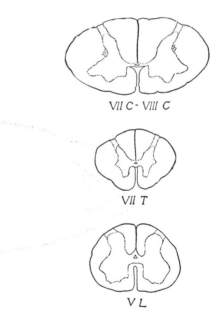

Figure 6.3 Outline drawings of sections through cervical, thoracic, and lumbar segments of the human spinal cord. (From Ranson and Clark: Anatomy of the Nervous System. 10th ed. 1959.)

increase in the size of the afferent bundles as they ascend, but also by the decrease in the descending bundles as they pass caudad. This results from termination of fibers from the higher centers as they form connections with other neurons of the effector pathways at successively lower levels. There are two conspicuous enlargements of the cord, one in the cervical and the other in the lumbar region; the volume of the gray matter is greatly increased at these levels by the many neurons whose fibers supply the arms and legs.

Spinal Nerves. The thirty-one pairs of spinal nerves correspond to segments of the spinal cord, and are classified as eight cervical, twelve thoracic, five lumbar, five sacral and one coccygeal. As pointed out in the previous discussion, the spinal nerves are formed by the fibers from the dorsal and ventral roots which join as they pass out through the intervertebral foramen. Spinal nerves continue for only a few millimeters before dividing into anterior and posterior branches. The roots and divisions are shown in Figure 6.4.

In general, the posterior divisions supply the muscles of the back acting on the vertebral column and the skin covering them. The anterior division is large and forms the main part of the spinal nerve. The muscles and skin of the extremities and the remaining areas of the trunk are supplied by anterior divisions.

The fibers of the nerve are grouped into bundles called funiculi, and each funiculus is ensheathed with connective tissue called perineurium. A looser connective tissue, the epineurium, containing blood vessels and lymphatics, binds the funiculi together and completely surrounds the nerve trunk. A similar organization is found in the arrangement of tendon fibers and skeletal muscle fibers.

In all regions except the thoracic, the anterior divisions of the spinal nerves interlace to form networks of nerves, called *plexuses*. The plexuses thus formed are cervical, brachial, and lumbosacral. In each instance muscular and cutaneous branches are given off from the plexus to the parts supplied. These nerves receive special names. Figure 6.5 shows the distribution of spinal nerves.

The first four cervical nerves form the *cervical plexus*, which supplies structures in

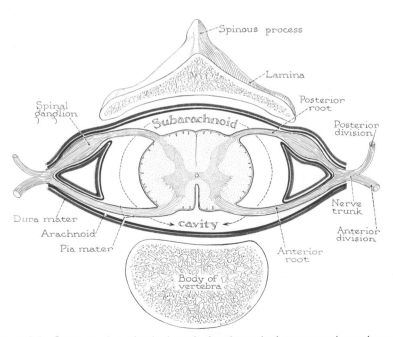

Figure 6.4 Cross section of spinal cord, showing spinal nerves and membranes.

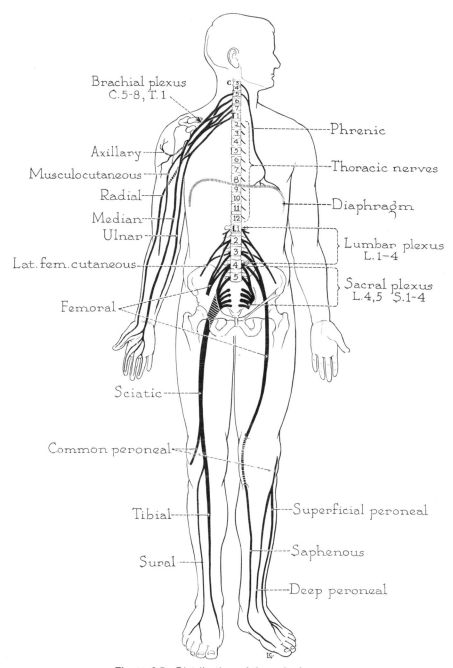

Brachial plexus
C.5-8, T.1

Phrenic

Axillary

Musculocutaneous

Thoracic nerves

Radial

Median

Diaphragm

Ulnar

Lumbar plexus
L.1-4

Lat. fem. cutaneous

Sacral plexus
L.4,5 S.1-4

Femoral

Sciatic

Common peroneal

Superficial peroneal

Tibial

Saphenous

Sural

Deep peroneal

Figure 6.5 Distribution of the spinal nerves.

the region of the neck. One important branch is the phrenic nerve, which supplies the diaphragm.

The *brachial plexus* is formed from the fifth, sixth, seventh, and eighth cervical and first thoracic nerves. This plexus sup-

plies the upper extremity. Important branches are the radial, median, and ulnar nerves of the arm.

The *lumbosacral plexus* is formed from the last thoracic and lumbar and sacral nerves. Its branches pass to the lower extremity. Its great nerves are obturator, femoral, and sciatic.

The thoracic nerves do not form a plexus, but pass out in the intercostal spaces as the intercostal nerves. They supply intercostal muscles, upper abdominal muscles and the skin areas of the chest and abdomen.

Spinal Meninges. The spinal cord and attached nerve roots within the vertebral canal are surrounded by three coverings: dura mater, arachnoid, and pia mater (Fig. 6.4). The *dura mater* is a strong fibrous layer attached by loose connective tissue to the periosteum of the vertebral canal. The dural sheath extends below the end of the spinal cord as far as the second sacral segment. In its lower part it encloses the root fibers of the cauda equina. The *pia mater* is a thin, highly vascular membrane which closely invests the cord and nerve roots. Between the dura and pia mater lies the delicate *arachnoid* of spider-web thinness, as its name implies. The arachnoid and pia mater are separated by the subarachnoid space, which contains the cerebrospinal fluid. The spinal cord, surrounded by the bony walls of the vertebral canal and suspended in a fluid bath, is well protected from injury. The meninges of the cord are continuous through the foramen magnum with those covering the brain.

REFLEX ACTIVITY OF THE SPINAL CORD

Principles of Neural Organization. It is extremely difficult to study the functional activity of the spinal cord of an intact mammal. This is so because of the complex pathways that connect the various segments of the cord with each other and with higher portions of the nervous system. We have learned that the anatomical organization of the spinal cord provides for responses that may involve only one, or several, or all its segments. The development of our knowledge of the spinal cord, and of the entire nervous system for that matter, has depended upon careful, stepwise experimental analysis of individual parts studied in isolation. Only after one

has gained some insight into the functional capabilities of such isolated parts can one begin to understand the complicated activity of the intact nervous system.

The most important single principle to come from such studies is the concept of *encephalization* in the process of neural development of animals. Simply stated, encephalization means the concentration of function at the head-end of the neural tube. We all know that if an earthworm is cut into two pieces both halves can move about. In the higher animals, if the cephalic portion of the nervous system is removed or separated from the lower segments, the lower portion ceases to function in many important respects. Nevertheless some rudimentary function does remain in the isolated lower portion, and an understanding of such remaining function is important to understanding the whole.

As one experiments with successively higher forms, the dominance of the cranial parts over more and more functions becomes increasingly obvious. Such observations have given rise to the concept of *levels of organization*. That is, as one studies higher and higher forms one finds more and more simple functions being taken control of by the higher parts of the brain. Many more functions are encephalized in man than in rats; for example: a rat deprived of its entire forebrain is a relatively normal-appearing rat, while a man deprived of only his cerebral cortex (the most cranial part of the forebrain) can no longer function as a man and cannot long survive.

Effects of Transection of the Cord. Our knowledge of the extent and limitations of independent activity of the spinal cord has come about largely as a result of studies on animals with the spinal cord surgically transected at a desired level, or from studies of humans with accidentally transected cords.

Transection of the spinal cord whether by design or accident is followed by symptoms that may be described as either (1) loss of function (those functions normally initiated by higher centers) or (2) release of function (activity normally held in abeyance or inhibited by the higher centers).

The most obvious symptoms that follow

immediately upon transection are: (1) all voluntary capability for muscular movement below the transection is lost and is never regained; (2) all sensation is lost from portions of the body innervated by parts of the cord below the cut, and is never regained; (3) there is a profound depression of all neural activity in the isolated part of the cord so that complete *areflexia* exists for a time. This latter phenomenon is referred to as *spinal shock*.

Spinal shock is a temporary condition the severity and duration of which varies depending upon the degree of encephalization. In the frog it is relatively mild and of very short duration (seconds or minutes). In primates it is complete and lasts months or even years. The explanation of spinal shock lies in the fact that the resting level of excitability of spinal neurons depends upon their afferent connections. In lower forms most of these afferent connections are of intraspinal origin. In higher forms they are of supraspinal origin. After all or part of the afferent connections to a particular neuron are destroyed, its excitability is decreased proportionately and returns only gradually. The more connections lost the longer will be the period of recovery.

Before continuing our discussion of spinal shock it is necessary to describe some basic spinal reflexes.

Reflex Arc (Fig. 6.6). The general pattern of a spinal reflex arc includes:

1. A receptor;
2. An afferent neuron, with its peripheral process, a cell body lying within a dorsal root ganglion, and a median or central process that enters the posterior gray column of the spinal cord;
3. A synapse;
4. The interneurons that lie within the gray matter of the spinal cord;
5. A synapse;
6. The efferent neuron, with axon, leaving the cord in the ventral root of a spinal nerve;
7. The motor end plate in skeletal muscle, which is the effector.

In the simplest type of spinal reflex, the afferent and efferent neurons may synapse directly without an interneuron. This is characteristic of reflexes initiated by striking tendons of the large skeletal muscles as they cross such joints as the elbow, wrist, knee, and ankle.

Reflex Time. If we initiate a reflex by stimulation of a sensory nerve ending, there is a delay before the muscle responds. The delay is determined by (1) the time for passage of the impulse along the afferent nerve, (2) the time for passage across the synapse or synapses, (3) the time for passage along the efferent nerve, and (4) the latent period of the muscle. The *central* or *reduced reflex* time is the time for passage of the impulse over that part of the reflex arc which lies within the spinal cord. The greater part of the reduced reflex time is consumed in transmission of the impulse across the synapse. In general, the longer reflex times indicate a greater number of synapses in the reflex arc.

Spinal Reflexes. The word *reflex* means a discharge in afferent neurons that is *reflected* back from the central nervous system to the periphery of the body and

Figure 6.6 Diagrammatic section through spinal cord and a spinal nerve to illustrate a simple reflex arc.

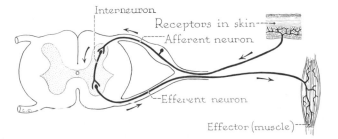

that results in muscular or glandular *reflex activity*. Such reflex activity may be either excitatory or inhibitory.

The simplest type of spinal reflex is the *stretch reflex* (basis for the common knee jerk). This reflex requires only a two neuron chain with a synapse in one segment of the spinal cord (Fig. 5.2). The afferent arm of the stretch reflex is one nerve fiber, beginning with a muscle spindle or neuromuscular sensory receptor, that is sensitive to stretch and that is located within a muscle. This afferent neuron synapses upon a motor neuron in the ventral horn of the spinal segment, innervating the muscle concerned. The motor neuron when fired brings about a contraction of the muscle fiber, thereby counteracting the stretch. The stretch reflex is important in maintaining body posture, e.g., when the muscles of the thigh and leg are stretched while standing, they contract and maintain the knee in a fixed position.

The *flexion reflex* is another simple and primitive reflex. The stimulus for setting up this reflex is a nociceptive or uncomfortable stimulus applied to the skin. The discharge set up by the skin receptors affects several segments of the cord and results in a contraction of the flexor muscles, which withdraws the limb from the source of painful or damaging stimulation.

The afferent arm of the flexion reflex also affects other neuron pools in the same and other spinal segments, which brings about contraction of the extensor muscles in the opposite limb. This is the *crossed extension* reflex. Its usefulness to the individual who steps upon a sharp object with one foot is obvious. Well coordinated (by higher centers) alternating flexion and crossed extension reflexes are also useful in locomotion.

Finally, certain *long spinal reflexes* must be considered. Like the flexor and crossed extension reflexes, the long spinal reflexes involve multineuron chains and several segments of the cord. These are reflexes that bring about well-timed contraction of muscles in other parts of the body when a reflex is set up in one limb. The long spinal reflexes form the basis for such actions as alternate extension of the arms to maintain balance, as, for example, when walking a tightrope or when standing on one leg. Such long spinal reflexes are important in walking, standing, swimming, and other such complicated neuromuscular activities.

Now we return to the temporal sequence of recovery of reflexes after spinal shock. The first reflex to return in all animals is the simplest one, the knee jerk. In frogs it is either never lost or is absent for only a matter of seconds. In carnivores this reflex is observable within a few minutes after cord section. In man it is absent for hours or days thereafter.

The second reflex to reappear is the flexion reflex. The interval is minutes for frogs, hours for carnivores, and days, weeks, or even months for man. In man this reflex always develops sooner or later if the cord below the level of transection is not damaged or destroyed.

Crossed extension reflexes and the long spinal reflexes (the scratch reflex in frogs and carnivores) also reappear after longer intervals. The comparative time course in lower animals and man parallels that described in regard to the simple reflexes.

The "scratch reflex" in carnivores and frogs demonstrates an important characteristic of the spinal cord in response to stimulation of sensory receptors. If one pinches or strokes an area of skin of an experimental animal below the level of the cord section, a hind limb will accurately scratch the area stimulated. This is called *local sign* and demonstrates that the mechanisms for locating a particular stimulus with reference to body area are located within the spinal cord. The animal will, of course, be quite unaware of either the stimulus or the response of its isolated spinal cord.

A reflex which appears after a very long interval in lower animals and man warrants special comment. It is not seen in individuals with intact spinal cords—it is seen only in paraplegics. This is the *mass reflex*. The effective stimulus is tactile. The efferent pathway involves both somatic and visceral structures. In the chronic spinal preparation after many months of survival a very slight tactile stimulus applied to almost any skin area innervated by the isolated cord may evoke a convulsive type of reflex pattern in which legs, trunk musculature, and urinary and gastrointestinal sphincters are all involved. This reflex does not always develop but it can be a troublesome problem for man, since even a light bed cover can elicit it.

Visceral reflexes also are affected by spinal cord section and spinal shock. During spinal shock the detrusor muscle of the bladder loses its tone, and the sphincters become tightly contracted as a result of the loss of inhibitory influence from above. This condition leads to retention of urine and harmful distention of the bladder. In man it can be alleviated by catheterization. As spinal shock wears off, tone returns to the detrusor muscle and the sphincters become less spastic. Reflex emptying of the bladder will follow slight pressure exerted upon the abdominal wall or tactile stimulation of the perineum or lower extremities. This reflex emptying is at first incomplete but may become normal later. This so-called "cord bladder" develops in carnivores after one or two weeks. In primates it develops only after a month or longer.

Reflexes that control emptying of the rectum are also depressed during spinal shock, but later return. As in the case of the bladder, tactile stimulation of the skin innervated by the lower spinal segments may evoke reflex defecation in man and in animals.

Sexual reflexes that are important in copulation are inherent in the cord but normally are controlled by higher centers. In humans with transected spinal cord, erection can be evoked by tactile stimulation of the external genitalia or of the perineum. Ejaculation rarely if ever occurs in "spinal" males. There are no data available on human females. From the results of experiments on other primates, however, one might predict that the human female with a complete cord section should be capable of conception, normal gestation, and parturition.

Some Mechanisms of Conduction and Integration in Nerve Pathways. When the critical excitatory level in a receptor is reached, the generator potential is repeti-

tively discharged and decreases in rate during the time the stimulus is being applied. This decrease in the rate of discharge with continued application of a constant stimulus is a phenomenon known as *adaptation*. Naked nerve fibers adapt most quickly, as may be shown by the fact that one or at most two or three discharges occur from maximal stimulation. Touch receptors stimulated by bending a hair give rise to a volley of impulses that die in about one-fifth of a second. Pressure endings show a somewhat longer period of adaptation. The proprioceptors such as are involved in the maintenance of posture, however, adapt very slowly, continuing to discharge for many minutes or even hours. Pain endings also continue to discharge over such long periods of time that it appears questionable whether adaptation exists for this type of ending.

In general there is multiple innervation of sensory areas: (a) one fiber may connect with several receptor cells, (b) a given receptor cell may receive innervation from two or more sensory fibers, and (c) sensory fields of individual neurons may overlap, sometimes to a considerable extent.

The direction of travel of impulses is determined by the synapse. Whereas excitation in a nerve process may spread in both directions, the transmission across a synapse is always from axon terminals to the succeeding neurons. Synaptic potential may be either excitatory or inhibitory. The type of response appears to depend on the properties of the synapse.

The structural arrangements in which the axon terminals of one axon synapse with the dendrites of several succeeding neurons, or in which several axons converge on a single neuron, provide for a wide variety of structural combinations that could determine the nature of individual responses.

The *divergent* mechanism provides for excitation of two or more neurons by a single axon whose rami or branches form synaptic connections with them. The principle of *convergence* describes the structural arrangement whereby the axons of two or more neurons may converge and provide dual or multiple innervation of a single neuron (Fig. 6.7).

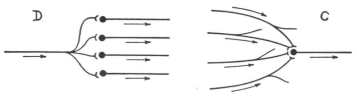

Figure 6.7 Diagrammatic schemata of divergent mechanism (*D*) and of convergent mechanism (*C*). Arrows indicate direction of impulse conduction. (David P. C. Lloyd in Fulton. Textbook of Physiology. 17th ed. 1956.)

This may be illustrated by considering a *motor unit*, i.e., a ventral horn cell or efferent unit together with the muscle fibers it innervates. Let us visualize a pool of six ventral horn cells (Fig. 6.8, *A*). We will assume that the fiber from an afferent nerve *a* synapses with two of these motor units; a fiber from nerve *b* synapses with two other motor units. Fibers from both *a* and *b* converge on each of the two remaining ventral horn cells providing for their dual innervation. If we should measure the strength of contractions resulting from intense stimulation of nerve *a* and nerve *b* separately, the sum of the work performed would be greater than the total work obtained by simultaneous stimulation. Since we have chosen an intensity of stimuli that, when applied to one nerve, will discharge the motor units having overlapping innervation, these motor units will be unaffected by impulses arriving over the other nerve. This phenomenon is known as *occlusion.*

Let us now assume another situation for the pool of the six ventral horn cells (Fig. 6.8, *B*). Here, a moderate stimulus to the peripheral receptor of nerve fiber *a* will cause the discharge of one ventral horn cell and like stimulation of *b* will also discharge one motor unit. Stimulation of *a* is also assumed to have a subthreshold effect on three other ventral horn cells, two of which may also be affected subliminally

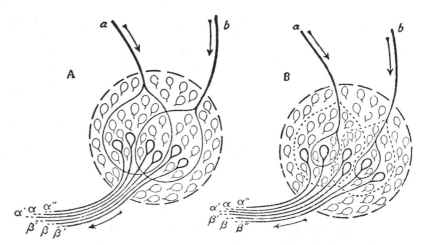

Figure 6.8 Diagrams to illustrate occlusion (*A*) and facilitation (*B*). *A,* Broken line encloses a pool of neurons some of which are discharged by presynaptic path *a,* some by path *b.* Fields overlap so that when *a* and *b* are stimulated together, the discharge is less (6 neurons in diagram) than sum of the discharges evoked by *a* and *b* severally (which would be 8 neurons). *B,* Broken line encloses a pool of neurons some of which are discharged by presynaptic path *a,* some by path *b.* The subliminal fields of path *a* and path *b* are enclosed by dotted lines. These subliminal fields overlap. According to diagram *B,* stimulation of *a* or *b* would cause discharge of one neuron each; the sum, 2 neurons; but, stimulated together, *a* and *b* cause 4 neurons to discharge because of summation in subliminal fringe. Two neurons are represented as remaining in subliminal fringe on combined stimulation of *a* and *b.* (From Sherrington: Proc. Roy. Soc., 1929, *105 B:*332-362.)

by stimulation of *b*. If we now stimulate fibers *a* and *b* at the same time or in rapid succession, the impulses from one fiber may not only discharge one motor unit, but also set up a local excitatory state in the three neurons in its subliminal fringe. The discharge of the second fiber, if it occurs before the excitation in the two neurons with common innervation dies down, will bring about summation of subthreshold stimuli and these two neurons also respond. Thus stimulation of the first nerve contributing to the dual innervation provides for *facilitation*, so that an additional subliminal stimulus through the fibers of nerve *b* results in a discharge of the motor units. Facilitation allows for *spatial summation* of subthreshold stimuli, i.e., subliminal stimuli from different areas of the body.

If we increase the strength of stimulation so as to obtain a higher frequency of discharge of the receptor end organs of nerve *a*, facilitation may again occur by summation of successive stimuli, i.e., *temporal summation*, so that all four of the motor units with which it synapses will respond.

CONDUCTING PATHWAYS OF THE SPINAL CORD

The white matter of the spinal cord serves as a conducting pathway for the long *ascending* and *descending* tracts by which afferent impulses reach the brain and efferent impulses pass from motor centers in the brain to the anterior gray column cells of the cord and so modify muscular movement. The fibers are arranged in bundles which show a functional as well as an anatomic grouping. A bundle of fibers having the same origin, termination, and function is called a fiber tract. The funiculi of the spinal cord are composed of a number of such tracts that have definite locations (Fig. 6.2). The origin means the location of the cell bodies giving rise to processes forming the tract. The termination refers to the point at which the axons forming the tract end.

We can follow the course of a tract in experimental animals by sectioning a part of the conducting pathway, observing all the deficiencies that appear upon recovery, and allowing degeneration of the fibers that have been separated from their cell bodies so that they may be identified in postmortem histologic sections. This procedure involves using the most refined surgical techniques under conditions which parallel those in operating rooms for human patients. The experimental animals must be given the best postoperative care. All sensory and motor changes must be noted and related to specific areas of the body during the period that is allowed for degeneration to take place. In this way we learn that sensory receptors, located on either the same or the opposite side of the body, cease to function and that the response to one or several types of sensation is lost. Subsequent study of histologic sections at various levels of the nervous system shows degenerating areas which can be followed to determine whether the tracts continue on the same side of the cord throughout their course or whether they cross to the opposite side, and the direction and extent of displacement within the funiculi. We can also determine whether a single neuron or a chain of neurons makes up the pathway between two levels of the nervous system. The experimental results on animals are carefully related to clinical and postmortem findings on man. Detailed, precise and orderly observation and careful recording, and analysis and summary of the findings of individual experiments over a period of many years afford us a background for interpreting the pathways of conduction and for understanding the structural and functional basis for sensory and motor deficits and pathologies.

Pathways and Fiber Tracts. The successive links of an ascending (afferent) pathway are referred to as first order neurons, second order neurons, and so forth. The first order neuron is associated with the receptor end organ. The location of its synapse with the second order neuron varies with the pathway. In descending (efferent) pathways we speak of upper motor neurons and lower motor neurons. The lower motor neuron is associated with the effector organ, while the upper motor neuron includes the cells of origin and interneurons that lead to the ventral horn cell, i.e., the cell body of the lower motor neuron.

The fiber tracts form a link in the pathway for conduction of afferent or efferent impulses between the higher centers and the cord. With some exceptions, the names of these tracts are sufficiently descriptive to indicate the funiculus in which they travel in the cord, the general location of the cells of origin, and the level of the location of the axon terminals that connect with the neurons making up the next succeeding link in the pathway. For example, we may conclude that, in the *lateral spinothalamic tract*, the fibers run in the lateral funiculi of the cord, that the cells of origin lie within the spinal cord, and that the terminal processes of its axons make their connections with other neurons at a thalamic level. Since it passes from the lower level of the spinal cord to the thalamus at the higher level, it is an ascending or afferent tract. The axon fibers of the *ventral corticospinal tract* lie in the ventral funiculus, its cells of origin in the cortex, and its terminal connections in the spinal cord. We would conclude from this that it was an efferent or descending pathway.

Description of specific pathways will be limited to several of the major ascending and descending tracts (Fig. 6.9). If the

time allotted for study of the conducting pathways permits, the student is urged to refer to the standard texts on neurology and neuroanatomy for a more comprehensive treatment than is warranted in an anatomy and physiology text.

ASCENDING TRACTS

1. Fasciculus Gracilis and Fasciculus Cuneatus. These are the two major afferent fiber tracts that make up the posterior funiculus or dorsal white columns (Fig. 6.10). They are fibers of *first order neurons* that form the first link in the pathway for sensations of position, movement, and touch-pressure. The cells of origin lie in the posterior root ganglia. The peripheral processes of these neurons are associated with neuromuscular and neurotendinous spindles, Pacinian corpuscles, and free nerve networks. All these receptors may be located as proprioceptor nerve endings that, through their connections, give rise to the sense of position and movement. The peripheral processes of other posterior root cells of origin of fasciculi cuneatus and gracilis are associated with exteroceptors that, upon stimulation, give rise to sensation of discriminative touch, and those that are concerned with deep or massive pressure. The axons of the spinal ganglia cells enter the cord through the posterior roots, where they divide to form

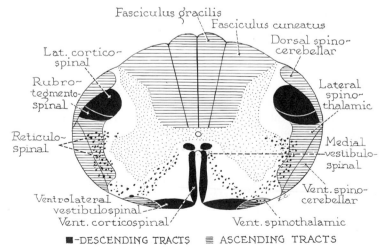

Figure 6.9 Diagram of a cross section of the spinal cord, showing the position of fiber tracts in the white matter.

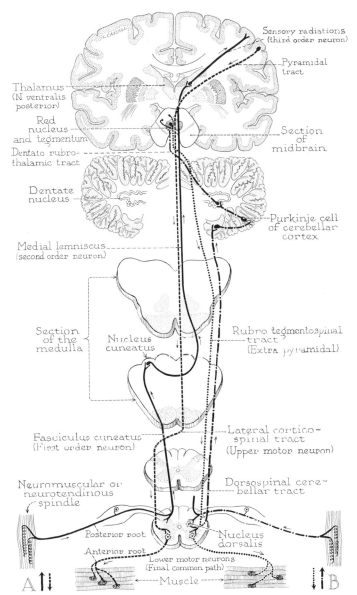

Figure 6.10 Diagram showing pathways of muscle sense impulses. *A*, Conscious muscle sense impulses. *B*, Unconscious muscle sense impulses.

reflex connections, short descending branches, and short and long ascending branches. The long ascending branches which make up the fasciculi gracilis and cuneatus pass upward and terminate in the medulla on the same side of the cord; i.e., the fibers are uncrossed. The fibers of fasciculus gracilis which occupy the most medial position in the posterior columns

(Fig. 6.9), above the midthoracic region, come from the sacral, lumbar and lower thoracic segments. In consequence, they are associated with sense of position, movement and pressure-touch in the lower extremities and the lower part of the trunk. The fibers of fasciculus cuneatus which occupy the lateral positions (Fig. 6.9) in the posterior funiculus have their cells of origin in the upper five thoracic and cervical segments.

The terminal rami of fibers of these tracts are located in the nucleus gracilis and the nucleus cuneatus of the medulla oblongata. Here they form synapses with other neurons whose fibers cross to the opposite side; the final link in the pathway is made up by neurons from the thalamus to the cerebrum. Thus, while the fasciculi cuneatus and gracilis are uncrossed, crossing of the second order neurons results in the central representation of one side of the body lying in the cerebral hemisphere of the opposite side (Fig. 6.10).

A great deal of information is derived from sensory impulses conveyed over the posterior columns. Our knowledge of the position and exact movement of the extremities eliminates the need for following them with our eyes when we are performing a task. We walk without looking at our thighs, legs or feet as long as the dorsal columns are intact. When we hit or kick an object, we look only at the object, since we know where our feet and hands are and can continuously adjust their route until contact is made. Sensation of touch-pressure enables us to recognize objects by feeling their shape and texture, and to be aware that an object or objects are touching our body at one or more points. Sensations of pressure enable us to discriminate between weights of objects. Because of the local sign of the receptors, we can identify the points on the body at which tactile stimuli or pressure is being applied.

2. Ventral Spinothalamic Tracts. These tracts, which, like the fasciculi gracilis and cuneatus, convey impulses arising from stimulation of proprioceptor nerve endings and Meissner's and Pacinian corpuscles, are formed by fibers of *second order neurons.* They ascend in the ventral funiculus (Figs. 6.9, 6.11). The first order neuron lies in the posterior root ganglion. The central fibers of the spinal ganglia may synapse in the dorsal gray matter with neurons whose axons leave the gray matter, cross to the opposite side of the cord and pass to the ventral spinothalamic tract in the contralateral ventral funiculus. A second route for the first link in the pathway is by way of the short ascending branches that pass up with the fibers of the posterior white columns and, after giving off collaterals, synapse with neurons in the gray matter at a higher segmental level; the axons of neurons cross the midline and join with the other fibers of the ventral spinothalamic tract. Thus the cells of origin of the second order neurons that make up the ventral spinothalamic tract lie in the gray matter of the opposite side. They terminate in the ventral posterior nucleus of the thalamus. The third order neuron of the pathway passes between the thalamus and the homolateral cerebral hemisphere. Groups of short fibers which re-enter the spinal cord gray for multiple synapses accompany these tracts as *ascending reticular components.*

The structural arrangement that provides the uncrossed fasciculi gracilis and cuneatus and the crossed ventral spinothalamic tracts as pathways for afferent impulses of position and movement, touch and pressure, explains why hemisection of the cord does not result in a complete loss of these sensations; the crossed fibers provide for functional receptors after homolateral hemisection of the cord (Fig. 6.11).

3. Spinocerebellar Tracts. These tracts lie in the lateral funiculi. They are composed of fibers of *second order neurons.* The first link in the pathway between the neuromuscular spindles and the cerebellum is formed by the spinal ganglion cells. Central processes of these neurons pass to cells of the posterior gray column. Here they synapse with the cells of origin whose axons pass to the outer margin of the lateral funiculus to form the spinocerebellar tract (Figs. 6.9, 6.10). The ascending fibers are grouped as *dorsospinocerebellar* and *ventrospinocerebellar tracts.*

The spinocerebellar tracts, although ascending or afferent pathways to the higher centers, do not result in conscious sensation. The afferent impulses that arise in the neuromuscular receptors are those of "unconscious muscle sense" that, when integrated in the cerebellum, are concerned with muscular coordination.

4. Lateral Spinothalamic Tracts. These tracts are made up of second order neurons which constitute the second part of the pathway for pain and temperature.

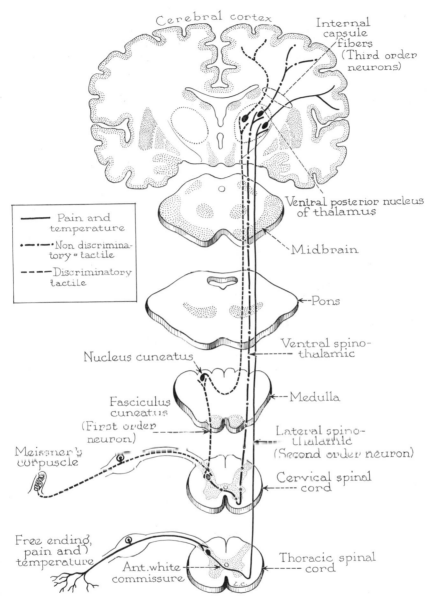

Figure 6.11 Diagram of sensory mechanisms for pain, temperature, and touch.

The peripheral processes of spinal ganglion cells are associated with the free nerve endings that are the pain receptors, and the end bulbs of Krause and brushes of Ruffini that are the receptors for cold and heat, respectively. The central processes enter the cord and bifurcate into short ascending and descending branches. They give off collaterals to the gray matter at several levels. The collaterals and terminal rami synapse with the cells of origin of the lateral spinothalamic tract that lie in the dorsal portion of the posterior gray columns. Axons from the cells of origin pass to the opposite side of the cord and ascend without interruption in the lateral funiculi to end in the thalamus (Figs. 6.9, 6.11). The majority of the afferent neurons for pain and temperature impulses from the face enter the brain stem and spinal cord in the trigeminal cranial nerve. Second order fibers ascend in close association with the spinothalamic tracts. The third order neurons for pain and temperature pass from the thalamus to the cerebrum. *Reticular* fibers accompany the lateral spinothalamic tract.

Since these tracts are crossed, hemisection of the cord results in loss of the sensations of pain and temperature on the opposite side of the body below the level of the section.

DESCENDING TRACTS. The somatic efferent tracts have their cells of origin in the higher centers and terminate in the anterior gray columns of the spinal cord. Though such connections may afford an uninterrupted pathway between the higher level and the anterior horn cell of a motor unit, the more usual structural arrangement includes one or more interneurons. Axons from a number of areas of the higher centers may have synapses with a single anterior horn cell; in consequence, this cell with its peripheral axon in the anterior root of the spinal cord is called *the final common pathway*. Efferent impulses that reach the final common pathway may be either excitatory or inhibitory.

1. Corticospinal Tracts. The two corticospinal tracts (pyramidal tracts) form the great motor pathways from the cerebral cortex and carry impulses for voluntary movement. They are for the most part concerned with skilled voluntary movement requiring participation by a small number of muscle groups. Both tracts take their origin from the large pyramidal cells in motor area 4 of the cerebral cortex. Just before entering the spinal cord, about four-fifths of the fibers undergo a decussation or crossing in the medulla oblongata. These decussating fibers, together with a lesser number of uncrossed fibers, form the large *lateral corticospinal tracts*; the remainder of the uncrossed fibers pass downwards to continue in the ventral funiculus as the *ventral corticospinal tracts* (Figs. 6.9, 6.10). The fibers of the ventral corticospinal tract that do not decussate in the medulla cross over a few at a time in the anterior white commissure at the suc-

cessive levels of the cord at which they terminate; it is believed that a small number of these fibers do not cross at all. Fibers from both tracts end directly, or through interneurons, on anterior horn cells. The lateral tracts supply muscles of the extremities. The fibers of the ventral tract convey motor impulses that reach the muscles of the trunk.

As in the afferent system, there is a crossed relation between cortical representation and peripheral structure. Cortical representation of the great majority of the efferent pathways is located on the side opposite to that of the effector muscles receiving the impulses. Lesions of the cortical areas or of the pyramids of the medulla result in a weakness in the opposite side of the body and marked decrement in performing precise movements. The paralysis is not complete, however, because other fibers, which pass in the extrapyramidal tracts, remain. The results of lesions of the cord are more severe, since greater numbers of fibers may be involved. If inhibitory influences of the higher centers are interrupted, the reflex activity of the postural reflexes may be greatly exaggerated, and spastic paralysis results.

2. Rubrotegmentospinal Tract. This tract arises in the cells of the red nucleus and adjacent tegmental gray matter of the midbrain. The majority of fibers cross to the opposite side at once and descend in the lateral funiculus to end in relation to motor cells in the anterior columns of the cord. Since the red nucleus and tegmentum receives fibers from the cerebellum, the rubrotegmentospinal tracts may be said to carry impulses of unconscious muscle coordination, or, in other words, through it muscular movements are unconsciously adjusted to proprioceptive impulses.

3. Vestibulospinal Tracts. These tracts have their origin in the cells of the vestibular nuclei of the medulla. They descend in the anterior funiculus and end in the anterior columns around motor cells. These tracts adjust muscular movements to impulses received from the semicircular canals and so assist in the maintenance of muscle tone and equilibrium.

4. Reticulospinal Tracts. Groups of short

fibers which reenter the spinal cord gray for multiple synapses in their descending course are intermingled with the other paths, particularly those in ventral and lateral funiculi, as reticulospinal tracts. Part of their termination is upon the cells of the anterior column. The coordinating influence of basal ganglia, brain stem, and cerebellum upon the final common path is brought about in part by these reticulospinal tracts.

The position of the corticospinal pathways in the brain has provided the designation of *pyramidal tracts* as a term of common use. Rubrotegmentospinal, vestibulospinal, and reticulospinal pathways are *extrapyramidal tracts* in their location and function.

CONDUCTION AND INTEGRATION IN THE PERFORMANCE OF A SIMPLE TASK. If we trace a typical impulse through the nervous system we shall see how the tracts of the spinal cord function as conducting pathways, and understand more clearly the operation of the nervous system as a whole. The course over which this impulse passes may be followed on the diagram in Figure 6.10.

The use of the muscles of the forearm and hand in carrying a suitcase requires almost constant adjustment of muscular movements. Although the act is initially consciously directed by the cerebral cortex, the details of these adjustments are largely automatic, and attention (consciousness) is centered mainly on where we are going rather than on the discrete muscular movements involved in supporting the burden while walking over uneven surfaces. These unconscious adjustments are made in response to proprioceptive impulses of stretch. The cell body of such tendons of the arm and hand. Specialized receptors (neuromuscular and neurotendinous spindles) of afferent neurons receive impulses of stretch. The cell body of such a neuron is in the posterior root ganglion. Its axon enters the cord through the posterior root and, as previously described, divides into a long ascending and a short descending branch having collaterals and terminal rami. The impulse passes to a second neuron in the posterior column gray. The axon of this neuron carries the

impulse by way of the dorsal spinocerebellar tract to the cerebellum. Connection is here made through internuncial neurons with the Purkinje cells of the cerebellar cortex. These large cells may be said to form the beginning of the efferent path. Their axons end in the dentate nuclei of the cerebellum. The cells of the dentate nucleus give rise to the great efferent tract from the cerebellum that reaches to the red nucleus of the midbrain. Here the impulse is relayed to the cells of origin of the rubrospinal tract, which descends in the lateral funiculus of the cord to end around motor cells in the anterior column. The axons of these cells pass out in the nerves of the brachial plexus to the muscles of the forearm and hand, and the impulses passing over them stimulate the muscles to contract.

The path traveled by this impulse is that of an elaborate neural arc with components comparable to a spinal reflex arc. It differs from a spinal reflex in that it involves many parts of the brain as well as the cord and many neurons instead of two or three. The principle, however, is the same and the response is reflex in nature; that is, it is an involuntary response to a stimulus.

Continuing with the same illustration, we know that we are conscious of sensations of stress and strain in the forearm and hand. What are the pathways by which the impulse reaches the conscious centers and by which the response is made?

The stimulus is received as before by special receptors in muscles, joints, and tendons, and is carried by afferent neurons of the spinal nerves. The cell bodies of the neurons are in the posterior root ganglia, and their central processes pass into the cord in the posterior root. The impulse passes by way of the long ascending branches of the processes. These fibers form the fasciculus cuneatus, which ends in the medulla at the nucleus cuneatus. The axons of the cells of the nucleus cuneatus cross in the medulla and relay the impulse to the thalamus, from which it passes to the sensory area of the cerebral cortex by a third neuron. The impulse has now reached consciousness. Connection is established between the sensory area and

motor area of the cerebrum by an internuncial neuron, and the impulse passes
to the large pyramidal cells. The axons of
these cells form the corticospinal tracts,
the great motor pathways from the cerebrum. Since the impulse is destined for
the muscles of the arm, it will be carried
in the lateral corticospinal tract, which
crosses in the medulla and ends in the cord
around cells in the anterior column. These
neurons carry the impulse by way of the
nerves of the brachial plexus to the muscles of the upper extremity, and the position of arm is voluntarily changed. The
diagram of these pathways (Fig. 6.10)
shows that impulses which enter the cord
on one side of the body pass to the opposite side of the brain. In like manner,
the motor area on one side of the cerebrum
controls movements of the opposite side of
the body. Sensory and motor pathways
both cross at some point in their course.

It is probable that any given impulse
travels, not over one or two pathways as
we have pictured it, but over many. It
should be understood that the possibilities
of the nervous mechanism are almost infinite.

QUESTIONS FOR DISCUSSION

1. How are the right and left sides of
the brain related to the right and left sides
of the trunk and extremities?

2. Describe the passage of a nerve impulse from its initiation at the receptor
over the nerve pathways to an effector
organ. State the possibilities of following
alternative pathways on the basis of convergence, divergence, spatial and temporal
summation, and occlusion.

3. What would be the effects of the following injuries: severance of posterior
roots L4, 5, S1—4; severance of anterior
roots C5—T11; bullet wound in right half
of T5 spinal cord; injury to the right
pyramidal tracts above their decussation
in medulla; injury to the posterior column
white matter?

THE BRAIN

The brain is a suprasegmental monitoring apparatus concerned with all somatic and visceral functions. It serves as a center for integrating responses to sensory stimuli arriving by way of the ascending tracts of the spinal cord and of the cranial nerves, and to nervous activity of its various component parts. It contains centers (i.e., groups of neurons with their functional connections which provide for integrated responses; apexes of several functional neural arcs) that control respiration, circulation, temperature regulation, and fine adjustment of voluntary movement, as well as areas for the senses of sight, smell, hearing, balance, touch, and taste. There are areas for associative memory, which allow us to store, recall, and make use of past experience through the establishment of the relatively simple conditioned reflexes and through the more complex and less well understood process of learning.

The brain is defined anatomically as that part of the nervous system which lies within the cranial cavity of the skull. It arises in the embryo as a development of the head end of the neural tube. The canal extending throughout the length of the tube, which in the spinal cord is reduced almost to obliteration, widens out in the different parts of the brain to form spaces called *ventricles* which are filled with cerebrospinal fluid.

Differences in size, shape, and function of the different portions of the brain assist in its division for convenience of description into three chief masses, the *brain stem*, the *cerebellum*, and the *cerebrum*. The parts of the brain stem from below upward are *medulla, pons, midbrain, and interbrain*. The cerebrum appears as a huge flowering outgrowth from the upper end of the brain stem. It covers most of the interbrain and midbrain. The cerebellum develops as an extension from the lower part of the brain stem or hind brain. The main divisions of the central nervous system are shown in Figure 7.1.

A rich blood supply is needed to sustain the high metabolic requirements of the

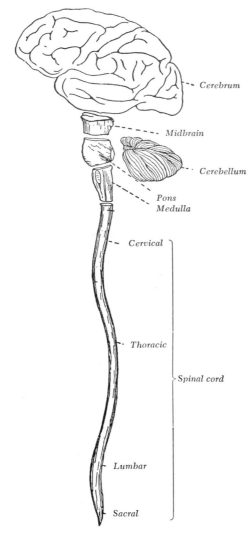

Figure 7.1 Diagram illustrating the gross divisions of the central nervous system. (From Morris: Human Anatomy. The Blakiston Co.)

Labels on figure: Cerebrum, Midbrain, Cerebellum, Pons, Medulla, Cervical, Thoracic, Spinal cord, Lumbar, Sacral

The capillaries in brain substance have endothelial cells which are tightly adherent to each other. Their basement lamina is continuous and supported by processes of astrocytes. Collectively these constitute an effective *blood-brain barrier*. Only water, carbon dioxide, and oxygen pass across the blood-brain barrier easily; glucose appears to be dependent upon active transport into neural tissues.

CRANIAL MENINGES

The membranes covering the brain are the same as those covering the cord: namely, dura mater, arachnoid, and pia mater (Fig. 7.2).

Dura Mater. The dura mater is adherent to the inner surface of the cranium, where it serves the double function of an internal periosteum and a covering for the brain. Two conspicuous folds of dura mater, the falx cerebri and the tentorium cerebelli, are given off from the deep surface.

The *falx cerebri* is a sickle-shaped partition which passes in the great longitudinal fissure between the hemispheres. Its inferior border arches over the corpus callosum.

The *tentorium cerebelli* forms a roof for the posterior cranial cavity and separates the cerebellum from the posterior part of the cerebrum.

The two layers of dura mater separate along certain lines to form venous channels, sinuses, for the return of blood from the brain (Fig. 15.11, p. 283). The more important sinuses are the superior sagittal sinus along the superior border of the falx cerebri, the inferior sagittal sinus on the inferior border, the straight sinus where the falx cerebri joins the tentorium, the transverse sinus along the occipital and temporal bones, and the cavernous sinus in the region of the sella turcica. There is a rich sensory innervation to the dura. Irritation of those sensory nerve endings is responsible for many headaches.

Arachnoid. The arachnoid membrane is a fine membrane loosely disposed over

brain. Glucose and oxygen are utilized continually in the activities of the brain which is never at rest. Gray matter receives a better distribution of the capillary branches of the cerebral circulation than does white matter. The pattern of arterial supply and venous drainage of the brain is illustrated and discussed on pages 282 to 283. The larger blood vessels are well supplied by sensory nerves. Marked distention of these blood vessels is reflected in headache, as the vascular receptors for pain are intensely stimulated.

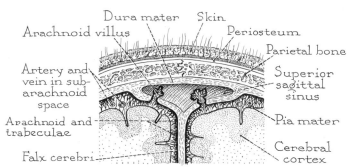

Figure 7.2 Meninges. (After Netter.)

the surface of the brain. It does not dip down into the sulci between convolutions. The arachnoid membrane forms finger-like projections, called villi, which penetrate the walls of the venous sinuses and extend into them. The subarachnoid space, like its counterpart in the spinal cord, contains the cerebrospinal fluid. The cerebrospinal fluid tends to pool in *cisterns* where subarachnoid space is relatively large.

Pia Mater. The pia mater is closely adherent to the surface of the brain and is carried down into the sulci between convolutions. Cells of the pia mater reinforced by astrocyte processes form a *pia-glial membrane* similar to the blood brain barrier (p. 94). The pia mater lines the ventricles and covers the choroid plexuses of these spaces. Close association of some arachnoid and pia mater may be referred to as the leptomeninges.

space under pressure equivalent to that of 150 mm. of water. It forms a watery cushion for the brain and spinal cord, thus protecting them from injury. Since it contains nutrient substances and waste products, the cerebrospinal fluid apparently plays an important part in metabolism also.

This fluid is formed principally by diffusion and secretion in the tela choroidea of all four ventricles. Tela choroidea are blood capillary networks covered by pia mater and ependymal cells and found on the roofs of the third and fourth ventricles and portions of the wall of each lateral ventricle. Fluid formed in the lateral ventricles passes (Fig. 7.3) through the interventricular foramina (Monro), where it is joined by the fluid produced in the third ventricle, to pass through the cerebral aqueduct (Sylvius) into the fourth ventricle. The fluid from all four ventricles

CEREBROSPINAL FLUID

The cerebrospinal fluid is a clear, slightly viscous liquid circulating in the subarachnoid space about the brain and spinal cord. Its chemical composition is somewhat similar to that of lymph and closely resembles that of the aqueous humor of the eye. The major constituents include water, 70 mg. per cent glucose and 700 mg. per cent NaCl. Small amounts of other inorganic salts, proteins, urea, and cholesterol, along with a few white blood cells, are also found in the fluid. About 150 cc. of the fluid are found in the subarachnoid

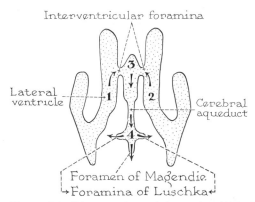

Figure 7.3 Diagram of ventricles and course of cerebrospinal fluid.

passes from the roof of the fourth ventricle through the foramen of Magendie and foramina of Luschka to the subarachnoid space.

It slowly circulates through subarachnoid space to the arachnoid villi. These villi are minute, fingerlike processes of the arachnoid, projecting into the venous sinuses on the superior surface of the brain. As the cerebrospinal fluid reaches the arachnoid villi it is absorbed into the venous sinuses and systemic circulation. Along the route of the cerebrospinal fluid are spaces or *cisterns* in which the fluid tends to collect as it circulates. These cisterns in the subarachnoid space are in relation to the end of the spinal cord and ventral surface of the brain. A large cerebellomedullary cistern is located over the roof of the fourth ventricle.

PARTS OF THE BRAIN — STRUCTURE AND FUNCTION

Medulla.　The medulla lies between the spinal cord and the pons (Fig. 7.1, 7.4). Its structure closely resembles that of the cord. All the ascending and descending pathways of the cord are represented in it. Some of the fiber tracts end in the medulla (fasciculi gracilis and cuneatus), while others pass through it, crossing from one side to the other without interruption (lateral corticospinal tract). The central canal of the cord opens out on the dorsal surface of the medulla into the large space, the fourth ventricle. The medulla contains the nuclei (i.e., a large group of cell bodies) of origin of the last five cranial nerves, eight to twelve inclusive. The reticular formation occupies a large portion of the medulla. Within the medulla are such vital centers as the cardiac, vasomotor, and respiratory centers. These mechanisms are discussed throughout the text under Vegetative Functions (p. 131), Control of Heart and Blood Pressure (p. 310), and Respiration (p. 235).

Pons.　(Figs. 7.1, 7.4) The pons lies above the medulla and in front of the cerebellum. It consists of a bridge of fibers that connect to the cerebellum and join the midbrain above with the medulla below. The pons forms an important part in the corticopontocerebellar path by which the cerebral hemispheres and the cerebellum are integrated. Nuclei of the fifth, sixth, and seventh cranial nerves are located in the pons.

Midbrain.　The midbrain is the short part of the brain stem which lies just above the pons (Figs. 7.1, 7.4). It consists dorsally of the tectum, ventrally of the cerebral peduncles, with the tegmentum lying between. The *cerebral aqueduct* passes lengthwise through the midbrain tectum to connect the third and fourth ventricles. The tectum presents two pairs of rounded elevations, the corpora quadrigemina. The superior colliculi (anterior quadrigeminal bodies) correlate visual reflexes. The inferior colliculi (posterior quadrigeminal bodies) correlate auditory reflexes.

The *cerebral peduncles* are two large diverging stalks that pass into each half of the cerebrum (Figs. 7.4, 7.7). They are composed of pyramidal and corticopontine bundles of fibers that form conducting pathways for impulses from the cerebrum to the pons, cranial nerves, and spinal cord. Nuclei of the third and fourth cranial nerves are located in the tegmentum of the midbrain. The *red nucleus*, which contains some of the cells of origin of the rubrotegmentospinal tract, is in the rostral part of the midbrain tegmentum. Most of this pathway takes its origin from the tegmental cells caudal to and encircling the red nucleus. These areas of the midbrain are under the influence of the cerebellum, dorsal thalamus, and basal ganglia. This pathway becomes important in *extrapyramidal tract* regulation of automatic and associated skeletal muscular movements.

Interbrain.　The *diencephalon* or interbrain is located between the midbrain and the cerebrum. Diencephalic structures may be subdivided further into the dorsal thalamus, ventral thalamus, hypothalamus, and epithalamus. The *epithalamus*, which includes the pineal gland, is closely related to olfactory connections which lead by multisynaptic pathways to the cranial nerve nuclei involved in feeding reflexes.

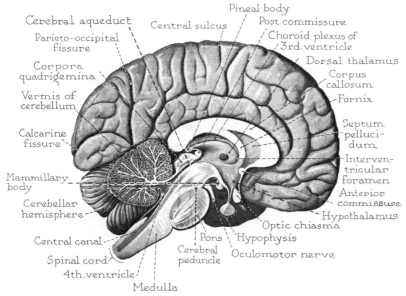

Figure 7.4 Midsagittal section of the human brain. (After Sobotta and McMurrich.)

The *ventral thalamus* is closely related to the basal ganglia of the cerebrum and the tegmentum of the midbrain, with which it is continuous. Extrapyramidal neural impulses from cerebral cortex to midbrain may synapse in the ventral thalamus in their descending course through the brain stem. An imaginary line connecting the anterior commissure to the posterior commissure across the third ventricular space (Fig. 7.4) would separate the dorsal thalamus from the hypothalamus. The dorsal thalamus lies above the imaginary line and is bounded superiorly by the fornix. The hypothalamus lies below the imaginary line and includes the optic chiasm, hypophysis, and mammillary body.

The *dorsal thalamus* contains a number of separate nuclear centers. Functional and anatomic relations can be utilized as a method of classification of these nuclei. *Relay* nuclei transmit the ascending sensory impulses to the cerebral cortex. Auditory radiations relay through the medial geniculate nucleus. Visual radiations relay from the lateral geniculate nucleus. Somatic sensory radiations of pain, and thermal, proprioceptive, and tactile impulses relay from the posterior part of the ventral nucleus. Cerebellar impulses re-

lay from the lateral portion of the ventral nucleus.

The *association* nuclei of the dorsal thalamus are interconnected with the cerebral cortex and receive neural impulses from the adjacent dorsal thalamic nuclei. An important association nucleus is the dorsomedial nucleus, closely related to the (posterior) ventral nucleus and to the orbital surface of the frontal portion of the cerebral hemisphere. It is concerned with emotional or *affective tone* (state) in the individual. This is expressed as feelings of pleasantness or unpleasantness to environmental stimuli.

The *diffuse conducting* nuclei of the dorsal thalamus will be discussed in relation to the *reticular* formation.

HYPOTHALAMUS. Neural impulses reaching the hypothalamus are derived principally from the dorsal thalamus, reticular formation, basal ganglia, cerebrum, and olfactory formation. A wide variation in function is found among the cellular groups of the hypothalamus. Some are particularly sensitive to the osmotic pressure of the blood plasma (osmoreceptors), others to the level of the blood glucose (glucostats), and still others to the fluctuations of the temperature of the blood in the capillaries of the hypothalamus. Several nuclei are known to be capable of forming neurosecretions.

Neurosecretions are important in the influence of the hypothalamus upon the hypophysis, i.e., the pituitary gland (p. 137). Hypothalamohypophyseal tracts extend from groups of hypothalamic cells, manufacturing polypeptides which migrate through the axoplasm, to storage areas in the posterior lobe of the pituitary gland. These secretions are released as vasopressin and oxytocin, the hormones of the posterior pituitary gland. Hyperosmotic blood stimulates the hypothalamic osmoreceptors to initiate the release of the antidiuretic hormone (ADH) or vasopressin. ADH acts upon the kidney (p. 321) to increase the resorption of water back into the blood stream. Other neurosecretions are manufactured at or near the eminence of the hypothalamus just caudal to the hypophyseal stalk. They are secreted into the capillaries in this region and circulate through a portal system of blood vessels (p. 282) which convey them to the anterior lobe of the pituitary gland. In this manner the *hypothalamic-releasing factors* regulate the activity of the ovaries and testes, adrenal glands, and thyroid gland. Six releasing factors have been extracted from the hypothalamus. These hormonal polypeptides include corticotrophin-releasing factor (CRF), thyrotrophin-releasing factor (TRF), growth hormone-releasing factor (GHRF, SRF), follicle-stimulating hormone-releasing factor (FSHRF), luteinizing hormone-releasing factor (LRF), and prolactin inhibitory factor (PIF).

Appetitive mechanisms for food and thirst are under hypothalamic control. A *feeding center* and *satiety center* are found in the lateral walls of the hypothalamus. The feeding center appears to be active at most times and subject to transient inhibition by the satiety center. The glucostat cells are found within the satiety center. As the glucostat cellular utilization becomes low the feeding center cellular activity is high and the individual is hungry. Anterior to the feeding center are osmoreceptor cells whose response to increased osmotic pressure in the circulating blood initiates thirst and *drinking*.

There are numerous adjustments of the viscera involved in *temperature regulation* (p. 378). Groups of cells in the anterior portion of the hypothalamus initiate the processes which result in heat loss. Dilation of blood vessels in the skin and sweating promote loss of heat from the body. The constriction of cutaneous blood vessels, erection of the hair, and shivering result in conservation of the heat of the body. These latter processes are regulated from the posterior hypothalamus.

The complex mechanisms that maintain chemical and thermal constancy of the internal environment are integrated in the hypothalamus. There is some general localization of the visceral regulation (p. 381), which is characterized as *parasympathetic* in the anterior portion of the hypothalamus and *sympathetic* in the posterior portion of the hypothalamus. No sharp separation of such regulation exists and *homeostasis* appears to be the result of interaction of the various groups of cells in the formation of neurosecretions or visceral nerve impulses.

Cerebellum. The cerebellum lies in the posterior cranial fossa. Covered by the tentorium of the dura mater, it is separated from the cerebrum. The *vermis* is the middle portion which grossly resembles a segmented worm and, when sectioned (Fig. 7.4), has the foliated pattern of arbor vitae leaves. Large right and left cerebellar *hemispheres* are joined to the vermis. A *superior cerebellar peduncle* containing the efferent *dentatorubrothalamic tract* connects the cerebellum to the midbrain. The *middle cerebellar peduncle* containing the afferent *pontocerebellar tracts* relates the pons to the cerebellum. Numerous afferent and efferent pathways between the medulla and the cerebellum are the substance of *the inferior cerebellar peduncle.* Dorsospinocerebellar, reticulocerebellar, and vestibulocerebellar tracts are representative of afferent connections in this peduncle. Cerebelloreticular and cerebellovestibular tracts complete the respective efferent side of the arc of fibers from the cerebellum to the medullary nuclei.

The outermost layer of cerebellum (Fig. 7.4) is composed of strata of gray matter, the *cerebellar cortex*. The large Purkinje cells (Fig. 5.4,*D*) are a conspicuous layer of the cerebellar cortex. The *dentate nucleus* is the largest and most important of non-cortical, deeply placed masses of gray in the cerebellum. The efferent dentato-rubrothalamic tract is formed by axons of these cells.

Voluntary movement of skeletal muscles can proceed without the cerebellum. However, these movements are clumsy and disorganized. Although all neural activities in the cerebellum are below the level of consciousness it functions as a reflex center for coordination and refinement of muscular movements. The general scheme of cerebellar function allows nerve impulses to be returned or *fed back* to the same region from which they originated. This is indicated by the fact that there are both vestibulocerebellar and cerebellovestibular fibers. Such connections are ipsilateral automatic control devices or analogs of *servomechanisms.* A great proportion of the information transmitted to the cerebellum is derived from proprioceptive and tactile sources (spinocerebellar, reticulocerebellar, and vestibulocerebellar tracts) and from the cerebral cortical areas (corticopontine tracts) also serving voluntary motor controls (pyramidal tracts). The cerebellar cortical relay from Purkinje cells directs the efferent signals from the deep-seated cerebellar nuclei (dentatorubro-thalamic, cerebelloreticular, and cerebellovestibular tracts) that are necessary to make the appropriate muscular adjustments.

These muscular adjustments are variations in action of synergistic groups of muscles, relative to tone and length of contraction. Subsequent to injury of the cerebellum there may be disturbances in posture and walking. The strength and fine coordination of muscular contraction may be inappropriate for a task such as buttoning buttons. It may not be possible to maintain the sequence of muscular contraction, for example, to bring the hand up to the mouth. Given sufficient time, other mechanisms of the brain can compensate for cerebellar injury.

Cerebrum. The cerebrum is the largest and most prominent part of the brain. It is divided into right and left hemispheres by a deep cleft, the great *longi-*tudinal fissure*, in which the falx cerebri is located. As in the cerebellum the outer covering of the cerebral hemispheres is composed of gray matter, called the cerebral cortex, spread over an inner mass of gray and white matter. The lateral ventricles within each hemisphere connect with the third ventricle through the interventricular (Monro) foramen.

THE CEREBRAL CORTEX. The cortex or gray mantle of the cerebrum is thrown into numerous folds called convolutions or *gyri* (Fig. 7.5). The grooves between the convolutions are *sulci*. Such an arrangement makes it possible for a large surface area (estimated at about 220,000 square millimeters) to be contained within the narrow confines of the cranial cavity. Deep sulci or fissures divide each hemisphere into distinct areas known as frontal, parietal, temporal, and occipital lobes. The *central sulcus* (fissure of Rolando) separates the frontal and parietal lobes. The *lateral fissure* (fissure of Sylvius) separates the temporal lobe below from the frontal and parietal above. The *parieto-occipital fissure* marks off the boundaries of the occipital lobe. There are five lobes in each hemisphere: frontal, parietal, temporal, occipital, and insula. The insula lies within the lateral fissure and is not visible on the surface. The fissures and lobes, with the exception of the insula, are shown in Figures 7.5 and 7.6.

LOCALIZATION IN THE CEREBRAL CORTEX. Physiologic and anatomic studies show two kinds of localization in the cerebral cortex, the functional and the topographic. These studies involve such processes as direct electrical or chemical stimulation of the surface of the cortex, excitation of receptor organs with simultaneous recording of electrical potentials in the cortex, and surgical removal of various parts of the cortex. There are three general types of cortical tissue: motor cortex, sensory cortex, and associational cortex.

Different areas of the cortex have distinctive types of histologic organization and in some cases distinctive cell types (such as the pyramidal cells of the motor cortex). These different types of cortex have been numbered on the basis of their histologic appearance. Such numbers are

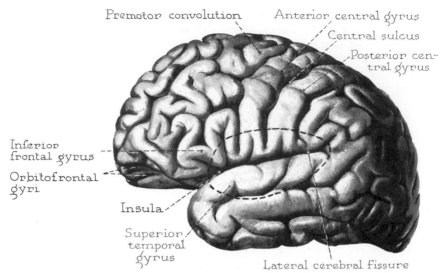

Premotor convolution   Anterior central gyrus

Central sulcus

Posterior central gyrus

Inferior frontal gyrus

Orbitofrontal gyri

Insula

Superior temporal gyrus

Lateral cerebral fissure

Figure 7.5 Lateral view of the human cerebral hemisphere. Dotted lines outline the insula. (After Sobotta and McMurrich.)

an aid to learning and some are used frequently in the literature and in discussion. The more widely used numerical designations will be noted subsequently.

The motor (or pyramidal) cortex is, as its name implies, concerned with the voluntary movement of skeletal muscles. Electrical stimulation of this portion of the cortex in a lightly anesthetized animal or in a conscious human (under local anesthesia) results in movement of certain muscle groups. These areas of the cortex lie ahead of the central sulcus. There is detailed localization within the motor cortex. Different body areas have discrete representation within areas 4 and 6 (Fig. 7.6). That is, if a stimulus is applied far down on the lateral surface of the hemisphere in area 4, the face muscles will contract, but if the part of area 4 near the midline is stimulated, the leg muscles will respond. As a result of the decussation of the corticospinal tracts, the left motor cortex controls the muscles of the right side of the body, and vice versa (Fig. 7.7).

Surgical removal or injury of a part of the motor cortex will result in a deficit in movement of the muscle group represented in the areas removed or damaged.

The degree of impairment varies with the species, being least in the rat and most in the great apes and man.

The somesthetic sensory areas 1, 2, and 3 lie behind the central sulcus. These areas serve both cutaneous and deep sensibility, including touch, pressure, pinprick, and muscle sense. Electrical stimulation of these areas produces neither movement nor discrete sensations. Such stimuli, applied to conscious humans under local anesthesia, produce feelings of numbness, tingling, or constriction, which are referred by the patient to a particular area of the body. Pain is *never* reported from such stimulation.

As in the case of the motor cortex, various parts of the body have neural connections with definite portions of the sensory areas. This *somatotopic localization* has been carefully studied in lower forms and in man. An idea of the extent of such localization may be gained from Figure 7.8. Note that the arrangement is similar to that of the motor cortex, with the face represented laterally and the foot medially. The somesthetic impulses are relayed to areas 1, 2, 3 from the posterior portion of the ventral nucleus of the dorsal thalamus.

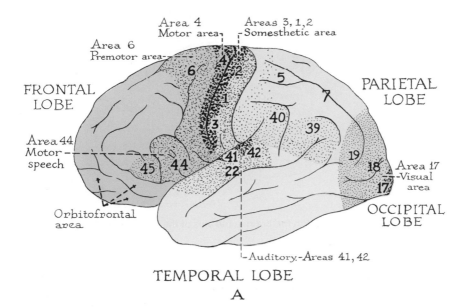

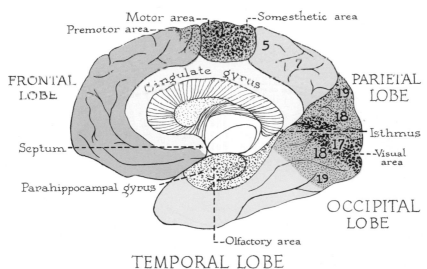

Figure 7.6 Diagram of localization areas. *A*, Lateral aspect of human cerebral hemisphere, showing areas 3, 2, 1 (somesthetic); area 4 (motor); area 6 (premotor); area 17 (visual); areas 22, 41, 42 (auditory); and area 44 or Broca's area (motor speech). *B*, Medial aspect of human cerebral hemisphere, showing various localization areas in section, the olfactory area, and the limbic lobe.

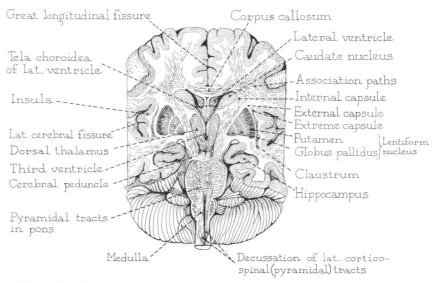

Figure 7.7 Section through the brain in the axis of the brain stem. (After Toldt.)

Area 17 receives impulses from the retina, relayed by the lateral geniculate nucleus of the dorsal thalamus. Areas 41 and 42 receive auditory impulses from the medial geniculate nucleus. Damage to area 17 in primates results in blindness, although light and dark may still be distinguished. Removal of the auditory cortex in man does not result in total deafness, but it does cause serious symptoms in-

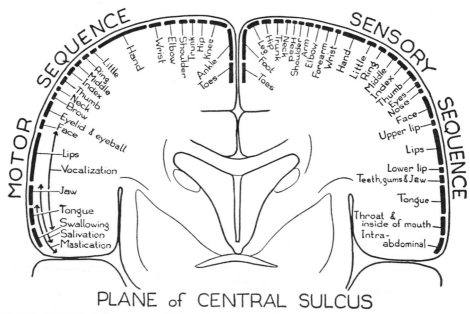

Figure 7.8 Diagrammatic representation of sensory and motor sequences as mapped by threshold stimulation of cerebral cortex in man. Length of bars indicates in a general way extent of cortical areas devoted to each structure. This is subject to considerable variation, however. (From Rasmussen and Penfield, Fed. Proc., 1947, 6:452-460.)

volving the interpretation of auditory information. Gustatory impulses are relayed to somesthetic areas along with exteroceptive and proprioceptive information about the mouth. Olfactory impulses terminate at the region of the parahippocampal convolution (Fig. 7.6).

WHITE MATTER OF THE CEREBRAL HEMISPHERES. The integration of functions of the cerebral hemispheres is maintained by systems of fiber pathways which join the cerebrum to other parts of the central nervous system as *projection tracts*, coordinate the right and left hemispheres as *commissural paths*, and relate adjacent and distal convolutions within the same hemisphere as *association paths*. Most of the large projection paths are grouped together within the *internal capsule* (Fig. 7.7). Visual, auditory, and somesthetic radiations are found in the posterior portion of the internal capsule. The pyramidal tracts are at the central part of the capsule, and radiations from the dorsomedial thalamic nucleus and frontocorticopontine projections are found in the anterior portion of the capsule. A restricted hemorrhage (stroke) within the internal capsule can produce extensive sensory and motor losses in an individual.

A large commissure of white fibers, the corpus callosum (Figs. 7.4, 7.7), relates most of the right and left sides of the cerebral cortex. Such reciprocal connections allow coordination of right and left sided motor acts and integration of sensory information into concepts of the body and its environment. The much smaller anterior commissure relates the olfactory parts of the brain and temporal lobes (Fig. 7.4).

CORTICAL ASSOCIATIONS. The connection of the afferent (sensory) and efferent (motor) sides of the long reflex arcs is brought about by short association tracts between adjacent convolutions, such as areas 1, 2, 3, to area 4. More complex long associations relate visual areas 18 and 19 to auditory association area 22. External and extreme capsules contain association pathways from visual 18, 19, somesthetic 5, 7, and auditory 22 to a correlation region in areas 39 and 40. Such associations are largely responsible for the recognition and uses made of the visual, auditory, gustatory, olfactory, and somesthetic sensory information about the environment.

Comprehension of and response to the sensory symbols of communication represent the important role of the associative cerebral cortex. The motor speech areas 44 and 45 are on the inferior frontal convolution of the *dominant hemisphere*. The left cerebral hemisphere is dominant in most individuals. The receptive areas for speech include auditory association, visual association, somesthetic association, and the correlation region. Injuries at the receptive sites impede the processing of sensory data which underlies the speech. For example, there may be word deafness or word blindness present that prevents speaking although there is no paralysis of the laryngeal muscles.

THE CONDITIONED REFLEX. The cerebrum is essential to the establishment of conditioned reflexes that play an important part in habit formation and reactions of human beings. In the unconditioned reflexes that have already been discussed, a stimulus brings about the response without previous training, and the response is specific for the stimulus. Thus chemical and mechanical stimuli from food in the mouth bring about salivation. In conditioned responses previous training is necessary for forming associations, and the stimulus may be neutral or quite unrelated to the response. Salivation from visual and olfactory stimuli associated with the presentation of food is a familiar example. Even to think of sucking a lemon is sufficient to cause salivation if the taste of a lemon is familiar. If puppies are allowed to see and smell meat, however, no salivation will occur if they have been kept on a milk diet and are unfamiliar with meat as a food.

In the conditioned reflex, the response that would normally accompany or follow the unconditioned stimulus occurs when neutral stimuli that have been associated with that response are given. Experimentally, such widely diverse responses as constriction of the pupil, sleeping, or vomiting have been elicited by the ringing of a bell. Previous training has established the association of the ringing of the bell with the unconditioned stimuli bringing about these responses. Formation of conditioned responses may be easily recognized when observing reactions of young children. Conditioned reflexes may also be observed in many routine responses of adults. Examples of such reactions are applying the brakes or shifting gear when driving, turning out lights when leaving a room, and "automatically" sorting objects such as surgical instruments.

ELECTROENCEPHALOGRAM AND RETICULAR FORMATION. Activity goes on in the brain even during sleep. A record of the electrical activity can be obtained by placing electrodes on the outside of the head or upon the cerebral cortex and attaching the electrodes to a recording apparatus. The *electroencephalogram* (EEG) is in the form of waves (Fig. 7.9) which vary in frequency, amplitude, and rhythm. The EEG is not similar in all parts of the cortex. The alpha type of rhythm is illustrated in the record of the right and left occipital areas of Figure 7.9. *Alpha waves*, 8 to 12 per second with electrical potential of 50 microvolts, are associated with relaxed awaken-

ing. *Beta waves*, with a rhythm of 18 to 32 per second and 5 to 10 microvolt potentials, are seen in the records of frontal, parietal, and temporal areas. *Delta rhythms* are slow waves, 0.5 to 5 per second with 20 to 200 microvolt potentials, typical of the sleeping state. Alpha waves are high voltage slow waves (HVS) of a *synchronized* pattern of activity of the cerebral cortex. Beta waves are low voltage fast waves (LVF). They desynchronize the alpha rhythm. When the beta rhythm is present the individual is mentally active. EEG is profoundly affected by an oxygen lack or marked lowering of blood sugar.

The term *reticular formation* has been given to the nerve cells and fibers which are interwoven as a network. This network is in contrast to the separation of gray and white matter into nuclei and fiber pathways. Reticular formation is present throughout the central nervous system. This term now signifies a core from the spinal cord through the brain stem which processes a tremendous quantity of sensory and motor neural impulses.

Collateral branches off the major ascend-

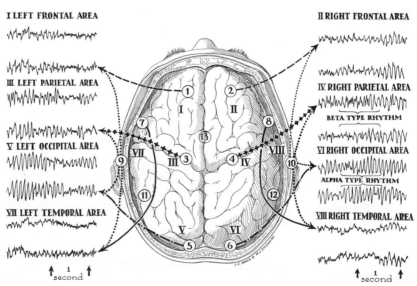

Figure 7.9 Diagram of electroencephalogram: 1, 2, 3, etc., are corresponding locations on the brain to electrodes placed on the subject's scalp. These may be used in several combinations; one combination is shown above where 1, 2, 3, etc., are attached to 9, 10. The region of the brain represented by records of electrical waves are indicated by Roman numerals. Typical alpha rhythm of 8 to 12 waves per second and beta rhythm of 18 to 32 waves per second are shown.

ing sensory pathways, such as the fasciculi gracilis and cuneatus, spinothalamic, fifth and eighth cranial nerves, synapse within the reticular core. The multiple synapses in the course of neural transmission through the reticular formation change the characteristics of specific sensory information to that of nonspecific, slowly ascending repeatedly synapsing trains of impulses. At the level of the dorsal thalamus the *nonspecific thalamic nuclei* such as nucleus reticularis and other intralaminar nuclei transmit the multineuronal trains of impulses through the internal capsule into the frontal, temporal, parietal, and occipital lobes of the cerebrum. The *arousal* of the cerebral cortex by reticular formation can be observed in the desynchronization of the EEG to an activation pattern in which the beta waves predominate.

The integration of numerous impulses from the ascending side of the reticular formation, cerebellum, basal ganglia, and cerebral cortex, likewise occurs within the reticular core. Multisynaptic descending reticulospinal tracts (p. 90) terminate upon anterior and lateral column cells of the spinal cord and their cranial nerve equivalents. The reticulospinal tracts influence the motor performance of skeletal muscles which are utilized in patterns of movements such as walking and standing upright. Descending fibers which regulate autonomic visceral functions in the brain stem and spinal cord are a part of these reticulospinal pathways.

BASAL GANGLIA. Embedded in the white matter of the cerebral hemispheres are paired masses of cells, the *basal ganglia* (Fig. 7.7). Some of the interrelations are indicated below:

| Extra pyramidal system | { | Caudate nucleus Putamen Globus pallidus Claustrum | } Lentiform nucleus | } Corpus striatum |
| Limbic system— | | Amygdala | | |

Some authors have included the ventral thalamus, red nucleus, and surrounding tegmentum of the midbrain with the corpus striatum as basal ganglia. It is apparent that a close functional relationship does exist. Fiber connections from midbrain

and thalamus, particularly from the cells receiving the dentatorubrothalamic tract of the cerebellum, are reciprocally linked to the corpus striatum and cerebral cortex such as in premotor area 6. The major efferent outflow of corpus striatum is the *lenticular fasciculus* from the globus pallidus to the midbrain tegmentum. The cells of the midbrain tegmentum, as mentioned before, are the origin of reticulospinal and rubrotegmentospinal descending motor pathways with terminations upon anterior column cells of the spinal cord and comparable cranial nerve nuclei. The majority of these connections traverse the white matter of the cerebrum and brain stem in positions which are not in physical proximity to the pyramidal tracts. They are parts of the *extrapyramidal system* which activates and coordinates the ceaseless postural adjustments, automatic associated, and stereotyped movements of the body. Through the highly complex circuitry of the basal ganglia the strength, tone, coordination, and pattern of movements to play the violin, type, eat, dress, and walk are regulated.

LIMBIC SYSTEM. Some of the structures which may be included in the term limbic system are outlined below:

Cerebral hemisphere
  Septum
  Cingulate gyrus
  Isthmus   } Limbic lobe (Fig. 7.6)
  Parahippocampal gyrus
    Amygdala
    Hippocampus
  Insula
  Orbitofrontal cortex (Fig. 7.6)
Olfactory nerve and tracts
  (Fig. 8.1)
Papez' circuit (Fig. 7.10)

The anterior nuclear group of the dorsal thalamus which receives afferent impulses from the hypothalamus is reciprocally connected to the cingulate gyrus. Reference to Figure 7.10 will permit the student to follow the sequence of *Papez' circuit* from the (1) anterior nuclear group of the dorsal thalamus to (2) cingulate gyrus to (3) isthmus to (4) parahippocampal gyrus to (5) hippocampus to (6) fornix to (7) mammillary body to (8) mammillothalamic tract to (9) anterior nuclear group of the dorsal thalamus.

In addition to the sensory impulses transmitted from the reticular formation

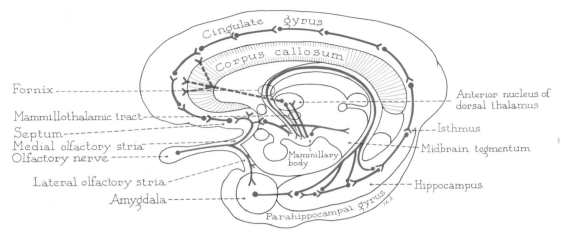

Figure 7.10 Diagram of medial surface of the brain. "Papez circuit" and portions of the "septal circuit" and "amygdalar circuit" are shown in red.

into this circuit, the olfactory connections enter by way of two groups of fibers. One portion, the medial olfactory pathway, synapses in and near the septum with reciprocal discharge into adjacent hemispheric structures such as insula, orbitofrontal gyri and cingulate gyrus. These connections may be referred to as the *septal circuit*. It is currently believed that these structures are concerned with emotional affective tone that is conducive to sociality, sexual attraction, and copulation. The septal circuit provides the neuroanatomic substrate for preservation of the species in the autonomic visceral controls from the hypothalamus and the automatic associated movements integrated by the extrapyramidal system requisite to sexual arousal and copulation. Another group of olfactory fibers, the lateral olfactory tract, synapses in and near the amygdala with reciprocal discharge into the adjacent temporal lobe, insula, and orbitofrontal gyri. These connections may be referred to as the *amygdalar circuit*. It is currently believed that these structures are concerned with the emotional affective tone that is necessary for feeding and survival. The amygdalar circuit provides the neuroanatomic substrate for the preservation of self in autonomic visceral controls from the hypothalamus and the automatic associated movements integrated by the extrapyramidal system requisite to obtain-

ing food, eating, and defense of self by fighting or fleeing from potential harm. Studies on man and animals show conspicuous changes in the cardiovascular, respiratory, and gastrointestinal systems, in the skin, and in the pupil of the eye when areas of the limbic system are involved. "Pleasure centers" and "punishing centers" located in experimental animals by self-stimulating devices are found to be in parts of the limbic system. Injury in the hippocampal formation of the dominant hemisphere impairs the memory for recent events. An instruction or experience of a few minutes ago in time may be forgotten while those events of several years past are recalled with no difficulty.

QUESTIONS FOR DISCUSSION

1. What substances may cross the blood-brain barrier and pia-glial membrane? What influence would this have on the administration of drugs given for their effect upon the central nervous system?

2. Distinguish or characterize the following:

Brain stem	Localization areas
Cisterns	of cerebrum
Ventricles	Basal ganglia
Reticular formation	Limbic system

Lobes of   Electroencephalogram
   cerebrum   Reciprocal innervation
        Servomechanism

3. How are conditioned reflexes formed? Relate the conditioned reflex to learning.

4. Summarize the functions of the dorsal thalamus and hypothalamus. How is the hypothalamus related to the endocrine system? To vegetative functions? To emotions?

5. What type of neural integration of postural and locomotor movements is carried out by the pyramidal tracts? Extrapyramidal tracts? Cerebellum? Reticular formation? Limbic system?

CRANIAL NERVES: SPECIAL SENSES AND VEGETATIVE FUNCTIONS

CHAPTER EIGHT

CRANIAL NERVES

In the early discussion of nervous tissue it was noted that the cerebrospinal nerves form a part of the peripheral portion of the nervous system. Cerebrospinal nerves, as the name implies, include the spinal and cranial nerves. Cranial nerves are designated as those, attached to the brain, which pass through the foramina of the skull (Fig. 10.15). Twelve pairs symmetrically arranged are distributed mainly to the structures of the head and neck (Figs. 8.2, 8.3).

Because of the diversity of their function, the nerves have been given names as well as numbers (Fig. 8.1). Most of the nerves have motor and sensory roots. A few have sensory roots only. The sensory nerve roots have their cell bodies in ganglia outside the brain; the cell bodies of the motor roots are in nuclei within the brain.

A summary of the data pertinent to a particular cranial nerve is given in the figure description of the illustration of distribution of that nerve. This information will appear as shown in the example below:

Number	Name	Exit from skull	Structures supplied by sensory fibers (Function)	Structures supplied by motor fibers (Function)
I	Olfactory	Cribriform plate	Mucosa of upper third of cavity (smell)	None

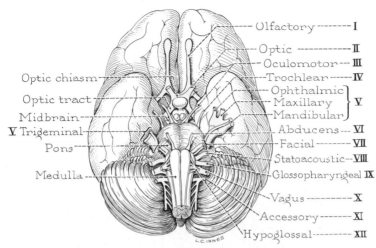

Figure 8.1 The base of the brain, showing cranial nerves.

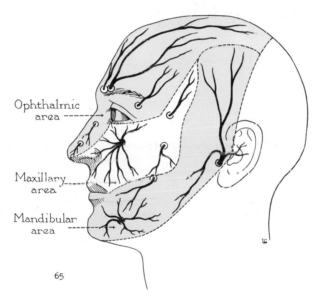

Figure 8-2. Diagram showing skin area supplied by three divisions of the fifth cranial nerve. (Redrawn from Gray.)

| V. | Trigeminal (See also Figs. 8.6, 8.7, 8.9, 8.11, 12.1) | Three divisions: Ophthalmic-superior orbital fissure Maxillary-foramen rotundum Mandibular-foramen ovale | Skin of face and anterior one half of scalp Mucous membranes in head Teeth Anterior two thirds of tongue (Pain, cold, heat, touch) Chewing muscles (Muscle sense) Cornea of eye (Pain) Lacrimal gland (Reflexes) | Muscles of mastication (Muscle movement) |

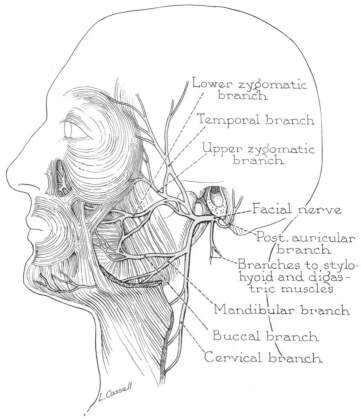

Figure 8.3. Diagram showing distribution of the facial nerve. (Redrawn and modified from Cunningham.)

| VII. Facial (Fig. 12.1) | Internal acoustic meatus Stylomastoid foramen | Taste buds of anterior two thirds of tongue (Taste) Muscles of facial expression (Muscle sense) | Muscles of facial expression (Motion) Submaxillary gland Sublingual gland Lacrimal gland (Secretion) |

It will be of particular assistance at this time to consult Figures 10.15, 10.16, and 10.17 to aid in visualization of the points of exit by which cranial nerves leave the cranial cavity in their courses toward the structures innervated. Wherever possible the descriptions and illustrations of the cranial nerves are incorporated into the text material relevant to structures associated with special senses and vegetative functions.

SPECIAL SENSES

CHARACTERISTICS OF TELERECEPTORS

In the discussion of receptors and their neuronal pathways, some special characteristics of the sensory mechanisms were stressed. We have learned that the receptors may respond to several types of stim-

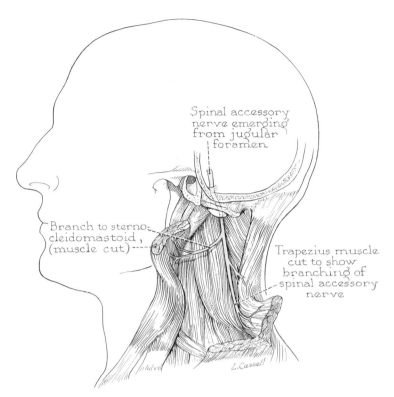

Figure 8.4. Diagram showing distribution of the spinal accessory nerve.

XI.	Accessory (spinal) (Figs. 12.9 and 12.4)	Jugular foramen	Sternocleidomastoid and trapezius (Muscle sense)	Sternocleidomastoid Trapezius (Motion)

ulations, but have the lowest threshold for a specific type of stimulus. Sensory nerve endings adapt to continuous stimulation by decreasing their frequency of discharge. They display a local sign through which the stimulus is referred to a specific location. Further, if the central nervous system is intact, each receptor always signals its characteristic sensation regardless of the type of stimulus applied; a blow on the eye or ear results in our "seeing stars" or "hearing" a "ringing."

We have also learned that sensation, as interpreted at the thalamic level, cannot be localized or identified. There is only a noncritical level of awareness that something pleasurable or painful is happening. The somesthetic, visual, auditory, and olfactory areas of the cortex, though concerned with localization, depend upon association areas for interpretation of the qualities of a sensation.

Combinations of visual, auditory, superficial, deep, and visceral sensations may be simultaneously involved in determining comfort or discomfort; the combination of taste, smell, vision, and touch may indicate the palatability of a food; touch, pressure, heat, and pain may all be felt upon coming in contact with a solid object. It is not only the modalities of sensation, but also their relative intensities in combination that, interpreted upon the basis of past experience, determine our subjective and objective reactions.

So far we have considered senses related to the present or immediate environment, stimulated by environmental changes acting directly on or within the body. We will now consider the special senses that, taste excepted, respond to more distant environmental changes and hence are concerned with the "immediate future." These telereceptors or distance receptors are end organs of the cranial nerves.

OLFACTION

All living organisms generate their own particular odor and the very old vertebrate special sense has provided a widespread method of identification. Olfactory epithelium, as distinguished from respiratory epithelium (Fig. 4.5), is found in the upper third of the nasal cavity on the surface of the superior conchae and nasal septum (Fig. 8.5). Ciliated neuroepithelial cells are the receptors for this chemical sense. The olfactory epithelium is kept moist by secretions of the mucous membrane. Aromatic substances entering the nose in gaseous form must circulate by convection currents, or be "sniffed" into the olfactory area, enter physical solution, and contact the receptor cells.

Use of synthetic chemicals and olfactometers has allowed the differential recognition of odors by human subjects. The stereochemical theory of odors classifies the different odors according to molecular shape or electric charge into seven groups: camphorous, musky, floral, peppermint, ethereal, pungent, and putrid. Some of the characteristics of substances which stimulate the olfactory mucosa result from excitation of the exteroceptive endings of the trigeminal nerve (Fig. 8.7). Man is able to distinguish several thousand odors in spite of the small size of his olfactory apparatus as compared to other animals. Adaptation to olfactory stimuli occurs with relatively great rapidity.

Axons from the neuroepithelial cells collect into aggregates of olfactory fila and enter the cranial cavity at the roof of the

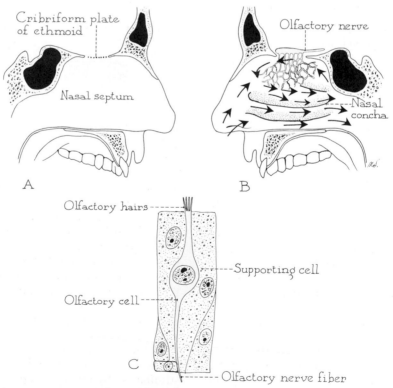

Figure 8.5 Distribution of olfactory nerve fibers on medial surface (A) and lateral surface (B) of the nasal cavity. Direction of air currents is shown by arrows. (C) Neuroepithelial cell in olfactory mucosa.

nose through the cribriform plate of the ethmoid. Synapses occur within the olfactory bulb of cranial nerve I. Integration of the incoming olfactory nerve impulses into conscious recognition of odor is believed to occur in the temporal lobe cortical area 28 covering the hippocampus (Fig. 7.6). Further associations of this olfactory information are made by widespread connections which include the septal region and subcallosal gyrus; amygdala and hippocampus; epithalamus and hypothalamus (see pages 96-98). Complex neuronal connections form the substrate for associa-tion of cutaneous, gustatory, and olfactory sensations and their reflex connections to cranial nerves involved with movements of the mouth, face, and digestive tract in the various responses to olfactory sensations.

GUSTATORY SENSATION AND THE ORAL CAVITY

The receptors for taste are the taste buds, located chiefly on the tongue, but present also in the pharynx, on the epiglottis, and on the roof of the mouth (pp.

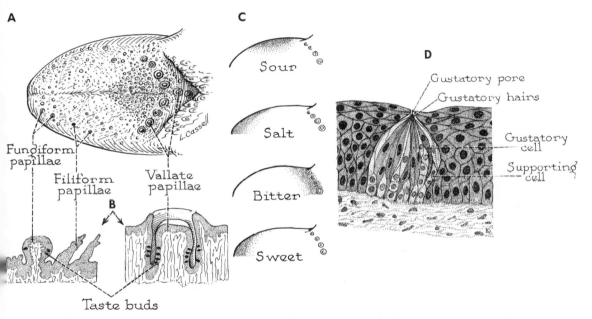

Figure 8.6. Receptors for taste. *A*, Dorsal surface of the tongue, showing taste papillae. *B*, Three types of papillae in section and enlarged. *C*, Areas of maximum sensibility to four primary taste qualities. *D*, Vertical section of a taste bud.

V.	Trigeminal (Fig. 8.7)	Mandibular division foramen ovale	Anterior two Thirds of tongue (Heat, cold, pain, touch)
VII.	Facial (Fig. 8.3)	Internal acoustic meatus Stylomastoid foramen	Taste buds of anterior two thirds of tongue (Taste)
IX.	Glossopharyn-geal (Fig. 8.8)	Jugular foramen	Taste buds of posterior one third of tongue (Taste)
X.	Vagus (Fig. 8.17)	Jugular foramen	Taste buds of soft palate and epiglottis (Taste)

340-341. Those on the tongue are located in the vallate and the fungiform papillae. Although the taste buds give rise to different qualities of taste, they have the same general structure (Fig. 8.6). They are composed of clusters of cells submerged in the epithelium, but communicating with the surface through a small pore into which their microvilli project. These gustatory cells are shed and renewed from the adjacent epithelium about every four to seven days. Such a renewal of cells tends to decline with age. The base of the gustatory cell is associated with plexiform nerve endings of cranial nerves VII, IX, and X. The mucous membrane of the oral cavity, except for the taste bud cells, is innervated by the trigeminal nerve (V) (Fig. 8.7).

Although taste sensations are numerous only four basic qualities are recognized: bitter, sour, salty, and sweet. It is believed that gustatory cells are responsive to several chemical stimuli and that the discrimination of taste is based upon the pattern of neuronal discharge from a population of multiple receptors among the approximate 9000 taste buds of the oral cavity. The distribution of the principal sensations is depicted in Figure 8.6.

Neuronal impulses from the facial, glossopharyngeal, and vagus nerves synapse in the nucleus of the fasciculus solitarius in the pons and medulla (Fig. 18.22). The secondary gustatory pathways travel through the brain stem to the diencephalon. Sensory radiations from the thalamus

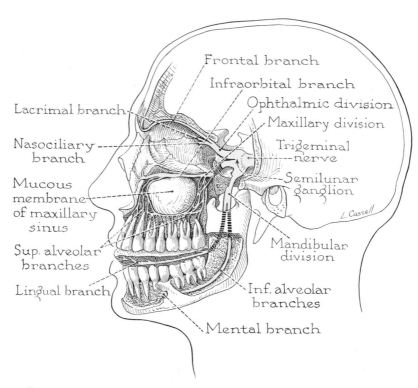

Figure 8.7. Diagram showing distribution of the trigeminal nerve.

| V. | Trigeminal (See also Figs. 8.2, 8.6) | Three divisions: Ophthalmic- superior orbital fissure Maxillary-fora- men rotundum Mandibular-fora- men ovale | Teeth Anterior two thirds of tongue Mucous membranes in head (Heat, cold, pain touch) |

are believed to project gustatory sensations into consciousness at the inferior portion of the somesthetic parietal cortex (1, 2, 3, Fig. 7.6).

The many taste sensations which we experience are the result of (a) the fusion or blending of the fundamental qualities, (b) the combination of some exteroceptor sensation in the tongue with the taste sensation, or (c) reinforcement of taste by smell. The oral and nasal cavities communicate freely through the pharynx and are frequently stimulated by the same substances. Taste plays a critical role in nutrition and preservation of the constancy of the internal environment. It often provides the

sensory clues by which important discriminatory dietary selections are made.

A description of the tongue, teeth, palates, jaws, and cheeks comprising the oral cavity is given in Chapter 18, pages 341 to 343. A partial appreciation of functions of this part of the digestive system can be gained at this time. The muscular activity of the jaws, cheeks, and tongue are combined in biting, chewing, swallowing, and the exposure of food to salivary secretions and taste buds. Muscles of the cheeks and their innervation by the facial nerve (VII) are shown in Figure 8.3. Muscles of mastication (Fig. 12.1) are innervated by the trigeminal nerve (V). Pharyngeal and

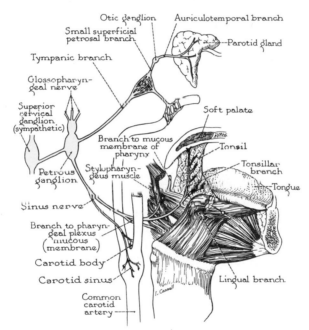

Figure 8.8. Diagram showing the distribution of the glossopharyngeal nerve. (Redrawn and modified from Cunningham.)

IX.	Glossopharyngeal (See also Fig. 13.2)	Jugular foramen	Carotid sinus (Cardiac reflex) Mucous membrane of pharynx, soft palate, tonsils, posterior one third of tongue (Swallowing reflex) Taste buds posterior one third of tongue (Taste)	Muscles of pharynx (Swallowing) Parotid gland (Secretion)
XII.	Hypoglossal	Hypoglossal foramen	Muscles of tongue (Muscle sense)	Muscles of tongue (Motion)

tongue musculature with innervation by the glossopharyngeal (IX) and hypoglossal (XII) nerves is illustrated in Figure 8.8. Secretory mechanisms of the large salivary glands controlled by cranial nerves VII and IX appear in Figures 8.8 and 18.22. The small salivary glands are innervated by the glossopharyngeal nerve (Fig. 8.8). These oral secretions are necessary for taste as well as digestion.

VISION

The Eye and Associated Structures.
The eye is in many ways comparable to a camera. Some of its structures form an optical system that bends or focuses the light rays from outside objects, located at various distances, to form sharp images within the eye. Other structures, comparable to the film of a camera, react to these light rays composing the image, and set up nerve impulses giving rise to the sensations of form, contrast, and color by which the objects are recognized. The eye, however, is an exceedingly adaptable, highly complex camera that may seem to work automatically, since we are seldom aware of the adjustments for distance, amount of light, and the position or location of the object. The associated structures that protect the eye and aid in its function are the orbital cavities, the eyelids, the lacrimal apparatus, and the eye muscles.

Outer Parts of the Eye.
The eyeballs, lying in the anterior part of the orbital cavities, are protected above and at the side by the prominent margins of the orbits, below by the zygomatic bones, and medially by the bridge of the nose.

THE EYELIDS. The eyelids are placed in front of the eyeball (Figs. 8.9, 8.11). They are formed of muscular tissue attached to dense fibrous plates which give shape to the lids. Externally, they are covered by skin, and internally, by mucous membrane, called conjunctiva, which is reflected upon the anterior surface of the eyeball. Hairs project from the free margins to form the eyelashes. Along the margin of the lids are the tarsal (meibomian) glands; these glands secrete an oily liquid which keeps the lids from becoming adherent. The muscular tissue of the lids forms sphincters, or the orbicularis oculi muscles, which close the eyelids (Fig. 12.1). The levator palpebrae superioris muscle raises the upper eyelid. The origin is the posterior part of the orbit, above and in front of the optic foramen; the insertion is the upper eyelid (Fig. 8.11).

THE LACRIMAL APPARATUS (Fig. 8.9). The anterior surface of the eye is protected by a constant stream of tears secreted by the lacrimal gland lying above the eye. The excess secretion is drained off from the eye through the nasolacrimal duct into the nose. The tears pass into the duct through two small openings at the medial corner of the eye. In this way the surface of the eye is kept moist and free of irritating particles.

THE EXTRINSIC EYE MUSCLES. Each eyeball is attached to six muscles that hold it in place and control its movements. There are four straight or rectus muscles, superior, inferior, lateral, and medial, and two oblique muscles, superior and inferior (Fig. 8.10). All except the inferior oblique arise from the apex of the orbit near the optic canal. The inferior oblique arises from the medial margin of the orbit. The six muscles are inserted into the outer coat of the eyeball. The tendon of the superior oblique muscle passes through a cartilaginous ring or pulley attached to the upper and inner part of the orbit to reach its attachment on the eyeball. The movements of the muscles of both eyes are coordinated so that both move together to focus on a single field of vision. The conjugate movement of the eyes upward, downward and horizontally right or left, convergence, and blinking are mediated by neuronal connections among the motor centers of the III, IV, and VI nerves. These pathways in the brain stem may be influenced by nerve impulses from the cerebral cortex reflecting visual stimulation or a voluntary decision to move the eyes. Auditory and proprioceptive stimulation from lower brain stem centers may also result in deviations of the eyes through conjugate action of the extrinsic muscles of the eyes.

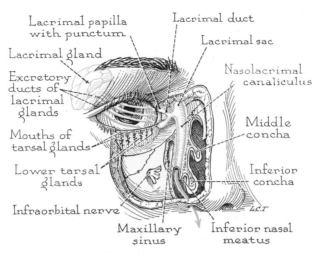

Figure 8.9. The lacrimal apparatus and eyelids.

III.	Oculomotor (Fig. 8.11)	Superior orbital fissure	Levator palpebrae superioris (Muscle sense)	Levator palpebrae superioris (Motion)
V.	Trigeminal (Fig. 8.2)	Superior orbital fissure: ophthalmic division	Cornea (Pain) Conjunctiva and skin of eyelids (Heat, cold, pain, touch)	
VII.	Facial (Figs. 8.3, 12.1)	Internal acoustic meatus Stylomastoid foramen	Lacrimal gland (Reflex)	Lacrimal gland (Secretion)
			Orbicularis oculi (Muscle sense)	Orbicularis oculi (Motion)

The Structure of the Eyeball (Fig. 8.11). The eyeball is roughly spherical in shape. Its walls are formed of three layers: an outer fibrous coat, a middle vascular coat, and an inner nervous coat.

The fibrous coat has two parts, the sclera and the cornea. The *sclera* invests the eye except for a small area at the front. It is tough and opaque and gives form to the eyeball. The *cornea* is the clear, transparent tissue that completes this coat anteriorly.

The vascular coat or uvea has many blood vessels and is concerned chiefly with nutrition of the eye. There are three parts: choroid, ciliary body, and iris. The *choroid* contains a rich plexus of blood vessels and a large amount of dark brown pigment, which reduces reflection and scattering of light after it has fallen on the retina. It is continuous with the ciliary body in front. The ciliary muscle and ciliary processes

make up the *ciliary body*, which projects into the cavity of the eye at the sclerocorneal junction to form a circular band. The ciliary muscle forms the main part of the ciliary body. The longitudinal fibers arise from the sclera near its junction with the cornea and pass backward to be inserted into the choroid. Other muscle fibers radiate from the sclera into the ciliary body. The ciliary muscle functions in accommodation of the eye. The ciliary processes consist of fibers that radiate from the free border of the ciliary muscle and give attachment to ligaments supporting the lens. The *iris*, or colored portion of the eye, is a muscular diaphragm that is attached at its circumference to the ciliary body and has an opening (the pupil) in the center. It controls the amount of light admitted to the eye. Its circular fibers, when stimulated, produce constriction of

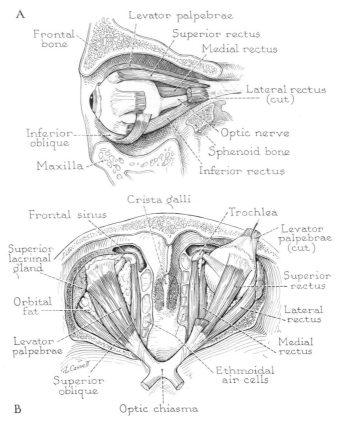

Figure 8-10. Muscles of the orbit. *A*, Lateral view. *B*, Superior view. (Modified after Sobotta and Uhlenhuth; and Grant: An Atlas of Anatomy. The Williams & Wilkins Co.)

III.	Oculomotor (See also Fig. 8.11)	Superior orbital fissure	Levator palpebrae Superior rectus Medial rectus Inferior rectus Inferior oblique (Muscle sense)	Same group of eye muscles (Eye movement)
IV.	Trochlear	Superior orbital fissure	Superior oblique (Muscle sense)	Superior oblique (Motion)
VI.	Abducens	Superior orbital fissure	Lateral rectus (Muscle sense)	Lateral rectus (Motion)

the pupil; its radial fibers contract to dilate the pupil. The ciliary muscle and the circular fibers of the iris are supplied by the third cranial nerve.

The nervous coat or *retina* forms the lining layer of the eyeball. A layer of pigment cells and five types of neurons supported by glial cells comprise the retina, as indicated in Figure 8.12. The neurons include the photoreceptive *rods* and *cones*,

bipolar cells, horizontal cells, amacrine cells, and *ganglion cells* whose axons form the optic nerve II. When the retina is illuminated an *electroretinogram* can be recorded from the cornea by instrumentation similar to that for electroencephalograms. Analysis of this record suggests the participation of the pigment cells and neurons in the transduction of light stimulation into a nerve impulse. The *optic*

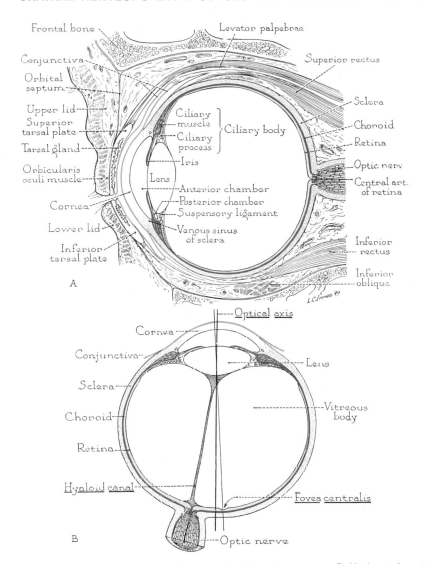

Figure 8.11 *A,* Vertical section of the anterior part of orbit and contents. *B,* Horizontal section of right eye. Underlined labels indicate structures and optical axis not shown in the vertical section.

II.	Optic	Optic foramen	Retina of eye (Sight)	None
III.	Oculomotor (Fig. 8.10)	Superior orbital fissure		Ciliary muscle (Accommodation) Iris (Constriction of pupil)
V.	Trigeminal (Fig. 8.2)	Ophthalmic division: superior orbital fissure Maxillary division: foramen rotundum	Cornea (Pain) Conjunctiva Skin of eye lids (Heat, cold, pain, touch)	
VII.	Facial (Fig. 8.6)	Internal acoustic meatus, stylomastoid foramen	Orbicularis oculi (Muscle sense)	Orbicularis oculi (Motion)

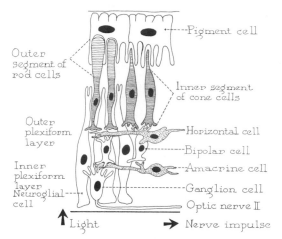

Figure 8.12 Diagram of the types of cells found in the retina.

nerve leaves the eye slightly to the nasal side of center. The point is marked by a white circular area called the *optic disc.* Since there are no rods or cones in this area, it is called the blind spot. Near the center of the posterior pole is a yellowish spot called the *macula lutea.* In the center of the macula lutea is a small depression, the *fovea centralis.* At this point the rods are absent, but cones are greatly increased in number. It is the region of keenest vision. Circulation to the retina is provided by the central artery and vein, branches of the ophthalmic blood vessels. They pass through the center of the optic nerve and appear at the center of the optic disc, where they divide into branches.

The coordinated movements of both eyes, particularly in convergence, brought about by the extrinsic ocular muscles are requisite to the focusing of both foveae upon the same spot. Without such a focus a double visual image or diplopia occurs.

The *crystalline lens* lies just behind the pupil and iris. It is held in position by the suspensory ligaments, which are attached to the ciliary processes. The iris separates the anterior and posterior chambers. The posterior chamber is the small recess between the iris in front and the lens and suspensory ligament behind. Posterior to the lens is the large cavity of the eye filled with a jelly-like material called the vitreous humor.

The aqueous humor, secreted by the ciliary process, fills the space anterior to the lens. From the posterior chamber it permeates the vitreous body and passes forward between the iris and the lens, through the pupil into the anterior chamber. Drainage from the anterior chamber is mainly by way of the spaces of Fontana and the venous sinus at the junction of the cornea and sclera. Formation and resorption of aqueous humor maintains an intraocular pressure at 28 mm. Hg. This fluid supplies a linkage between the circulatory system and the lens and cornea, both of which are lacking in blood vessels. The intraocular pressure permits a precise geometric position of the retina that is necessary to ensure the formation of a clear visual image.

Physiology of Vision

REFRACTION. In vision, rays of light reflected from an object must enter the eye and be brought to a focus on the retina. In coming to a focus on the retina, rays of light reflected from objects must be bent. This bending of light rays is called refraction. A ray of light is refracted when it passes from a medium of one density into a medium of a different density. When passing from a less dense to a more dense medium light is bent toward the perpendicular, and when passing from a denser to a less dense medium it is bent away from the perpendicular. The degree of ability of a substance to bend rays of light is referred to as the *refractive index.*

The refractive index of air is taken as the standard and is said to be 1. The refracting media of the eye are the cornea, aqueous humor, lens, and vitreous humor. All except the lens have the same refractive index as water, 1.33. The lens has a refractive index of 1.42. A ray of light passing into the eye receives its greatest refraction as it enters the cornea from the air and as it enters and leaves the lens.

In the normal or emmetropic eye the optical system is adequate for bringing rays from distant objects (i.e., objects at a distance of more than 20 feet) into a sharp focus on the retina, so that no activity of the eye muscles is necessary for adjustment. If, however, a person is near-sighted (myopic) or far-sighted (hypermetropic), the rays come to focus in front of or behind the retina, respectively. Near-sighted people whose eyes have a greater than normal anterior-posterior diameter wear lenses that diverge the light rays; far-sighted people, i.e., those with eyeballs having a relatively short anterior-posterior diameter, wear convex lenses that converge the entering rays.

ACCOMMODATION. Rays of light from objects close at hand require a greater degree of bending or refraction in order to bring them to a focus on the retina. The structure of the lens permits such an adjustment. It is an elastic organ held in place by the suspensory ligaments, which in turn are attached to the ciliary processes. Contraction of the ciliary muscle pulls the choroid forward and allows the ciliary processes to release tension on the lens. Since the lens is highly elastic, release of tension causes it to become more nearly spherical in shape. The greater the convexity of the lens surface, the greater the index of refraction. By this mechanism rays of light from near objects are brought to a focus on the retina.

The elasticity of the lens changes with age. The near point, i.e., the shortest distance at which an object can be seen distinctly, moves further and further away as we grow older, since the lens becomes progressively less elastic and hence cannot assume so great a curvature.

FUNCTION OF RODS AND CONES. The rods and cones are the specialized receptor organs of the eye. The adequate stimuli for these end organs is the radiant energy of the visible spectrum. The rods are associated with vision under conditions of low illumination; this is called *scotopic* vision and enables us to get around fairly well at night once the eyes have become adapted to darkness. Vision is improved fairly rapidly, but complete dark adaptation may require twenty to thirty minutes. Night vision is not discriminative; we see no detail or color, but rather vague outlines of forms of objects which are more readily detected when they are moving. Under higher levels of illumination, peripheral vision — that is, vision resulting from light rays falling on the peripheral areas of the retina that contain only rods — signals the presence of stationary or moving objects. When the eyes are then turned so that the rays fall upon the central area of the retina, we can see fine details of form, contrast and color. Discriminative, or *photopic*, vision is a function of the cones. Whereas impulses from many rods or from a number of rods and cones may converge on a single bipolar neuron, the cones in the fovea centralis, or region of highly discriminative vision, may have direct line connections with one bipolar cell.

The visible spectrum is a relatively narrow band of wavelengths between the longer infra-red waves and the shorter ultraviolet waves. The chemical changes which stimulate the end organs are brought about by absorption of light of various wavelengths by light-sensitive pigments. The pigment of the outer segment of the rods, *rhodopsin*, has the characteristic of maximum absorption of green light; this pigment is chemically unstable under conditions of high illumination, a fact that accounts for loss of rod sensitivity in daylight vision. A photosensitive pigment, *iodopsin*, is associated with cone vision. It is thought that three pigments with absorption maxima in red, blue, and green parts of the spectrum are lodged in iodopsin in separate cone cells. Thus the cones acting separately or in concert are responsible for the entire range of color perception. The visual pigments are combinations of *retinenes* and a protein. All retinenes are related to vitamin A complex, and retinal function is dependent upon an adequate supply of vitamin A.

Recognition that vision is the result of photochemical reactions dependent upon absorption of light of various wavelengths aids us in understanding the three important factors determining retinal response: (1) the *wavelength*, (2) the *state of adaptation* of the eye, i.e., the chemical state of the pigments, and (3) the *quantity of light* falling on the retina, which is determined by the intensity and duration of the stimulus.

Visual acuity is a specific term for the ratio of 1 to the least angle that must be subtended to recognize a white area between two black lines, i.e., an area of stimulation between two unstimulated areas. It describes the ability to see fine detail.

To use the example of Luckiesh and Moss in their book "Science of Seeing," if we should progressively decrease the size of the letters on a printed page, the detail and finally the letters themselves would eventually become invisible; here we have gone beyond the limits of visual acuity. Reference to the three factors determining retinal response listed in the preceding paragraph should indicate to you that visual acuity is not a fixed value, but may vary with adaptation, quantity of light, and wavelength.

JUDGMENT OF DISTANCE. An effective telereceptor provides information as to separation between man and the stimulus at a distance. In vision, not less than eleven clues are provided. Interpretation of these clues is dependent, however, upon experience and associative memory. The clue provided by the slight differences in the images of a single object falling on the two retinas, which are separated by a distance of about 60 mm., is important for judging the distance of near objects. This ability to see part of the way around or see "two sides" of an object because of the separation of the eyes is called *stereoscopic vision.* Further, we judge distance by the size of the retinal image of familiar objects and by perspective, which is illustrated by the sides of a street appearing to come closer together as we gaze into the distance. Near objects appear to move greater distances than far objects as we move our head from side to side; near objects may also overlap or blot out parts of more distant objects. Clues are also provided by sensory endings in the eye muscles which contract in accommodation and convergence when viewing near objects.

THE VISUAL PATHWAY. The regions from which objects are seen are called the visual fields. The visual field of each eye is divided into a right and left half. The medial half is called the nasal visual field; the lateral half is called the temporal visual field. The retina is divided in the same way: nasal half of the retina and temporal half of the retina. Rays of light from objects in the temporal visual field fall on the nasal half of the retina; accordingly, rays of light from objects in the nasal visual field fall on the temporal half of the retina.

It will be noted in the diagram (Fig. 8.13) that the fibers from the nasal halves of two retinas cross in the *optic chiasm,* while fibers from the temporal halves of the retinas pass uncrossed to the visual cortex of the same side. Both crossed and uncrossed fibers synapse in the lateral geniculate bodies in the thalamus, from which point the fiber tracts pass to the visual area 17 in the occipital lobes of the cerebrum. Thus the visual cortex in the left cerebral hemisphere receives visual impulses from objects in the temporal visual field of the right eye and the nasal visual field of the left eye (Fig. 7.6).

The effect of injury at several points along the visual pathway is reflected by losses in portions of the visual fields as suggested in Figure 8.13. Although the great majority of fibers in the optic tract terminate in the lateral geniculate body, a few end in the pretectal area and the superior colliculus of the midbrain. The

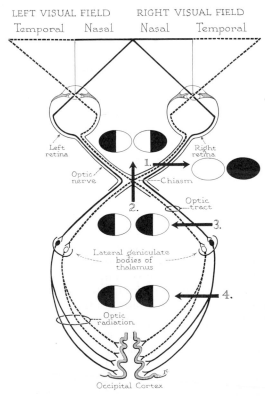

Figure 8.13 Arrows indicate possible sites of injury of the pathway. Black portion of the oval suggests the visual field loss resulting from the injury.

pretectal fibers provide the afferent pathway to the nucleus of the oculomotor nerve III, whose motor fibers complete the *light reflex* response of pupillary constriction. The neurons synapsing in the superior colliculus are concerned with following movements of the head and eyes in response to visual stimulation.

HEARING AND EQUILIBRIUM

The ear is concerned with the functions of hearing and equilibrium. On the basis of structure it is divided into three parts: external ear, middle ear, and internal ear. The first two portions serve to conduct sound waves to the receptor in the internal ear.

The External Ear (Fig. 8.14). The pinna and the external acoustic meatus constitute the external ear. The *pinna*, the expanded portion composed of cartilaginous framework covered with skin, projects from the side of the head and serves to collect and direct sound waves into the external acoustic meatus. The *external acoustic meatus* is a canal a little over an inch in length which leads from the outside to the ear drum or tympanic membrane, which separates the external ear from the middle ear. The canal is lined with skin which presents many fine hairs and sebaceous glands near its orifice. Along the upper wall are the ceruminous glands, modified sweat glands that secrete the ear wax or cerumen. The hairs and cerumen help to prevent the entrance of foreign particles or insects into the ear.

The Middle Ear (Fig. 8.14). The tympanic cavity, or middle ear, is a small air cavity located in the petrous portion of the temporal bone. The *auditory tube*, which connects the cavity with the nasal pharynx, serves as an air channel by which air pressure within the cavity is equalized with that outside. Equalization of pressures is aided by swallowing. Through the posterior wall is an opening into the mastoid antrum and mastoid cells. Two openings covered with membrane (the round and oval windows) separate the cavity from the inner ear. A chain of three small bones extends across the cavity from the tympanic membrane to the oval window. Derived from their shape, their names are *hammer* (malleus), *anvil* (incus) and *stirrup* (stapes). The malleus is attached to the drum membrane; the stapes fits into the oval window. Vibrations set up in the tympanic membrane by sound waves reaching it through the external auditory meatus are transmitted to the inner ear through the ossicles that bridge the cavity.

The Internal Ear. The internal ear contains the receptors for hearing and equilibrium. The *osseous labyrinth* is composed of a series of canals tunneled out in the petrous portion of the temporal bone (Fig. 8.14, *b*). The *membranous labyrinth* lies within the osseous labyrinth. It conforms to the shape of the osseous labyrinth, but is much smaller (Fig. 8.15, *A*).

The osseous labyrinth is filled with a liquid called *perilymph*; the membranous labyrinth contains *endolymph*. The parts of the bony labyrinth are cochlea, vestibule, and semicircular canals. The vestibule occupies a central position between the cochlea in front and the semicircular canals behind. The cochlea is concerned with hearing, the vestibule and semicircular canals with equilibrium.

The *cochlea* resembles a snail shell. It is in the form of a spiral wound two and one half times around a central axis called the modiolus. A cut through the cochlea from apex to base shows five cross sections of the tube (Fig. 8.14, *c*, *d*). Examination of the cross section shows the tube to be divided into three compartments. A bony lamina projecting from the modiolus, together with the basilar membrane, forms a partition which divides the tube into upper and lower passageways. The upper passage is the scala vestibuli; the lower passage is the scala tympani. The two connect at the apex by a small opening. The scala vestibuli ends at the oval window, the scala tympani at the round window. They are filled with perilymph. Between these two canals is the cochlear duct filled with endolymph. It is bounded above by the vestibular membrane and below by the basilar membrane. The *basilar membrane* consists of tightly stretched fibers which increase in length from base to apex. Resting on the basilar membrane is the *spiral organ*, the receptor for hearing, composed of a num-

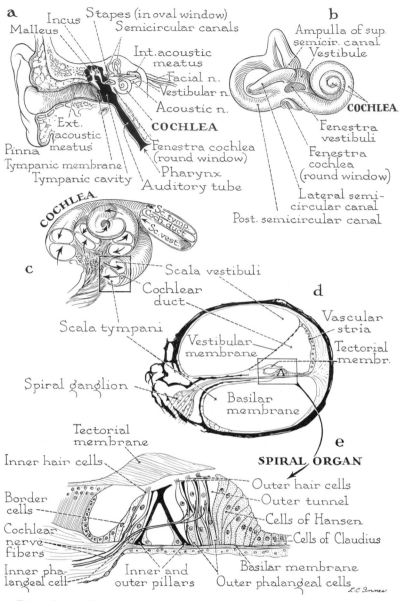

Figure 8.14. External, middle, and inner ear. See text for discussion.

VIII.	Statoacoustic (Auditory)	Cochlear division— internal acoustic meatus	Cochlear division spiral organ (Hearing)	None

ber of columnar cells with cilia on their free borders. These are the hair cells. Over them projects the tectorial membrane. The fibers of the cochlear nerve are in contact with the hair cells. These structures are shown in Figure 8.14, *e.*

Physiology of Hearing. The transmission of sound through the structures of the ear to the auditory receptor for transduction into a nerve impulse can be followed in Figure 8.16. Sound waves coming to the ear through the external

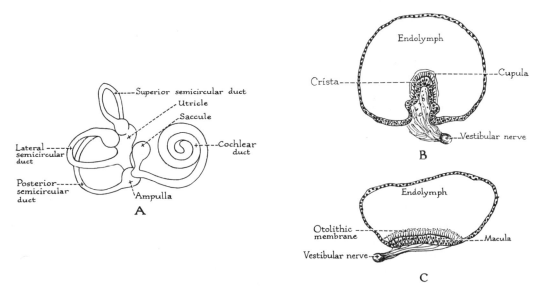

Figure 8.15.   *A*, Membranous labyrinth. *B*, Crista of semicircular duct. *C*, Macula of saccule.

VIII.	Statoacoustic (Auditory)	Vestibular division— internal acoustic meatus	Vestibular division Utricle Saccule Semicircular canals (Equilibrium)	None

acoustic meatus set the tympanic membrane in vibration. The chain of ossicles transmits the vibration to the oval window. The mechanical characteristics of the systems of ossicles are well adapted for the transfer of air-borne vibrations to pressure waves in a fluid system. The area of the tympanic membrane is nearly thirty times as great as that of the oval window, so that the pressure acting on the smaller surface area is amplified; the amplitude

of the excursion is reduced, since the piston-like movement of the tympanum results in a rocking-like movement of the stapes. When the vibrations of the stapes impinge upon the oval window, the whole fluid system is set in motion. The vibrations of the perilymph begin in the scala vestibuli and pass through the opening in the apex of the cochlea to the fluid in the scala tympani. Descending over this course, the force of the wave expends itself against

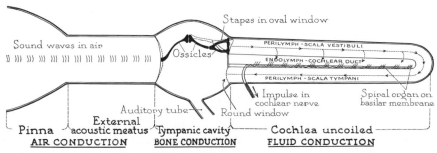

Figure 8.16 Diagram of sound transmission from the air to impulse in cochlear nerve. Dotted lines indicate the position of the ossicles and various membranes after inward displacement of the tympanic membrane.

the membrane of the round window. From this point on, the knowledge of the mechanism of hearing is incomplete. Our current concept is that a sound will set a portion of the basilar membrane into vibration. There is one point of maximum excursion of the membrane, so that the nerve fibers associated with this point will discharge at the highest frequency. It is the hair cells in contact with the tectorial membrane that are stimulated by vibration, and that set up impulses in the acoustic nerve that pass to the auditory area in the temporal lobe, where sound is perceived (Fig. 7.6).

In general, the *intensity*, that is, the loudness, of sounds within the audible range is related to the magnitude of the sound waves. Physiologically, differences in intensity are described in terms of the ratio of the intensities of two sounds. The standard or reference intensity for describing loudness is the lowest intensity at which a sound of a frequency of 1000 cycles per second can be heard by a person with normal hearing. The power or physical equivalent of this intensity is 0.0002 dyne per cm.^{2}. Since the range of energy between the threshold intensity and the loudest tolerable intensity is 1 to 1,000,000,000,000, logarithmic units are used to express the ratios: the term *decibel* or one-tenth of a bel is customarily used. For example, if we compare two sounds, and state that the loudness of the second sound is 1 bel, or 10 decibels, we mean that the intensity of the second sound is 10 times that of the first sound; if it is 2 bels or 20 decibels it is 100 times louder (you will remember that the log of 10 is 1; the log of 100 is 2).

In general, *pitch* is determined by the frequency of the sound waves, i.e., the number of vibrations per second. The pitch is said to be high when the frequency is high. The normal ear can hear frequencies of from 16 cycles per second to 20,000 cycles per second. Maximum amplitude of vibration of the membrane of the basal turn of the cochlear duct is associated with high pitch, and maximal amplitude toward the apex with low pitch.

In speaking of intensity and pitch we have qualified the discussion by use of the term "in general." Space does not permit discussion of the exceptions, but such qualification is necessary for relating the physical characteristics of vibration to physiological sensations such as "loudness" and "pitch." As might be expected in the case of sensory mechanisms, loudness is determined by the frequency of discharge of neurons, and pitch is a form of localization depending on the portion of the basilar membrane responding maximally.

Localization of sound, that is, recognition of the direction of its source, depends upon the differences in the time (or phase) of sound waves reaching the two ears. Movements of the head and body are used in detecting these differences. The detection of the source is called *binaural* localization. It is an important telereceptor function for warning of danger at a distance. The auditory reflex centers are in the inferior colliculi of the midbrain. In an auditory reflex, animals and men will turn their eyes and possibly their heads and bodies toward a sound. A loud sound brings about a "startle" reaction.

THE AUDITORY PATHWAY. The hair cells of the spiral organ form the receptors for sound waves. The afferent pathway for hearing is composed of at least three units. Neurons of the first order are afferent neurons that constitute the fibers of the cochlear division of the auditory nerve. The cell bodies of these neurons are in the spiral ganglion embedded in the modiolus of the osseous labyrinth. Their axons terminate in the dorsal and ventral cochlear nuclei of the medulla. The tract formed by the axons of the cochlear nuclei transmits impulses to the medial geniculate body of the thalamus. From the thalamus auditory impulses pass to the auditory area in the superior temporal gyrus of the temporal lobe.

Equilibrium. The saccule, utricle, and semicircular ducts contain the receptors for the senses of position and movement of the head. (Fig. 8.15).

The *saccule* and *utricle* form the membranous labyrinth in the vestibule. Their maculae contain sensory hair cells in contact with *otoliths* of calcium carbonate.

Changes in the position of the head cause the otoliths to bend the cilia of the hair cells. The hair cells synapse with the fibers of the vestibular nerve. The utricle and perhaps the saccule are concerned with the relationship of the body (really the head) with the pull of gravity. These organs supply the information that leads to shifts in muscular support of body weight.

The *semicircular ducts* form the membranous labyrinth of the semicircular canals. Each ear has three semicircular canals placed at right angles to each other in the three planes of space: posterior, anterior, and horizontal canals. There are groups of hair cells called *cristae ampullaris* in the dilated portion (ampulla) of each duct (Fig. 8.15). Agitation of the endolymph occasioned by turning of the head stimulates the hair cells, and impulses are initiated in the vestibular nerve endings. The semicircular ducts can be excited, inhibited, or unaffected as they work in right and left pairs, e.g., both horizontal ducts, right anterior and left posterior. They are responsive to angular acceleration of the head. The vestibular system is thought to project, in the company of the auditory pathways, to the temporal lobe of the cerebrum for the subjective sensation of equilibrium. The important reflex connections of the vestibular system are by way of the cerebellum and vestibulospinal tracts to the motor neurons of the spinal cord in the innumerable and continual adjustments of tone and muscular contraction requisite to posture. Vestibular reflexes are responsible via interconnections with extrinsic eye muscle motor neurons III, IV, and VI for the coordination of eye movements that maintain an image on the fovea of the retina. Disturbance of these reflexes may be evident in abnormal movements of the eye in *nystagmus.*

Impulses from these special proprioceptors are augmented by impulses from other receptors. Images or successions of images on the retina provide a source of information as to our position in relation to the external environment. If sensations from the labyrinths and the eyes tell us we are disoriented, we may adjust the position of the head to its normal relation to outside objects. If the body is not aligned with the head, the proprioceptor nerve endings in the neck are stimulated and discharge. In addition, the cutaneous tactile receptors and proprioceptors in the feet signal the relation of the feet and body to gravitational forces. Impulses from these many sensory receptors, located on widely different areas of the body, alter integration in the higher centers, converge upon the final common pathway and bring about the effective and coordinated response of the antigravity muscles that enable us to retain or to recover our normal orientation in space.

VISCERAL INTEGRATION

By definition, the term "autonomic" implies self-control and independence of outside influences. So the autonomic nervous system has often been given the alternate names of involuntary or vegetative nervous system. However, the implication that the autonomic system functions free of influence from higher centers is incorrect.

The term *autonomic nervous system* may be used to include both the visceral efferent fibers, and the visceral afferent fibers, which convey (a) afferent impulses from viscera, which do not reach the level of consciousness, (b) organic sensation such as hunger, nausea, distention, and sexual sensations, and (c) pain.

ARCHITECTURE OF THE AUTONOMIC SYSTEM

The autonomic nervous system is divided into a parasympathetic (craniosacral) and a sympathetic (thoracolumbar) division (Fig. 8.17). The efferent pathway is always composed of a two neuron chain that has its synapse outside the central nervous system. Cell bodies of the *preganglionic neurons* lie within the central nervous system, and the axons leave the system via cranial nerves or via the *white rami* of spinal nerves (Fig. 8.18). Cell bodies of the postganglionic neurons are located in the autonomic ganglia: (a) vertebral ganglia, a chain of which lies on either side of the vertebral column, (b)

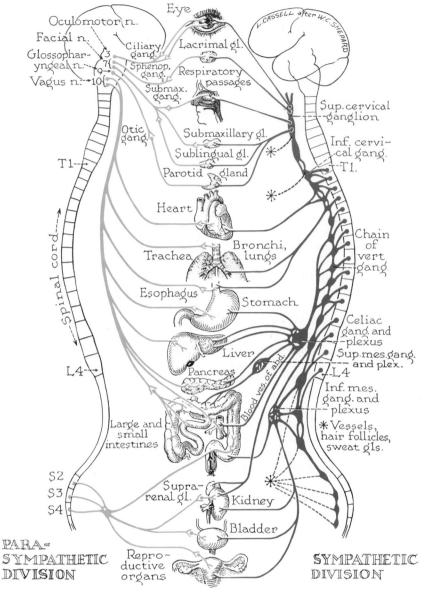

Figure 8.17 Diagram of the autonomic nervous system. The craniosacral division is shown in blue, the thoracolumbar division in red.

prevertebral ganglia, which lie along the aorta, or (c) terminal ganglia, which are located in the walls of the organs innervated. The axons of the postganglionic fibers innervate viscera of the ventral body cavities, blood vessels, glands, and arrector muscles. The vertebral and prever-

tebral (collateral) ganglia are associated with the sympathetic division, and the terminal ganglia are related to the parasympathetic division of the autonomic system.

The chain of vertebral ganglia is connected to each of the spinal nerves by one

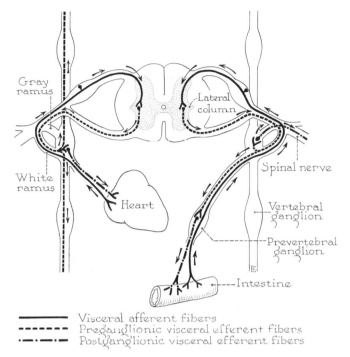

Figure 8.18 Diagram of reflex arc of the autonomic nervous system.

or more strands of delicate fibers called *rami communicantes*. A *gray ramus* from the autonomic trunk runs to each spinal nerve. It is made up of postganglionic unmyelinated efferent fibers. *White rami* are limited to the thoracic and first three or four lumbar nerves. These rami are composed of visceral afferent and preganglionic myelinated efferent fibers (Fig. 8.18).

The visceral afferent fibers have their cell bodies in the posterior root ganglion or in comparable ganglia near the brain, just as do any other sensory nerves.

Autonomic Reflex Arc (Fig. 8.18). The reflex arc of the autonomic system follows the same general pattern as the reflex arc of the somatic nervous system (Fig. 6.6):

1. An interoceptor (Table 5.1).
2. The visceral afferent neuron.
3. A synapse.
4. Preganglionic visceral efferent neuron transmitting impulses to cells in vertebral, prevertebral, or terminal ganglia. Synaptic vesicles contain *acetylcholine*.

5. A synapse.
6. Postganglionic visceral efferent neuron.
7. A visceral effector, i.e., cardiac muscle, smooth muscle, or gland.

The diagram of the autonomic reflex arc (Fig. 8.18) presents three possibilities for the course of the preganglionic fiber of the sympathetic division after it has entered a vertebral ganglion. (1) The fiber may synapse with cells in this ganglion. (2) It may pass up or down the chain of vertebral ganglia for some distance and terminate in a ganglion at a higher or lower level. (3) The neuron may pass through the vertebral ganglion to synapse in a prevertebral ganglion.

All the preganglionic neurons of the autonomic system can be influenced by other parts of the nervous system. The connections of the cells in the lateral column shown in Figure 8.18 are the simple ones, and to them may be added both ascending and descending fibers in the spinal cord, particularly those in the reticular formation.

Parasympathetic Division (Figs. 8.17, 8.19). The bodies of the preganglionic

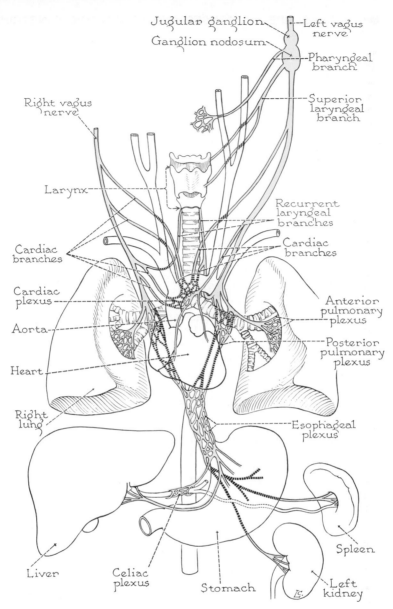

Figure 8.19. Diagram showing the distribution of the vagus nerve. (Redrawn and modified from Cunningham.)

| X. | Vagus | Jugular foramen | Mucous membrane of larynx, trachea, bronchi (Respiratory reflex) Lungs (Reflex control) Arch of aorta (Reflex inhibition of heart) Stomach (Hunger) | Muscles of palate, pharynx, esophagus (Swallowing) Muscles of larynx (Speech) Heart (Inhibition) Smooth muscle of stomach and small intestine (Peristalsis) Smooth muscle of trachea, bronchi, bronchioles (Contraction) Glands of stomach and pancreas (Secretion) |

cells of this division are located in the midbrain, medulla, and sacral portion of the spinal cord. Preganglionic fibers from the midbrain run in the oculomotor nerve; from the medulla in the facial, glossopharyngeal, and vagus nerves; in the sacral portion of the cord from the anterior column of the second, third, and fourth sacral segments of the cord through the anterior roots of the corresponding spinal nerves.

The axons of these cells synapse in terminal ganglia with postganglionic fibers. Because of the close relation of the efferent neurons with the organs innervated, the responses of the craniosacral division of the autonomic system are usually limited rather than widespread. *Acetylcholine* is the neurohumor secreted at the axon terminations in the effector organ.

Sympathetic Division (Figs. 8.17, 8.18). The bodies of the preganglionic cells of this division are located in the lateral column of gray matter of the spinal cord from the first thoracic to the third lumbar segment. These fibers leave the cord by way of the anterior roots of the corresponding spinal nerves and pass through the white ramus to connect with postganglionic neurons in the vertebral or prevertebral ganglia.

A preganglionic fiber may control a number of postganglionic fibers. For example, it has been found that there are about thirty-two cell bodies of postganglionic fibers in the superior cervical ganglion (a vertebral ganglion) to every preganglionic fiber in the chain of vertebral ganglia. Such an arrangement would explain the widespread responses to stimulation in the thoracolumbar system. *Norepinephrine* is the neurohumor secreted at the axon terminations in most of the effector organs (see pp. 143 to 144).

VEGETATIVE FUNCTIONS

The autonomic system governs the activities of such visceral structures as heart, lungs, digestive tube, glands, blood vessels, uterus, urinary bladder, and certain endocrine organs. As previously explained, it does not function automatically as an independent unit in the sense of controlling the organs from ganglia unrelated to the central nervous system, but control is exerted from several levels within the central nervous system—cerebral cortex, hypothalamus, and medulla. The hypothalamus integrates the finely adjusted balance that is effected between the parasympathetic and sympathetic functions of the autonomic system.

The autonomic nervous system performs the important function of maintaining the constancy of composition of the internal environment. Through its manifold activities the autonomic nervous system works to resist forces that tend to alter the internal environment. Regulation of the body fluids in respect to composition, temperature, quantity, and distribution is brought about through the action of this system on circulatory, respiratory, excretory, and glandular organs.

Most visceral structures receive fibers from both divisions of the autonomic system, and effects exerted by the two types of fibers on a given organ are relatively antagonistic. Thus the heart rate is slowed by the parasympathetic division (vagus) and accelerated by the sympathetic division. In general, the parasympathetic system is concerned with conservative and restorative processes, while the sympathetic division governs processes involving an expenditure of energy. In the parasympathetic division the slowing of the heart rate, constriction of coronary arteries, contraction of the pupil for protection of the eye from intense light, action of the liver inhibiting glycogen mobilization, and effects on the gastrointestinal tract favoring digestion and absorption through which energy supplies are restored, furnish evidence of conservative activities controlled by this division.

The sympathetic division has been called the emergency mechanism of the body because it is brought into activity by conditions that call for unusual effort on the part of the body to perform work or to resist threatened dangers. In such crises the sympathetic division is stimulated, and, since this division supplies secretory fibers to the suprarenal glands, the hormone epinephrine is added to the blood,

TABLE 8.1 VEGETATIVE FUNCTIONS OF THE AUTONOMIC NERVOUS SYSTEM

Organ	Parasympathetic Effects: Conservation and Restoration of Energy	Sympathetic Effects: Expenditure of Energy
Eye { Iris	Contraction of circular fibers	Contraction of radial fibers
Eye { Ciliary muscle	Contraction accommodates for near vision	Relaxation
Lacrimal gland	Secretion	
Cerebral blood vessels	Dilatation	Constriction
Salivary glands	Secretion—large amount of thin watery saliva	Secretion—thick viscid and scanty saliva
Respiratory passages	Secretions stimulated, blood vessels dilated	Secretions inhibited, blood vessels constricted
Bronchi	Constriction	Dilatation
Heart	Inhibition	Acceleration
Coronary arteries	Constriction	Dilatation
Stomach { Wall	Increased tone, motility	Inhibition
Stomach { Sphincter	Inhibition	Contraction
Stomach { Glands	Secretion	Inhibition
Intestine { Wall	Increased tone, motility	Inhibition
Intestine { Internal anal sphincter	Inhibition	Contraction
Liver	Inhibits glycogen breakdown Secretion of bile	Increases glycogen breakdown
Pancreas	Stimulates secretion of pancreatic enzymes and hormones	Diminishes enzyme secretion
Adrenal gland—medulla		Secretion
Blood vessels of abdominal and pelvic viscera		Constriction
Urinary bladder { Wall	Contraction	Inhibition
Urinary bladder { Sphincter	Inhibition	Contraction
Uterus—nonpregnant		Inhibition
Uterus—pregnant		Contraction
Blood vessels of external genitalia	Dilatation	Constriction
Sweat glands		Secretion
Blood vessels of skin		Constriction
Arrector muscles of hair follicles		Contraction

and this in turn augments the action of this division. A review of the actions of the sympathetic division will show how well these bodily reactions fit an animal (or man) to meet emergencies demanding defense or flight:

1. A rise in arterial blood pressure by acceleration of heart rate, increase in force of cardiac contractions and constriction of arterioles, especially in skin and splanchnic areas; dilatation of coronary arteries and blood vessels in contracting muscles brings about a state of maximum efficiency in the circulatory system.

2. Stimulation of glycogen breakdown in the liver releasing large amounts of glucose into the blood stream insures a fuel supply for active muscles.

3. Dilatation of bronchi and inhibition of secretions of respiratory tract permit an increase in oxygen intake.

4. Decrease in coagulation time lessens danger from hemorrhage.

Visceral integration is discussed in greater detail at applicable points throughout this book. Your attention is directed to control of respiration (pp. 251–254), control of the heart (pp. 310–312) and of blood pressure (pp. 314–315), emptying of the urinary bladder (pp. 329–331), and mechanism of salivary secretion (pp. 363–365). An enhanced appreciation of these complex vegetative functions can be obtained by looking over the sections cited in this paragraph at this time, then later reviewing the autonomic nervous system in conjunction with the study of regulation of heart and blood pressure and the other listed subjects.

QUESTIONS FOR DISCUSSION

1. While at a football game the following sequence of events occurred: You saw the halfback running down the field; turned your head to follow the play; listened to the cheers of the crowd and shouted your own; clapped your hands as the touchdown was scored; sat down and ate a hot dog. Name localization areas, tracts of the cerebrum, and cranial nerves involved.

2. Beginning with the external ear, list the structures through which sound waves must pass to reach the receptor. Follow light waves through the eye to the receptor.

3. State the relationship between special senses and somesthetic senses; between special senses and kinesthetic senses; between special senses and exteroceptors and proprioceptors.

4. How is the ciliary muscle affected in close work over a long span of time?

5. Why do older persons hold newspapers and books at great length from their eyes?

6. How will vitamin A deficiency affect the photoreceptors?

7. Describe your appearance and physiological reactions when you are thoroughly frightened. How are these related to the autonomic nervous system?

8. How is the function of the sympathetic portion of the autonomic system related to summation, facilitation, and convergence?

9. What is there about the metabolism of chemical transmitters that helps to explain the fact that parasympathetic activity is quite localized while sympathetic activity is usually widespread?

10. How can autonomic responses be influenced by the cerebral cortex, hypothalamus, and reticular formation?

ENDOCRINE MECHANISMS

CHAPTER NINE

THE ENDOCRINE SYSTEM

The endocrine system is closely related to the nervous system. There is overlap in some of their respective areas of control. The endocrines do, however, assume a principal role in the control of a number of physiological functions; indeed, direct participation by the nervous system may be lacking or negligible. In other functions the endocrines may mimic and supplement the vegetative controls of the autonomic nervous system. Endocrine controls, which are exerted through glandular secretions, i.e., hormones, usually evoke somewhat slow but sustained responses.

The endocrines exert the principal control of the metabolic functions of assimilation, storage, and energy metabolism; maintenance of the physiological integrity

and functioning of the endocrine glands themselves; maintenance of the physiological integrity and functioning of other systems of the body, particularly the reproductive, nervous, and circulatory systems. In many instances control and integration involve more than one endocrine gland.

The endocrine system includes the following endocrine glands: pituitary (hypophysis cerebri), suprarenals, thyroid, parathyroids, pancreas, reproductive glands (ovaries and testes), placenta, and gastrointestinal mucosa (Fig. 9.1). In discussing the pituitary, we will be concerned with two principal structures, each having three component parts. The suprarenals have two structural and functional parts, and the pancreas has two main types of endocrine cells. In addition there are or-

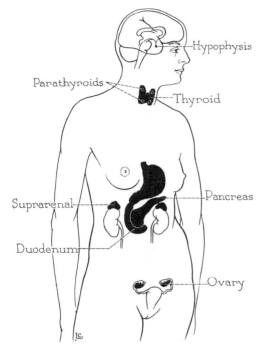

Figure 9.1 Location of the glands of internal secretion.

gans and tissues that may carry out endocrine functions but their status with respect to the endocrine system is as yet uncertain. These include the pineal and thymus glands and certain cells of the kidney (juxtaglomerular cells). It is well to recognize their existence but they will not be discussed because of the degree of uncertainty about their function.

The endocrine glands are usually the last of the body's coordinating mechanisms to appear in embryological development.

The following summary table (Table 9.1) listing the endocrines, their secretions, and principal functions is presented for guidance in the detailed discussion of the individual organs and their hormones and for review. Although the glands controlling the reproductive system and the gastrointestinal mucosa have been included in the table, they will be discussed in the sections on reproduction and digestion.

Definitions. Endocrines are glands of *internal secretion* or *ductless glands*. They discharge their secretions directly into the blood so that all cells in the body are ex-

posed to endocrine secretions. Thus endocrines differ from the mammary, sweat, salivary, and gastrointestinal glands, which discharge their secretions into ducts that carry the secretions only to the site of their action or use.

The active principles of the endocrine glands are called hormones, from the Greek word meaning "stir up or set in motion." In this text the use of hormone will be limited to the secretions of endocrine or ductless glands that exert their specific effects on other specific cells and tissues by stimulation or inhibition.

Methods of Study. Several methods of experimentation that apply particularly to this field may be mentioned. Not all have been profitably used in any one case. They include the removal of a gland, followed by careful study of the subsequent deficiencies; the treatment of an animal following removal of an endocrine gland by administration of an extract of that organ or with its active principle; administration of an extract or active principle of a gland to normal animals; the isolation, characterization, and synthesis of active principles from glandular extracts; the analysis of arterial blood entering and of venous blood leaving a gland, to determine that a hormone is actually added to the blood during its passage through the gland, as only this method can establish positive proof of the endocrine function of a tissue; and clinical studies of diseases that can be related to dysfunction of one or more glands. Dysfunction may take the form of either increased secretion, *hyperfunction*, or decreased secretion, *hypofunction*.

Mechanism of Action. Hormones regulate the *rate* at which a cell functions or its metabolic transformations occur. Hormones do not initiate action themselves; they act by influencing enzyme reactions. There are two hypotheses concerning the mechanism involved. According to one hypothesis they influence cellular enzyme systems directly. According to the other, they exert an indirect effect by changing the permeability of cell membranes and thus facilitating transfer of substrate or other substances involved in effective functioning of the enzyme system.

TABLE 9.1 ENDOCRINE SECRETIONS AND FUNCTIONS

Endocrine and Hormone	Metabolic Functions; Water and Salt Balance (Assimilation, Storage, Energy Metabolism; Retention, Excretion)	Maintenance of Integrity; Control of Function (System or Organ)
Pituitary: Adenohypophysis		
pars distalis		
Adrenocorticotrophin (ACTH)		Endocrine, suprarenal cortex
Thyrotrophin (TSH)		Endocrine, thyroid
Gonadotrophins		
Follicle stimulating (FSH)		Endocrine, ovaries, testes
Luteinizing (LH or ICSH)		Endocrine, ovaries, testes
Prolactin	Stimulates milk production.	Endocrine, ovaries, mammary
Somatotrophin (GH or STH)	Growth; carbohydrate, protein, lipid metabolism; glycogen storage; sustained lactation	All body cells
Pituitary: Adenohypophysis, pars intermedia		
Intermedin (MSH)	Pigmentation of skin	Skin
Pituitary: Neurohypophysis		
Antidiuretic hormone (ADH) or vasopressin	Water retention	Urinary, kidney
Oxytocin	Ejection of milk from mammaries	Mammary, uterus
Suprarenals: Adrenal cortex		
Cortisone, hydrocortisone	Conversion of protein to carbohydrate	
Aldosterone	Sodium retention, potassium excretion	Kidney, all cells
Suprarenals: Adrenal medulla		
Epinephrine	Carbohydrate, glycogenolysis; liberation of fat; calorigenic	Cardiovascular
Norepinephrine	Carbohydrate, glycogenolysis	Sympathetic nervous system, cardiovascular
Thyroid		
Thyroxine and triiodothyronine	Increases metabolic rate, O_2 consumption; growth; supports lactation	Heart, all cells
Calcitonin	Mineral metabolism; reduces resorption of bone Ca^{++}; reduces blood Ca^{++}	Skeletal
Parathyroid		
Parathormone	Mineral metabolism, Ca^{++}; PO_4; increases blood Ca^{++}; increases PO_4 excretion	Skeletal, muscular
Pancreatic islets		
Insulin	Carbohydrate utilization; lowers blood sugar	Digestive, liver
Glucagon	Glycogenolysis of liver glycogen; elevates blood sugar	Digestive, liver
Testes		
Testosterone	Protein anabolism; nitrogen, salt, water retention	Reproductive, testes
Ovaries		
Estrogens	Protein anabolism; nitrogen, salt, water retention	Reproductive, ovaries
Progestins		Reproductive, uterus, mammary
Relaxin		Reproductive, cervix, symphysis pubis
Placenta		
Estrogens	Same as for ovaries	Reproductive, ovaries
Progesterone		Reproductive, uterus, mammary
Relaxin		Reproductive, cervix, symphysis pubis

Table 9.1 *(Continued)*

Endocrine and Hormone	Metabolic Functions; Water and Salt Balance (Assimilation, Storage, Energy Metabolism; Retention, Excretion)	Maintenance of Integrity; Control of Function (System or Organ)
Chorionic gonadotrophin	Supplements pituitary gonadotrophin	Reproductive, ovaries
Gastrointestinal mucosa		
Secretin	Chemical digestion	Digestive
Cholysystokinin	Chemical digestion	Digestive
Enterogastrone	Inhibits gastric motility	Digestive
Intestinal gastrin	Chemical digestion	Digestive

Hormones become bound to plasma proteins when they are released into the blood stream. The specificity which they have with respect to site of action suggests that there may be an affinity between a hormone and its effector tissues.

The control of secretion and release of hormones may be exercised by other endocrine glands, by nerves in response to chemical changes in the environment of a receptor or center, or by nervous control mediated directly through chemical means. The control of some endocrines has been likened to negative feedback in a servomechanism, i.e., reduction in the amount of a hormone from endocrine A in the blood stream stimulates increased activity on the part of endocrine B which controls endocrine A. Conversely an increase in the hormone from A decreases the activity of endocrine B. These and other control mechanisms will be presented in the discussion of the individual glands and their secretions.

HYPOPHYSIS CEREBRI

The *hypophysis cerebri*, or *pituitary gland*, is a small organ about the size of a pea in man. It lies in the sella turcica of the sphenoid bone, below the optic chiasma (Figs. 9.1, 9.2). It is attached to the brain by the *infundibular stem*, which extends downward from the floor of the third ventricle. Current terminology distinguishes the different parts of the hypophysis on functional and embryologic grounds.

All of the adenohypophysis is derived embryologically from the ectoderm of the roof of the mouth. All of the neurohypophysis is derived from neural ectoderm; it is actually an outgrowth of the nervous system. (See adrenal medulla, p. 142; and eye, p. 410.)

The blood supply of the hypophysis is analogous to that of the liver (see p. 352) in that it has an arterial supply, a portal venous supply, capillaries, sinusoids, and veins. The arterial supply is derived from the superior and inferior hypophysial arteries, which are branches of the internal carotids, from the arterial circle, and from the posterior communicating artery. The hypophysial portal veins arise from the capillaries of the median eminence of the hypothalamus. These portal veins empty into a network of sinusoids in the pars distalis. This provides a functional vascular linkage between the hypothalamus and the adenohypophysis for neurohumoral control of the activity of pars distalis. The capillaries and sinusoids empty into the hypophysial veins, which drain into the cavernous and circular sinuses. Blood supply to the neural lobe is entirely arterial (from the inferior pair of arteries), and venous drainage is the same as that of the adenohypophysis. The nerve supply, which the hypophysis receives from the sympathetic plexus around the internal carotid artery, is entirely vasomotor. The neurohypophysis is the termination of the hypothalamohypophysial tract from the hypothalamus.

Adenohypophysis

Pars Distalis. Much more is known about the function of the pars distalis of the adenohypophysis than is known about the functions of its other two divisions. There are three basic cell types that may be distinguished in histologic section (Fig.

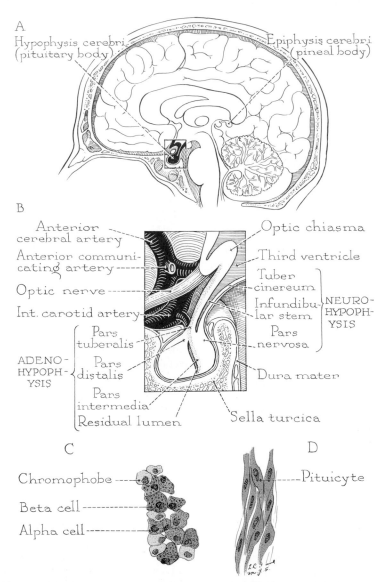

A
Hypophysis cerebri
(pituitary body)

Epiphysis cerebri
(pineal body)

B

Anterior
cerebral artery

Optic chiasma

Anterior communi-
cating artery

Third ventricle

Optic nerve

Tuber
cinereum

Infundibu-
lar stem

NEURO-
HYPOPH-
YSIS

Int. carotid artery

Pars
tuberalis

Pars
nervosa

ADENO-
HYPOPH-
YSIS

Pars
distalis

Dura mater

Pars
intermedia

Residual lumen

Sella turcica

C

Chromophobe

D

Pituicyte

Beta cell

Alpha cell

Figure 9.2 Hypophysis cerebri. *A,* Blackened inset draws attention to relation of hypophysis to gross structures of the brain in midsagittal section. *B,* An enlargement of the inset showing gross details of the hypophysis and surrounding structures. *C,* Typical cells of adenohypophysis. *D,* Typical cells of neurohypophysis.

9.2). These are the chromophobes, i.e., cells that do not stain readily; the acidophils, or alpha cells, which take up acid stains; and the basophils, or beta cells, which take up basic dyes. Secretion of each of the trophic principles mentioned below can now be assigned to a particular cell type in the pars distalis by the use of appropriate histotechnique or cytochemical methods.

The pars distalis elaborates at least six hormones, five of which have their primary site of action in other endocrine glands. They are called trophic hormones. This term, which means "pertaining to nutrition," was applied to these compounds when they were first discovered, because the pituitary principles were found to be necessary for the growth and morphologic integrity of the thyroid, suprarenals, and gonads. We now know that the pituitary hormones also have other actions, but the term is well entrenched. The glands that utilize these trophic principles are called "target organs." All of the trophic hormones are of a protein nature; they are either proteins or polypeptides. The trophic hormones and their functions are as follows:

Adrenocorticotrophic hormone (ACTH) has as its target organ the adrenal cortex. It can be extracted from the basophils, but in man it may be secreted by chromophobes. It is now available in very pure form as a polypeptide of low molecular weight. It is essential for the integrity of the adrenal cortex, and also stimulates the suprarenal glands to increase their production of certain steroid hormones.

Thyrotrophic hormone (TSH) has the thyroid as its target organ. It is secreted by modified basophils called "thyrotrophs." It is a glycoprotein with a high molecular weight. The hormone is required for the maintenance of the thyroid cells, and stimulates the production of thyroid hormones.

Gonadotrophic hormones (FSH, ICSH, and LTH) all have a role in the reproductive process. *Follicle-stimulating hormone (FSH)* has as its target organ the follicles of the ovary. It is responsible for the maturation of these follicles and hence is necessary for ovulation. It probably also acts upon the thecal cells which form the capsule surrounding the follicles (see p. 390). In the male, FSH maintains spermatogenesis by stimulating the cells in the seminiferous tubules. It maintains testicular weight in hypophysectomized animals, but does not stimulate production of the hormone testosterone.

Interstitial cell-stimulating hormone, or *luteinizing hormone (ICSH or LH)*, has several actions in the female and one in the male. In the male it stimulates the production of testosterone by the interstitial cells of the seminiferous tubules. In the female it is synergistic with FSH in bringing about follicular maturation; it intiates rupture of the ripe follicle and hence is sometimes called the "ovulating hormone"; it acts upon the thecal cells to cause the formation of the *corpus luteum*; and it stimulates the production of estrogenic hormones by the thecal cells during follicular development (after FSH has prepared these cells for secretion).

Prolactin stimulates milk production in the mammary gland after estrogens and progesterone have prepared the mammary cells for milk synthesis. It is important to remember that prolactin stimulates milk production, not milk ejection. The latter is a function of the neurohypophysis (see p. 140). The function of prolactin in the male, if any, is not known.

In addition to these five trophic hormones, the pars distalis secretes *growth hormone (GH or STH)*, which is also called *somatotrophin* because its target cells are somatic cells, particularly cells in the epiphyseal cartilage in developing long bones (p. 155). This hormone is secreted by the acidophils; it is now available in purified form. It is necessary for growth and development and it affects carbohydrate, protein, and fat metabolism. Hypersecretion of growth hormone in childhood and adolescence causes *gigantism*. Hyposecretion results in *dwarfism*. The administration of growth hormone alone will not bring about normal growth in hypophysectomized animals or in naturally occurring hypopituitarism. Other endocrine substances, principally thyroxin and insulin, are also required for growth.

The factors that control the secretion

of the pars distalis are probably very similar, from a mechanistic point of view, for all the hypophysial hormones, perhaps even for growth hormone. Four important factors are:

First, there exists a wealth of evidence to show that the rate of secretion of the various trophic hormones is increased or decreased by some control mechanism of the central nervous system, particularly by centers in the hypothalamus. There is evidence that there are specific releasing factors, i.e. corticotrophic-releasing factor and releasing factors for TSH, LH and FSH.

Second, the primary capillary plexus lies in the floor of the hypothalamus and is fed by arterial blood. This plexus empties into portal veins that terminate in a secondary capillary bed in the pars distalis. This arrangement obviously bestows upon the hypothalamus the capability of modifying the constituents of the blood bathing the cells of pars distalis.

Third, the pars distalis receives no nerve supply from the brain.

Fourth, there is a reciprocal relationship between the rate of secretion of individual hypophysial trophic hormones and the target organ hormones concerned. In the case of the gonadotrophins this relationship is complex and will be discussed in the Unit on reproduction. In the case of the suprarenals and the thyroid the relation is clear: when the concentration of adrenal hormones, e.g., cortisone, or of thyroxin increases, the rate of secretion of ACTH or of TSH decreases. Also, a decrease in the blood level of the target organ hormones results in an increase in secretion of the appropriate trophic hormones. This arrangement is referred to as "negative feedback of a servomechanism," by which an increase in output retards the stimulating mechanism and vice versa.

Thus, in summary, it may be seen that the nervous system is able to influence secretion of the adenohypophysis by a chemical process.

The influence of the central nervous system on the secretion of prolactin is a special case. The hypothalamus is thought to release a prolactin-inhibiting factor (PIF); this is believed to involve a reciprocal relation between the PIF and the LH release factor, or some factor serving a dual function in control of PIF and LRF. Finally, there is a reciprocal relationship between trophic hormone secretion and the blood level of the target organ hormone concerned.

It should be again emphasized that all cells in the body are exposed to the same concentration of each hormone. For example, every cell in the body is exposed to the same concentration of ACTH, but only the cells of the adrenal cortex respond to it. Further, all pituitary cells are exposed to an identical concentration of adrenal steroids, but only the adrenocorticotrophs respond to them. These facts imply an inherent specificity of response. We do not have sufficient evidence yet even to venture an intelligent guess as to the mechanism of specificity.

PARS INTERMEDIA. The pars intermedia secretes *intermedin* or *melanocyte stimulating hormone* (MSH), which causes changes in the pigmentation cells of the skin. The secretion is under the control of the brain. It endows some lower animals, such as amphibians, with the ability to change the color of their skin under various environmental conditions. In man MSH appears to be similar to a portion of the molecule of ACTH in the number and position of several amino acids.

Neurohypophysis. The infundibular process, the neural portion of the stem, and the median eminence (which is really part of the brain) are considered a unit. For purposes of description, however, it is just as well to discuss the three as separate parts. The *infundibular process* (posterior pituitary) contains some cells, called *pituicytes*, that appear to be glandular and were formerly thought to be secretory elements. Axons in the stalk, which have their cell bodies in particular nuclei of the hypothalamus, terminate on or near these pituicytes. The present concept is that the hormones of the neural hypophysis are synthesized in the hypothalamic nuclei and then pass down the nerve fibers into the infundibular process, to be stored or released directly into the capillaries of the circulatory system.

Two hormones are produced by the pars nervosa, or neurohypophysis. Both are polypeptides consisting of eight amino acids. The chemical structure of each is known, and pure synthetic forms of each are available. One, the *antidiuretic hormone* (ADH), or *vasopressin*, acts on the kidney to decrease the rate of urine formation. It is important in the maintenance of the proper state of hydration in land animals. This substance also stimulates the smooth muscle of arterioles and arteries to contract, thus increasing the blood pressure, and giving rise to the term "vasopressin." It is questionable, however, whether this pressor action is important under physiological conditions.

The lack of ADH, which may occur from damage to the pituitary or hypothalamus, results in a condition called *diabetes insipidus*. This is entirely different from *diabetes mellitus* (see p. 148). There is no disturbance of carbohydrate metabolism in *diabetes insipidus*, only an inability to control water excretion by the kidneys. This results in a large urine production, *polyuria*, and a large fluid intake, *polydipsia*.

The second hormone produced by the neurohypophysis is *oxytocin*. It has two important actions in pregnant females. It is secreted during parturition and causes contraction of the pregnant uterus, the process of labor. The nonpregnant uterus is not affected by physiological concentrations of oxytocin. Second, it is secreted during suckling and causes active ejection of milk from the mammary glands. It has no known function in males.

CONTROL OF SECRETION OF THE NEUROHYPOPHYSIS. The secretion of antidiuretic hormone is controlled, ultimately, by the osmotic pressure of the blood and by the volume of blood in the pulmonary circulation. Changes in osmotic pressure of arterial blood entering near the region of the optic chiasm of the hypothalamus result in changes in ADH secretion. If the osmotic pressure increases, ADH secretion increases, so that less water is excreted by the kidneys and the osmotic pressure of the blood again approaches a normal

value. On the other hand, if the blood is diluted, that is, its osmotic pressure decreased by the ingestion of a large amount of fluid, the secretion of ADH will be stopped, allowing the kidneys to excrete the excess fluid. Some commonly used drugs, such as ethyl alcohol and caffeine, act directly on the hypothalamus to inhibit ADH secretion.

Nerve impulses originating in volume-sensitive receptors in the pulmonary veins and in the atria of the heart may also modify ADH secretion. An increase in effective blood volume decreases ADH secretion; a decrease in effective volume increases ADH secretion.

Although it is well established that oxytocin is necessary for parturition, the mechanism that causes its release at the proper time is not known. The mechanism controlling oxytocin release during suckling, however, is known. Sensory receptors located in the nipples send nerve impulses through the ascending reticular system in the spinal cord and brain stem to the hypothalamus which cause oxytocin release.

Since the "final common path" for ADH and oxytocin secretions originates in the hypothalamic nuclei, it is possible for higher centers of the brain to affect these nuclei. Psychologic factors can influence the secretion of oxytocin at the time of labor and during lactation. For example, psychic trauma can result in premature labor, or in a failure of milk ejection. It also may be demonstrated that psychic influences can produce changes in ADH secretion.

SUPRARENAL GLANDS

The suprarenal glands are paired structures, one of which is located at the superior pole of each kidney (Figs. 9.1, 9.3). They are also called *adrenal glands*, both names meaning "above the kidney." Each gland consists of an outer portion called the *cortex*, and an inner portion, the *medulla* (Fig. 9.4). The cortex is surrounded by a

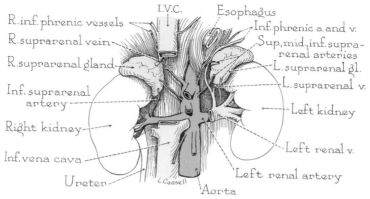

Figure 9.3 Suprarenal glands and related structures.

dense connective tissue capsule. The two parts of the gland, as in the case of the pituitary, have separate embryologic origins. The adrenal cortex develops from embryologic mesoderm, while the medulla develops as an outgrowth from neural ectoderm, that is, from the same part of the neural tube from which the autonomic nervous system develops. The cortex is essential to life in all the higher mammals; the medulla is not. Secretory activity of the cortical cells is under the control of the pituitary gland (the adenohypophysis). Medullary secretion is under the control of sympathetic preganglionic visceral efferent nerves (p. 129).

Adrenal Cortex. The adrenal cortex secretes several different hormones, all of which belong to the family of organic chemicals called steroids. These hormones are usually referred to collectively as the "adrenal corticoids." The most important ones are cortisone, hydrocortisone, and aldosterone. In the female, some androgens, or male hormones, are secreted by the cortex; androgens also are steroids.

The corticoids are divided into two groups, depending upon whether their

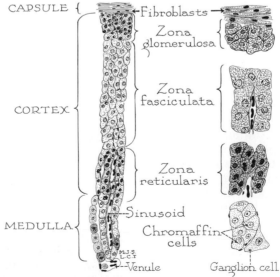

Figure 9.4 Section through suprarenal gland showing proportional zones of medulla and cortex with their respective types of cells.

main effect is upon carbohydrate or salt metabolism. These are called glucocorticoids (cortisone, hydrocortisone) and mineralocorticoids (aldosterone), respectively.

The glucocorticoids act upon many different kinds of cells, particularly liver and muscle, to promote conversion of protein to carbohydrates. The mineralocorticoids act upon all cells to change their permeability to various salts. Their most important action is upon renal cells, promoting the excretion of potassium and the retention of sodium. It is the loss of this adrenal cortical function that is fatal to the adrenalectomized mammal and to the human with *Addison's disease*. Loss of large amounts of sodium and retention of potassium leads to changes in the nervous and cardiovascular systems, particularly in the heart, which are incompatible with life.

So far as is known, the glucocorticoids are under the control of ACTH, while mineralocorticoid secretion is apparently independent of hypophysial control.

Adrenal Medulla. The adrenal medulla secretes two hormones, *epinephrine* and *norepinephrine*. They belong to a family of chemicals called *catechol amines*. The actions of epinephrine and norepinephrine, and those of other catechol amines, mimic the action of the sympathetic nervous system, i.e., they are sympathomimetic agents. These hormones also influence metabolism and act on the central nervous system.

Epinephrine has both excitatory and inhibitory effects, depending upon the type of receptor that predominates in the effector cells of the target organ, and also upon its concentration. The peripheral excitatory receptors in the cardiac nodes and cardiac muscle are β receptors. Epinephrine stimulates the β receptors and increases both the vigor of the contraction of the heart and the heart rate. The increase in the vigor of contraction is called an *inotropic effect*, the increase in the rate a *chronotropic effect*. The smooth muscle of the blood vessels supplying the skeletal muscles and the splanchnic area has a preponderance of β receptors that are inhibitory, hence epinephrine exerts an inhibitory effect or vasodilation (see pages 314 and 315). The cerebral blood flow may also be increased but to a somewhat lesser extent than in muscle and the splanchnic area. Smooth muscle of blood vessels of the skin, mucosa, and kidney are constricted by the excitatory effect of epinephrine on their α receptors. The overall effect is that of a powerful cardiovascular stimulant. The initial increase in the strength of contraction of the heart, the increase in heart rate, and the constriction of the blood vessels of the skin increase systolic blood pressure and blood flow through the areas in which vasodilation has occurred. The initial increase in rate is followed by a compensatory slowing of the heart as a result of stimulation of the vagus by the increased blood pressure. This is followed by a reduction in blood pressure.

For the most part epinephrine relaxes and reduces the activity of the smooth muscle of the gastrointestinal tract. The peripheral inhibitory receptors are β receptors, although there are also some of α type receptors of the intestinal muscle that have an inhibitory effect. The response to epinephrine may be different when the tone and the level of activity of the smooth muscle of the gastrointestinal tract is low. Under these circumstances epinephrine may stimulate the excitatory receptors and increase muscular tone and the frequency and amplitude of contraction. The pregnant and nonpregnant uterus differ in their response to epinephrine. The bronchial smooth muscles of the respiratory system are relaxed by epinephrine.

Epinephrine exerts an important effect on carbohydrate and fat metabolism; it also has a significant calorigenic effect. It has a *hyperglycemic* action, increasing blood sugar levels by stimulating glycogenolysis, i.e., the conversion of carbohydrate stored as liver and muscle glycogen into glucose. It also increases the level of blood lactate which is converted to glucose in the liver. Epinephrine also stimulates the liberation of free fatty acids from the adipose tissues, increasing the free fatty acid level in the blood.

The influence of epinephrine on the central nervous system is not great. However, it causes affective reactions, particularly the feeling of anxiety and restlessness; tremors may also occur in some people. The reactions appear to be associated with passive rather than aggressive states, i.e., tending to lead to "flight rather than to fight."

Norepinephrine, like epinephrine, has both excitatory and inhibitory effects, again depending upon its concentration and upon the peripheral receptors. In general, it is a less powerful stimulant than epinephrine and acts predominantly upon the α receptors, except in the heart where the β receptors are excitatory. It has an overall vasoconstrictor (excitatory) effect on the circulatory system; systolic and diastolic blood pressure and peripheral resistance are increased. The effects of norepinephrine on smooth muscle of the gastrointestinal tract, the respiratory system, and the reproductive system are similar to those of epinephrine. It influences carbohydrate metabolism and liberation of stored fat. It is calorigenic. Its action on the central nervous system appears to be associated with an aggressive state, i.e., anger conducive to "fight not flight." It has been found that the more aggressive species secrete large amounts of norepinephrine, and the more docile types secrete smaller amounts.

A most important function of norepinephrine is the chemical mediation of nerve impulses. It is the neurohumoral transmitter of postganglionic adrenergic fibers. Norepinephrine which is stored in the axon terminals is synthesized by the nerve cells as well as picked up from the blood stream. This contributes to the capability of the postganglionic fibers to sustain a prolonged response.

THYROID GLAND

The thyroid gland has two lobes. These are connected across their midline by a bridge of cells called the *isthmus* (Figs. 9.5, 9.7). The two lobes lie on either side of the trachea and extend from the caudal border of the thyroid cartilage of the larynx down to the region of the sixth tracheal ring. The isthmus crosses the anterior surface of the trachea at about the third ring. Two arteries supply each lobe. A pair of superior thyroid arteries arise from the external carotids and a pair of inferior thyroid arteries branch off from the subclavian arteries. These four arteries combine on the surface of the gland to form a dense plexus from which multiple branches enter the gland. The capillaries drain into the superior and middle thyroid veins, which empty into the internal jugular veins and the inferior thyroid veins, thus joining the left brachiocephalic vein. The gland is innervated from the superior and inferior cervical ganglia (sympathetic fibers) and from the superior and inferior laryngeal branches (parasympathetic fibers) of the vagus nerve. There is no direct nervous control of thyroid secretion; these nerves serve a purely vasomotor function.

The secretory portion of the thyroid is made up of many *follicles* (Fig. 9.6) that are composed of a single layer of epithelial cells. The shape of the cells varies with the activity of the gland. The follicular cells perform three functions. These are the uptake of iodide from the blood stream against a steep concentration gradient by active transport; synthesis and storage of the thyroid hormones; and secretion of the hormones into the blood stream.

The thyroid secretes *thyroxin*, *triiodothyronine*, and *calcitonin*, which will be discussed separately. The first two hormones are iodinated amino acids. Thyroxin is *tetraiodothyronine*. The ratio of thyroxin to triiodothyronine in venous blood leaving the gland is about 10:1 under basal conditions. No qualitative difference in the physiological action of the two compounds is known, although triiodothyronine is several times more potent on a weight-for-weight basis. Both hormones are stored in combination with a protein (globulin), and the storage form of the hormone in the thyroid follicle is called *thyroglobulin*. Thyroglobulin is never found in the circulation under normal conditions. Thyroxin, which constitutes the principal blood hormone, and triiodothyronine are rapidly attached to serum proteins once they enter the circulation. Since there are no other important iodine-containing compounds in the body, a measurement of protein-bound iodine (PBI) can be used as a clinical test for the

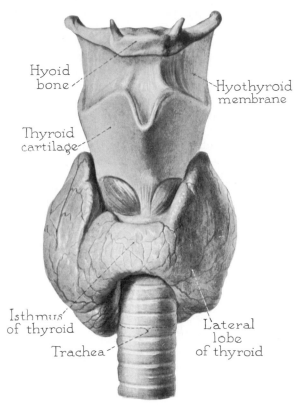

Figure 9.5 The thyroid gland, larynx, upper portion of the trachea, and hyoid bone from in front. (From Sobotta and McMurrich.)

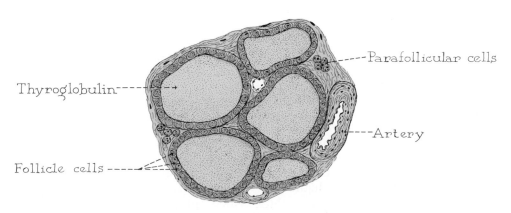

Figure 9.6 Several thyroid follicles.

amount of thyroid hormone in blood. A normal value for PBI is 5.9 to 7.6 μg. per 100 ml. serum. The follicular cells cannot synthesize the thyroid hormones unless the concentration of iodine in the blood is adequate.

The thyroid hormones have five important physiological effects. (1) They increase basal metabolism, i.e., heat production under basal conditions (see p. 369). There are other clearly evident effects on protein and fat intermediate metabolism and upon the rate of absorption of carbohydrates and fatty acids; they vary greatly with hormone balance and metabolic state. (2) Thyroid hormones are necessary for proper growth in man; this effect seems to be exerted independently of action on the basal metabolic rate. (3) They are essential for the growth and proper functioning of the nervous system. (4) They play a special role in cardiac metabolism, affecting the heart rate, output, and physiological condition of its tissues. (5) They have an effect on water balance and electrolyte balance that influences excretion and physiological cellular hydration.

Lack of thyroid secretion may result in *cretinism* in the young. This condition is characterized by small stature, arrested mental development, and retarded sexual development. In adults, hypofunction of the thyroid results in *myxedema*. Both of these conditions are associated with edema, skin and hair texture changes, reduction in excitability of the central nervous system, reduction in basal metabolic rate, and reduced tolerance to cold. Excess of thyroid hormones results in *hyperthyroidism* and is characterized by an increased basal metabolic rate, loss of weight, rapid heart rate, increased perspiration, and increased sensitivity to heat.

So far as is known, the rate at which thyroid hormone is secreted into the blood is controlled solely by TSH. There is a feedback mechanism that governs the reciprocal relation between secretion of TSH and thyroid hormones. If the circulating levels of thyroid hormones are high, the output of pituitary TSH is reduced; if the blood level of the thyroid hormone is low, TSH secretion is stimulated. Environmental stimuli, such as cold, and internal stimuli, such as goitrogens (antithyroid chemical agents) from certain foods, affect thyroid activity indirectly by first altering pituitary TSH secretion.

Calcitonin. A hypocalcemic hormone can be obtained from the perfusate from the thyroid gland. Also a purified hypocalcemic substance has been prepared from thyroid glands of hogs and other species. Since it has been established that these substances can be derived from the thyroid, the agent has been called *thyrocalcitonin*. It was once believed that it was a secretion of the parathyroid rather than the thyroid. The results of recent studies suggest that the parathyroid may also secrete a hypocalcemic agent. Regardless of whether it is derived from one source or two, its action in regulating extracellular calcium concentration seems to be firmly established. Calcitonin or thyrocalcitonin lowers plasma calcium by reducing calcium resorption from the bone. A high calcium plasma concentration, i.e., hypercalcemia, stimulates the release of calcitonin.

PARATHYROID GLANDS

The parathyroid glands are small yellowish-brown bodies usually located on the posterior surface of each thyroid lobe near its medial border (Fig. 9.7). The number of parathyroids present in the human body is variable. Seventy to eighty per cent of all persons have two pairs; some, however, have only one pair, while others have three. Often accessory parathyroid tissue is located in the mediastinum or in the fascia of the neck. The total mass of parathyroid tissue is fairly constant, but it may be distributed in bodies of varying size.

The parathyroid glands secrete *parathormone*. This hormone controls calcium and phosphate metabolism and is essential to life. In its absence, serum calcium decreases and serum phosphate increases. Their combined effect causes tetany and eventually convulsions and death. A purified preparation of a hypercalcemic agent has recently been extracted from parathyroid glands. This causes both calcium mobilization from bone and in-

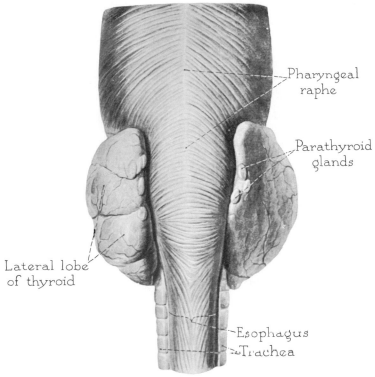

Pharyngeal
raphe

Parathyroid
glands

Lateral lobe
of thyroid

Esophagus
Trachea

Figure 9.7 The thyroid and parathyroid glands with the lower portion of the pharynx and upper end of the esophagus from behind. Usually there are four parathyroid glands, but there may be more, as in this figure. (From Sobotta and McMurrich.)

creased urinary excretion of phosphate. It is a polypeptide and its amino acid content is known.

The stimulus for secretion of parathormone is probably a decrease in calcium ion concentration in the blood. There is also a possibility that an elevated level of phosphorus in the blood may indirectly stimulate the glands to secrete. The pituitary has no direct control over the parathyroids. Parathyroid size is not affected by hypophysectomy, nor is the calcium-phosphorus ratio in serum, which is normally about 3:1, altered appreciably.

PANCREAS

The pancreas is an organ that extends transversely across the posterior abdominal wall from the duodenal loop on the right to the hilus of the spleen on the left (Fig. 9.1). The duodenal portion is called

the head, the splenic portion the tail. The portion in between these is referred to as the body of the pancreas.

The pancreas receives arterial blood from the three divisions of the celiac artery and from the superior mesenteric artery. Venous drainage is by way of the splenic and superior mesenteric veins. The gland is innervated by sympathetic fibers (from the celiac plexus) and parasympathetic (vagal) fibers.

This gland contains both exocrine and endocrine tissue. The exocrine functions of the pancreas were dealt with in Chapter 18. Here we are concerned only with the endocrine tissue, the islets of Langerhans (Fig. 9.8). Most islet cells are of two types, alpha (α) cells and beta (β) cells. The α cells secrete the hormone *glucagon* and the β cells secrete *insulin*.

The nature and importance of insulin have been appreciated for over fifty years

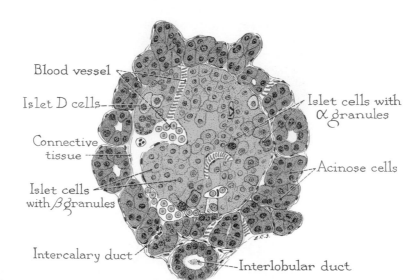

Figure 9.8 Section of human pancreas comparing endocrine cells of the islet of Langerhans with surrounding glandular cells.

and the pure compound (a polypeptide) was first prepared in 1926. Insulin is essential to life; if deficient, hyperglycemia (elevated blood glucose) and consequent glycosuria (glucose in urine) develop. This condition is known as *diabetes mellitus*. In the absence of insulin, blood sugar rises to toxic levels, which, if untreated, lead to coma and death. Hyperinsulinemia, whether brought about by pancreatic secretion or by the injection of insulin, results in a profound fall in the blood sugar level, *hypoglycemia*, which if severe enough also leads to coma, convulsions, and death.

The sequence and interrelationships of the known effects of insulin administration and deprivation have not been satisfactorily explained. It is possible to interpret these phenomena with a conceptual model in which insulin provides a mechanical connection between hexokinase and a mitochrondrion in the presence of Mg^{++}. The transport of certain substances across the cell membrane along with numerous biochemical reactions within the cell are facilitated because of this connection. The major biochemical reactions which are affected by insulin include:

Synthesis of: DNA, mRNA, proteins, glycogen;
Oxidative phosphorylation;
Intracellular transportation;
Glucose utilization, lipogenesis, antiglycogenolysis, antilipolysis, antiproteolysis, antigluconeogenesis.

The net accomplishments of insulin's effect upon metabolism are the generation and storage of energy with regulation of its release and utilization.

The second islet cell hormone, *glucagon*, has been identified in the past ten years. It is also a polypeptide and is available in pure form. The administration of glucagon results in a rise in blood sugar, hyperglycemia. This hormone has an opposite effect to that of insulin. This hyperglycemia is effected by glycogenolysis of liver glycogen.

The control of insulin secretion is vested in the level of blood sugar itself. That is, if blood sugar rises, insulin secretion is enhanced and the concentration of blood sugar will return toward normal. Conversely, if blood sugar is depressed, as during a prolonged fast, insulin secretion is retarded or halted. Although it is known that parasympathetic nerves to the β cells can stimulate insulin secretion, the physiological importance of this innervation is poorly understood. Blood sugar levels may also control glucagon secretion but the evidence for this is less convincing than in the case of insulin.

QUESTIONS FOR DISCUSSION

1. Compare and contrast the control of TSH secretion with the control of parathormone secretion.

2. Relate the effects of low iodine (iodide) concentration in the blood to a secretory activity of the pituitary adenohypophysis.

3. Explain the difference between diabetes mellitus and diabetes insipidus.

4. Cushing's disease is a disorder of the pituitary, but its symptoms are always related to hypersecretion of the suprarenal glands. Which part of each gland do you think is involved in this disease?

5. Enumerate the endocrine glands that are essential to life, and state briefly what the cause of death would be if each were removed individually in a series of experimental animals.

6. A chemical agent is capable of blocking stimulation of β receptors of smooth muscle of the intestine. Discuss the effect of epinephrine on the tone and activity of the muscle following use of the blocking agent.

UNIT 3

BIOMECHANICS

10. THE SKELETAL SYSTEM   11. THE DYNAMICS OF MUSCLE   12. POSTURE AND MOVEMENT

In this unit interest is centered upon the musculoskeletal system and its particular features of mechanical advantage and abilities for adaptation to stress and strain.

The development and growth of osseous tissue furnish an important background for this study. The physiology of muscle describes the properties of muscle, analyzes muscle action, and discusses the source of energy for muscular contraction.

The attachment of muscles to the bony framework makes possible the maintenance of posture, the movements of the parts of the body, and protection of organs within the cavities of the body. The student is referred to Figures 10.9, 12.60, and 12.61 for orientation in studying the organs of the musculoskeletal system.

THE SKELETAL SYSTEM

CHAPTER TEN

CHARACTERISTICS OF BONE

Composition and Function. The bones of the body constitute the organs of the skeletal system. Together they form the supporting framework of the body, they serve as the basis of attachment for the muscles, in certain regions of the body they protect delicate structures, they supply calcium, phosphate, and citrate to the blood, and they are important in the formation of blood cells (for hemopoietic function, see p. 267).

Bones may be considered as *organs* because (1) they are made up of several kinds of tissue—osseous tissue, cartilage, fibrous tissue, nervous and vascular tissues; and (2) they function as integral parts of the skeletal system as a whole.

Bone Formation, Development, and Reconstruction. The skeleton of the young embryo is composed of fibrous membranes and hyaline cartilage. The formation of bone begins in these two tissues in the eighth week of embryonic life (see p. 409 also). Bone formed in a membrane is called intramembranous bone; bone formed in cartilage is called endochondral bone. It is important to understand that these terms indicate solely the method by which the bone starts to develop; they do not imply and difference in structure once the bone is fully formed.

Intramembranous Ossification. This is the simpler, more direct type of bone formation. The flat bones of the face and cranial vault and a part of the clavicle form in membrane. In the area in which bone formation is about to begin, *mesenchymal* cells congregate and many small blood vessels are present. The mesenchymal cells cluster to form long strands that run in all directions. Delicate bundles of fibrils, produced by the secretory action of the cells, form the axis of each elongated group. In a short time the fibrous axis is

153

well defined and the cells are arranged in a layer around the outside of the strand. The fibers of the axis become saturated and cemented together with a mucopolysaccharide. The fibers are then less distinct, and in a short time they are masked to such an extent that the strand has a homogeneous appearance. This organic fibrous material forms a preliminary framework in which calcium salts are deposited. The framework may be called *osteoid*. As soon as the deposit of calcium salts begins, the osteoid becomes true bone matrix and the mesenchymal cells are then called *osteoblasts* (bone-formers). The osteoblasts secrete alkaline phosphatase, an enzyme that speeds the formation of phosphate ions and subsequently the synthesis of hard hydroxyapatite crystals $[Ca_{10} (PO_4)_6 (OH)_2]$. When an original strand is completely invested with bone matrix it is called a *trabecula*. With the deposit of successive lamellae of bone, some of the osteoblasts become entrapped in their own secretions. These cells are *osteocytes*, and the spaces in the bone matrix which they occupy are called lacunae (see Fig. 10.1).

As the trabeculae in any ossification center grow, they soon touch each other and fuse. The pattern formed by the coalescence of the trabeculae resembles a latticework (Latin, *cancellus*), and bone showing this structure is, accordingly, primary cancellous bone. Between the trabeculae are the marrow spaces. They contain mesenchymal elements that are gradually converted into marrow. Layers of compact bone form on the outer and inner surfaces by periosteal ossification. In this process, layers of the original mesenchyme condense to form *periosteum* shortly after bone forms at the inner centers. Osteoblasts from the inner surfaces of the periosteum deposit layers of cancellous bone. Much of the newly formed bone is destroyed and resorbed. In the surface areas the dissolving bone is replaced at a rapid rate; by means of considerable internal reconstruction, bone of the compact type is formed. The cancellous bone at the inner ossification center also undergoes reconstruction; some bony strands are resorbed, while osteoblasts reinforce and construct other parts

of the meshwork. The large multinuclear cells, *osteoclasts* (bone-destroyers), are usually present in areas in which bone destruction is taking place. The bones of the skull, when fully formed, consist of inner and outer *tables* of compact bone joined by the mass of spongy bone, *diploe* (see Fig. 10.4).

Endochondral Ossification. This type of bone formation involves the same processes as intramembranous ossification, but these processes are preceded by an initial period of cartilage destruction. The endochondral course of development occurs in the bones of the thorax, the limbs, some of the bones of the skull, and the hyoid bone. These bones are represented in the embyro by temporary cartilaginous models. Bone begins to form in the eighth week of embryonic life, and at birth a large part of the skeleton is composed of bone.

The process occurring in a long bone is typical. Figures 10.1, *A-F*, and 10.2, *G-I*, show stages in the ossification of the tibia. The contour of the cartilaginous model suggests the general form of the future bone (*A*). There is a central shaft called the *diaphysis* with an *epiphysis* at each end. The cartilage model is covered with *perichondrium*. Bone formation begins in an area surrounding the center of the diaphysis. The fibroblasts of the perichondrium adjoining the cartilage enlarge, become osteoblasts, and begin the formation of bone, depositing a ring or collar of bone surrounding the middle of the diaphysis (*B*). As soon as the perichondrium begins to form bone, it is called periosteum. While the periosteal bone is forming, changes take place in the cartilage of the diaphysis; the cartilage cells swell into vesicles, and the matrix between them calcifies. Blood vessels and mesenchymal cells penetrate the collar of spongy bone and make their way into the interior of the altered cartilage (*C*). The calcified cartilage matrix surrounding the cartilage cells dissolves, and large spaces are opened up which soon become filled with embryonic marrow (*D, E*). These spaces are the primary marrow spaces. Cells of the embryonic marrow become osteoblasts and begin to form layers of bone about the remnants of cartilage matrix. Some cartilage cells also become osteoblasts; others degenerate.

The osteoblasts form columns or trabeculae of spongy bone, and the cartilage matrix is gradually absorbed. Osteoclasts are also formed and can usually be seen in places in which the newly formed bone is being resorbed.

Meanwhile, the cartilage has grown steadily so that the whole model has increased in size. The periosteum has deposited successive layers of bone on the outside, gradually extending the collar toward each epiphysis. In the interior of the cartilage the process of cartilage destruction and endochondral bone formation has extended from the center of the diaphysis toward the epiphyses. As these areas of cartilage disintegration become removed somewhat from the center, the cartilage cells show a more definite arrangement and are seen in regular rows (E). Before long, mesenchymal elements of the periosteum invade the cartilage of the epiphyses and establish secondary ossification centers. In the tibia a center appears in the proximal epiphysis soon after birth and distally in the second year (F, G). The process is similar to that occurring in the diaphysis and results in spongy bone.

Plates of cartilage, known as epiphyseal cartilage (Fig. 10.2, G), lie between the diaphysis and epiphysis at the *metaphysis* (H). This cartilage persists for some time and provides for the growth in length of the bone. Cartilage grows by mitosis on the epiphyseal side of the disc; it is destroyed and replaced by bone on the diaphyseal border, so that the disc remains approximately the same thickness. The metaphysis, or growth zone, is composed of the epiphyseal cartilage disc, a zone of calcified cartilage, and a zone of spongy bone deposited on the trabeculae of cartilage matrix. The process extends progressively, and the bone increases in length as the growth zone continues to move away from the center.

All bone is spongy when it is first formed; later, by processes of bone destruction and resorption, the bone at the surface is reconstructed into the compact type. To accomplish this, the irregular channels in the spongy bone are enlarged and concentric lamellae of bone are laid down on the inside to construct the *osteons* (haversian systems). In the center of the diaphysis extensive dissolution of bone sculptures out a cylindrical space that is the medullary cavity. Eventually the cavity extends into the spaces of the spongy bone near the epiphysis. The design of the growing bone is suited to support body weight and muscular activity.

Ossification is complete when the cells of the cartilage cease to divide and the discs are entirely replaced with bone. The epiphyses are then united with the diaphysis, and growth in length is no longer possible. In the tibia this union occurs in the distal epiphysis at the age of 17, and in the proximal one at about the twentieth year (H, I). Growth in the circumference of the bone is accomplished by layers of bone formed by the periosteum. Ossification is not complete in all the bones of the body until about the twenty-fifth year.

Histophysiology of Bone. Although it appears to be unyielding, bone is a living, plastic structure that continually adapts to gradual change of growth. It also yields to transient forces, such as those imposed by walking and muscular contraction. There is a constant turnover of materials, which reflects the dynamics of growth, maintenance, and reconstruction.

Metabolism of the cells and matrix in osseous tissue requires a constant dietary supply of calcium and phosphorus varying with the physiologic state of growth and development of the body as a whole (see p. 146). The absorption of these minerals from the intestine into the blood is dependent upon an appropriate dietary source of vitamin D. A deficiency of minerals and vitamin D prevents hardening of bone in both child and adult. The connective tissues are unable to produce and maintain the collagenous fibers and ground substance of bone matrix with inadequate supplies of vitamin C. Rate of growth of the skeleton from the activity, distribution, and coordination of modulation of the osteoblasts, osteoclasts, and osteocytes requires an appropriate dietary source of vitamin A.

Normal *calcium deposition* in the matrix appears to depend upon acid hydrolases of

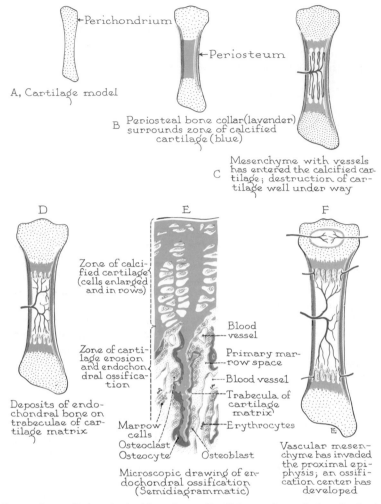

←Perichondrium

A, Cartilage model

←Periosteum

B Periosteal bone collar(lavender) surrounds zone of calcified cartilage(blue)

C Mesenchyme with vessels has entered the calcified cartilage; destruction of cartilage well under way

D

E

F

Zone of calcified cartilage (cells enlarged and in rows)

Zone of cartilage erosion and endochondral ossification

Deposits of endochondral bone on trabeculae of cartilage matrix

Marrow cells
Osteoclast
Osteocyte

Osteoblast

Microscopic drawing of endochondral ossification (Semidiagrammatic)

Blood vessel

Primary marrow space

Blood vessel

Trabecula of cartilage matrix

Erythrocytes

Vascular mesenchyme has invaded the proximal epiphysis; an ossification center has developed

10.1 Ossification and growth in a typical long bone, the tibia, as shown in longitudinal sections. (Part I, early stages.)

lysosomes from the enlarged mesenchymal cells and cartilage cells and the chemical configuration in the collagenous fibrils. Normal *calcium mobilization* for blood plasma levels (see p. 146) occurs partly by simple diffusion between blood and the readily available calcium in newly formed osteons. Another portion of the blood plasma calcium results from the interaction of parathyroid hormone and thyrocalcitonin from the thyroid gland. Coordination of the numerous processes of skeletal growth and maturation also requires hormonal stimuli from the gonads, and the thyroid and pituitary gland (see p. 136).

Closely related to the hydroxyapatite $[Ca_{10}(PO_4)_6(OH)_2]$ crystals in bone matrix are the blood plasma reservoirs of citrate $(C_6H_3O_7^{\equiv})$, carbonate $(CO_3^{=})$, magnesium (Mg^{++}), and sodium (Na^+) ions. It is possible for radioactive isotopes of calcium and phosphorus to substitute for the usual forms of calcium and phosphorus in bone. The hydroxide (OH^-) may be replaced by fluoride (F^-). Detrimental effects upon surrounding tissues may occur when calcium is supplanted by lead (Pb^{++}), strontium (Sr^{++}), or radium (Ra^{++}).

Repair of fracture initiates bone formation. The bleeding that occurs with injury

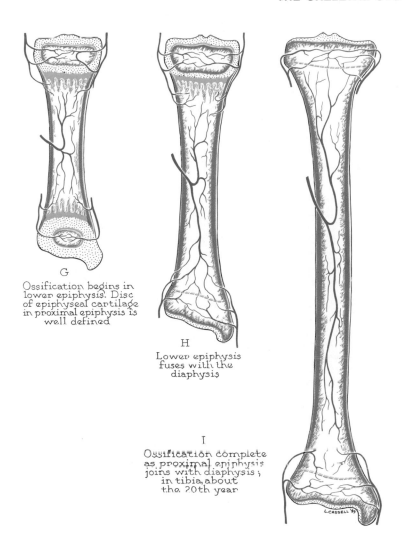

G
Ossification begins in
lower epiphysis. Disc
of epiphyseal cartilage
in proximal epiphysis is
well defined

H
Lower epiphysis
fuses with the
diaphysis

I
Ossification complete
as proximal epiphysis
joins with diaphysis;
in tibia, about
the 20th year

Figure 10.2 Ossification and growth in a typical long bone, the tibia, as shown in longitudinal sections. (Part II, late stages.)

to the blood supply and vascular membranes of bone organizes into a clot of procallus. Fibrocartilaginous connective tissue modifies the procallus into callus. The osteoblasts that have migrated from the periosteum and endosteum at the line of fracture replace the callus with bone matrix, which calcifies. Resorption of excess bone and remodeling of the new bone complete the repair of the fracture.

The numerous sources of constant mechanical stress upon the microscopic structure of bone include hydrostatic pressure of circulating blood, recoil of the heart, gravity and the concomitant resistance to it by contraction of antigravity muscles,

and growth and movement in adjacent soft tissues as well as locomotion of the entire body. Coincident with the deformation of bone is the generation of *electrical activity* in the matrix of bone. It is postulated that junctions of hydroxyapatite crystals and collagenous fibers act as piezoelectric materials to develop an electric charge under deformation. Electrically negative regions appear to be associated with bone formation and electrically positive regions with bone destruction.

Structure of Bone. The structure of a long bone is shown in Figure 10.3 Compact bone is found on the exterior of all bones and cancellous bone in the interior.

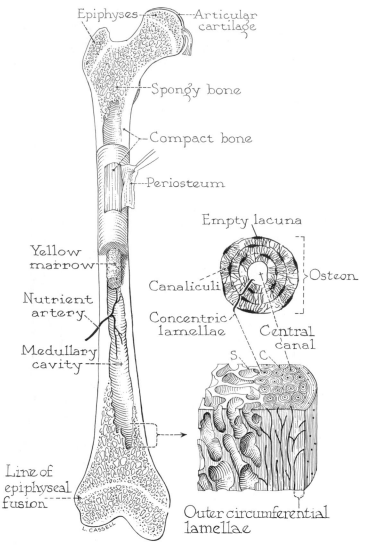

Epiphyses
Articular cartilage
Spongy bone
Compact bone
Periosteum
Empty lacuna
Osteon
Yellow marrow
Canaliculi
Nutrient artery
Concentric lamellae
Central canal
Medullary cavity
S.   C.
Line of epiphyseal fusion
L. CASSELL
Outer circumferential lamellae

Figure 10.3 Diagram of a structure of a long bone. *S*, on inset, indicates spongy bone; *C*, compact bone. (Inset adapted from Toldt.)

In the long bones of the extremities the epiphyses are composed of the spongy type of bone covered by a thin layer of compact bone.

The diaphysis is made up almost entirely of compact bone, most of which is composed of osteons and their interstitial lamellae. A set of lamellae, known as inner and outer circumferental lamellae, runs parallel to the surface of the bone on the interior and exterior. Extending throughout the center of the diaphysis is a cavity containing marrow.

The surface of the bone is covered by a fibrous membrane or *periosteum*. It has an outer fibrous layer composed of dense fibrous tissue with blood vessels and an inner osteogenetic layer containing many fibroblasts. The periosteum is attached to the surface of the bone by the collagenous fibers of Sharpey, which extend from the osteogenetic layer into the bone tissue. A thinner, more delicate membrane, the *endosteum*, which resembles periosteum in structure, lines the medullary cavity.

Bone is well supplied with blood. If we

strip the periosteum from a fresh specimen of bone we see blood oozing from minute pores on the surface of the bone. At these points, blood vessels from the periosteum enter the bone and pass through channels, *Volkmann's canals*, to enter and leave the central canals of the osteons (Fig. 10.3).

The lymph fluid from the blood vessels of the central canals reaches all parts of the osteons through the circulatory tract formed by the canaliculi and lacunae. The circulation of the fluid in an osteon is probably independent of those of neighboring systems. In a long bone, an artery and vein enter the marrow cavity through an opening, *the nutrient foramen*, which is usually near the center of the shaft. These divide into branches that run through the marrow and supply it. Other vessels penetrate the bone through Volkmann's canals to enter the osteons. Branches of the nutrient artery connect with arteries of the compact and cancellous bone. In this way, blood vessels entering the bone from the periosteum are united with blood vessels entering from the marrow cavity, so that through the osteons nutritive materials of the blood penetrate to all parts of the tissue. In the short, flat, irregular bones composed largely of spongy bone, several large openings in the surface transmit vessels that penetrate deep into the marrow spaces and resemble the nutrient arteries of long bones.

Bone marrow is found filling in the spaces of spongy bone and the medullary cavity of long bones. It is composed of a supporting framework of reticular tissue in which there are blood vessels and blood cells in various stages of development. In the adult, there are two kinds of marrow, red and yellow. Red blood cells and some white blood cells are formed in the red bone marrow (see also p. 267). In the newborn, all marrow is red; in the adult it is found in spongy bone, such as the proximal epiphyses of long bones, in the sternum, ribs, vertebrae, and diploe of the cranial bones. Yellow marrow, which contains many fat cells, is in the medullary cavity of long bones. Bone marrow aids in the nutrition of bone.

Articulations of the Skeleton. The bones of the skeletal system are joined together to form the supporting framework of the body. The joints, or articulations, may be classified by their most characteristic structural feature into fibrous, cartilaginous, and synovial (see Table 10.1).

The architecture of the *fibrous joints* (Figs. 10.4, 10.5) and some *cartilaginous joints* (Fig. 10.6) is that of a continuous union of the bones with fibroelastic connective tissue. The sutures and synchondroses of the adult skeleton may change entirely into bone and become *synostoses*. Comparison of Figures 10.6, 10.7, and 10.8 will show the similarity of symphysis and synovial articulations. The disc is a prominent feature of the symphysis. There is little or no movement at the fibrous and cartilaginous joints.

The *synovial joints* have a more elaborate structure (Figs. 10.7, 10.8). The two or more bones are united by an encircling band of fibrous tissue called the articular capsule. This capsule is often strengthened by ligaments, which withstand stress and assist in securing the joint. The articular capsule is lined with synovial membrane. Articulating ends of bone are covered by a layer of hyaline cartilage. A disc or meniscus of fibrous cartilage may divide the cavity of some joints, such as tibiofemoral articulation (Fig. 10.8).

Most of the joints of the body are synovial. Some are more freely movable than others; this variation in the degree of movement is determined to a large extent by the shape of the articulating surfaces forming the joint and the effect of activity of skeletal muscles related to the articulation. A division into groups illustrating the association of structure and movement can be made as follows:

1. Ball and socket joints (Fig. 10.9): Movement is freest in this type of joint, in which a rounded head on one bone moves in a cuplike cavity of another. Examples of ball and socket joints are the shoulder joint, formed by the head of the humerus and the glenoid cavity of the scapula, and the hip joint, formed by the head of the femur and the acetabu-

TABLE 10.1   CLASSIFICATION OF ARTICULATIONS

Type	Characteristics	Examples
Fibrous joints	Joint cavity absent; motion very limited	
Sutures (Figs. 10.4, 10.21, 10.10, 10.11)	Serrated bone ends approximated by several layers of fibroelastic tissue	Bones of the skull; teeth in mandible and maxilla
Syndesmoses (Fig. 10.5)	Bone margins approximated by fibroelastic membrane	Laminae of vertebrae; distal ends of tibia and fibula; borders of radius and ulna
Cartilaginous joints	Joint cavity absent; motion limited	
Synchondroses (Figs. 10.3, 10.42)	Bone ends approximated by hyaline cartilage	Metaphysis; ribs and costal cartilages; acetabulum
Symphyses (Fig. 10.6)	Bone ends covered by hyaline cartilage and separated by a disc of fibrocartilage; approximated by a fibroelastic capsule	Bodies of vertebrae; pubic bones
Synovial joints (Figs. 10.7, 10.8)	Joint cavity present; bone ends covered by cartilage, may be separated by disc; approximated by fibrous capsule lined with fibroelastic synovial membrane and fluid; freely movable	Extremities; articulatory processes of vertebrae; jaw

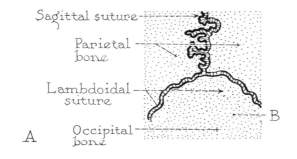

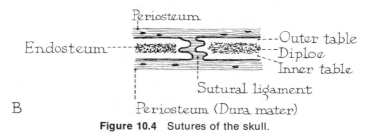

Figure 10.4 Sutures of the skull.

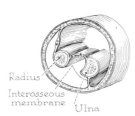

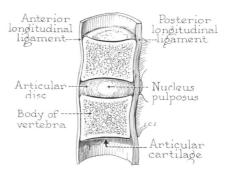

Figure 10.5 Syndesmosis between radius and ulna.

Figure 10.6 Symphysis between bodies of vertebrae.

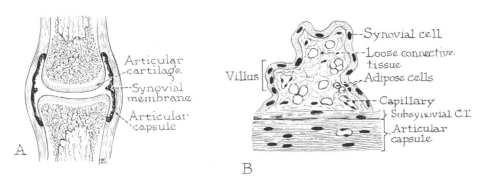

Figure 10.7 *A*, Diagram of a synovial joint; *B*, synovial membrane.

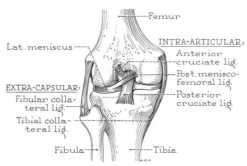

Figure 10.8 Hinge joint at the knee.

lum of the hip bone. Functionally, the wrist and ankle perform as ball and socket joints.

2. Saddle joints (Figs. 10.9, 10.40): Opposing articulating surfaces that are convex and concave alternately, such as the carpal-metacarpal articulation in the thumb, allow great freedom of motion.

3. Hinge joints (Fig. 10.9): Action in a hinge joint is limited to movement in one plane, usually forward or backward. The elbow, knee, and interphalangeal joints of fingers and toes are examples of this type.

4. Pivot joints: These joints exhibit a rotary movement in which a ring rotates around a central axis as in the articulation between the first and second cervical vertebrae (atlas and axis) (Figs. 10.27, 10.28), or in which an axis turns within the ring as in the articulation between the head of the radius and the radial notch of the ulna (Fig. 10.38). In this case the ring is completed by the annular ligament that encircles the head of the radius and is attached to the margins of the radial notch.

5. Plane joints: Very little movement takes place in these joints. The articular surface of one bone slides upon that of the other to a limited extent, the form of the articulating parts often serving to restrict the movement. The joints between the articular processes of the vertebrae (Figs. 10.25, 10.26) and those between the carpal and tarsal bones are of this type (Fig. 10.9).

Synovial Membrane. Synovial membrane (Fig. 10.7, *B*) varies in structure according to the tissue upon which it lies such as muscle, adipose tissue, dense or loose connective tissue. Small sacs of synovial membrane or *bursae* are found near the skin, tendons, ligaments, and muscles which are related to articulations and subject to friction.

Synovial membrane lining the dense fibrous articular capsule rests upon less dense fibroelastic connective tissue. A discontinuous layer of fibroblasts at the joint cavity surface covers loose connective tissue which is abundantly supplied with blood vessels, lymphatic vessels, and sensory nerve endings. Macrophages and mast cells are found in the synovial membrane in addition to the fibroblasts. This membrane may be thrown into large temporary folds or small permanent villi. Synovial fluid is a dialysate of blood filtered through the synovial membrane to which the fibroblasts have added hyaluronic acid. This mucopolysaccharide imparts viscosity to synovial fluid which lubricates and possibly nourishes the adjacent structures.

Viscosity of the synovial fluid increases with cold and decreases with heat. Injury to the synovial membrane may induce an inflammatory reaction and formation of excess synovial fluid and result in pain and limitations in the movements of the musculoskeletal organs.

DIVISIONS OF THE SKELETON

The bones of the body fall into two main groups (Fig. 10.9): those comprising the axial skeleton, and those forming the appendicular skeleton. The former is made up of the bones of the skull, vertebral column, and thorax; the latter consists of the bones of the upper and lower extremities.

The number of bones in the skeleton varies at different ages. At birth the human body contains about 270 bones. This number is slightly reduced during infancy by the union of some of the separate segments to form single bones, but from then on through puberty and adolescence the number increases steadily as the epiphyses and bones of wrists and ankles develop. After adolescence reduction is again brought about by a gradual union of independent bones. Ultimately the adult human skeleton consists of 206 bones.

The number of bones in the axial and appendicular divisions of the skeleton is listed in tabular form:

Axial Skeleton

Skull	29
Cranium, 8; face 14, ear ossicles 6, hyoid 1	
Vertebral column*	26

---

*Twenty-six bones when the nine or ten terminal segments which fuse to form the sacrum and coccyx are counted as two bones.

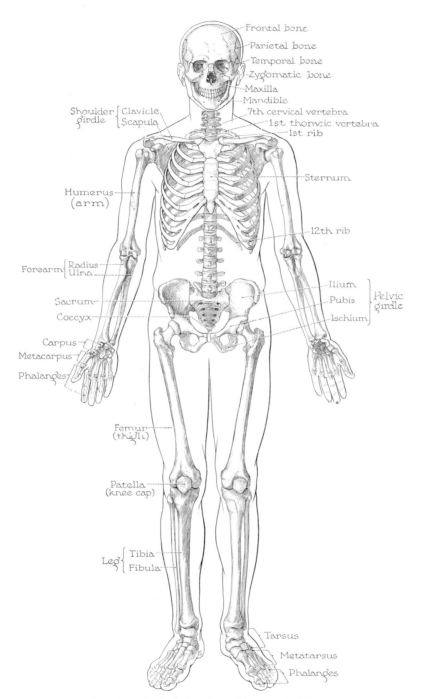

Figure 10.9 Anterior view of human skeleton.

Thorax (sternum and ribs) <u>25</u>

Total axial   80

Appendicular Skeleton
Upper extremities   64
Lower extremities   <u>62</u>

Total appendicular   <u>126</u>

Total all bones   206

THE AXIAL SKELETON

Bones of the Skull. The bones of the skull form the cranium, or brain case, and the face (Fig. 10.14):

BONES OF THE CRANIUM (8)
Single bones:
  Occipital
  Frontal
  Sphenoid
  Ethmoid
Paired bones:
  Parietal
  Temporal

BONES OF THE FACE (14)
Single bones:
  Mandible
  Vomer
Paired bones:
  Maxillae
  Zygomatic
  Lacrimal
  Nasal
  Inferior nasal conchae
  Palatine

The bones of the calvaria form the floor and domelike cranial cavity that enclose the brain. On looking at the skull from the side (Figs. 10.11, 10.21), it appears that the frontal bone forms the anterior part of the calvaria and the occipital bone the posterior part, the parietal bones form the superior and lateral walls of the cranial cavity, while a portion of the temporal bone forms the lower part of the lateral wall in the center.

THE CALVARIA. Examining the base of the skull in Figures 10.15 and 10.17, we note that the sphenoid bone occupies the key position. Extending transversely through the center of the skull, it joins anteriorly with the orbital plates of the frontal bone and posteriorly with the central part of the occipital bone. Both frontal and occipital bones curve far underneath toward the center, forming considerable portions of the base of the cranium. Wedgelike parts of the temporal bone fit between the occipital and sphenoid bones. The ethmoid bone separates the cranial cavity above from the nasal fossae below.

SPECIAL FEATURES PERTAINING TO THE SKULL AS A WHOLE. *Sutures.* The sutures are the lines of union of the cranial bones (Figs. 10.10, 10.11, 10.21). The sagittal suture is in the midline between the parietal bones. The coronal suture is at right angles to the sagittal suture and separates the frontal and two parietal bones. The lambdoidal suture marks the boundary line between the occipital and parietal bones. The squamous suture is between the parietal bone and the squamous portion of the temporal. (See Figures 10.11, 10.21.) At birth the frontal bone consists of two parts which later become fused to form the single bone, but occasionally this suture persists as a line of division between the halves of the frontal bone. It is called the interfrontal or metopic suture.

Fontanels. The spaces between the converging bones in which intramembranous ossification is incomplete at birth are called fontanels. The newborn infant usually has six fontanels, found at the angles of the parietal bone. The anterior fontanel is diamond-shaped (Fig. 10.10). It lies at the junction of the frontal and parietal bones. This fontanel usually closes about the eighteenth month. The posterior fontanel, lying at the junction of the occipital and parietal bones, is triangular in shape (Fig. 10.10). It is smaller than the anterior fontanel and usually closes by the second month. The sphenoid fontanels lie at the junction of the frontal, parietal, temporal, and sphenoid bones (Fig. 10.11). They usually close by the third month. The mastoid fontanels lie at the junctions of the parietal, occipital, and temporal bones and do not close completely until the second year (Fig. 10.11).

The incomplete ossification of the bones of the skull at birth points to an adaptive mechanism for childbirth. During labor the bones of the skull override each other, and the infant's skull, being reduced in its diameters, accommodates itself to the size of the birth canal to a considerable extent.

Sinuses. The air sinuses are cavities within the skull. The spongy bones has

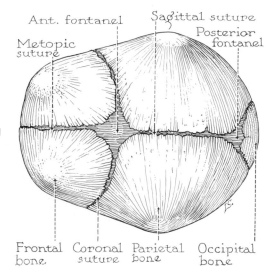

Figure 10-10 Skull at birth, showing anterior and posterior fontanels.

been resorbed and replaced by air-filled spaces lined with a mucous membrane. Mucosa of the paranasal sinuses (frontal, maxillary, ethmoid, and sphenoid) is continuous with the mucosa of the nasal fossae (see Figures 13.1 and 13.2). Similar air spaces are found in the mastoid portion of the temporal bone. The air sinuses lessen the weight of the skull and contribute to resonance of the voice. They may be involved when the upper portion of the respiratory tract (p. 236) becomes infected.

The blood sinuses are channels in the external membrane covering the brain, which convey venous blood from the brain. Those that lie against the cranial bones make impressions or grooves on the inner surface of the bone. Examples of venous sinuses are the superior sagittal and transverse sinuses (Fig. 10.13).

Nasal Fossae. The bony portion of the external nose is formed by the maxillae and the nasal bones (Fig. 10.14). The anterior aperture of the nose is divided into two nasal fossae by a median vertical partition, the nasal septum (Fig. 10.12). The perpendicular plate of the ethmoid forms the upper part, the vomer the lower, and the septal cartilage completes the anterior portion (p. 236). On the lateral walls (Fig. 10.13) of each nasal fossa are the superior, middle, and inferior conchae with spaces beneath that are called meatuses. The roof is formed principally by the following

bones: nasal, frontal, cribriform plate of the ethmoid, and body of the sphenoid. The horizontal plate of the palatine bone and the palatine process of the maxilla constitute the floor of the nasal fossa. Posterior apertures of the fossae are the choanae.

Orbital Fossae or Orbits. The orbit (Fig. 10.14) is the bony socket for the eyeball. It is formed by the frontal, zygomatic, ethmoid, sphenoid, lacrimal, maxillary, and palatine bones. The fossa is cone-shaped, with the apex directed backward and somewhat medialward. Near the apex are two openings, the optic canal and the superior orbital fissure.

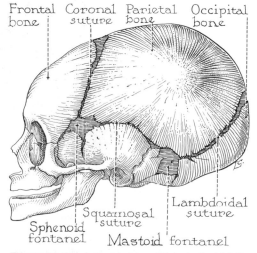

Figure 10-11 Lateral view of the skull at birth.

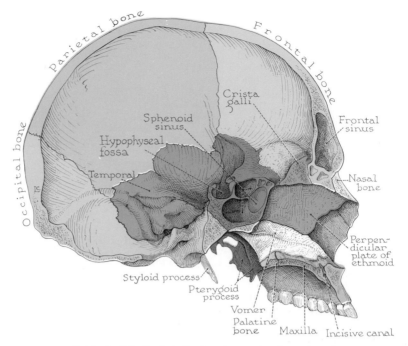

Figure 10.12 Left half of skull, showing parts of nasal septum.

The *vomer* is a thin bone, shaped like a ploughshare. It forms the back and lower part of the nasal septum.

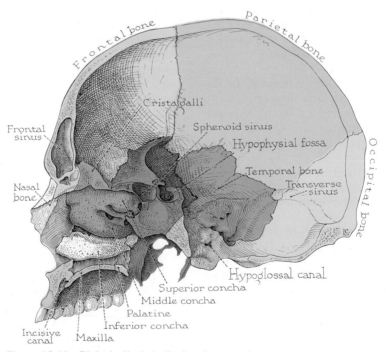

Figure 10.13 Right half of skull, showing conchae on lateral nasal wall.

The *inferior nasal concha* is an elongated, curved bone placed horizontally along the lateral wall of the nasal fossa below the superior and middle conchae, which are parts of the ethmoid.

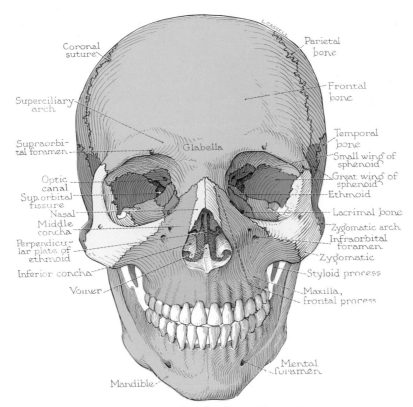

Figure 10.14 Anterior view of the skull.

The *frontal* bone forms the forehead, the anterior part of the cranial vault and the greater part of the roof of the orbits. On either side of the nose, where the frontal and orbital portions of the bone meet, there is a sharp curved border, the supraorbital margin. Toward the medial part each margin is crossed by a groove, the supraorbital notch, which transmits the supraorbital nerve and artery. Occasionally the notch is converted into a foramen. Above the margin are two ridges, the superciliary arches, which give prominence to the eyebrows. In the middle, just above the nose and between the ridges, is a smooth area called the glabella. Inside the bone in the position corresponding with the superciliary arches are two cavities, the frontal sinuses. These are air sinuses.

The *zygomatic* bone forms the prominence of the cheek and outer margin of the orbit. It joins with the zygomatic process of the temporal bone to complete the zygomatic arch.

The *nasal* bones are thin, rectangular pieces of bone that form the upper part of the bridge of the nose; the lower part is composed of cartilage.

The *maxilla* has been described as the key to the architecture of the face, since all bones of the face except the mandible touch it. This bone meets its fellow in the midline to form the whole of the upper jaw. Each bone shares in forming the floor of the orbit, the lateral and inferior walls of the nasal cavities and the hard palate (Fig. 10.17). The lower border of the bone, which contains cavities for the teeth, is the alveolar process. In the body of the bone is a large air space, the maxillary sinus. The opening just below the orbit on the external surface is the infraorbital foramen.

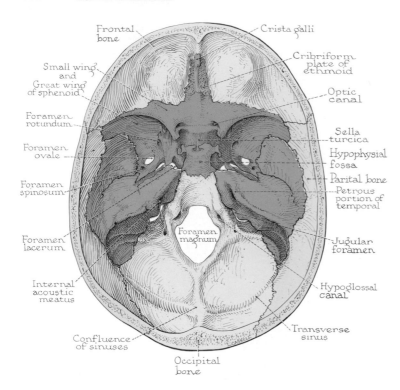

Figure 10.15 View of base of skull from above.

The *sphenoid* bone forms the central part of the base of the cranium (Figs. 10.15, 10.17). It is bounded by the ethmoid and frontal bones anteriorly and the temporal and occipital posteriorly. It has been compared to a bird with wings outspread and feet dependent. It presents a body, two great wings, two small wings and hanging feet (the pterygoid processes). The body extends from its connection in front with the ethmoid through the midline to its union posteriorly with the occipital bone. In the center of the superior surface of the body is a fossa which holds the hypophysis, or pituitary body. In the interior of the body are two large cavities, the sphenoidal air sinuses (Figs. 10.12, 10.13). The great and small wings extend laterally from the sides of the body. The small wings form a small part of the posterior part of the orbits. In the orbital portion of each small wing is an opening, the optic canal, which transmits the optic nerve. The great wings form part of the floor and lateral walls of the orbits (Fig. 10.14). Each great wing is perforated by several openings: foramen rotundum, foramen ovale, and foramen spinosum. At either side of the body where the lesser wings overhang the greater wings there are irregular, slitlike openings, the superior orbital fissures. The pterygoid processes consist of medial and lateral plates. They extend downward from the sides of the body. The medial plate forms part of the lateral wall of the nose; the lateral plate forms the back part of the framework of the upper jaw (Fig. 10.12).

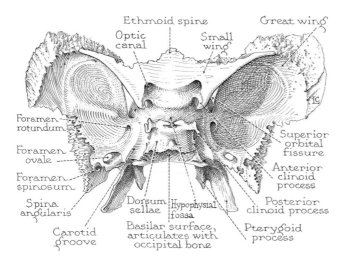

Figure 10.16 Sphenoid bone, upper surface.

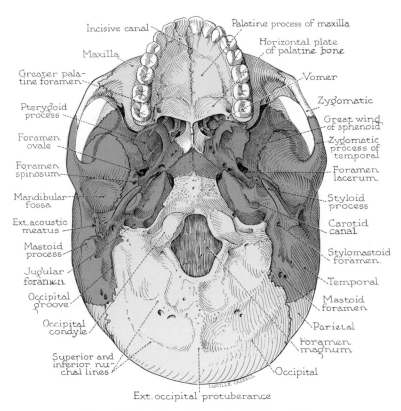

Figure 10.17 View of base of skull from below.

The *occipital* bone forms the posterior part of the floor and vault of the cranium. In the middle of the inferior surface is a large opening, the foramen magnum, through which the spinal cord passes to make connection with the brain stem. On either side of the foramen magnum, externally, are two oval-shaped processes, the condyles. These processes are curved anteroposteriorly, resembling rockers. Fitting into shallow depressions on the upper surface of the atlas (the first cervical vertebra), they form a joint allowing nodding movements of the head. Just above each condyle and visible on either side of the foramen magnum are the hypoglossal canals. On the posterior part of the external surface is a projection called the external occipital protuberance, and extending out from it on either side are curved ridges, the superior nuchal lines, and a short distance below are the inferior nuchal lines. On the inner surface are well-defined grooves for the transverse sinuses (Fig. 10.15).

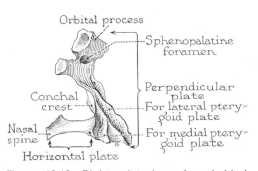

Figure 10.18 Right palate bone from behind.

The *palatine* bones are situated at the back part of the nasal cavities between the maxillae and the pterygoid processes of the sphenoid bone. Each consists of a horizontal and a perpendicular plate. The union of the horizontal plates in the midline forms the posterior part of the hard palate. These bones help to form the walls of three cavities, the floor and lateral walls of the nasal cavities, the floor of the orbits, and the roof of the mouth (Fig. 10.17).

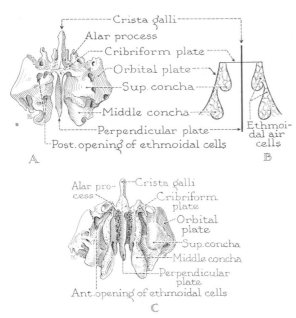

Figure 10.19 *A,* Ethmoid bone from behind. *B,* Diagram of the parts of the ethmoid bone. *C,* Ethmoid bone from in front and below.

The *ethmoid* bone (Figs. 10.15, 10.19) is located in the anterior part of the base of the cranium, between the two orbits, at the roof of the nose, and it contributes to each of these cavities. The main parts are a perpendicular plate, a horizontal plate, and two lateral masses. The perpendicular plate descends into the nasal cavity in the midline, forming the superior part of the nasal septum (Fig. 10.12). The horizontal or cribriform plate extends at right angles to the perpendicular plate on either side, in which situation it roofs in the nasal fossae and joins the corresponding portion of the floor of the cranial cavity (above). The cribriform plates have perforations through which pass nerves of smell to the mucous membrane of the nose. Extending into the cranial cavity as an upward extension of the perpendicular plate is a process called crista galli. The lateral masses, or ethmoidal labyrinths, are attached to the margins of the cribriform plates. They are composed of the orbital plates, superior and middle conchae, and ethmoidal cells. The orbital plates are thin, rectangular sheets of bone that form the main part of the medial wall of the orbits. The medial surface of the lateral mass, forming the lateral wall of the nose, presents two scroll-shaped convoluted masses, the superior and middle conchae (Fig. 10.13). Between the orbital plate and the superior and middle conchae is an intricate, honeycombed arrangement of bone that consists of many spaces or compartments called the ethmoidal cells. These are air spaces that connect with the nasal cavity, and collectively they comprise the ethmoid sinus.

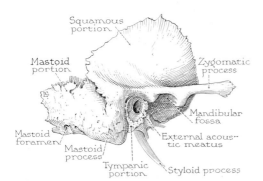

Figure 10.20 Right temporal bone, external surface.

The *temporal* bones form part of the base and lateral wall of the cranium. Viewed from the side, the external surface presents an important landmark, the external acoustic meatus. This canal forms part of the passageway leading to the middle ear and is a convenient point of reference in describing the parts of the temporal bone. Above the meatus is a thin, fan-shaped sheet of bone, the squamous portion; backward and slightly below is the petrous portion. The tympanic part is a curved plate that forms the inferior and lateral walls of the acoustic meatus. The petrous portion extends inward and forward from the meatus, forming a prominent elevation on the floor of the cranial cavity. It is best recognized in a view of the base of the skull from above (see Fig. 10.15). The petrous portion is hard and rocklike, as its name implies, and in the interior are cavities containing the specialized organs of hearing and equilibrium. The internal acoustic meatus on the posterior wall of the petrous elevation transmits nerves leading to these structures. Closely related to the internal ear is the carotid canal for the passage of the internal carotid artery into the brain by way of the petrous temporal bone. Posteriorly and laterally the petrous portion continues into a mastoid region, which is marked internally by the groove for the sigmoid sinus. Externally, the mastoid process forms a conspicuous bony prominence behind the ear. The interior of this process contains mastoid air cells, which communicate with the middle ear. The zygomatic process, a conspicuous bar of bone, projects forward from the lower part of the squamous portion and joins with the zygomatic bone of the face to form the zygomatic arch. Below the zygomatic process and just in front of the external acoustic meatus is a depression, the mandibular fossa (Fig. 10.17), which receives the condyle of the mandible. The inferior surface of the temporal bone is rough, and from it extends a sharp projection, the styloid process. Between the styloid process and the mastoid process is an opening, the stylomastoid foramen.

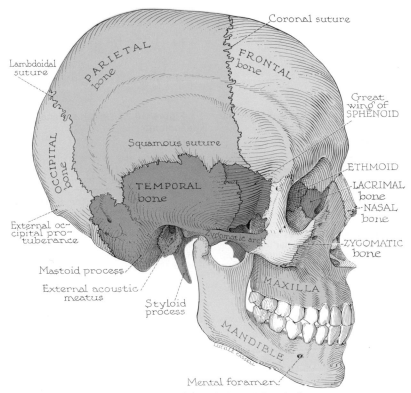

Figure 10.21 Lateral view of the skull.

The *parietal* bones form a large part of the superior and lateral walls of the cranium. The two bones meet in the midline to form the sagittal suture. On the inner surface along the line of the suture is a groove for the superior sagittal sinus, called the sagittal sulcus. The *lacrimal* bone forms a small part of the medial wall of the orbit. It lies between the orbital plate of the ethmoid bone and the frontal process of the maxilla. The orbital surface is di-

vided into two parts by a vertical ridge, the posterior lacrimal crest. In front of the crest is a longitudinal groove that joins with a corresponding groove on the maxilla to form the lacrimal fossa. The crest ends below in a hook-like projection that curves forward to articulate with the maxilla and complete the upper orifice of the nasolacrimal canal (see also p. 117).

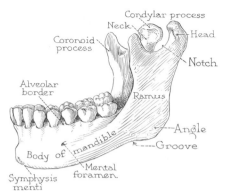

Figure 10.22 The mandible as seen from the left side.

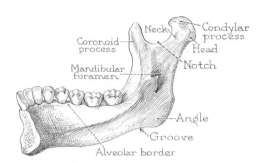

Figure 10.23 Inner surface of right half of the mandible.

The *mandible,* or lower jaw, consists of a central horizontal portion, the body, which forms the chin and supports the teeth, and two perpendicular portions, the rami, which project upward from the back on either side. The body is curved and presents on its upper border the alveolar process for the teeth. Just below the first bicuspid, about halfway between the upper and lower margins of the jaw, is the mental foramen. Each ramus has a condylar process for articulation with the mandibular fossa of the temporal bone and a coronoid process for attachment of

the temporal muscle. The angle of the mandible is at the point of union of its posterior and inferior borders. On the medial surface of the ramus is an opening, the mandibular foramen, through which pass the vessels and nerves for the teeth. The terminal branches emerge through the mental foramen to supply the chin. At the base of the mandible where the body joins the ramus is a groove for the external maxillary artery. A synostosis, the symphysis menti, marks the junction between the two halves of the mandible.

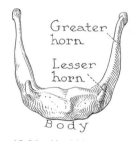

Figure 10.24 Hyoid bone, front view.

The *hyoid* bone is a **U**-shaped bone suspended by ligaments from the styloid processes of the temporal bones. It is not a bone of the skull, but it is considered here for convenience. It may be felt in the neck between the mandible and the larynx. It consists of a central portion, the body, and two projections or horns on each side.

Bones of the Vertebral Column. The *spine* or vertebral column, a part of the axial skeleton, is a strong, flexible rod that supports the head, gives base to the ribs, and encloses the spinal cord. The 33 (or occasionally 34) bones composing the

spinal column are called *vertebrae.* These are divided into five groups according to their distinguishing characteristics. The cervical region has seven vertebrae; the thoracic, twelve; the lumbar, five; the sacral, five; the coccygeal, four or five.

In the adult the vertebrae of the sacral and coccygeal regions are united into two bones, the sacrum and the coccyx.

A lateral view of the vertebral column shows four curves, alternately convex and concave ventrally (Fig. 10.25). In fetal life the vertebral column is uniformly curved so that it is concave ventrally. In the thoracic and sacrococcygeal regions these concavities persist, providing space for accommodation of the viscera. The two convex curves are the cervical and the lumbar. The cervical curve appears when the infant learns to hold his head erect, usually about the third month; the lumbar curve appears when the child has learned to walk, between the twelfth and eighteenth months. The thoracic and sacrococcygeal curves present in the fetus are primary; the cervical and lumbar appearing after birth are secondary and compensatory. Intervertebral foramina appear laterally, formed by the successive attachments of the vertebrae.

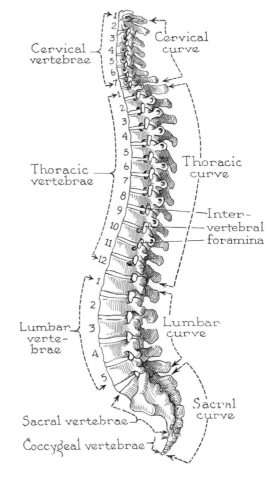

Figure 10.25 Vertebral column from the left side.

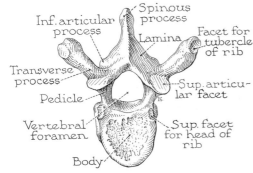

Figure 10.26 Sixth thoracic vertebra viewed from above.

A TYPICAL VERTEBRA. The vertebrae differ in size and shape, but in general show a uniform plan of structure. The sixth thoracic vertebra exhibits this typical structure (Fig. 10.26). A vertebra is composed of the following parts:

a weight-bearing portion, the body; a part that protects the spinal cord, the neural arch; three levers on which muscles pull, the spinous process and right and left transverse processes; and four processes or projections, the articular processes, which restrict movements.

The body is the central mass of bone that forms the anterior part of the vertebra. The pedicles or pillars of the arch are two short, thick columns that extend backward from the body to meet with the laminae in the formation of the neural arch. The body and neural arch enclose a foramen, the vertebral foramen. Seven processes arise from the arch: one spinous, two transverse, two superior articular, and two inferior articular. Extending backward from the point of union of the two laminae is the spinous process. Projecting laterally at either side from the junction of lamina and pedicle are the transverse processes. The articular processes arise near the junction of the pedicle and lamina, the superior processes project upward, and the inferior project downward. The surfaces of the processes are smooth, the inferior articular processes of the vertebra above fitting into the superior articular processes of the vertebra below. These are true joints, but the contact established serves to restrict movement, preventing forward displacement of an upper vertebra on a lower.

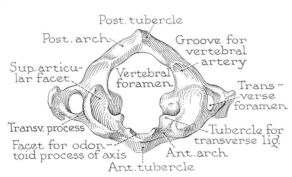

Figure 10.27 First cervical vertebra, or atlas, from above.

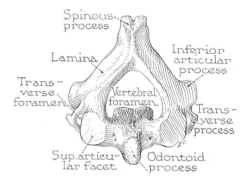

Figure 10.28 Second cervical vertebra, axis or epistropheus, from above.

DISTINGUISHING FEATURES OF DIFFERENT REGIONS. *Cervical Region (Figs. 10.27-10.29)*. All vertebrae of this region have foramina in the transverse processes; those of the upper six vertebrae transmit the vertebral artery. The spinous processes are short; the third, fourth, and fifth are bifurcated, while the seventh is unusually long and may be felt as a prominence at the back of the neck. In general, the bodies of the cervical vertebrae are small, and the vertebral foramina large and somewhat triangular in outline. The first cervical vertebra, the *atlas,* has no body but is composed of an anterior and a posterior arch and two lateral masses (Fig. 10.27). The superior articular processes articulate with the condyles of the occipital bone. The second cervical vertebra is the *axis* (Fig. 10.28). A process, the *dens,* on the upper surface of the body, forms a pivot about which the atlas rotates. The dens represents the separated body of the atlas that has fused with the axis.

Thoracic Regions (Fig. 10.26). The presence of facets for articulation with the ribs is the distinguishing feature of this group. All processes of the thoracic region are larger and heavier than those in the cervical region. The spinous process is directed downward at a sharp angle. The vertebral foramen is circular.

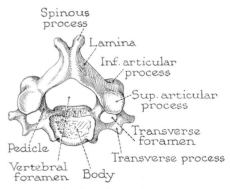

Figure 10.29 Fourth cervical vertebra from above.

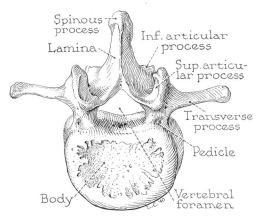

Figure 10.30 Third lumbar vertebra from above.

Lumbar Vertebrae. The bodies of the lumbar vertebrae are large and heavy. The superior articular processes face inward; the inferior articular processes face outward (Fig. 10.30).

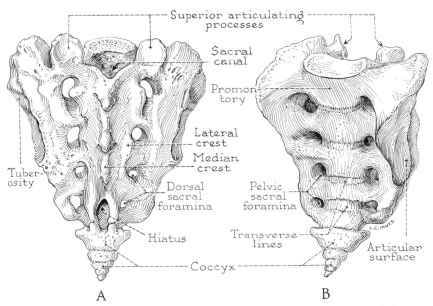

Figure 10.31 *A*, Posterior view of sacrum and coccyx. *B*, Anterolateral view.

Sacral Vertebrae. The sacrum is composed of five fused and modified vertebrae (Fig. 10.31). On the concave pelvic surface are four transverse lines separating the bodies of the vertebrae. The sacrum is triangular and is fitted like a wedge between the halves of the pelvis. On the anterior margin of the upper surface of the body of the first sacral vertebra is an important landmark, the promontory of the sacrum. Four pairs of dorsal sacral foramina communicate with four pairs of pelvic sacral foramina. A sacral hiatus is found in the midline dorsally where the spinous processes and laminae of the fifth and possibly the fourth sacral vertebrae have not formed.

Coccygeal Vertebrae. The coccyx is the terminal and most rudimentary part of the vertebral column. It is composed of four or five nodular pieces representing bodies of the vertebrae. The bone is triangular in shape with its base above, attached to the sacrum, and its apex below.

Bones of the Thorax. The thorax is a bony, cartilaginous cage whose walls are formed behind by thoracic vertebrae, at the sides by the ribs, and in front by the costal cartilages and the sternum (Fig. 10.32). It is cone-shaped, being narrow above and broad below. At birth the thorax is nearly round, but in adult life it is flattened from front to back.

The twenty-four *ribs*, placed twelve on each side of the thorax, form the greater part of its bony walls. They are long, flat bones which are curved and twisted. They are connected behind to the spine and continued forward by the costal cartilages. The first seven pairs are attached directly to the sternum through their costal cartilages and for this reason are called "true" ribs; the remaining five pairs are called "false" ribs. The cartilages of the eighth, ninth, and tenth ribs each join to the lower border of the cartilage of the preceding rib. Since cartilage endings of the eleventh and twelfth ribs are unattached, they are termed "floating" ribs. Each rib slopes downward from its posterior attachment so that its anterior end is considerably lower than its posterior end.

The anterior or costal end of the rib is often slightly expanded and contains a pitlike depression into which the costal cartilage sinks. The joint thus formed is called the costochondral junction. The parts are bound together by a fusion of the periosteum of the bone with the perichondrium of the cartilage.

The *sternum* or breast bone, likened to the Roman sword, is composed of the manubrium or handle, the body or blade, and the xiphoid process. The sternal angle formed at the articulations of manubrium, body, and second rib can be easily palpated through the soft tissues of the chest wall.

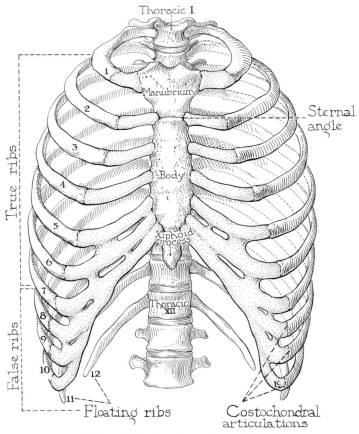

Figure 10.32 The thorax from in front.

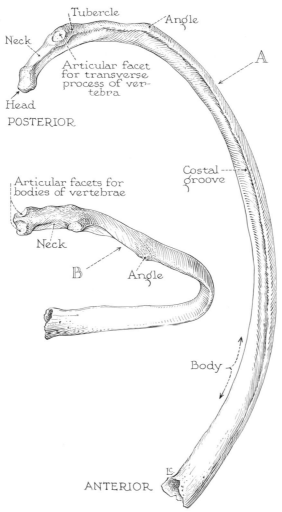

Figure 10.33 A central rib of the right side. *A*, Inferior surface. *B*, Posterior surface.

A central rib is regarded as typical, although certain ribs show variations. The head of the rib, which is on the posterior end of the bone, is expanded, and its medial surface presents two smooth areas which articulate with the demifacets on the vertebral bodies. Below the head is the slightly constricted region, the neck, and beyond this is the body or shaft. At the junction of the neck and shaft is a tubercle which consists of an articular and a non-articular portion. The articular portion connects with the facet on the transverse process of the vertebra; the non-articular portion is for the attachment of ligaments. The body of the rib shows a rather sharp bend near its posterior end, which is called the angle of the rib. On the lower border of the inner surface is a groove, the costal groove, which lodges intercostal vessels and nerve.

THE APPENDICULAR SKELETON

The upper and lower extremities comprise the appendicular skeleton.

The Upper Extremity. The following divisions constitute the upper extremity:

Shoulder — scapula ⎫ shoulder girdle
           clavicle ⎭
Arm   — humerus
Forearm — ulna, radius
Hand   — ⎧ carpus (wrist) — 8 small bones
         ⎨ metacarpus — 5 bones
         ⎩ phalanges (fingers) — 14 bones

SHOULDER. The shoulder girdle is made up of the collar bone (clavicle) and the shoulder blade (scapula). The clavicle articulates with the sternum, but the scapula has no bony attachment to the axial skeleton except through the clavicle. It maintains its position through muscular attachments and is thus free and mobile. This girdle serves to attach the upper extremity to the axial skeleton.

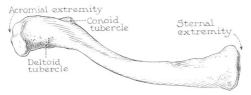

Figure 10.34 Right clavicle, superior surface.

The *clavicle* is a slender S-shaped bone that extends horizontally across the upper part of the thorax. The medial sternal end articulates with the manubrium of the sternum. The lateral end, articulating with the acromion, is the acromial extremity. The bone has important muscle attachments and gives support to the shoulder joint.

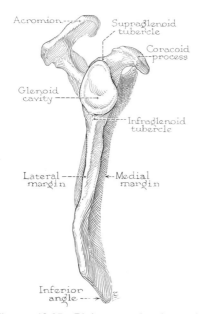

Figure 10.35 Right scapula, from the axillary border.

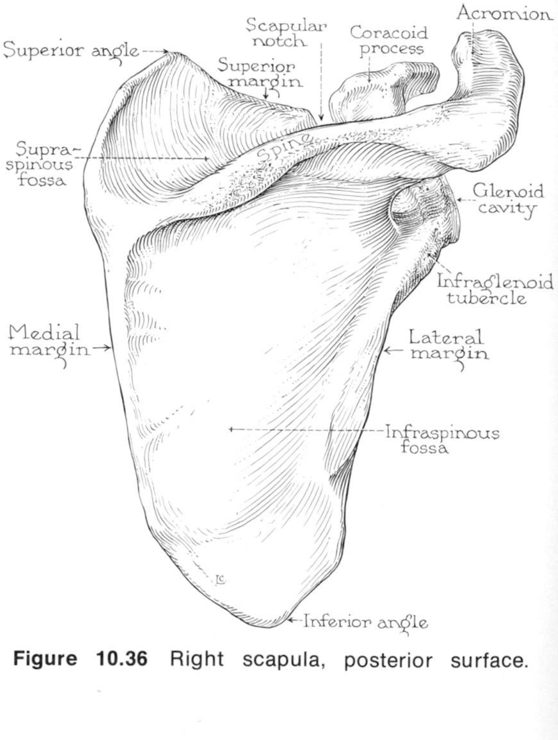

Figure 10.36 Right scapula, posterior surface.

The *scapula* or shoulder blade is a triangular bone with the base upward and the apex downward. The base of the triangle forms the superior border; the medial margin, the side toward the vertebral column; the lateral margin, the axillary border. The angles of the triangle are named superior, lateral, and inferior. The lateral angle forms an expanded portion known as the head. On its lateral aspect is an oval, hollowed surface, the glenoid cavity, which receives the head of the humerus. The neck is the slightly constricted part that supports the head. Above the glenoid cavity is a process called the supraglenoid tubercle; below is a prominence called the infraglenoid tubercle. Extending across the upper part of the posterior surface is a ridge of bone, the spine, which expands laterally into a broad, flat projection, the acromion. The acromion forms the point of the shoulder and gives attachment to the clavicle. The coracoid process projects anteriorly from the upper part of the neck of the scapula.

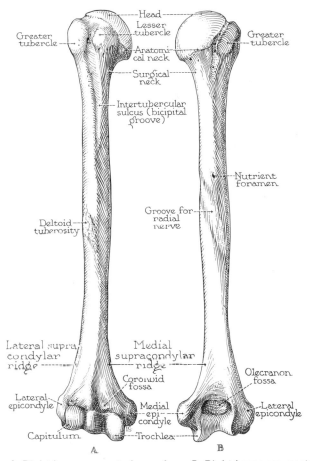

Figure 10.37 *A*, Right humerus, anterior surface. *B*, Right humerus, posterior surface.

The *humerus* or arm bone consists of a shaft and two enlarged extremities. On the proximal extremity is the smooth, rounded head that fits into the glenoid cavity of the scapula. Just beneath the head are two rounded processes, the greater and lesser tubercles, and lying between them is the intertubercular (bicipital) groove. Between the head and the tubercles is the anatomic neck; the region below the tubercles is called the surgical neck, from its liability to fracture. The shaft exhibits on its posterior surface a groove for the radial nerve, and a rough area midway down the lateral border, the deltoid tuberosity. The distal end of the bone has two articulating surfaces, the condyles, the lateral of which, called the capitulum, articulates with the head of the radius; the medial one, the trochlea, articulates with the ulna. Above the trochlea on the anterior surface is a depression, the coronoid fossa, and on the posterior surface, the olecranon fossa, into which the corresponding processes of the ulna slip in flexion and extension, respectively. On either side just above the capitulum and trochlea are the lateral and medial epicondyles.

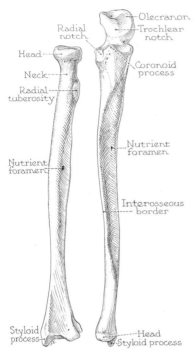

Figure 10.38 Right radius and ulna, anterior view.

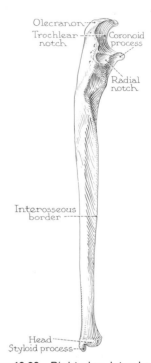

Figure 10.39 Right ulna, lateral surface.

FOREARM. The *radius* is the lateral bone of the forearm. It is shorter than the ulna, but is broad below, where it forms the whole of the articulation with the wrist. The proximal end of the radius has a disc-shaped head that articulates with the humerus and with the radial notch of the ulna. Below the head on the medial side is a rough elevation, the radial tuberosity. The distal end has a styloid process on its lateral side.

The *ulna* is on the medial side of the forearm and therefore on the little finger side in relation to the hand. It forms a conspicuous part of the elbow joint and has been described as belonging to the arm, while the radius may be considered to belong to the hand. The proximal end is large, presenting on its superior and posterior aspect the olecranon, which forms the point of the elbow. The curved surface articulating with the trochlea of the humerus is the trochlear notch. Below this is a rough projection, the coronoid process. On the lateral side near the trochlear notch is a concave articular surface, the radial notch for reception of the head of the radius. The distal end has a sharp styloid process and a head which articulates with a disc of fibrocartilage, separating it from the bones of the wrist, and a small sharp projection, the styloid process.

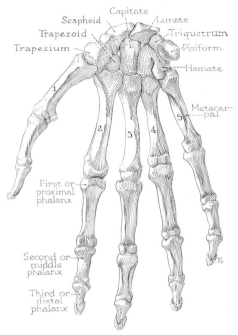

HAND. The eight *carpal* bones of the wrist are arranged in two rows of four each. Listed from lateral to medial aspects they are, in the proximal row: scaphoid, lunate, triquetrum, pisiform; in the distal row: trapezium, trapezoid, capitate, hamate.

The five *metacarpal* bones form the framework of the hand proper. They are numbered from one to five, beginning on the lateral or thumb side.

The *phalanges* form the framework of the fingers or digits. There are three phalanges in each finger and two in the thumb.

Figure 10.40 Bones of right hand, palmar surface.

The Lower Extremity. The following divisions comprise the lower extremity:

Hip	—pelvic girdle
Thigh	—femur
Kneecap	—patella
Leg	—tibia, fibula

Foot	—	tarsus (ankle)—7 bones
		metatarsus—5 bones
		phalanges (toes)—14 bones

HIP. The hip constitutes the pelvic girdle. It provides stability and is firmly united to the vertebral column. The pelvic girdle serves to attach the lower extremity to the axial skeleton.

The hip bone is a large irregular bone that in youth is composed of three parts. Although in the adult the parts are united into one bone, it is usual to describe the three portions separately. The union of the parts occurs below the center of the bone, and the location is marked by a cup-shaped cavity, the *acetabulum*. The large portion above, which is wide and flaring, is the ilium; the part passing medially is the pubis; the downward extension is the ischium. Ilium, pubis, and ischium share in the construction of the acetabulum, which forms the socket for the head of the femur.

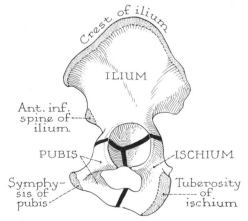

Figure 10.41 Plan of ossification of hip bone, showing union of the three parts in the acetabulum.

Figure 10.42 Right hip bone, or os coxae, external surface.

The *ilium*, broad and expanded, forms the prominence of the hip. The superior border is the crest. The projection at the anterior tip of the crest forms the anterior superior spine of the ilium. This is an important anatomical landmark. The prominence just below is the anterior inferior spine. Corresponding projections on the posterior part are called posterior superior and posterior inferior iliac spines. Beneath the posterior part is the greater sciatic notch. The outer surface of the ilium is traversed by three curved or gluteal lines, the posterior gluteal line, anterior gluteal line and inferior gluteal line, all of which end near the greater sciatic notch. On the inner surface is the terminal line, which begins below on the pubis and continues across the ilium to the sacrum. This line separates the lesser pelvis below from the greater pelvis above. Most of the ilium above the terminal line is a smooth concavity, the iliac fossa; posteriorly, there is a rough, pitted area, the auricular surface, which articulates with the sacrum in the formation of the sacroiliac joint.

The *pubic* bone comprises the anterior part of the os coxae bone and, joining its fellow in the midline, forms a joint known as the *symphysis pubis.* This bone con-

sists of a body and two arms of rami. The body forms about one fifth of the acetabulum. The superior ramus extends from the body to the median plane. The upper border of the superior ramus presents a rough ridge, the pubic crest. The crest ends laterally in a rounded process, the pubic tubercle. The terminal line of the ilium continues as a sharp border over the superior ramus of the pubis and includes the pubic tubercle, crest, and symphysis pubis. The inferior ramus passes downward and outward to meet the ischium. The *pubic arch* is formed by the inferior rami of both pubic bones, which converge above at the symphysis.

The *ischium* forms the lower and back part of the ox coxae bone. It consists of a body and a ramus. The body forms a little over two fifths of the acetabulum. Below is a large, rough process, the ischial tuberosity, which supports the body in sitting position. The sharp projection above the tuberosity is the spine of the ischium. The ramus of the ischium passes upward to join the inferior ramus of the pubis. The ischium and pubis combine to close in a large aperture, the obturator foramen.

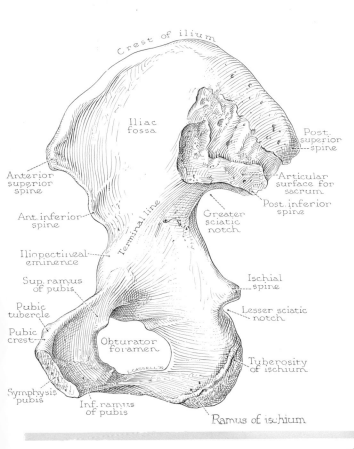

Figure 10.43 Right hip bone, or os coxae, internal surface.

THE PELVIS. Pelvis is the Latin word meaning basin. The pelvis is formed by the right and left hip bones, sacrum, and coccyx (Fig. 10.44) The promontory of the sacrum and the terminal line divide the pelvis into the lesser pelvis below and the greater pelvis above. The latter, bounded by the ilia and lower lumbar vertebrae, is deficient in front and for this reason is referred to as the "false" pelvis. The capacious iliac fossae give support to abdominal viscera, indicating clearly that the greater pelvis really belongs to the abdomen. The lesser or true pelvis has more complete bony walls than the greater pelvis, and a well-defined inlet and outlet. The inlet or brim of the pelvis corresponds to the sacral promontory and the terminal lines and marks out the circumference of the superior aperture. The inferior aperture or outlet is bounded by the tip of the coccyx, ischial tuberosities, and inferior rami of the pubis.

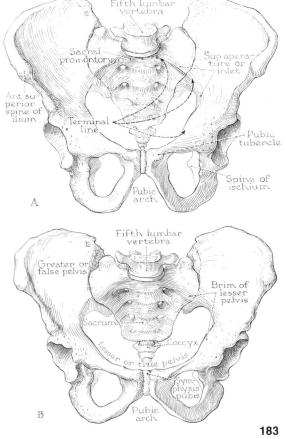

Figure 10.44 A, Male pelvis, anterior view. B, Female pelvis, anterior view.

183

Differences Between Male and Female Pelves. The female pelvis shows adaptations related to its function as a birth canal. The male pelvis is constructed along lines which contribute to motor power and speed. It is narrow, heavy, and compact; while the female pelvis is wide, light, and capacious. In the male pelvis the inlet is heart-shaped; in the female it is almost a perfect circle. The angle of the pubic arch of the male is acute; that of the female is obtuse. In the male the sacrum is narrow, long, and curved; the female sacrum is broad, short, and straight. Spines of the ischia are sharper and project inward farther in the male than in the female.

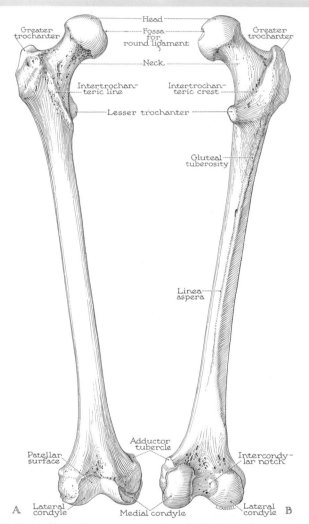

Figure 10.45 *A*, Right femur, anterior view. *B*, Right femur, posterior view.

THIGH. The thigh bone or *femur* is the longest and strongest bone of the body. It resembles the humerus in many ways. The proximal end shows a rounded head that articulates with the acetabulum, a constricted portion, the neck, and two processes, the greater and lesser *trochanters*. On the posterior surface the two trochanters are connected by a prominent ridge, the intertrochanteric crest; on the anterior surface is a more delicate ridge, the intertrochanteric line. The shaft, almost cylindrical in form, is slightly arched so that it is convex anteriorly and concave posteriorly where it is strengthened by a prominent ridge, the *linea aspera*. This is formed above by the gluteal tuberosity and spiral line; below it diverges, forming the medial and lateral supracondylar ridges. The linea aspera affords attachment for numerous muscles. The distal end of the femur widens out into two large eminences, the condyles, separated posteriorly by a deep fossa, the intercondyloid notch.

KNEECAP. The *patella* (Fig. 10.9) or kneecap is a sesamoid bone developed from and embedded in the tendon of the quadriceps muscle. It articulates with the femur, protecting the knee joint and affording greater leverage for the action of the muscle.

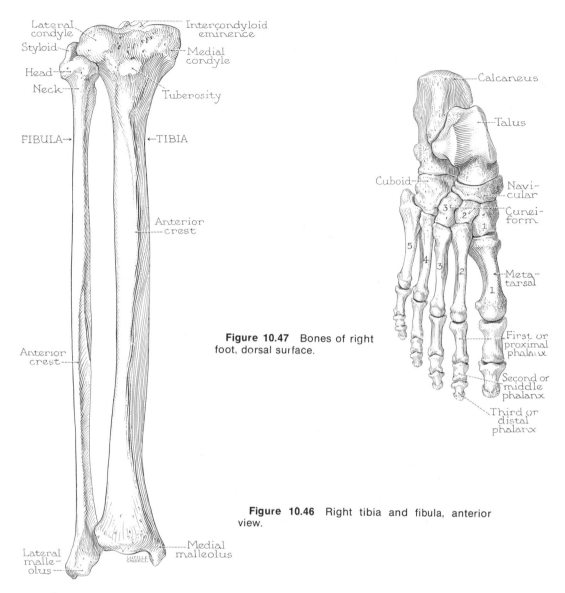

Figure 10.47 Bones of right foot, dorsal surface.

Figure 10.46 Right tibia and fibula, anterior view.

LEG. The medial bone of the leg is the *tibia*. The proximal end shows flattened surfaces, the condyles, which articulate with the femur. Between the condyles is the intercondyloid eminence. In front, at the junction of head and shaft, is a prominence called the tuberosity of the tibia. The shaft is triangular, showing anterior, medial and lateral borders. The anterior border, commonly called the *shin*, is prominent. The posterior surface is traversed by the soleal line, which runs obliquely across the upper third of the shaft. The distal end is continued downward on its medial side by a strong process, the medial malleolus. The inferior surfaces of the distal extremity and the malleolus articulate with the talus in forming the ankle joint.

The *fibula* is parallel with the tibia on its lateral aspect. It articulates with the lateral condyle of the tibia, but does not enter into the knee joint. The distal end projects as the lateral malleolus and assists the tibia in boxing in the talus.

ANKLE, FOOT, AND TOES. The bony structure of the foot corresponds roughly to that of the hands; the *tarsal* bones are the counterparts of the carpal bones, the *metatarsal* of the metacarpal bones, and the *phalanges* of the toes the counterparts of the phalanges of the fingers.

The *talus* occupies the uppermost and central position in the tarsus. The talus transmits and distributes the body weight from the tibia above to the other tarsal bones. Beneath the talus and extending posteriorly is the heel bone, the calcaneus. On its medial surface is a projecting process, the sustentaculum tali, and on its lateral surface the trochlear process, which give attachments to ligaments and may be used as bony landmarks in surface anatomy. In front of the talus on the medial side of the foot is the navicular, which in turn articulates with the three cuneiform bones distally. The cuboid bone of the lateral side of the foot lies in front of the calcaneus. Its medial border lies along the lateral borders of the navicular and the third cuneiform bones. The lst, 2nd, and 3rd metatarsals lie in front of the three cuneiform bones, and the 4th and 5th metatarsals in front of the cuboid bone. Distally, the phalanges of the toes are arranged with two in the great toe and three in each of the other toes.

The series of arches which characterize the structure of the foot provide an effective arrangement for supporting and distributing body weight. Architects have long recognized this principle and have used arches to serve the same functions. There are two longitudinal bony channels (arches) in the foot: the lateral arch formed by the calcaneus, the talus, the cuboid, and the 4th and 5th metatarsal bones, and the medial arch formed by the calcaneus, the talus, the navicular, the cuneiform bones, and the 1st, 2nd, and 3rd metatarsal bones. A series of transverse arches are formed by the tarsal and metatarsal bones. These bony arches are bound and strengthened by ligaments and tendons, assisted by the intrinsic muscles of the foot and long muscles of the leg.

In supporting the body, the foot may be likened to a triangular stool with one leg, the calcaneus, at the apex and five legs, the distal ends of the metatarsals, arranged along the base. The first metatarsal, which is twice as thick as the others, together with the second metatarsal, supports a quarter of the weight, the three lateral metatarsals a quarter and the heel the remaining half. The effectiveness of this arrangement may be appreciated when we realize that when we are walking or running the entire body weight is borne by one foot at a time with little or no conscious effort.

QUESTIONS FOR DISCUSSION

1. Summarize the steps in intramembranous ossification and in endochondral ossification.

2. Discuss the role of fibroblast-like cells of endosteum.

3. What is the significance of modulation of osteoblasts, osteocytes, and osteoclasts?

4. What would be the effect of insufficient dietary calcium and vitamin D upon the weight-bearing bones of the child? Adult?

5. What effect might the weightlessness of space travel have upon the skeletal system of an astronaut?

6. Explain how a long bone grows in circumference and length.

7. Describe and discuss the blood circulation in bone during growth and maturity. How does this relate to repair of bone?

8. In what situations do bones serve protective functions?

9. How is the relationship between the degree of motion and the structure of a joint manifest?

10. Cite examples in which the shape of the articulating surfaces and position of ligaments in synovial joints may provide variety of motion or limitation of motion.

THE DYNAMICS OF MUSCLE

CHAPTER ELEVEN

SOME PHYSIOLOGICAL ACTIVITIES OF MUSCLE

Voluntary muscle enables man to maintain erect posture and to hold his head, body, and extremities in a variety of positions. Skeletal muscular contraction, resulting in movement and locomotion, enables him to secure food and shelter, to escape danger, and to communicate his wishes, thoughts, or reactions to his fellows by speech, facial expression, signal, or body attitude. Voluntary muscle contractions are essential to breathing, as they are responsible for alterations in chest capacity that result in inspiration and expiration. Part of the energy liberated by muscular contraction is converted into heat, which aids in the maintenance of body temperature. Furthermore, skeletal muscle aids in hearing and in vision.

Cardiac muscle performs the work necessary for pumping the blood to all tissues of the body and for maintaining filtration pressures.

In the digestive system, the ureters and bladder, the ducts of the reproductive glands, and in the blood vascular system, smooth muscle activity propels ingested substances, body fluids, and excretions from place to place. Involuntary muscle in the skin and the blood vessels assists in regulation of body temperature. Smooth muscle of the ciliary body of the choroid controls light reflexes and accommodation of the eye.

THE STRUCTURE OF MUSCULAR TISSUE

The names given parts of muscle cells differ from those of analogous structures in the cells of other tissues. These include:

Muscle	Other Tissues
Fiber	Cell
Sarcolemma	Plasmolemma
Sarcoplasm	Cytoplasm
Sarcotubular system or sarcoplasmic reticulum	Smooth surfaced endoplasmic reticulum
Mitochondria	Mitochondria
Myofibrils	Neurofibrils
Myofilaments	Neurofilaments

COMMON PATTERNS IN MUSCLE TISSUES (Figs. 11.1-11.8)

While there are many variations in the detailed structure and organization of striated and smooth muscles, they all follow the same general architectural plan. Muscles are bundles or layers of muscle *fibers*. The long axes of the individual fibers are parallel to the direction of contraction.

The fibers or cells are the structural units of muscle. They are made up of *myofibrils* or bundles of thin parallel threads which extend the length of the cell. The myofibrils, in turn, are made up of groups of *myofilaments* containing the proteins of actin or myosin.

The myofibrils lie in the sarcoplasm. The sarcoplasm performs two functions; it assists in the nutrition of the myofibrils and in the conduction of excitation within the muscle fiber. In addition to the fibrils,

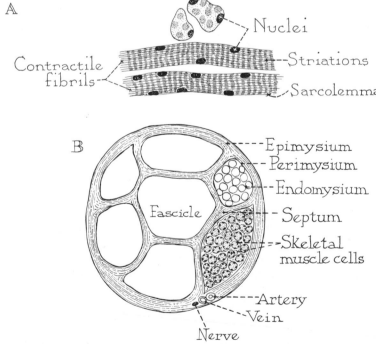

Figure 11-1 *A*, Longitudinal and cross sections of skeletal muscle fibers. *B*, Diagram shows organization of muscle cells by connective tissues into a skeletal muscle: e.g., biceps brachii.

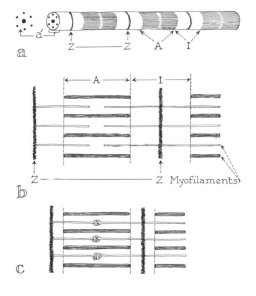

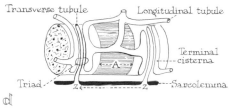

Figure 11.2 Diagram of a, myofibrils; b, myofilaments; c, myofilaments in contraction; d, sarcotubular system.

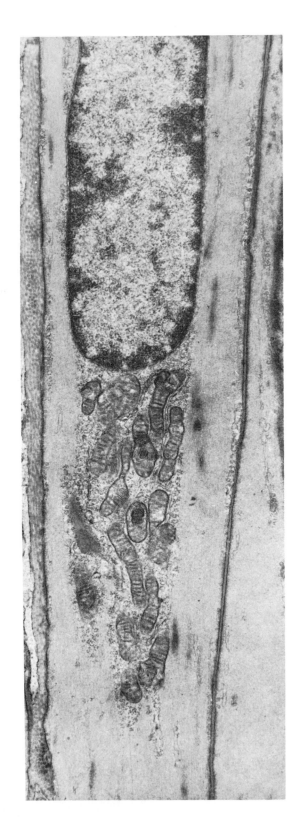

Figure 11.3 Electron micrograph of a portion of a smooth muscle cell from mouse ductus epididymidis cut longitudinally. The periphery of the fiber is occupied by myofilaments. Conical regions of cytoplasm extending from either pole of the elongated nucleus contain numerous mitochondria, a few profiles of endoplasmic reticulum, and many free ribosomes. × 20,000. (From Bloom and Fawcett: A Textbook of Histology, 9th Ed., 1968.)

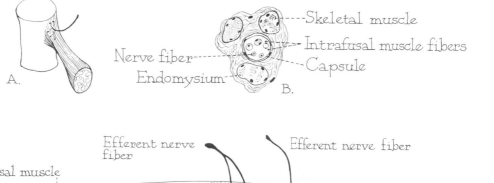

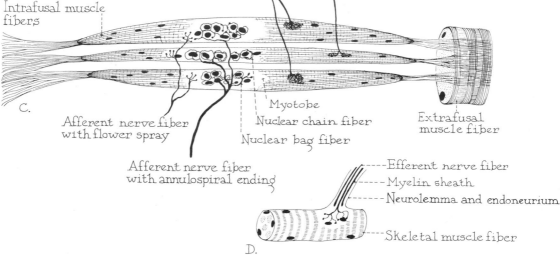

Figure 11.4 Nerve ending in relation to skeletal muscle. *A*, Golgi tendon organ; *B*, Cross section of neuromuscular spindle; *C*, Longitudinal organization of neuromuscular spindle; *D*, Motor end plate.

the sarcoplasm contains organelles and inclusions found in the cytoplasm of other cells. The nuclei are in general oval, with the long axis parallel to that of the myofibrils, but are not identical in size and shape in the different types of muscle. *Mitochondria* of muscular tissue have numerous compactly arranged cristae in contrast to those found in other cells. These specialized mitochondria are distributed close to myofibrils in longitudinal rows.

They constitute a source of adenosine triphosphate, which furnishes energy in carrying out cell functions.

The *sarcoplasmic reticulum* is an elaborate system of tubules within a muscle cell. It appears that it functions as a conduction system for activation of the contractile process. It is generally agreed that in most striated muscle, at least, the effect of excitation of the cell membrane is conducted inward to the immediate neighborhood

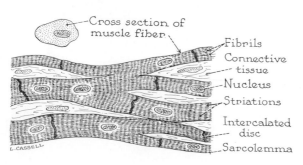

Figure 11.5 Cardiac muscle.

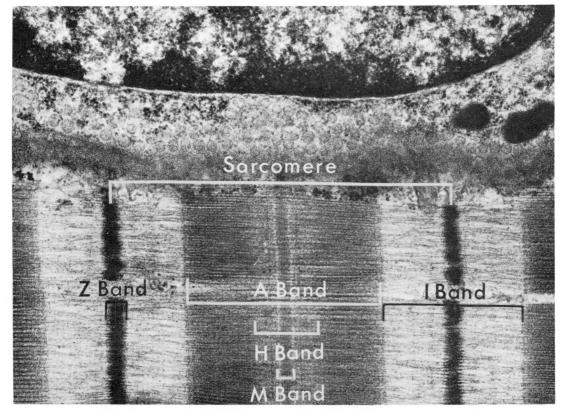

Figure 11.6 Electron micrograph of parts of two muscle fibers with the nucleus of one *(above)* and the most superficial myofibrils of the other *(below).* The principal features of the pattern of cross striations are identified on the figure. × 34,000. (From Bloom and Fawcett; A Textbook of Histology, 9th Ed., 1968.)

of the fibrils. The fact that activation of the contractile process is too rapid to be explained without a special conducting system is evidence in support of this concept. A *relaxing factor* has been isolated from fragments of sarcoplasmic reticulum. This factor has a strong affinity for calcium ions and binds them within a few milliseconds after their utilization in muscle contraction. The relaxing factor keeps the muscle fiber in its normal relaxed state.

Figure 11.7 Isolated smooth muscle cells.

SPECIAL FEATURES OF MUSCLE TISSUES

Skeletal Muscle (Figs. 11.1, 11.2, 11.4). The long, cylindrical cells of skeletal muscle range up to 12 cm. in length with widths of 10 to 100 microns. Fibers of large caliber occur in the powerful muscles such as those maintaining posture. The smallest fibers are those of rapidly acting extrinsic muscles found in the eye, ear, and larynx. The numerous small, oval nuclei are regularly distributed in the peripheral sarcoplasm of the cell.

Further distinctions can be made between two types of skeletal muscle fibers, i.e., the "red" and "white." In red fibers the abundant sarcoplasm contains greater numbers of nuclei, mitochondria, myohemoglobin, ion-containing enzymes, cytochromes, and lipids as compared to the white fibers. The red fibers usually

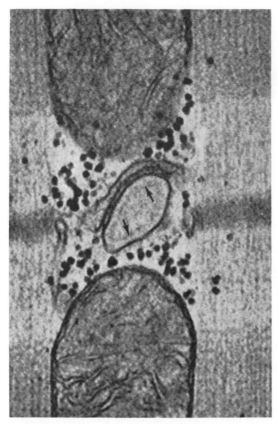

Figure 11.8 Longitudinal section of a small area of a cardiac muscle fiber illustrating a T tubule cut transversely and a tubule of the reticulum in close apposition to it. The T tubule is lined with a layer of protein-polysaccharide (at arrows) like that coating the sarcolemma at the surface of the fiber. The dense granules in the neighboring sarcoplasm are glycogen. × 70,000. (From Bloom and Fawcett: A Textbook of Histology, 9th Ed., 1968.)

mere extends from Z to Z. The Z line is a dense transverse band of sarcoplasmic reticulum. The thin actin-containing myofilaments pass through the position of the Z band. At regular intervals there are groups of thick myosin-containing myofilaments. Overlapping thick and thin filaments constitute the A band, while the thick filaments constitute the H band portion of the A band. The I band contains only the thin filaments. The arrangement of the myofilaments is responsible for the appearance of the striations.

The network of the sarcoplasmic reticulum consists of interconnecting tubules lying parallel to the myofibrils and transverse channels at the Z line or the AI junction running across the myofilaments as shown in Figure 11.2, *D*. Two longitudinal tubules approaching the transverse channels from alternate sides of adjacent sarcomeres expand into *terminal cisternae*. This group of channels and membranes is the *triad* (see Fig. 11.2, *D*). The transverse tubule connects the extracellular space around the sarcolemma. It is believed that this intimate arrangement of triad membranes provides a means for rapid spread of excitatory impulses among the myofibrils.

The organization of skeletal muscle fibers into muscles is accomplished by connective tissues (Figs. 11.1, 12.60, 12.61). The collagenous, elastic, and reticular fibers vary in proportion to the functions of the skeletal muscles. The fibers are covered by an *endomysium* of connective tissue elements. Bundles of fibers are held together as *fasciculi* by *perimysium*. The fascicles in turn are surrounded by *epimysium*, or *fascia* of the muscle. Blood vessels and voluntary cranial or spinal nerves penetrate these connective tissues to reach the muscle fibers (Fig. 11.4).

Attachments of skeletal muscles to the bony framework may be one of three types: direct to the periosteum, by means of a tendon, or by means of an aponeurosis. In a direct attachment the white fibers of the connective tissue framework of the muscle fuse with the fibrous layers of the periosteum of the bone. A *tendon* (Fig. 11.4) is a band or cord of white fibrous tissue connecting a muscle to a bone. An

respond more slowly and sustain contraction longer than white fibers. In man, the skeletal muscular organ contains a mixture of red and white fibers.

The myofibrils are marked by alternating light and dark striations oriented along the long axis of the cells (Figs. 11.1 and 11.2). Each myofibril possesses two types of myofilaments. The thicker myofilaments are rich in the protein *myosin*. *Actin*, another protein, is found in the thinner myofilaments. A complex system of bridges links the myofilaments in an orderly pattern, associating one thick filament to each of six adjacent thin filaments every 400 Å. As shown in Figures 11.2 and 11.6 a *sarco-*

aponeurosis (Fig. 12.61) is a heavy sheet of white fibrous tissue connecting a muscle to bone, or muscle to muscle. The more fixed attachment of the muscle is its *origin* (Fig. 12.4). The attachment where the effects of muscle contraction produce movement is the *insertion* (Fig. 12.4). Generally the origin is close to the midline of the body and the insertion is peripheral to this plane.

Skeletal muscles are innervated by craniospinal nerves arranged in *motor units* (p. 84). Naked and encapsulated nerve endings (Fig. 11.4) convey sensations of pain, pressure, and muscle tension. *Tendon spindles* and *free endings* are stimulated when the muscle is placed under tension. The highly specialized *neuromuscular spindles* play a part in the unconscious control of muscular contraction.

Annulospinal and flower spray endings signal the length of the muscle at any given instant. The annulospinal endings also give information on the velocity at which the muscle is being stretched. They do not contribute to the sense of position of a body part. The gamma motor endings in the spindle serve to adjust the sensitivity of the receptor mechanism to a level appropriate for the nature and extent of muscle response at that time. The motor nerves responsible for contraction of the muscle transmit excitatory impulses through specialized endings, the motor end plates (see p. 63 and Fig. 11.4, *D*) Skeletal muscle, whose activity varies widely, has an effective circulatory system with an elaborate system of minute vessels (see p. 276). The blood flow during exercise may increase twenty to thirty times.

Cardiac Muscle. The cells of cardiac muscle (Fig. 11.5), approximately 100 microns wide, are not single, cylindrical fibers. They tend instead to bifurcate and join adjacent fibers at all planes of space in a complex network covered by sarcolemma. Their sarcoplasm is more abundant and has a higher concentration of glycogen and mitochondria than skeletal muscle. The large elongated nuclei of each cellular unit are centrally placed. Myofilaments are less discretely organized into their respective myofibrils than one finds in skeletal muscle. The repeating pattern of cross striations has bands identical to those of the skeletal muscle. The transverse tubules are large and enter the fibers at the Z band to approximate small expansions of sarcoplasmic reticulum without the formation of triads (Fig. 11.8). The network of minute vessels provides for an abundant supply of blood to the cardiac muscle fibers (p. 276, 285).

The junctional surface of the fibers of cardiac muscle is specialized to maintain a tight cohesion through *intercalated discs* (Fig. 11.5) which occur at the I bands of myofibrils. The interfaces of the intercalated discs present degrees of closeness of contact between any two cells. Such contacts are similar to unions found among epithelial cells, e.g., desmosomes. It is believed that where the intercellular space is reduced a more rapid spread of electrical current of excitation for contraction will occur.

The aggregate of cardiac muscle fibers comprises the *myocardium* of the heart. Particular groups of specialized cardiac muscle cells make up the conducting system which generates the stimulus for heart beat. This system is composed of *sino-atrial node, atrioventricular node, atrioventricular bundles* and *Purkinje fibers* (see Fig. 15.30). The cells of the nodal and bundle tissue are smaller than ordinary cardiac muscle fibers and are embedded in an increased amount of loose connective tissue. Their myofibrils are fewer in number and their striations are indistinct. The sino-atrial node is well innervated by sympathetic and parasympathetic divisions of the autonomic nervous system (p. 132). The nerve endings are nonspecialized although it is possible to distinguish synaptic vesicles in the termination of axons. Purkinje fibers are larger than ordinary cardiac muscle fibers and have few myofibrils and a large mass of centrally placed sarcoplasma containing one or two nuclei.

Smooth Muscle. Smooth muscle occurs in a variety of forms, i.e., single fibers, in small groups, and in bundles and layers. Long, spindle-shaped cells vary in length from 20 to 200 microns with a thickness of about 5 microns (Fig. 11.7). An elongated nucleus occupies the center of the cell. The longitudinal axis of the cell has myofibrils composed of myofilaments with myosin and actin filaments arranged in a random fashion (Fig. 11.3). The sarcoplasm, which is scant in smooth muscle, gathers at both ends of the nucleus. Mitochondria and a few tubules of the sarcoplasmic reticulum lie within these accumulations of sarcoplasm.

Single cells or small groups are seen in connective tissue in the skin and elsewhere in the body. In the skin, their contraction causes wrinkling, as in the scrotum and mammary papillae. Small groups of fibers with their associated elastic connective tissue fibers cause erection of the hair, i.e., a *pilomotor* response. In blood vessels, the smooth muscle fibers form layers or sheets arranged in a spiral fashion around the large arteries and in a circular fashion in the arterioles. In hollow organs such as the uterus and bladder the fibers are arranged in layers around the viscus. The direction of fibers is the same within a layer, but different in different layers. In the intestine there is, in addition to the circumferential fibers, a longitudinal layer distributed as a long spiral.

Connective tissue covers bundles and layers of fibers and extends into spaces between cells. Nonspecialized autonomic nerve endings are found within the connective tissue. The arrangement of nerves and blood supply depends upon location and the organ with which the muscle is associated. A dense network of reticular connective tissue fibers penetrates the narrow intracellular spaces forming a sheath around the individual muscle cells and continues into the surrounding connective tissue. When individual muscle cells contract the force is transmitted through their sheaths to the reticular fiber network and associated connective tissue fibers. Thus the separate muscle cells act together and exert their combined force through a common linkage.

Within most groups of smooth muscle fibers the thin end of one cell lies adjacent to the thicker middle section of the neighboring cells. Each cell makes numerous membrane-to-membrane "contacts" with adjacent cells; contacts of a single cell have been estimated to amount to about 5 per cent of its total area. In vascular smooth muscle, interdigitated ends of the cells form the membrane-to-membrane contacts. Although the word "contact" is used to describe the relationship, the membranes of adjacent cells are reported to be separated always by a narrow intercellular space of approximately 100 Å in width. The area of close contact has important functional significance in terms of conduction of excitation from cell to cell.

PHYSIOLOGICAL MECHANISMS OF MUSCULAR CONTRACTION

The striated muscles, particularly skeletal muscle, have been studied more extensively than has smooth muscle. In consequence the fundamental mechanism of contraction will be described for voluntary muscle. The mechanical mechanisms are essentially similar for cardiac muscle, and they share many features in common with those for smooth muscle. The source of energy for contraction of all contractile tissues and for other cellular functions is *adenosine triphosphate*.

Contraction of muscle involves a series of events that occur with great rapidity. The excitation process involves a nerve impulse, transmission across a small synaptic gap between the nerve ending and a *motor end plate* (Fig. 11.4), and reaction with the end plate chemical receptors. The disturbance at the end plate travels away from it through the muscle in both directions. The contraction process involves complex chemical and mechanical mechanisms. The events, the mechanisms and the resulting types of muscular activity are described in the following sections.

NEUROMUSCULAR TRANSMISSION

The axon terminals of motor nerves have many vesicles, each containing varying numbers of molecules of acetylcholine (ACH). Some of the substance is being released continuously from these sites and creates a local potential at the nerve ending. Upon arrival of a nerve impulse, a quantity of ACH is released simultaneously from a number of the vesicles and diffuses from the motor nerve terminal to the post-synaptic membrane of the motor end plate.

The ACH reacts with one type of receptor to form an ACH-receptor which causes the end-plate potential to reach a critical value and increase the permeability and P_{Na} and the P_K values of the end-plate membrane. When the local depolarization reaches threshold, an impulse is propagated throughout the muscle fiber. Excitation of the sarcolemma is conducted from the surface of the fiber inward by the T system into the sarcoplasmic reticulum at the triads (Fig. 11.2, D, 11.8).

ACH also reacts with another post-synaptic membrane chemical receptor, acetylcholinesterase, ACHE, an enzyme inactivating ACH by hastening its hydrolysis. As ACH is inactivated more is released. The sequential process of the release of ACH, depolarization, destruction of ACH, and repolarization occurs sufficiently rapidly to permit muscle to respond effectively with different frequencies of stimulation. The steps in neuromuscular transmission are summarized in Table 11.1

CHEMICAL MECHANISMS

Energy for Muscle Contraction. In the contraction, chemical energy is converted to the mechanical energy apparent as shortening, and subsequently to heat. Energy sources for contraction are adenosine triphosphate (ATP), adenosine di-

phosphate (ADP), creatine prosphate (CP), glucose, and glycogen. With the exception of glucose these substances are present in sarcoplasm and myofibrils. A single muscle contraction may occur in less than 100 milliseconds and requires a very rapid supply of energy. The metabolic rate of muscle during exercise may increase a hundred-fold and require a sustained supply of energy. Some of the chemical reactions providing for immediate and for prolonged energy requirements of the myofilaments, and hence the entire muscle, are:

(1) $ATP + H_2O \rightarrow ADP + H_3PO_4 + energy$

(2) $CP + ADP \rightarrow Creatine + ATP + energy$

(3) Glucose $+ 2$ ATP $\left.\right\}$ $\xrightarrow[\text{reactions}]{\text{Anaerobic}}$ 2 Lactic acid $+$
or Glycogen $+ 1$ ATP $\left.\right\}$ 4 ATP + energy

(4) Glucose $+ 2$ ATP $\left.\right\}$ $\xrightarrow[\text{reactions}]{\text{Aerobic}}$ $6 CO_2 +$
or Glycogen $+ 1$ ATP $\left.\right\}$ $6H_2O + 40$ ATP

The enzymes for the breakdown of ATP and ADP are present in the cisternae of the sarcoplasmic reticulum. Excesses of glucose are stored as the polymer glycogen within the sarcoplasm.

The initial supply of stored energy from the hydrolysis of ATP is released without delay and the muscle contracts (reaction 1). Reactions that follow provide for the renewal of stored energy. Reaction 2 is concerned with the resynthesis of ATP by the breakdown of creatine phosphate (CP), an energy-rich phosphate stored in the muscle cell; CP furnishes phosphate and energy for this resynthesis. The other

TABLE 11.1 NEUROMUSCULAR TRANSMISSION

Axon Terminal PRESYNAPTIC MEMBRANE	SYNAPTIC CLEFT	Muscle Fiber End Plate POSTSYNAPTIC MEMBRANE
1. Synthesis and storage of ACH in vesicles		
2. Release of ACH by nerve impulse	Diffusion of ACH ACHE	Local action produces end-plate potential
3. Resorption of choline and resynthesis of ACH	Hydrolysis of ACH	Propagated muscle impulse and muscle contraction

reactions for the ready renewal of energy stores involve the breakdown of glycogen and glucose in the muscle. Glycogen is a long-chain polysaccharide made up of units of glucose bound together.

Glycogen, in the presence of the enzyme *phosphorylase*, takes up phosphate made available through the breakdown of ATP and splits off glucose phosphate, shortening the glycogen chain by one glucose unit. Successive glucose units are broken off at corresponding points in the linkage of the glucose molecules. This process is called *phosphorolysis*. The resulting glucose phosphate undergoes a series of chemical transformations, each catalyzed by its appropriate enzyme (see p. 371). Both glucose and glycogen are broken down to pyruvic acid. If oxygen supplies are insufficient during muscular activity, the pyruvic acid is reduced to lactic acid by anaerobic glycolysis (reaction 3). In physiological reactions within the body, it is probable that when resting muscle becomes active the initial contractions occur under conditions of low oxygen supply, since there has been insufficient time for adjustment of the circulation to the new level of activity. Thus short-term intensive muscular activity requires the breakdown of energy-rich organic phosphates (reactions 1 and 2) and anaerobic glycolysis (reaction 3). This is a self-limiting process, however, since the accumulation of lactic acid in the muscle fiber alters the pH required for normal enzymatic activity.

Under normal physiological conditions of muscular activity there is a metabolic readjustment following the initial contraction and sufficient oxygen is soon available for *aerobic glycolysis* (reaction 4). The pyruvic acid enters the *citric acid cycle* for metabolism by the respiratory enzyme pathway to CO_2 and H_2O.

The muscle employs effective mechanisms for taking up oxygen. Myohemoglobin has a greater affinity for oxygen than hemoglobin of the blood so that transfer occurs even when the oxygen supply (and oxygen tension) in the blood is low. In turn, oxygen is transferred from the myohemoglobin to the muscle enzyme system, and used in the oxidative processes of the cell. These reactions provide for the continuation of muscular activity for prolonged periods.

Oxygen Debt. When man exercises at a moderate rate he attains a steady state condition during which the oxygen supply meets the oxygen requirements for his level of work. Hence, at the end of the exercise he is "in debt" only for the oxygen required to resynthesize the products of the initial anaerobic contractions. If, however, he engages in very strenuous exercise, fifteen or twenty times as much oxygen may be required as during rest. For example, an athlete running two hundred meters takes in only a very small part of the oxygen necessary to furnish the energy he expends and his *oxygen debt* increases very rapidly. When exercise stops, however, the oxygen consumption is maintained at a higher than resting level until the lactic acid has been oxidized or is resynthesized to glycogen in the liver and the muscle glycogen has been built up again as a chain of glucose units restored to the muscle by blood sugar. Since there is a limit to the amount of debt a man can accumulate, the duration of very strenuous exercise or maximum work is limited.

Heat Production. In a motor driven by combustion of fuel, only part of the energy freed in combustion is converted into work, that is, into moving the parts of the machine. Most of the energy is lost as heat. This is true also for muscle. It has been estimated that only about 25 to 30 per cent of the energy is converted into mechanical work; the rest is liberated as heat. This compares favorably with the efficiency of the best types of gas engines. Although the heat produced in engines is largely wasted, that produced in muscles serves to maintain body heat at a fairly uniform level.

The internal temperature of the human body must not fall much below 37°C. if chemical reactions are to proceed at a rate rapid enough to meet normal physiological requirements. In this connection it is interesting to note the adaptation of the body to external cold; we exercise consciously in order to keep warm, or we shiver. Shivering is a phenomenon in which muscles are activated involuntarily and heat is produced.

The heat given off in muscle contraction is divided into initial heat and recovery or delayed heat. Initial heat is produced during contraction; delayed heat is produced in the recovery period. Although the delayed heat is usually only slightly greater in amount than the initial heat, it is produced much more slowly.

MECHANICAL MECHANISMS OF THE CONTRACTION PROCESS

Striated muscle fibers, when removed from the body and treated chemically to remove their surface membranes, will shorten in the presence of ATP. Further, a solution of actomyosin, i.e., a combination of actin and myosin, can be spun into threads that will contract in the presence of ATP. These and other observations led to our present concepts of the chemical-mechanical mechanisms of muscular contraction.

Physiological contraction involves interaction of actin and myosin to form *actomyosin*, and the presence of ATP and Ca^{++}. Practically all ATP in muscle is bound to myosin. One fraction of myosin, *heavy meromyosin*, is associated with the cross-bridges to the thin actin myofilaments (see Fig. 11.2). Actomyosin possesses *ATP-ase* activity, serving as an enzyme in splitting ATP. Actomyosin–ATP-ase, activated by Ca^{++}, produces contraction. It is postulated that Ca^{++} is released in the vicinity of the triad of the sarcoplasmic reticulum during the excitation process. ATP also furnishes energy for sequestering or reducing the local concentration of Ca^{++} below that associated with shortening. It is also postulated that fragments of sarcoplasmic reticulum, or a substance intimately associated with them, act as a Ca^{++} binding agent, producing very high Ca^{++} concentration ratios between the separate sites of storage and the contractile elements. These granules or particulate fractions of muscle are referred to as the *relaxing factor*.

Sliding Filament Theory. A "model" of muscular contraction has been developed which provides a plausible explanation of how a muscle may work. The model is based upon the *sliding filament theory* of contraction, a theory now generally accepted although many of the details of the mechanism are still obscure.

According to the sliding filament theory, shortening of the muscle is brought about by a chemical-mechanical mechanism which forces the opposing thin filaments closer together toward the center of the A band. The A band remains constant in length over a wide range of muscle shortening. Within the A band the H band, in which only the thick myofilaments are present during relaxation, narrows as the distance between the ends of the thin filaments gets smaller. The I band decreases in length with the increasing shortening. The relative constancy of A band width and reduction of I band width are consistent with the theory that the thick and thin filaments slide with respect to each other. Thus the shortening of the individual sarcomeres results in shortening of the muscle.

The model serves to explain the approximation of the thin filaments according to the sliding filament theory. Projections or bridges from three myosin filaments touch each thin filament at 60 degree intervals around its circumference (Fig. 11.2). It is postulated that these bridges can move — oscillate. As the result of interaction of actin, myosin, and ATP, the bridges contract and pull opposing thin filaments together. The actin of the three heavy filaments and the succession of movements of the cross-bridges would provide an effective mechanism for smooth, continuous shortening.

OBSERVATIONS OF MUSCULAR CONTRACTION

SKELETAL MUSCLES

Skeletal muscles normally adapt themselves to the tasks of developing tension and shortening, speed of movement, strength of contraction, and precision of movement. To gain an understanding of the mechanisms involved in physiological responses of muscle *in situ*, we can isolate and study muscles and even muscle fibers under controlled experimental conditions

(Fig. 11.9). The skeletal muscles of frogs are well suited to laboratory observations; a length of attached nerve is frequently removed with the muscle. Electrical stimulation is commonly used to substitute for nerve impulses from the motor neuron in the central nervous system; its strength, duration, and rate of change can be controlled and, within limits, it does not injure the tissues.

Two extreme conditions of contraction can be observed experimentally in an excised muscle. If the muscle is attached between two fixed points so as to permit only a minimal degree of shortening, it responds to stimulation by an *isometric* (equal length) contraction. Under these conditions there is a marked increase in the tension developed. Examples of the isometric type of contraction of muscles within the body are holding a weight at arm's length, pressing against a wall, or simultaneous contraction of flexor and extensor muscles in preventing movement at a joint. In isometric contraction energy is converted almost entirely to heat—no external work is done. The principal characteristic of *isotonic* (same tension) contraction is shortening with the performance of work, i.e., a weight is moved over a certain distance. The weight may be only that of an arm or leg, or that of an object, or of the body in motion. These two types of contraction have been described as extreme conditions although they more commonly fall into intermediate combinations which may be principally isometric or principally isotonic. During contraction, a muscle behaves like a series of springs. When stretched, the resulting tension or tightness has both passive and active components. The passive tension exhibited by an unstimulated muscle varies with the length of the muscle fiber. This elasticity is reversible for muscle stretched by about one-third of its resting length. Active tension is developed following excitation of the muscle and passage of the action potential. The events occurring between the action potential and contrac-

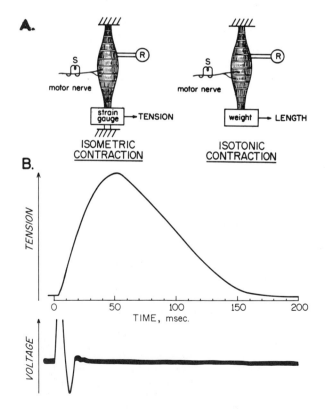

Figure 11.9 Twitch contraction of whole muscle. *A*, Arrangement for recording contractile responses of whole muscle. Left, isometric recording arrangement; length is held constant, and developed force (tension) is measured with a strain gauge and recorded as a function of time. Contraction is initiated by a supramaximal stimulus delivered to motor nerve via a pair of electrodes, S. Muscle action potential recorded by surface electrodes, R. Right, isotonic recording arrangement; tension is held constant by hanging a weight on muscle and changes in length are measured as a function of time. Stimulating and recording as at left. *B*, Action potential (below) and isometric tension (above) recorded in tibialis muscle of cat. Abscissae represent time; upper ordinate, tension in arbitrary units; and lower ordinate, voltage in arbitrary units (upward deflection incomplete). (After Creed et al., Reflex Activity of the Spinal Cord. Oxford, Clarendon Press, 1932.)

tion are referred to as *excitation-contraction coupling.*

Muscle Twitch. When a single stimulus is given, a muscle twitch results (Fig. 11.10). If the process is recorded, it can be seen to have three phases: a latent period, a period of contraction, and a period of relaxation. The latent period occurs from the moment of stimulation until the muscle shortens. During this time excitation-contraction coupling events occur. The slack in the elastic-series system is taken up by shortening of some sarcomeres and some fibers; this results in initial stretch and an increase in active tension in some parts of the entire system without change in length of the muscle itself. During the second or contraction phase, active tension continues to increase and the muscle as a whole shortens. The speed, strength, and degree of shortening are greatest when the muscle starts from its resting length in the body. The speed of contraction and degree of shortening decrease with increasing load. Because of the inertia involved in stretching elastic components within the muscle, active tension diminishes as the peak of contraction and sum of total active and

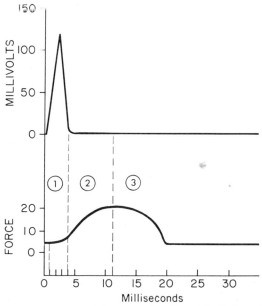

Figure 11.10 Diagram of spike potential and force developed during single muscle twitch: *1,* latent period; *2,* period of contraction; *3,* period of relaxation.

passive tension is reached. During the third phase of the twitch the muscle returns to its original length or passive tension.

Gradation in Response to Single Stimuli. Observation of excised muscle shows that total tension and shortening increase with an increase in the strength of the stimulus. This reaction represents the phenomenon of graded response to graded stimulus. It is dependent upon the fact that, as the strength of the stimulus is increased, more and more motor units (page 84), and hence more and more muscle fibers, enter into the response of the muscle. If a motor nerve is dissected so as to allow only a few nerve fibers to remain intact, the number of increases in the height of muscular contractions corresponds to the number of nerve fibers, and hence their motor units, which are stimulated in the preparation.

Summation of Contractions. If stimuli of adequate strength to cause maximum contraction are applied in rapid succession, the total tension and degree of shortening elicited exceed that developed by a muscle twitch. If the contractions are recorded while a muscle is being stimulated at a relatively low frequency, a succession of peaks may be seen rising during the time that the active tension of the immediately preceding contraction is falling. The amount of total tension and shortening depends on the time interval between stimuli. Thus, as the frequency of stimulation is increased, the successive peaks arise earlier and earlier in the period of relaxation of the preceding contraction and show successive increases in shortening and total tension. The response during which individual peaks can be observed is known as *clonus* or *incomplete tetanus.* At still higher rates of stimulation the peaks are fused and the tracing is seen as a plateau. This response is known as *tetanus.* During tetanic contraction the active component of tension is not permitted to diminish as it does prior to reaching maximum total tension in a muscle twitch. The responses are additive up to the limiting frequency for the reacting muscle as the Ca^{++} concentration is increased through its release by successive stimuli (Fig. 11.11).

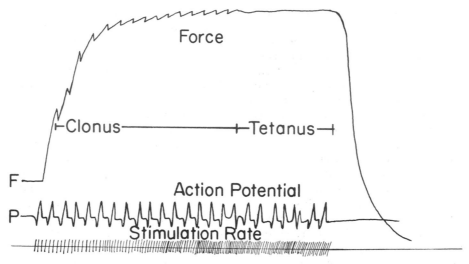

Figure 11.11 Summation of contractions.

If action potentials are recorded from a muscle, it will be noted that these continue to appear as separate, discrete responses even during complete tetanus.

Voluntary Muscle in Situ. The two major categories of response of voluntary muscles are movement and maintenance of posture. The degree of these responses shows wide variation in the rate and duration of expenditure of energy. The adjustment to voluntary contraction is brought about by (1) the frequency of response of single motor units, (2) the number of motor units involved, and (3) the interaction resulting from the different frequencies of response of single units.

Physiological rates of discharge of a nerve fiber of a motor unit may vary from 5/sec. to about 50/sec. At the lower rates a succession of twitches occurs. At the higher rates summation of contraction occurs, the force of the contraction is increased, and incomplete tetanus or clonus, or even complete tetanus or fusion, results. The rate of stimulation at which fusion occurs differs with different muscles: with rapid muscles the rate is about 50/sec.; with slow or postural muscles, about 30/sec. The responses of the separate muscle fibers in a single motor unit will not begin at the same time at the lower rates of stimulation due to differences in length of terminal branches of the associated axon, and hence time of arrival of the stimulus. The force of a contraction of a muscle is equal to the sum of the forces of single muscle cells contracting at one time.

The interaction of motor units in a muscle is influenced by both the number of units responding and the frequency of stimulation of each participating unit in the response. A single motor unit can respond repetitively for relatively long periods of time. The process of *facilitation* occurs when stimuli from two or more nerve impulses converge on a motor neuron *(final common path)*, and through *summation of subliminal stimuli* discharge additional motor units (see p. 84). Interaction of a relatively few units at relatively low rates of discharge can result in maintenance of fairly constant, sustained tension in the muscle. Further discussion of adjustments of neuromuscular structures in the maintenance of posture and locomotion can be found in Chapter 12.

CARDIAC MUSCLE

Turtle and frog hearts are quite resistant to the stresses attendant to their removal from the body. They continue to contract rhythmically and exhibit in slow motion many phenomena similar to those in skeletal muscle.

All-or-None Response. The degree of shortening of the myocardium is constant during successive rhythmic contractions in response to excitation from the acting pacemaker, usually the sino-atrial node, as long as the physiological conditions of the fibers remain relatively constant. The excitation process may arise in the sino-atrial node, or in other locations in the conducting system within the atrial and ventricular muscle. If electrical stimuli of increasing intensity are substituted and repeated at appropriate intervals, the heart will respond by the same degree of contraction and total tension. This illustrates the phenomenon of the all-or-none response in heart muscle. It results from the arrangement of the muscle tissue into a *functional syncytium* (Fig. 11.5). The heart responds much like a single motor unit.

Refractory Period. If the interval between stimuli is reduced so that a stimulus falls during the contraction phase of the previous beat, there is no response. During the contraction phase the myocardium cannot be excited by another stimulus regardless of its intensity. This phase of a cardiac cycle is called the *absolute refractory period*. When some fibers begin to relax, the heart will respond to supramaximal stimuli; this phase of the cycle is called the *relative refractory period*. During the relative refractory period the degree of shortening and total tension developed is reduced.

Gradation of Response. The extent of shortening of contracting myocardium is influenced by metabolic processes and by the resting length or passive tension of the cardiac fibers at the end of the diastolic period, i.e., the period of relaxation. In the intact heart the strength of the contraction increases with the amount of blood that flows into the heart during diastole. The degree of filling, of course, determines the resting length of the fibers.

Summation of Contractions. While cardiac muscle does show summation of contractions, it does not respond with clonic or tetanic contraction because of the duration of the refractory period.

Further discussion of the response of the heart and the normal mechanisms of cardiac contraction appears in Chapter 15.

SMOOTH MUSCLE

Smooth muscle behaves much like striated muscle if it is stretched rapidly — tension is proportional to length. However, it reacts quite differently following the initial response. If held at constant length the total tension decreases. If the tension is maintained constant, the length increases. These readjustments to new length or new tension proceed slowly. If smooth muscle is stretched slowly enough there is no appreciable rise in tension; this property of smooth muscle is termed *plasticity* (Fig. 11.12). When this muscle shortens without an increase in total tension its oxygen consumption does not increase; increase in total tension is accompanied by an increase in O_2 consumption.

Smooth muscles can be divided into two major categories on the basis of their mechanisms of activation and their responses — *multiunit smooth muscle* and *visceral smooth muscle* (Table 11.2). Such a classification emphasizes the differences. However, many smooth muscles have properties which range between these extremes and may behave as multiunit tissue at one time or single unit tissue at another. Both types are sensitive to chemical agents released at autonomic nerve endings (see p. 131) or present in circulating blood (see p. 315). Both respond to stretch — the

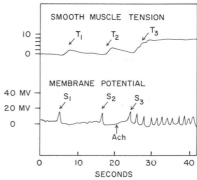

Figure 11.12 Comparison of membrane potential and tension developed in smooth muscle.

TABLE 11.2 CLASSIFICATION OF SMOOTH MUSCLE

Type	Response	Location	Analogous to:
Multiunit	Discrete, localized, like muscle twitch	Blood vessels, intrinsic eye muscles, erector pili, mammary papillae	Skeletal muscles
Intermediate	Pacemaker	Vas deferens	
Visceral	As a single unit, automatic, rhythmic and tonic contractions	Ureter, uterus, bile duct, intestine	Cardiac muscle

visceral muscle more readily than the multiunit type.

Multiunit Smooth Muscle. The organization of multiunit smooth muscle appears to be that of diffuse and overlapping motor units. Under physiologic conditions they contract only upon excitation of autonomic motor nerves (see also pages 131 and 132).

Visceral Smooth Muscle. Visceral smooth muscle frequently shows rhythmical activity for prolonged periods. Pacemaker cells develop prepotentials or pacemaker potentials, presumably as a result of variation of metabolism within the fibers. Subthreshold fluctuations in membrane potential occur locally; when a threshold is reached an action potential is initiated. In some visceral smooth muscle all the muscle cells can develop prepotentials and initiate impulses with the location of the pacemaker changing from time to time. In the intestine there is a gradient of metabolic rate and rythmicity which decreases from the upper to the lower portion of the intestinal tract. In the ureter, the end nearest the kidney acts as a pacemaker. Rhythmic activities of smooth muscles are modified by action of autonomic nerves. Visceral smooth muscle usually shows a partial state of contraction and tension. Under certain conditions a tonic contraction will occur which resembles tetanus in skeletal muscle. Combinations of rhythmic and tonic contractions are of particular value in functional movements of tubular structures such as glandular ducts and the intestinal tract. Visceral smooth muscle responds to stimuli in an all-or-none manner.

QUESTIONS FOR DISCUSSION

1. How might a deficiency of calcium in the diet or circulating blood affect muscle contraction?

2. In what ways might an oxygen debt be relieved?

3. Discuss the heat production of muscle metabolism in terms of basal metabolism, fever, and temperature regulation.

4. What similarities are there between the functions of nerve and muscle?

5. Explain the loss of strength and presence of tension in fatigued muscle.

6. What might be the mechanism of spasm in muscle?

POSTURE AND MOTION

CHAPTER TWELVE

BIOMECHANICS OF ARTICULATIONS

Mechanical Advantage. The movements associated with synovial joints are brought about by the contraction of skeletal muscles attached to or near the bones forming the articulations. The *axis* of a joint is taken as an imaginary line about which movement occurs. Since the articular surfaces are not regular, as they would be in a mechanical ball and socket, nor are hinge or pivot joints of uniform radius, there is no single center of movement. The "axis" shifts its position slightly during movement of the joint just as it would in an eccentric mechanical counterpart in which the opposing surfaces were somewhat irregular. The ball and socket joints of the skeletal system have many axes permitting movement in a number of directions, but the greatest motion is around the transverse, anteroposterior, and vertical axes (Fig. 12.11). In a hinge joint only a transverse axis is present (Fig. 12.18), while pivot joints have a vertical axis (Fig. 12.3). Flexion and extension take place on a transverse axis. Abduction and adduction of a part are performed around an anteroposterior axis. A vertical axis permits rotation to occur.

The axes represent the fulcrums in the lever systems made up by bones, their articulations, and associated muscles. The body part, or the part together with the external object it is moving or supporting, constitutes the weight or resistance of the system, while the muscles supply the power for performing work. Thus the architectural structure is admirably suited to function, for levers provide the mechanical advantage by which a small force can be made to overcome a larger counterforce, and by which the distance a weight is moved can be greatly increased beyond the distance through which the counterforce must act.

Mobility. *Flexion* is bending, decreasing the angle between the parts of the body. Flexion takes place at the elbow joint when the forearm is bent back on the arm (Fig. 12.21). *Extension* is straightening or stretching out, increasing the angle between the parts of the body. It is the reverse of flexion. Extension occurs at the

203

elbow joint when the forearm is straightened (Fig. 12.20). In anatomical position the foot is in *dorsiflexion* (Fig. 12.60), while extension of the foot is also *plantar flexion* (Fig. 12.56).

Abduction is movement away from the midsagittal plane. It occurs in the shoulder joint when the arm is raised. *Adduction* is the opposite of abduction. The part is moved toward the median plane, as when the raised arm is brought down to the side of the body (Fig. 12.14). Abduction and adduction of fingers and toes are movements from and toward the median planes of the hand and foot, that is, middle finger for the hand and second toe for the foot.

Circumduction is movement in which the end of a part describes a circle and the part itself the sides of a cone. It occurs in ball and socket joints and combines the movements of flexion, extension, abduction, and adduction.

Rotation is a turning on an axis without displacement, as in rotation of the atlas (first cervical vertebra) on the axis or epistropheus (second cervical vertebra). Turning the palm of the hand and forearm upward in *supination* or downward in *pronation* by the rotation of the radius about the ulna serves as another example of this movement (Fig. 12.25). Rotation of the foot upon axis 2-2 or 3-3 of Figure 12.50 which turns the plantar surface outward is *eversion*, and the opposite movement is *inversion*.

ILLUSTRATIVE TABULATION OF POSTURE AND MOTION

The skeletal muscles described in this chapter comprise only a small number of the more than 400 in the whole body (Figs. 12.60, 12.61). They are, nonetheless, representative, and serve to illustrate the principles of mechanics of muscle. The descriptions are designed not only to provide the student with information concerning the muscles that are discussed in this text, but also to indicate a method of approach for extension of his studies where such study is indicated by his professional requirements and interest. The muscles are arranged in opposing groups.

Agonistic muscles furnish the power for a particular movement. *Antagonistic* muscles contribute to the smoothness of the action while opposing the direction and force of the movement. The scheme of labeling used for all of the illustrations other than Figure 12.1 is that shown on Figure 12.4. The name of the muscle is in solid black, the origin in double stroke, and the related structures in upper and lower case lettering. Descriptions of additional skeletal muscles are found in reference to the eye (p. 118), respiratory (p. 246), and digestive (p. 335) structures and pelvic floor (p. 391). Refer also to Table 12.1.

Voluntary Movement. Muscular activity that results in movement or work involves two sets of muscles that act, in varying degrees, in opposition to one another. Normally, groups of agonists and antagonists, rather than two single opposing muscles, are engaged in voluntary movement. In movements involving flexion the flexors are the agonists and the extensors are the antagonists. The activity of the opposing muscle groups is well coordinated in respect to the degree of tension exerted from moment to moment; as the tension in the flexors is increased, the tone of the extensors is reduced or inhibited. The central nervous system integrates the complex activity pattern of the muscles which carry out the movements of the body. At the beginning of contraction only relatively little movement results, since most of the initial force is spent in pulling against the joint when the extremity is fully extended. This initial phase is isometric. Further shortening causes movement, i.e., isotonic contraction. The extent of the participation of various muscle groups will depend upon the force required for the voluntary act. For example, only immediately adjacent muscles and joints would be involved in an act requiring moderate flexion. Where greater force is required, outlying groups are brought into play and the more proximal joints are steadied or fixed.

The speed of voluntary movement depends upon the skeletal muscles that are acting, since individual muscles show great variation in the time required for contraction. (Text continued on page 227).

TABLE 12.1 ILLUSTRATIVE TABULATION OF POSTURE AND MOTION

MUSCLES OF MASTICATION

Name of Muscle	Origin	Insertion	Action
Temporalis (Figs. 12.1,A, 12.2)	Temporal fossa	Anterior border of ramus, and coronoid process of mandible	Closes jaws
Masseter (Figs. 12.1, A, 12.2)	Zygomatic arch	Coronoid process, lateral surface of ramus and angle of mandible	Closes jaws
Medial pterygoid (Figs. 12.1,B, 12.2)	Pterygoid process of sphenoid, palatine bone, tuberosity of maxilla	Medial surface of ramus and angle of mandible	Closes jaws
Lateral pterygoid (Figs. 12.1,B, 12.2)	Great wing and pterygoid process of sphenoid	Neck of condyle of mandible, articular capsule of temporomandibular joint	Opens jaws; side-to-side movements are produced by pterygoid muscles on two sides contracting alternately; protrudes mandible

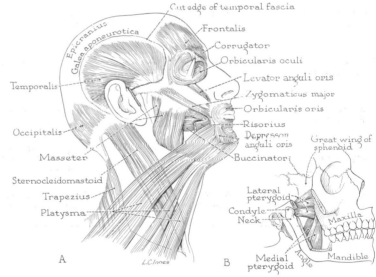

Figure 12.1 Muscles of mastication and facial expression. *A*, Muscles of the head and neck. *B*, Pterygoid muscles.

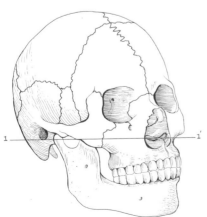

Figure 12.2 Transverse axis of temporomandibular joint.

MUSCLES OF FACIAL EXPRESSION

Epicranius (Fig. 12.1,A)			
Occipitalis	Lateral part of superior nuchal line	Galea aponeurotica	Draws scalp backward
Frontalis	Anterior border of galea aponeurotica	Fibers of orbicularis oculi	Raises eyebrows, wrinkles skin of forehead transversely
Orbicularis oculi (Fig. 12.1,A)			Closes eyelids, wrinkles skin of forehead, compresses lacrimal sac
Orbital portion	Frontal bone, frontal process of maxilla	Near own origin after encircling orbit	
Corrugator	Medial end of superciliary arch	Skin of forehead	
Palpebral portion	Medial palpebral ligament	Lateral palpebral raphe	
Lacrimal portion	Lacrimal bone	Joins palpebral portion after crossing lacrimal sac	
Orbicularis oris (Fig. 12.1,A)	Many layers of fibers surrounding the mouth	Skin of central part of lips	Closes lips and protrudes them
Levator anguli oris (Fig. 12.1,A)	Maxilla	Orbicularis oris	Draws upper lip upward
Zygomaticus major (Fig. 12.1,A)	Zygomatic bone	Angle of mouth, fibers of orbicularis oris	Draws angles of mouth upward and backward, as in laughing
Risorius (Fig. 12.1,A)	Fascia over the masseter	Skin of angle of mouth	Draws angle of mouth outward, gives strained expression to face
Depressor anguli oris (Fig. 12.1,A)	Mandible and platysma	Orbicularis oris	Draws lower lip downward
Platysma (Fig. 12.1,A)	Fascia of pectoralis major and deltoid	Lower border of mandible, skin of cheek and corner of mouth	Draws down lower lip and angle of mouth, wrinkles skin of neck
Buccinator (Fig. 12.1,A)	Alveolar arches of maxilla and mandible	Fibers of orbicularis oris at angle of mouth	Compresses cheeks, holds food in contact with teeth

MUSCLES THAT MOVE THE HEAD

Sternocleidomastoid (Figs. 12.3, 12.4)	Sternal end of clavicle, manubrium of sternum	Mastoid process of temporal bone	Both muscles acting flex head on chest against gravity; one muscle acting rotates head to side opposite contracting muscle
Splenius capitis (Figs. 12.3, 12.5)	Lower part of ligamentum nuchae, spinous processes of seventh cervical and upper three or four thoracic vertebrae	Mastoid process and lateral part of superior nuchal line	Both muscles acting extend head; one muscle contracting rotates and flexes head laterally to side of contracting muscle
Semispinalis capitis (Figs. 12.3, 12.5)	Transverse processes of upper six thoracic vertebrae, articular processes of lower four cervical vertebrae	Between superior and inferior nuchal lines of occipital bone	Extension, lateral flexion, rotation of head
Longissimus capitis (Figs. 12.3, 12.5)	Transverse processes of upper three thoracic vertebrae and articular processes of lower four cervical vertebrae	Mastoid process	Extension, lateral flexion, rotation of head

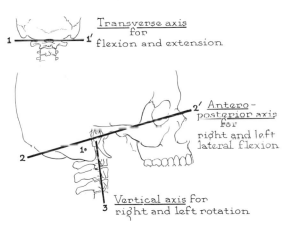

Figure 12.3 Axes of movement of skull on vertebral column.

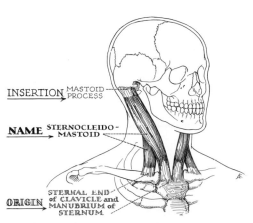

Figure 12.4 Sternocleidomastoid.

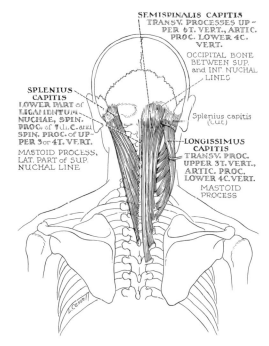

Figure 12.5 Splenius capitis; semispinalis capitis; longissimus capitis.

MUSCLES THAT MOVE THE VERTEBRAL COLUMN

Erector spinae (Figs. 12.6, 12.7)	Posterior part of iliac crest, posterior surface of sacrum, spinous processes of all lumbar vertebrae and last two thoracic vertebrae	Three divisions 1. Iliocostalis—angles of ribs 2. Longissimus—transverse processes of thoracic vertebrae and ribs 3. Spinalis—spinous processes of upper thoracic vertebrae	Extension, lateral flexion, rotation of vertebral column (and pelvis in walking)
Quadratus lumborum (Figs. 12.6, 12.8)	Posterior part of iliac crest, iliolumbar ligament, transverse processes of lower four lumbar vertebrae	Transverse processes of upper four lumbar vertebrae, last rib	Extension, lateral flexion, rotation of vertebral column
Rectus abdominis and Psoas major	See pages 217, 218		Flexion and lateral flexion of vertebral column

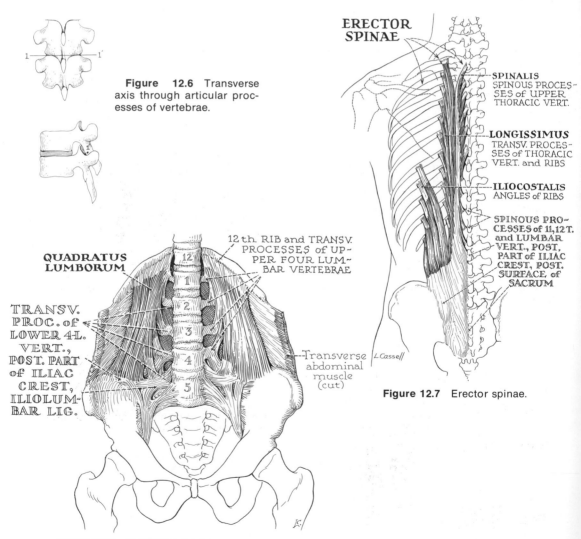

Figure 12.6 Transverse axis through articular processes of vertebrae.

ERECTOR SPINAE

SPINALIS SPINOUS PROCESSES of UPPER THORACIC VERT.

LONGISSIMUS TRANSV. PROCESSES of THORACIC VERT. and RIBS

ILIOCOSTALIS ANGLES of RIBS

SPINOUS PROCESSES of 11, 12 T. and LUMBAR VERT., POST. PART of ILIAC CREST, POST. SURFACE of SACRUM

Figure 12.7 Erector spinae.

QUADRATUS LUMBORUM

12 th RIB and TRANSV. PROCESSES of UPPER FOUR LUMBAR VERTEBRAE

TRANSV. PROC. of LOWER 4 L. VERT., POST. PART of ILIAC CREST, ILIOLUMBAR LIG.

Transverse abdominal muscle (cut)

Figure 12.8 Quadratus lumborum.

MUSCLES ACTING ON THE SCAPULA

Trapezius (Fig. 12.9)	External occipital protuberance, medial part of superior nuchal line, ligamentum nuchae, spines of seventh cervical and all thoracic vertebrae	Lateral third of clavicle, acromion and spine of scapula	Adduction and upward rotation of scapula
Serratus anterior (Fig. 12.10)	Upper eight or nine ribs	Medial margin of costal surface of scapula	Abduction of scapula

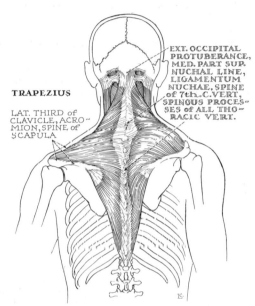

Figure 12.9 Trapezius. The right trapezius muscle is contracted, showing the scapula in adduction.

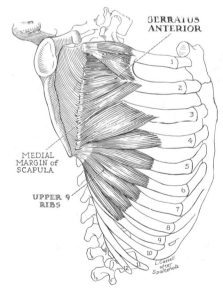

Figure 12.10 Serratus anterior.

MUSCLES THAT MOVE THE HUMERUS

Deltoid (Figs. 12.11, 12.12, 12.14)	Lateral third of clavicle, lateral margin of acromion, spine of scapula	Deltoid tuberosity of humerus	Abduction of humerus
Supraspinatus (Figs. 12.11, 12.12)	Supraspinous fossa of scapula	Highest facet on greater tubercle of humerus	Abduction of humerus
Pectoralis major (Figs. 12.11, 12.13, 12.14)	Medial half of clavicle, half of anterior surface of sternum, costal cartilages of upper seven ribs, aponeurosis of external oblique	Lateral margin of intertubercular groove of humerus	Adduction of humerus, medial rotation of humerus
Infraspinatus (Figs. 12.11, 12.15)	Infraspinous fossa of scapula	Middle facet of greater tubercle of humerus	Lateral rotation of humerus
Teres minor (Figs. 12.11, 12.15)	Lateral margin of scapula	Lowest facet of greater tubercle of humerus	Lateral rotation of humerus
Latissimus dorsi (Figs. 12.11, 12.16)	Spinous processes of lower six thoracic vertebrae, thoracolumbar fascia (by which it is attached to spinous processes of lumbar vertebrae, spine of sacrum, posterior fourth of iliac crest) and lower four ribs	Floor of intertubercular groove of humerus	Medial rotation and extension of humerus
Coracobrachialis (Figs. 12.11, 12.17)	Coracoid process of scapula	Middle of medial surface of humerus	Flexion of humerus

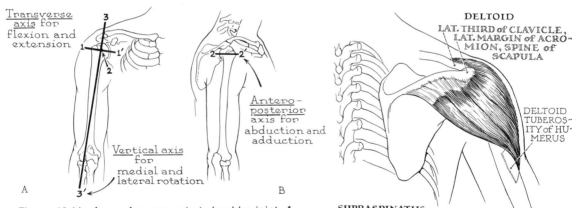

Figure 12.11 Axes of movement at shoulder joint. *A*, Anterior view. *B*, Lateral view.

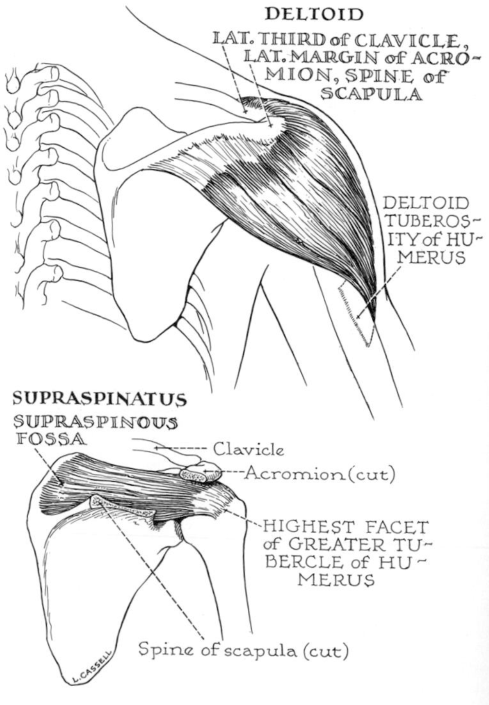

Figure 12.12 Deltoid and supraspinatus muscles.

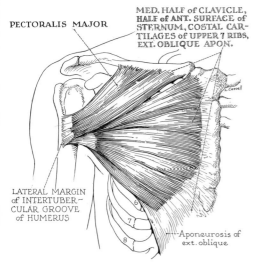

PECTORALIS MAJOR

MED. HALF of CLAVICLE,
HALF of ANT. SURFACE of
STERNUM, COSTAL CAR-
TILAGES of UPPER 7 RIBS,
EXT. OBLIQUE APON.

LATERAL MARGIN
of INTERTUBER-
CULAR GROOVE
of HUMERUS

Aponeurosis of
ext. oblique

Figure 12.13 Pectoralis major.

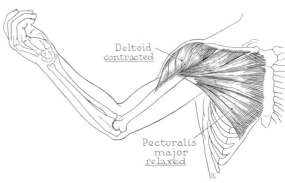

Deltoid
contracted

Pectoralis
major
relaxed

Figure 12.14 Diagram showing opposing action of deltoid and pectoralis major muscles.

Figure 12.15 Infraspinatus and teres minor muscles.

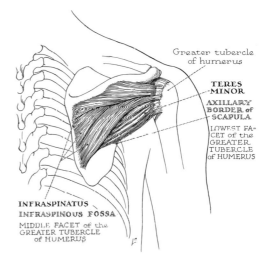

Greater tubercle
of humerus

TERES
MINOR

AXILLARY
BORDER of
SCAPULA

LOWEST FA-
CET of the
GREATER
TUBERCLE
of HUMERUS

INFRASPINATUS
INFRASPINOUS FOSSA
MIDDLE FACET of the
GREATER TUBERCLE
of HUMERUS

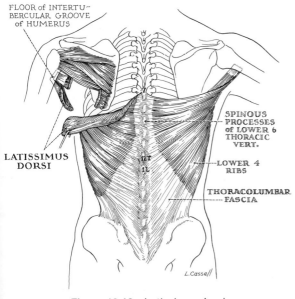

FLOOR of INTERTU-
BERCULAR GROOVE
of HUMERUS

LATISSIMUS
DORSI

SPINOUS
PROCESSES
of LOWER 6
THORACIC
VERT.

LOWER 4
RIBS

THORACOLUMBAR
FASCIA

Figure 12.16 Latissimus dorsi.

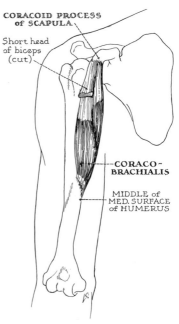

CORACOID PROCESS
of SCAPULA

Short head
of biceps
(cut)

CORACO-
BRACHIALIS

MIDDLE of
MED. SURFACE
of HUMERUS

Figure 12.17 Coracobrachialis.

MUSCLES ACTING ON THE FOREARM

Brachialis (Figs. 12.18, 12.19, 12.21)	Lower half of anterior surface of humerus	Coronoid process of ulna	Flexion of forearm
Brachioradialis (Figs. 12.18, 12.27,A)	Lateral supracondylar ridge of humerus	Lateral surface of radius above styloid process	Flexion of forearm
Triceps brachii (Figs. 12.18, 12.20)	Long head from infraglenoid tubercle of scapula, lateral head from posterior surface of humerus above radial groove, medial head from surface below radial groove	Olecranon process of ulna	Extension of forearm

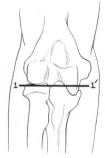

Transverse axis for flexion and extension of forearm

Figure 12.18 Axis of movement at elbow joint.

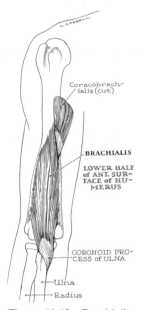

Figure 12.19 Brachialis.

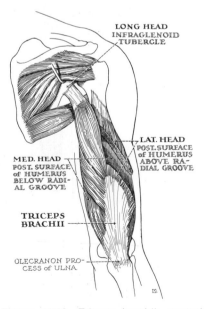

Figure 12.20 Triceps brachii; posterior view of right arm.

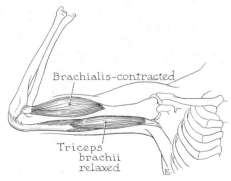

Figure 12.21 Diagram showing opposing action of brachialis and triceps brachii.

MUSCLES THAT MOVE THE HAND

Biceps brachii (Figs. 12.18, 12.22, 12.23, 12.25)	Long head from supraglenoid tubercle of scapula, short head from coracoid process of scapula	Tuberosity of radius; bicipital aponeurosis to fascia on medial side of forearm	Supinates hand and assists in flexion of forearm
Supinator (Figs. 12.22, 12.23)	Lateral epicondyle of humerus, crest of ulna	Lateral margin of tuberosity and oblique line of radius	Assists biceps in supination of the hand
Pronator teres (Figs. 12.22, 12.24, 12.25)	Medial epicondyle of humerus	Lateral surface of radius	Pronation, back of hand turned forward
Pronator quadratus (Figs. 12.22, 12.24, 12.25)	Distal part of ulna	Distal part of radius	Assists pronator teres in pronation
Flexor carpi radialis (Figs. 12.26, 12.27,A)	Medial epicondyle of humerus	Front of bases of second and third metacarpals	Flexes hand and assists in abduction
Flexor carpi ulnaris (Figs. 12.26, 12.27,A)	Medial epicondyle of humerus, medial surface of olecranon process, and by aponeurosis from posterior border of ulna	Pisiform, hamate, and base of fifth metacarpal	Flexes hand and assists in adduction
Flexor digitorum superficialis (Figs. 12.26, 12.27,B)	One head arises from medial epicondyle of humerus and medial surface of ulna; the other head from anterior border of radius	Anterior surfaces of middle phalanges two through five	Flexion of middle phalanges upon proximal phalanges
Flexor digitorum profundus (Figs. 12.26, 12.27,C)	Two-thirds of anterior surface of ulna and interosseous membrane	Bases of second through fifth distal phalanges	Flexion of distal phalanges upon proximal phalanges
Flexor pollicis longus (Figs. 12.26, 12.27,C)	Anterior two-thirds of radius	Palmar surface of distal phalanx of thumb	Flexion of thumb

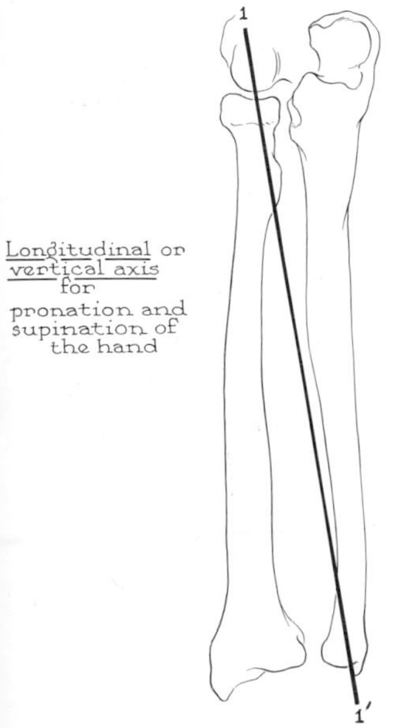

Figure 12.22 Axis of movement at the forearm.

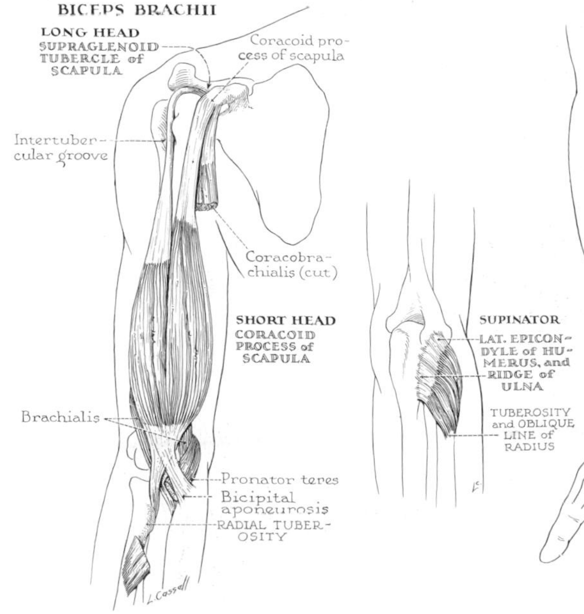

Figure 12.23 Biceps brachii and supinator muscles.

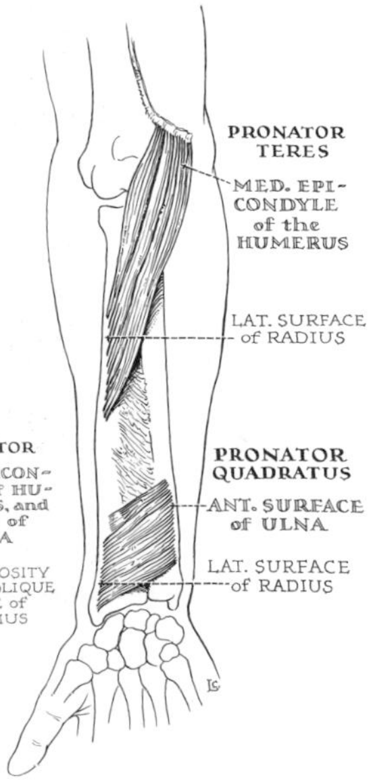

Figure 12.24 Front of right forearm, showing pronator muscles.

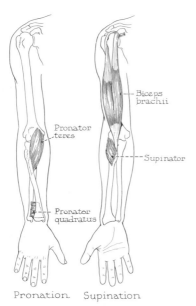

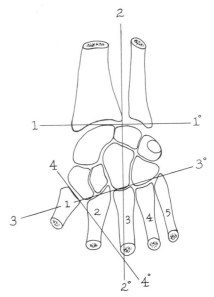

Figure 12.25 Diagram showing opposing action of pronators and supinators of the hand. *B*, Pronators contracted, forearm and hand pronated. *C*, Supinators contracted, forearm and hand supinated.

Figure 12.26 Axes of the wrist and hand.

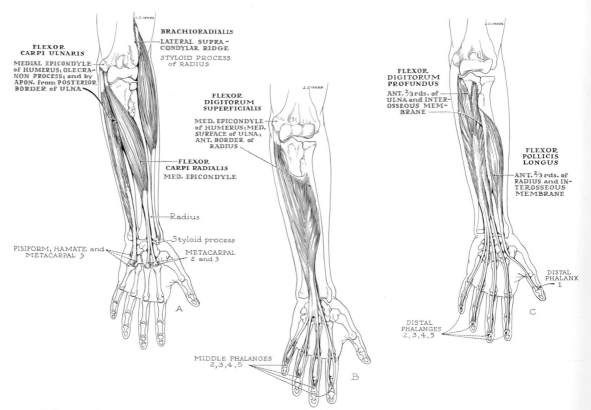

Figure 12.27 *A*, Brachioradialis; flexor carpi radialis; flexor carpi ulnaris. *B*, Flexor digitorum superficialis. *C*, Flexor digitorum profundus; flexor pollicis longus.

MUSCLES THAT MOVE THE HAND *(Continued)*

Extensor carpi radialis longus (Figs. 12.26, 12.28,*A*)	Lateral supracondylar ridge of humerus	Dorsal surface of the base of second metacarpal bone	Extension of hand, assists in abduction
Extensor carpi radialis brevis (Figs. 12.24, 12.28,*A*)	Lateral epicondyle of humerus	Dorsal base of second and third metacarpals	Extension of hand, assists in abduction
Extensor carpi ulnaris (Figs. 12.24, 12.28,*C*)	Lateral epicondyle of the humerus and at the oblique and posterior border of ulna	Fifth metacarpal	Extension of hand, assists in adduction
Extensor digitorum (Figs. 12.24, 12.28,*C*)	Lateral epicondyle of humerus	Dorsal bases of middle and distal phalanges two through five	Extension of fingers
Extensor digiti minimi (Figs. 12.24, 12.28,*C*)	Lateral epicondyle of humerus	Proximal fifth phalanx	Extension of finger
Extensor pollicis longus (Figs. 12.24, 12.28,*B*)	Lower posterior surface of ulna	Distal phalanx of thumb	Extends the thumb
Extensor pollicis brevis (Figs. 12.24, 12.28,*B*)	Lower posterior surface of radius	Proximal phalanx of thumb	Extends the thumb
Abductor pollicis (Figs. 12.24, 12.28,*B*)	Posterior surface of interosseous membrane	Lateral side of first metacarpal and trapezium	Abduction of thumb

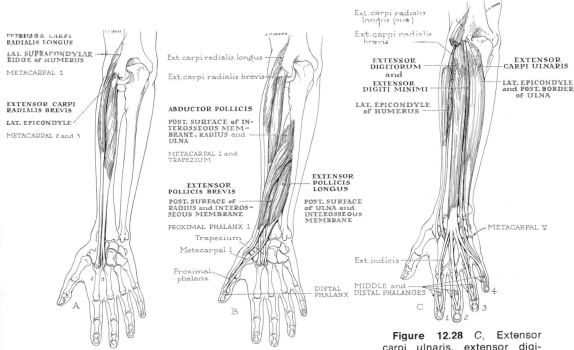

Figure 12.28 *A*, Extensor carpi radialis longus; extensor carpi radialis brevis. *B*, Extensor pollicis longus; extensor pollicis brevis; abductor pollics.

Figure 12.28 *C*, Extensor carpi ulnaris, extensor digitorum, and extensor digiti minimi.

MUSCLES OF RESPIRATION

Diaphragm (Figs. 12.29, 12.31)	Xiphoid process of sternum, costal cartilages of lower six ribs, medial and lateral tendinous arches; (two crura) right crus to bodies of first three lumbar vertebrae, left crus to bodies of first two lumbar vertebrae	Central tendon	Increases vertical diameter of thorax; lowers pressure in thorax; increases abdominal pressure
External intercostals (Figs. 12.30, 12.31)	Lower borders of upper eleven ribs	Upper borders of last eleven ribs	Elevate costal margins and increase transverse diameter of thorax
Internal intercostals (Figs. 12.30, 12.31)	Upper borders of lower eleven ribs and costal cartilages	Lower borders of upper eleven ribs and costal cartilages	Maintain intrathoracic pressure during forced expiration
External oblique (Fig 12.32)	Lower eight ribs	Anterior half of iliac crest, by means of an aponeurosis to linea alba	Compresses abdominal contents, assists in expiration and elimination (vomiting, defecation, micturition, parturition)
Internal oblique (Fig. 12.32)	Lateral half of inguinal ligament, anterior two-thirds of iliac crest, thoracolumbar fascia	Costal cartilages of ribs 10, 11, 12, linea alba, crest of pubis	Compresses abdominal contents, assists in expiration and elimination
Transversus abdominis (Fig. 12.33)	Lateral third of inguinal ligament, anterior half of iliac crest, thoracolumbar fascia, costal cartilages of lower six ribs	Linea alba and crest of pubis	Compresses abdominal contents, assists in expiration and elimination
Rectus abdominis (Fig. 12.33)	Crest of pubis	Xiphoid process of sternum, costal cartilages of fifth, sixth, and seventh ribs	Compresses abdominal contents, flexes vertebral column (pg. 208)

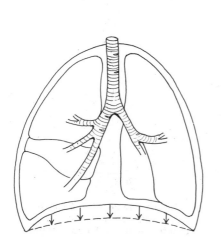

Figure 12.29 Vertical diameter of thorax.

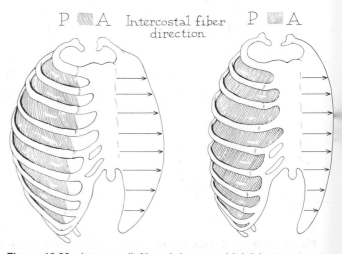

Figure 12.30 Increase (left) and decrease (right) in transverse diameter of thorax.

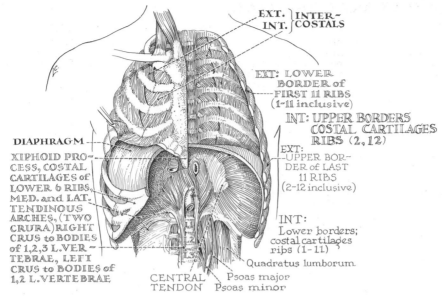

EXT.] INTER~
INT. } COSTALS

EXT: LOWER
BORDER of
FIRST 11 RIBS
(1-11 inclusive)

INT: UPPER BORDERS
COSTAL CARTILAGES
RIBS (2,12)

EXT:
UPPER BOR~
DER of LAST
11 RIBS
(2-12 inclusive)

INT:
Lower borders;
costal cartilages
ribs (1-11)

DIAPHRAGM

XIPHOID PRO~
CESS, COSTAL
CARTILAGES of
LOWER 6 RIBS,
MED. and LAT.
TENDINOUS
ARCHES, (TWO
CRURA) RIGHT
CRUS to BODIES
of 1,2,3 L.VER~
TEBRAE, LEFT
CRUS to BODIES of
1,2 L.VERTEBRAE

Quadratus lumborum

CENTRAL   Psoas major
TENDON   Psoas minor

Figure 12.31 Diaphragm and intercostal muscles.

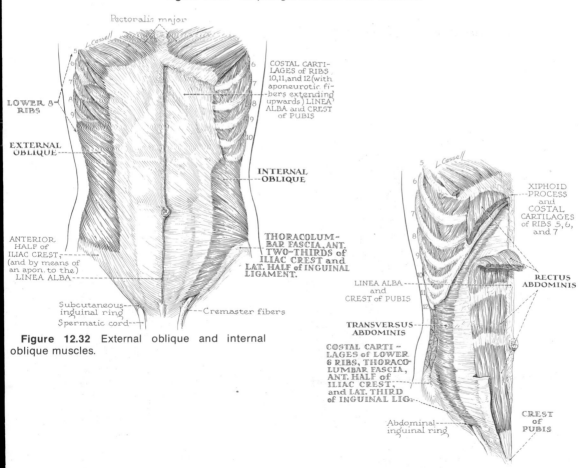

Pectoralis major

COSTAL CARTI-
LAGES of RIBS
10,11, and 12 (with
aponeurotic fi-
bers extending
upwards) LINEA
ALBA and CREST
of PUBIS

LOWER 8
RIBS

EXTERNAL
OBLIQUE

INTERNAL
OBLIQUE

ANTERIOR
HALF of
ILIAC CREST,
(and by means of
an apon. to the)
LINEA ALBA

THORACOLUM-
BAR FASCIA, ANT.
TWO-THIRDS of
ILIAC CREST and
LAT. HALF of INGUINAL
LIGAMENT.

Subcutaneous
inguinal ring
Spermatic cord

Cremaster fibers

Figure 12.32 External oblique and internal
oblique muscles.

XIPHOID
PROCESS
and
COSTAL
CARTILAGES
of RIBS 5, 6,
and 7

LINEA ALBA
and
CREST of PUBIS

RECTUS
ABDOMINIS

TRANSVERSUS
ABDOMINIS

COSTAL CARTI~
LAGES of LOWER
6 RIBS, THORACO-
LUMBAR FASCIA,
ANT. HALF of
ILIAC CREST,
and LAT. THIRD
of INGUINAL LIG.

Abdominal
inguinal ring

CREST
of
PUBIS

Figure 12.33 Transversus abdominis and rectus
abdominis muscles.

MUSCLES THAT MOVE THE FEMUR

Iliopsoas (Figs. 12.34, 12.35, 12.39)	Two divisions: Iliacus—iliac fossa Psoas major—sides of bodies and transverse processes of lumbar ver-brae	Lesser trochanter of femur	Flexes femur Flexes vertebral column (p. 208)
Gluteus maximus (Figs. 12.34, 12.36, 12.37, 12.39)	Ilium between crest and pos-terior gluteal line, sides of sacrum, coccyx, sacrotu-berous ligament	Gluteal tuberosity and ilio-tibial tract	Extends femur
Gluteus minimus (Figs. 12.34, 12.37)	Outer surface of ilium be-tween anterior and inferior gluteal lines	Anterior surface of greater trochanter	Medial rotation of femur
Piriformis (Figs. 12.34, 12.38)	Anterior surface of sacrum	Superior tip of greater tro-chanter	Lateral rotation of femur

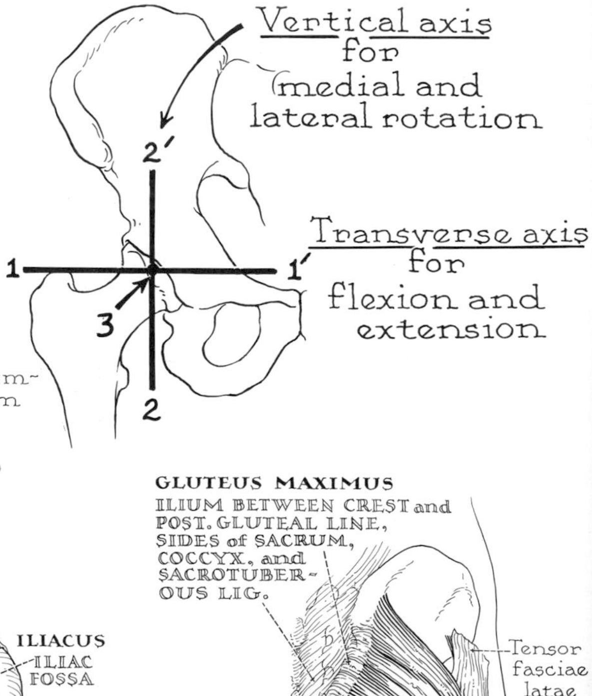

Vertical axis for medial and lateral rotation

Transverse axis for flexion and extension

Figure 12.34   Axes of movement at the hip joint.

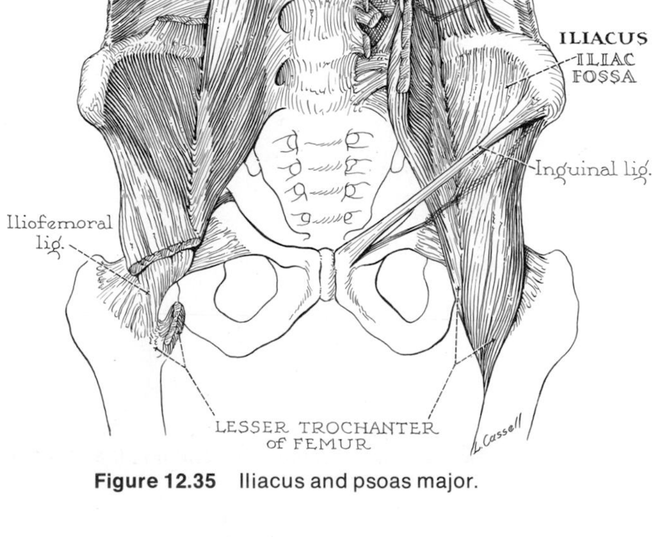

Psoas minor (cut)

PSOAS MAJOR SIDES of BODIES and TRANSV. PRO-CESSES of LUMBAR VERTE-BRAE

Quadratus lum-borum

ILIACUS ILIAC FOSSA

Inguinal lig.

Iliofemoral lig.

LESSER TROCHANTER of FEMUR

L. Cassell

Figure 12.35   Iliacus and psoas major.

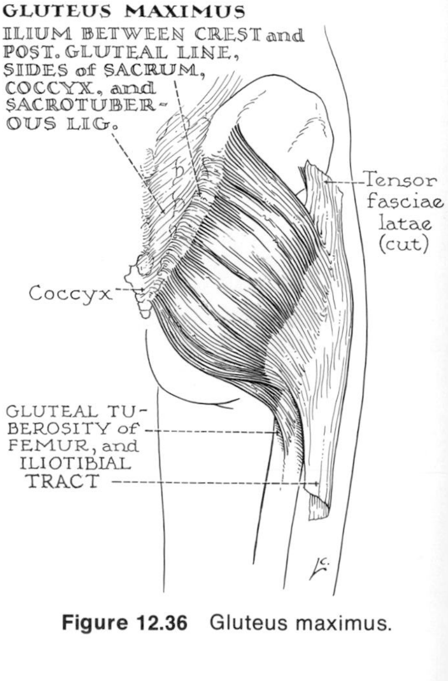

GLUTEUS MAXIMUS ILIUM BETWEEN CREST and POST. GLUTEAL LINE, SIDES of SACRUM, COCCYX, and SACROTUBER-OUS LIG.

Tensor fasciae latae (cut)

Coccyx

GLUTEAL TU-BEROSITY of FEMUR, and ILIOTIBIAL TRACT

Figure 12.36   Gluteus maximus.

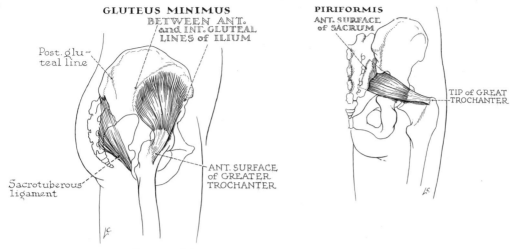

Figure 12.37 Gluteus minimus.

Figure 12.38 Piriformis.

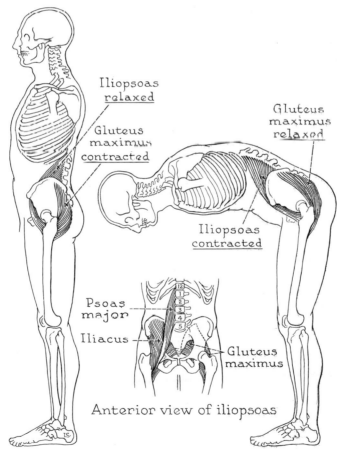

Figure 12.39 Diagram showing action of iliopsoas and gluteus maximus with femurs fixed.

MUSCLES THAT MOVE THE FEMUR (Continued)

Adductor brevis (Figs. 12.40, 12.41)	Inferior ramus of pubis	Upper third of linea aspera	Adducts femur
Adductor longus (Figs. 12.40, 12.41)	Pubis near symphysis	Middle third of linea aspera	Adducts femur
Adductor magnus (Fig. 12.40, 12.42)	Tuberosity and ramus of ischium	Linea aspera, adductor tubercle	Adducts femur
Gluteus medius (Figs. 12.40, 12.42)	Outer surface of ilium between anterior and posterior gluteal lines	Lateral surface of greater trochanter	Abducts femur
Tensor fasciae latae (Figs. 12.40, 12.43, 12.44)	Anterior part of iliac crest	Iliotibial tract	Assists in abduction, flexion, and medial rotation of femur

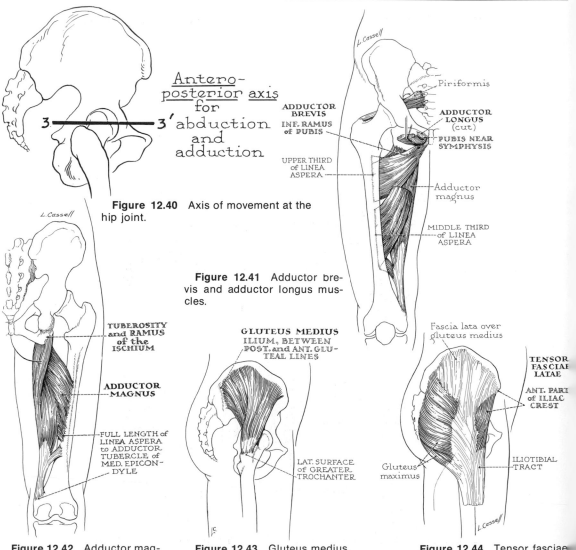

Figure 12.40 Axis of movement at the hip joint.

Figure 12.41 Adductor brevis and adductor longus muscles.

Figure 12.42 Adductor magnus.

Figure 12.43 Gluteus medius.

Figure 12.44 Tensor fasciae latae.

MUSCLES THAT MOVE THE LEG

Sartorius (Figs. 12.45, 12.46, 12.47)	Anterior superior spine of ilium	Upper end of shaft of tibia	Flexes leg; assists in abduction of femur
Gracilis (Figs. 12.45, 12.46, 12.47)	Inferior ramus of pubis	With sartorius, inner surface of tibia, just below the head	Flexes leg; assists in adduction of femur
Semitendinosus (Figs. 12.45, 12.46, 12.48)	Tuberosity of ischium	With sartorius and gracilis, upper end of shaft of tibia	Flexes leg
Semimembranosus (Figs. 12.45, 12.46, 12.48)	Tuberosity of ischium	Medial condyle of tibia	Flexes leg
Biceps femoris (Figs. 12.45, 12.46, 12.48)	Long head, tuberosity of ischium; short head, lower part of linea aspera	Upper end of fibula	Flexes leg
Gastrocnemius	(p. 225)		Assists in flexing leg
Quadriceps femoris (Figs. 12.45, 12.46, 12.49)	Four divisions: 1. Rectus femoris—anterior inferior spine of ilium, reflected tendon around margin of acetabulum 2. Vastus lateralis—lateral lip of linea aspera 3. Vastus medialis—medial lip of linea aspera 4. Vastus intermedius—anterior surface of femur	By a common tendon that encloses patella and inserts on tuberosity of tibia	Extends leg

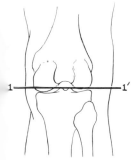

Transverse axis for flexion and extension

1 ———————— 1'

Figure 12.45 Axis of movement at the knee joint.

Figure 12.46 Diagram showing opposing action of quadriceps femoris and the flexors of the leg.

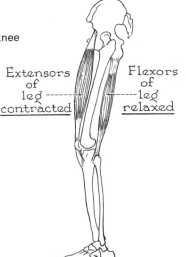

Extensors of leg contracted

Flexors of leg relaxed

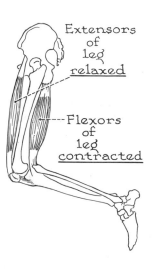

Extensors of leg relaxed

Flexors of leg contracted

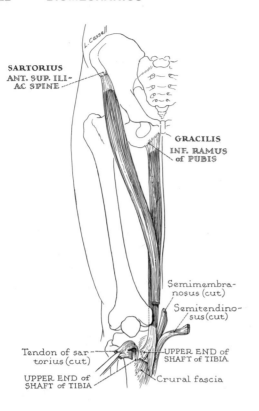

Figure 12.47 Sartorius and gracilis muscles.

Figure 12.48 Semitendinosus, semimembrano-sus, and biceps femoris.

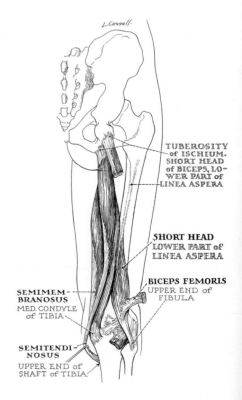

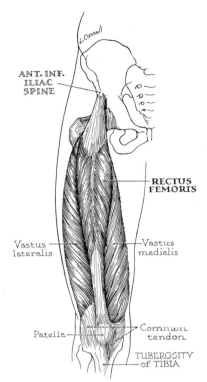

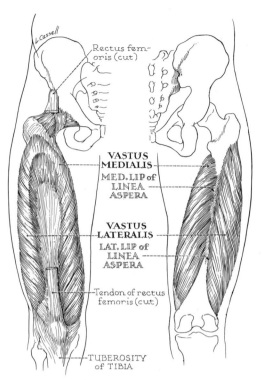

Figure 12.49A Quadriceps femoris, showing three heads of origin: vastus lateralis, vastus medialis, and rectus femoris. Origin and insertion of rectus femoris are given.

Figure 12.49B Lateral and medial heads of quadriceps femoris. Left, Anterior view. Right, Posterior view.

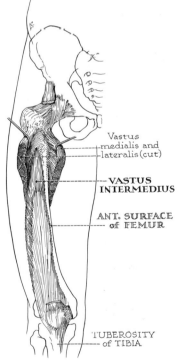

Figure 12.49C Vastus intermedius portion of quadriceps femoris.

MUSCLES ACTING ON THE FOOT

Tibialis anterior (Figs. 12.50, 12.51, 12.55)	Lateral condyle and upper two-thirds of shaft of tibia	Proximal end of first metatarsal and medial cuneiform	Flexes (dorsiflexion) and inverts foot
Peroneus tertius (Figs. 12.50, 12.52)	Anterior aspect of lower third of fibula	Base of fifth metatarsal	Flexes (dorsiflexion) and everts foot
Peroneus brevis (Figs. 12.50, 12.52)	Lower two-thirds of lateral surface of fibula, passes back of lateral malleolus	Dorsal surface, tubercle of fifth metatarsal	Extends (plantar flexion) and everts foot
Peroneus longus (Figs. 12.50, 12.53)	Lateral condyle of tibia and upper two-thirds of lateral surface of fibula	Tendon passes back of lateral malleolus, runs in groove of cuboid across sole of foot, inserted into proximal end of first metatarsal and medial cuneiform	Extends (plantar flexion) and everts foot
Gastrocnemius (Figs. 12.50, 12.54, 12.56)	Posterior supracondylar surfaces of femur	Calcaneus by means of tendo calcaneus	Extends foot (plantar flexion) assists in flexion of leg
Soleus (Figs. 12.50, 12.55, 12.56)	Head of fibula, soleal line of tibia	Calcaneus by means of tendo calcaneus	Extends foot (plantar flexion)
Tibialis posterior (Figs. 12.50, 12.57)	Interosseous membrane and adjacent surfaces of tibia and fibula	Tuberosity of navicular bone, medial cuneiform, cuboid, base of metatarsals 2, 3, 4	Extends (plantar flexion) and inverts foot
Extensor digitorum longus (Figs. 12.50, 12.58)	Lateral condyle of tibia, upper two-thirds of anterior surface of fibula and interosseous membrane	Four tendons insert on lateral four toes at metatarsal and proximal interphalangeal joints	Extends toes at metatarsal phalangeal joints; also dorsiflexion and eversion of foot
Extensor hallucis longus (Figs. 12.50, 12.58)	Middle half of anterior surface of fibula and interosseous membrane	Superior surface of base of distal phalanx of great toe	Extends the great toe and aids in dorsiflexion of foot
Flexor digitorum longus (Fig. 12.59)	Posterior surface of tibia below soleal line	Four tendons insert on the lateral distal phalanges	Flexion of toes
Flexor hallucis longus (Fig. 12.59)	Lower two-thirds of posterior surface of fibula and intermuscular septum	Inferior aspect of base of distal phalanx of great toe	Flexion of great toe

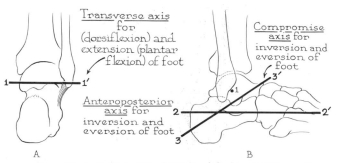

Figure 12.50 Axes of movement at the ankle joint and foot. *A*, Posterior view. *B*, Lateral view.

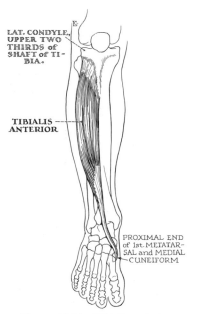

LAT. CONDYLE, UPPER TWO THIRDS of SHAFT of TIBIA.

TIBIALIS ANTERIOR

PROXIMAL END of 1st. METATARSAL and MEDIAL CUNEIFORM

Figure 12.51 Tibialis anterior.

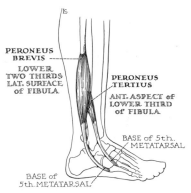

PERONEUS BREVIS

LOWER TWO THIRDS LAT. SURFACE of FIBULA

PERONEUS TERTIUS

ANT. ASPECT of LOWER THIRD of FIBULA

BASE of 5th. METATARSAL

BASE of 5th. METATARSAL

Figure 12.52 Peroneus brevis and peroneus tertius muscles.

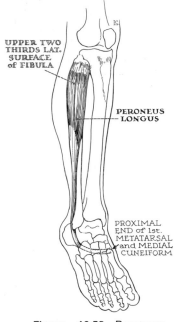

UPPER TWO THIRDS LAT. SURFACE of FIBULA

PERONEUS LONGUS

PROXIMAL END of 1st. METATARSAL and MEDIAL CUNEIFORM

Figure 12.53 Peroneus longus.

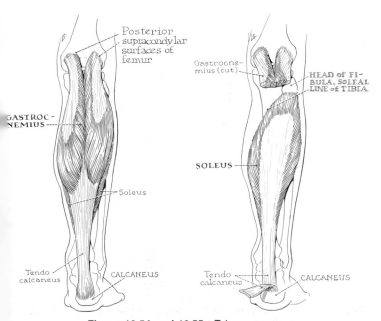

Posterior supracondylar surfaces of femur

GASTROC-NEMIUS

Soleus

Tendo calcaneus

CALCANEUS

Gastrocnemius (cut)

HEAD of FIBULA, SOLEAL LINE of TIBIA

SOLEUS

Tendo calcaneus

CALCANEUS

Figure 12.54 and 12.55 Triceps surae.

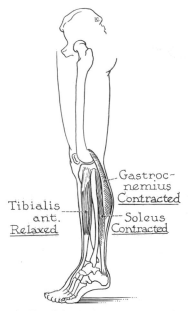

Figure 12.56 Triceps surae opposing the action of tibialis anterior.

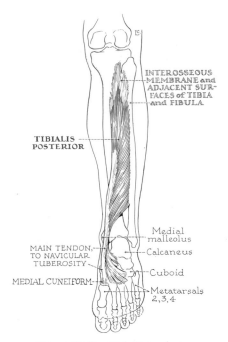

Figure 12.57 Tibialis posterior

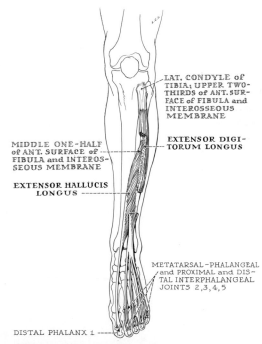

Figure 12.58 Extensor digitorum longus and extensor hallucis longus.

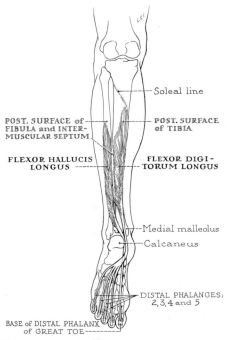

Figure 12.59 Flexor digitorum longus and flexor hallucis longus.

The muscles which move the eyeball contract rapidly, i.e., in less than 0.01 second, though muscles in the leg may require two to four times as long. Further, a limb may be moved over a considerable distance during the time it takes for a muscle to shorten; the shorter the distance between the insertion of the muscle and the joint, the greater is the extent of movement of the distal point of the extremity. Fairly precise movements over a distance of 1 to 15 inches can be carried out with the hand moving at an average speed of 2 to 3 feet per second; a maximum speed of about 4½ feet per second may be attained momentarily in a movement of this type. Even higher rates may occur in less precise movements.

CONTROL OF POSTURE AND MOVEMENT

Biomechanical Factors. Comparison of Figures 12.60, 12.61, and 12.62 will illustrate some of the characteristics of upright balanced stance of man. Equilibrium of the body is maintained by the biomechanical functions of the musculoskeletal system against gravitational force. The ideal erect posture (Fig. 12.62) is considered to have a line of pull of gravity through a midsagittal plane which would intersect horizontal lines projected from (1) the mastoid processes, (2) anterior to the shoulder joint, (3) at the hip joint, (4) in front of the center of the knee, and (5) anterior to the ankle joint. The center of mass of the body is (3) at the hip joint. In most individuals this stance is supported by contraction of gastrocnemius, soleus, other plantar flexor muscles of the calf of the leg, erector spinae, iliopsoas, supraspinatus, ligaments anterior to the hip, and ligaments posterior to the knee. Tendons of the powerful plantar flexors have the additional function of support to the weight-bearing arches of the foot (see p. 186). Tibialis posterior and flexor hallucis longus contribute to the longitudinal arch and peroneus longus to the transverse arch of the foot.

Skeletal muscle is characterized as having voluntary nervous control. However, the volition or will of the cerebral cortical motor control (see p. 100) dictates the direction of the movement taken in the multiplicity of postural adjustments rather than the control of an individual skeletal muscle. The skeletal muscles infrequently act alone. They are more commonly participants in *automatic patterns of movement*. Arrangement of skeletal muscles in Table 12.1 calls attention to prime movements and to groups of muscles whose position and attachments upon the skeleton give them mechanical advantage in executing a particular motion in relation to a pattern of movement. It can be observed from the table that a group of *antagonistic muscles* must undergo a corresponding degree of relaxation in order that a group of *synergistic muscles* of *agonists* can carry out their movement in an efficient manner. Some of the complex forms of posture require fixation of a joint by action of antagonistic muscle groups for synergists to be effective. For example, *fixation* of the scapula by simultaneous contraction of trapezius and serratus anterior allows a strong abduction of the arm by the deltoid and the supraspinatus. Fixation of the knee by quadriceps femoris and the flexor group assists in the flexion of the lower extremities upon the hip by iliopsoas such as in kicking a ball.

Associated actions of the musculoskeletal system are readily appreciated. In looking backward one is aware of the lateral flexion of the head. This movement is associated with adjustments of the eyes and fixation of the trunk and the extremities. The large variety of facial expression utilizes patterned activity for rapt attention, joy, and despair. An alternating coordination of activity of temporalis, masseter, and medial pterygoid on one side of the mandible and lateral pterygoid on the opposing side of the mandible is associated with contraction of orbicularis oris, buccinator, and the tongue in voluntary chewing movements. The mobility of the ball and socket joint of the shoulder allows a wide range of associated movement for the upper extremity. The hand can be brought into position with any part of the body. Freedom of the associated movements of the thumb and fingers at widely

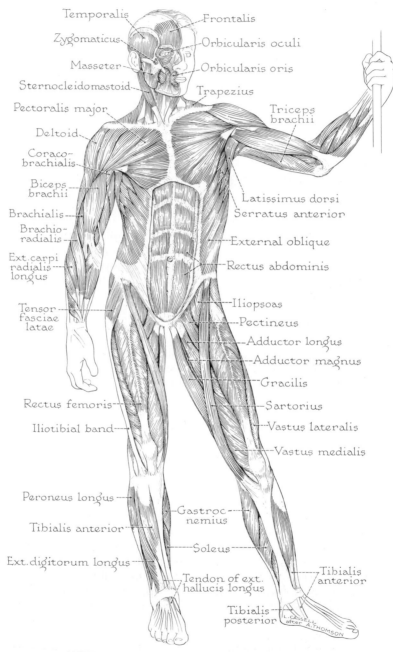

Figure 12.60 Muscles of the body, anterior view.

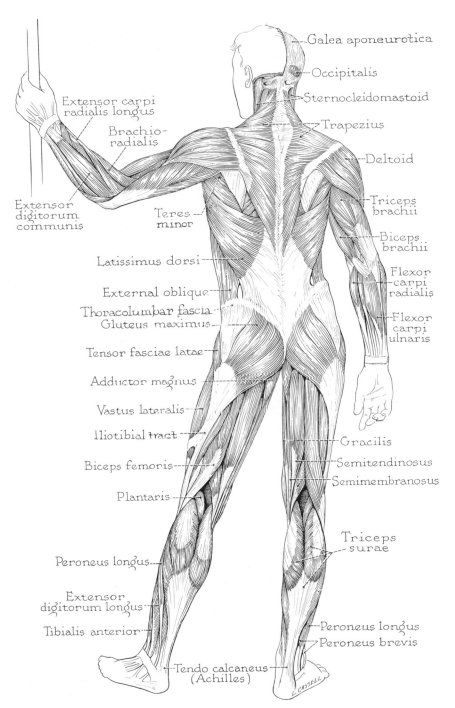

Galea aponeurotica

Occipitalis

Sternocleidomastoid

Trapezius

Deltoid

Triceps
brachii

Biceps
brachii

Flexor
carpi
radialis

Flexor
carpi
ulnaris

Extensor carpi
radialis longus

Brachio-
radialis

Extensor
digitorum
communis

Teres
minor

Latissimus dorsi

External oblique

Thoracolumbar fascia

Gluteus maximus

Tensor fasciae latae

Adductor magnus

Vastus lateralis

Iliotibial tract

Biceps femoris

Plantaris

Gracilis

Semitendinosus

Semimembranosus

Triceps
surae

Peroneus longus

Extensor
digitorum longus

Tibialis anterior

Peroneus longus

Peroneus brevis

Tendo calcaneus
(Achilles)

L. CASSELL

Figure 12.61 Muscles of the body, posterior view.

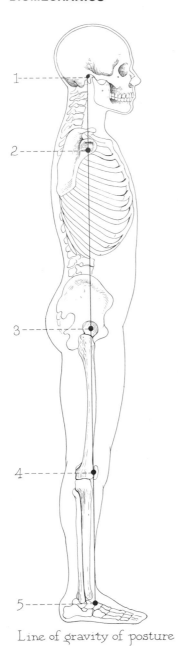

Line of gravity of posture

Figure 12.62 Diagram of ideal correct posture.

and adductors such as gluteus maximus, quadriceps femoris, gastrocnemius, adductor magnus, adductor longus, and adductor brevis are the powerful muscles in the lower extremities. Weight-bearing of the lower extremity is assisted by oscillation of the trunk by erector spinae and quadratus lumborum so it will be positioned over the center of mass toward the side supported while the flexor muscles may elevate the stepping foot.

Postural Reflexes. A number of neural reflexes functioning at centers in the spinal cord, medulla, cerebellum, midbrain, basal ganglia, and cerebrum are important in coordinating the constant adjustments in the patterns of movements that provide the postural background for voluntary activity. At levels of the nervous system above the spinal cord, motor nerve impulses are traveling extrapyramidal pathways such as rubrotegmentospinal tract, vestibulospinal tract, and reticulospinal tract (see p. 90). Voluntary motor controls, on the other hand, are mediated by nerve impulses in the pyramidal or corticospinal tracts of the spinal cord. All of these motor pathways will bring about their effect by termination near or upon anterior or ventral horn cells in the spinal cord. A portion of reticular pathways and vestibular tracts facilitates the activity of gamma efferent cells. Influence of the basal ganglia, cerebrum, and cerebellum is largely inhibitory to the gamma efferent neurons.

If a skeletal muscle with its nerve supply intact is stretched, it contracts. This is the usual response of the *stretch or myotatic reflex*. Afferent impulses from the neuromuscular spindle (Fig. 11.4) reach anterior column cells innervating the motor end plates of both extrafusal and intrafusal muscle fibers. The effect of the nerve impulse to motor units of the large muscle fibers is the observable contraction of the muscle. The effect of the gamma efferent nerve impulse to the intrafusal muscle fibers places tension upon the neuromuscular spindle and it is then in a ready state for additional stimulation by stretch of the muscle.

Muscle tone is the degree of resistance of the skeletal muscle. In *hypertonic or spastic*

different strengths and precision of movement allow a grasp from one that is light and delicate to a grasp that is heavy and firm. The musculature of the lower extremity provides a versatile combination of actions in the support of one side of the body while the opposing side advances in walking, running, and climbing. Extensors muscles this tone has been elevated substantially by extrapyramidal facilitation of the gamma efferent neuronal discharge. The opposite prevails in *hypotonic or flaccid* muscles where very little influence of gamma efferent discharge is present when there has been extrapyramidal inhibition of these neurons.

At the time a stretch reflex activates the agonist muscle *reciprocal innervation* inhibits contraction in the antagonist muscle. Such a reflex arrangement allows for the coordination of synergistic muscles in a particular pattern of movement.

Protection of a contrasting muscle is provided by the *inverse myotatic reflex*. As stretch of the muscle increases very markedly, the Golgi tendon organ (Fig. 11.4) discharges a nerve impulse into the spinal cord reflex. The effect of this reflex is observed in relaxation of the muscle, which thereby reduces the excessive pull upon its tendon through inhibition of the motor nerve supply to the muscle. In this reflex, stretch has brought about the reverse effect, or relaxation of the muscle, to that seen by activation of the neuromuscular spindle.

QUESTIONS FOR DISCUSSION

1. Consider the difference in heights of heels of different shoes. What effects might these have upon posture and the muscles which stabilize posture?

2. Under what conditions might muscular hypotonicity and hypertonicity occur?

3. Examine the body position in supine posture, sitting, and walking. Describe the patterns and associated movements involved, joint axes utilized, and synergistic muscles producing the movements.

4. Compare a muscular response elicited by tapping the patellar tendon to that obtained by touching a hot stove.

UNIT 4

EXCHANGE AND TRANSPORT

13. RESPIRATION 14. CIRCULATING BODY FLUIDS 15. CIRCULATION 16. MAINTENANCE AND REGULATION OF BLOOD PRESSURE 17. CONSTANCY IN COMPOSITION OF BODY FLUIDS

In unicellular forms such as the ameba, the physiochemical structure in the organism is maintained within the limits necessary for life by direct exchange with an external fluid environment. Constancy in the cells of man is maintained by exchange between the cells and the fluids that surround and bathe the tissues, and so constitute an internal, rather than an external, liquid environment. So effective are the mechanisms of homeostasis that serve to maintain the physiological range of constancy that man can enjoy the freedom of living under a wide variety of conditions involving extremes of environmental temperature, levels and types of activity, and differences in the chemical composition of ingested substances. Claude Bernard, a great physiologist of the last century, pointed out that freedom and independence of existence is possible only because of the liquid environment or "milieu interieur," i.e., the interstitial fluid, which "is diffused through the tissues and forms the ensemble of intercellular liquids, and is the basis of all local nutrition and the common factor of all elementary exchanges." It is the purpose of this unit to provide some understanding of how each of the various mechanisms of respiration, circulation, and excretion contributes to the continual readjustments or reactions preserving the constant physiochemical conditions necessary for life.

RESPIRATION

**CHAPTER
THIRTEEN**

CHARACTERISTICS OF RESPIRATION

Respiration involves the exchange of gases at two sites. The exchange across the respiratory membrane of the lungs with the blood in the capillaries of the pulmonary circulation is known as *external respiration*. Diffusion of gases between the blood of systemic capillaries and cells of the body is called *internal respiration*. The respiratory and cardiovascular systems working together provide a continuous supply of arterialized blood, high in oxygen and low in carbon dioxide content. The two systems are capable of wide variation in their responses so that the supply of arterialized blood is closely adjusted to the level of bodily activity.

It is common knowledge that we are only rarely conscious of breathing, which continues rhythmically without voluntary effort on our part. We have, however, some voluntary control of this vital process, for we can hold our breath for a limited time; we can increase this time by first breathing deeply and rapidly. We can interrupt the outflow of air in speaking, singing, and whistling. If we perform work we breathe more deeply and more rapidly.

If we take a breath of smoke or irritating gas we involuntarily stop inhaling and then exhale or cough or sneeze. These accessory functions of coughing and sneezing protect the body by propulsively eliminating irritating foreign materials from the respiratory tract. Talking, which makes possible the communication of ideas and wishes, is also an accessory function of respiration. Finally, the sensation of smell is dependent upon the respiratory system (see pp. 112, 113).

ARCHITECTURE OF THE RESPIRATORY SYSTEM

Air-Conducting Passageways (Figs. 13.1-13.8). The system of passageways that conduct air to the respiratory membrane of the lung is made up of the nasal cavity, the pharynx, the larynx, and the trachea and bronchi. Sensory receptors throughout this duct system can initiate the protective reflexes, which include coughing, sneezing, swallowing, bronchial constriction, slowing of the heart, and cessation of respiration. The type of mucosa found in the *upper respiratory tract* (passageways up to their point of entrance into the lung) is very well adapted for air conditioning. The air which reaches the primary bronchi has been warmed or cooled to body temperature, humidified, and filtered. Foreign particles from 10 to 0.3 microns in size are trapped in the sheet of mucus found in the lumen of the ducts and moved by the cilia in a continuous upward escalation. The work necessary to provide an exchange of air in the air-conditioning passages is supplied by the contraction of the muscles of respiration, principally those related to the thorax.

THE NASAL CAVITY. The bony structures forming the walls of the nasal cavity, together with the paranasal sinuses, have been described in Chapters 8 and 10. The cavity is divided into right and left nasal fossae by a central partition, the septum (Fig. 13.1). The anterior openings of the fossae are the nostrils or nares; the posterior openings into the nasal pharynx are the choanae. Each fossa may be divided into a vestibule, lying just inside the nostrils, the spheno-ethmoidal recess lying above the superior nasal concha, and the superior, middle, and inferior meatuses, lying underneath the superior, middle, and inferior concha, respectively (Fig. 13.2).

The entire fossa and paranasal sinuses are lined with mucous membrane richly supplied with blood vessels. The epithelial lining of the mucosa is highly specialized, being composed of pseudostratified ciliated columnar epithelium in which goblet cells are richly interspersed. The endings of the olfactory and trigeminal nerves lie in the mucosa of the nasal fossae and communicating sinuses (see pp. 112, 114).

As air enters into the fossae, the fine hairs at the nares screen out the grosser particles of foreign matter. As it passes over the membrane, the air is warmed and takes up moisture from the mucus secreted by the goblet cells. The ciliary activity of the epithelium removes the finer dust particles.

The nasal cavity assists in phonation, acting as a resonator for the voice. Olfaction has been discussed in Chapter 8.

THE PHARYNX (Fig. 13.2). The pharynx is a musculomembranous tube extending from the base of the skull above to

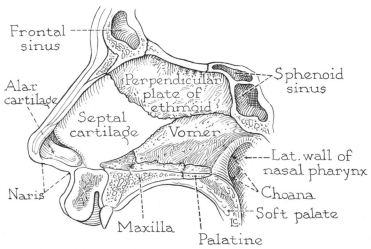

Figure 13.1 The nasal septum from the left side. (Redrawn from Spalteholz.)

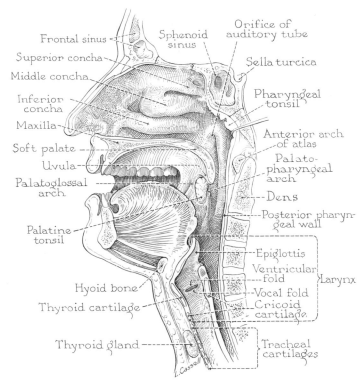

Figure 13.2 Sagittal section through mouth, larynx, pharynx, and nasal cavity.

the esophagus below. The posterior wall rests against the bodies of the cervical vertebrae. The lateral wall has openings communicating with the middle ear, while the anterior wall has openings through which connection is established with the nose, the mouth and the larynx. The pharynx is divided accordingly into three parts: nasal pharynx, oral pharynx, and laryngeal pharynx.

The soft palate separates the nasal pharynx from the oral pharynx. It is a pliable sheet, containing muscle and covered with mucous membrane, which is attached to the bone of the hard palate. On either side it is prolonged downward in the two arches of the fauces. Of these arches, the anterior palatoglossal arch passes to the side of the tongue, and the posterior palatopharyngeal arch passes to the posterior pharyngeal wall. Between the two arches on either side are the palatine tonsils. Posteriorly, the soft palate has a median prolongation, the uvula. Soft palate, palatine tonsils, and palatine arches are shown in Figure 13.3.

The *nasal pharynx* is that part of the pharynx lying behind the choanae and above the soft palate. On each lateral wall is the opening of the *auditory tube*, which connects with the cavity of the middle ear. The mucosa of the roof and posterior wall of the nasal pharynx contains much lymphoid tissue, which constitutes the pharyngeal tonsil or adenoids.

The *oral pharynx* extends from the soft palate above to the level of the hyoid bone below. It opens into the mouth at the palatoglossal arch.

The *laryngeal pharynx* lies posterior to the larynx and below the level of the hyoid bone, extending to the cricoid cartilage of the larynx opposite the sixth cervical vertebra. It communicates anteriorly with the larynx and posteriorly with the esophagus.

The oral and laryngeal portions of the pharynx belong both to the respiratory and digestive tracts. The swallowing reflex which is initiated in this region of the pharynx does not operate in an unconscious person. These two tracts cross each

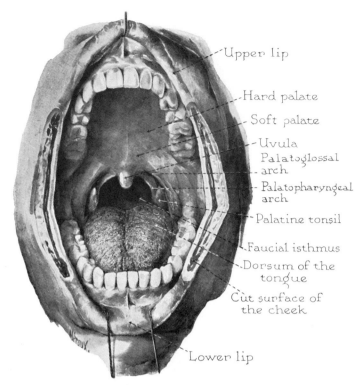

Upper lip

Hard palate

Soft palate

Uvula

Palatoglossal arch

Palatopharyngeal arch

Palatine tonsil

Faucial isthmus

Dorsum of the tongue

Cut surface of the cheek

Lower lip

Figure 13.3   The mouth cavity. (Modified from Spalteholz.)

other in the oral pharynx, so that the respiratory is anterior below this point (Fig. 13.2). The nasal pharynx is lined with "respiratory epithelium" like that in the nose; the oral and laryngeal portions are lined with stratified squamous epithelium. The principal muscles of the pharynx are three constrictor muscles overlapping each other from inferior to middle to superior. Separation of the respiratory and alimentary passages in swallowing is brought about by contraction of these muscles.

THE LARYNX.   The larynx is placed between the trachea and the root of the tongue (Fig. 13.2). It forms a prominence in the midline of the neck anteriorly, where it lies close to the surface, covered only by skin and fascia. The cartilages that form the supporting framework are the thyroid, the cricoid, the epiglottis, and the paired arytenoid corniculate and cuneiform cartilages. The *thyroid* (Fig. 13.4) is the largest cartilage of the larynx; it is

made of two laminae fused together at an angle to form a shield-shaped structure, the laryngeal prominence or "Adam's apple." This is considered larger with a sharper angle of laminar fusion in the male than in the female. The *cricoid cartilage* is below the thyroid and forms the lower limit of the larynx. It is shaped like a signet ring; the wide portion is placed at the back, and attached to its upper border are the two *arytenoid* cartilages that resemble small pyramids.

Two piriform fossae are formed at the lateral sides of the larynx by the junction of mucosa from the arytenoid and thyroid cartilages with the wall of the laryngeal pharynx. A median and anterior recess, the *vallecula*, occurs as membranes of the pharynx and epiglottis are fused. Foreign bodies aspirated into the air-conducting passages of the respiratory tract may lodge at either location (Fig. 13.5).

The *epiglottis* is a leaf-shaped elastic cartilage; the stem is attached to the thy-

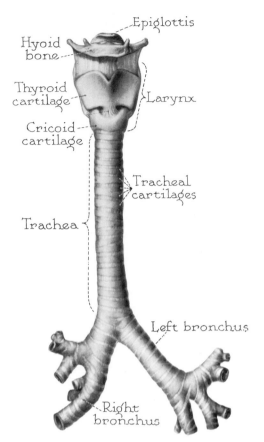

Figure 13.4 The hyoid bone, the larynx, the trachea, and its principal branches from in front. (From Sobotta and McMurrich.)

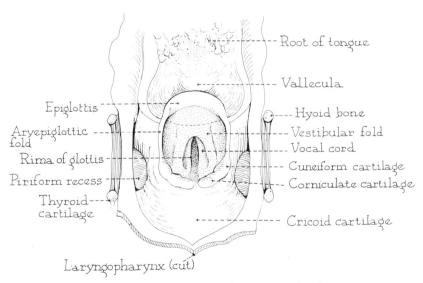

Figure 13.5 Larynx shown from a posterior view.

roid cartilage at the junction of the two laminae. It projects upward behind the root of the tongue anterior to the opening of the larynx. *Corniculate* and *cuneiform* cartilages are found as small nodules in the aryepiglottic folds between arytenoid cartilages and epiglottis.

The cartilages of the larynx are connected by ligaments. Epithelium of the mucosa lining the larynx is mainly of the respiratory type. Laryngeal mucosa is very sensitive to contact with foreign materials. This contact initiates the cough reflex or even cessation of respiration. In an unconscious person these reflexes are depressed or absent.

Extrinsic muscles of the larynx depress or elevate the larynx as a whole. The two synovial joints of the larynx are *cricothyroid* and *cricoarytenoid*. The elastic ligaments in these articulations, along with the small intrinsic laryngeal muscles, operate in the course of respiration, speech, and swallowing. Intrinsic muscles may close or open the laryngeal inlet, the rima of the glottis, by pulling the arytenoid cartilages toward the epiglottis. The adductor intrinsic muscles close the rima of the glottis by drawing the arytenoid cartilates together. Lateral rotation of the arytenoid cartilages by the abductors opens the rima. Tensors of the vocal folds are cricothyroid muscles and relaxors of the vocal cords are thyroarytenoid muscles.

The details of the voice mechanism are not completely known. Production of speech sounds is brought about by the vibration of expired air into sound waves in the vocal portion of the respiratory tract. The parts which are most concerned include mouth cavity, tongue, teeth, palates, nasal cavities, pharynx, and larynx. A range and pitch of vocal sounds is achieved principally by the variations in length, thickness, or tension of the vocal folds. Volume is regulated by size and duration of the opening between the vocal folds or the *rima glottidis* (Fig. 13.4). The selection of overtones for resonation of the voice occurs essentially in pharyngeal, oral, and nasal cavities. The neurologic processes which are requisite to speech are described in Chapter 7.

THE TRACHEA (Fig. 13.4). The trachea is a cylindrical tube about 11 cm. long and 2.5 cm. wide inclined slightly toward the right side. It begins at the lower end of cricoid cartilage and, passing into the thorax, terminates by dividing into right and left bronchi at the level of the junction between the manubrium and body of the sternum. The trachea is composed of a fibroelastic membrane in which hyaline cartilaginous rings, sixteen to twenty in number, are embedded. The cartilage gives firmness to the walls and prevents their collapse. The rings are deficient behind, and the interval is filled in with smooth muscle and fibroelastic connective tissue. Pseudostratified ciliated columnar epithelium with numerous goblet cells forms the surface of the mucosa and rests upon thick basement lamina. An abundance of mucoserous glands is found in the underlying connective tissue with ducts leading to the surface of the mucosa. The relationships of the trachea to the thyroid gland and great blood vessels of the neck are shown elsewhere (pp. 145 and 282).

THE BRONCHI AND THE BRONCHIAL TREE. The principal bronchi (Fig. 13.4) are the two tubes into which the trachea divides. The right is shorter, wider, and more nearly vertical in direction than is the left. The structure of the main bronchi is the same as that of the trachea, except that the cartilaginous rings are complete. On entering the lungs, the principal bronchi divide into a number of branches, lobar bronchi (Fig. 13.6). The right lobar bronchi include the superior lobe bronchus, the middle lobe bronchus, and the inferior lobe bronchus, which enter their respective lobes in the right lung. Superior and inferior lobe bronchi enter comparable lobes or portions of the left lung. In a similar manner, the segmental bronchi resulting from the division of lobar bronchi enter segmental portions of each lobe of the right and left lungs (Fig. 13.6).

The successive divisions of the bronchial tree include right and left primary bronchi; three right and two left secondary bronchi; ten right segmental bronchi and eight left bronchi; fifty to eighty terminal bronchioles in each segment; two or more respiratory bronchioles for each terminal bronchiole; two or more alveolar ducts for each respiratory bronchiole; several

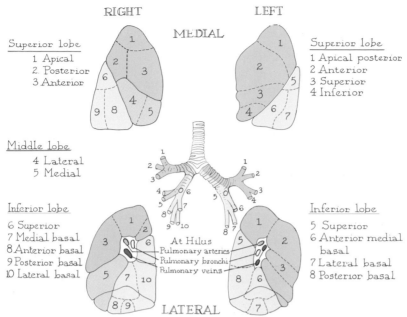

RIGHT   MEDIAL   LEFT

Superior lobe
1 Apical
2 Posterior
3 Anterior

Superior lobe
1 Apical posterior
2 Anterior
3 Superior
4 Inferior

Middle lobe
4 Lateral
5 Medial

Inferior lobe
6 Superior
7 Medial basal
8 Anterior basal
9 Posterior basal
10 Lateral basal

At Hilus
Pulmonary arteries
Pulmonary bronchi
Pulmonary veins

Inferior lobe
5 Superior
6 Anterior medial basal
7 Lateral basal
8 Posterior basal

LATERAL

Figure 13.6 Diagram of bronchopulmonary segments. (Modified from Huber.)

alveolar sacs and alveoli for each alveolar duct.

The structure of primary and secondary bronchi is similar to that of the trachea. Intrapulmonary bronchi and their branches to those bronchioles of about 1 mm. in diameter are cylindrical with irregularly distributed hyaline cartilage plates embedded in a complete layer of elastic connective tissue encircling the tube. Mucosa lining the intrapulmonary bronchial branches contains pseudostratified ciliated columnar epithelium, a prominent basement membrane, and fibroelastic connective tissue. Between the mucosa and outer bronchial wall is an interlacing myoelastic feltwork of smooth muscle and connective tissue penetrated by a rich network of blood vessels.

The Lungs. The lungs are cone-shaped organs that lie in the pleural cavities of the thorax (Fig. 13.7). The base of each lung lies in contact with the upper surface of the diaphragm, extending to the level of the seventh rib anteriorly and the eleventh rib posteriorly. The apices reach a little over an inch above the level of the clavicles.

The right and left pleural cavities are formed by two serous sacs into which the lungs are invaginated. The visceral pleura covers the surface of the lung and is reflected from the root of each lung onto the inner surface of the chest wall, the diaphragm and the lateral aspect of the mediastinum, to form the parietal pleura. The two layers of pleura are separated by only a thin layer of fluid about 0.02 mm. thick. Under normal conditions the layers are so closely in apposition that the space between them is potential rather than real.

The interpleural space between the two lungs is called the *mediastinum*. It extends from the sternum in front to the thoracic vertebrae behind, and from the thoracic inlet above to the diaphragm below. It contains the heart, the great vessels and some of their proximal branches, the thymus gland, the esophagus, the phrenic, vagal and sympathetic nerves, a portion of the trachea, and the principal bronchi. Anteriorly, the borders of the lungs reach nearly to the midline from the level of the second to the fourth costal cartilages, where they turn laterally, making room for the heart. The posterior borders, which are rounded and less well defined, extend almost vertically from the level of the

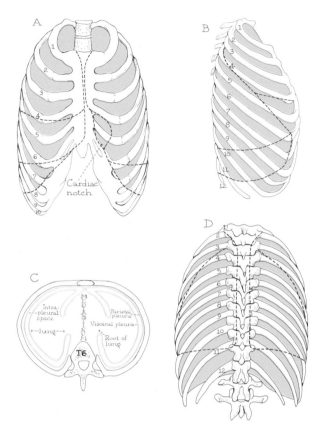

Figure 13.7 Relation of pleural cavities to thorax and mediastinum.

second rib to the base. The notch for the heart is not apparent in the posterior view.

On the medial surface of each lung (Fig. 13.6) is a vertical slit, the hilus, where structures enter and leave the lung. These structures, blood vessels, nerves, bronchi, and lymphatics, taken together, constitute the root of the lung (Figs. 13.6, 13.7).

The right lung, which is larger than the left, is divided by two interlobar fissures into superior, middle, and inferior lobes. The left lung is divided into a superior and an inferior lobe; the superior lobe is marked by the cardiac notch.

Additional units of the lung are recognized as associated with the segmental bronchi. Their delicate fibroelastic connective tissue boundaries can be demonstrated by dissection. These *bronchopulmonary segments* are named in Figure 13.6.

Structures beyond the terminal bronchioles are respiratory in function; that is, gaseous exchange between blood and air occurs here. The microscopic group of structures that consists of the respiratory bronchiole, alveolar ducts, alveolar sacs, and alveoli together with associated blood vessels, nerves, and lymphatics is the functional unit of the lung (Fig. 13.8).

Epithelium in the respiratory bronchiole shifts from ciliated columnar without goblet cells to cuboidal cells. The walls of respiratory bronchioles have no cartilage and are formed by collagenous fibers interwoven with smooth muscle and elastic fibers. Alveoli bud off the sides of respiratory bronchioles. The respiratory membrane through which the gas exchange of external respiration occurs is present beyond this point in the alveolar ducts, alveolar sacs, and alveoli. Three types of cells are found in the membrane on the side of the air-conducting passages. These cells rest upon a continuous basement lamina adjacent to capillary endothelium (Fig. 13.9). Thin squamous cells predominate as *small alveolar cells*; numerous cuboidal *large alveolar cells* contain a multilaminar cell inclusion of phospholipid which has been implicated as the precur-

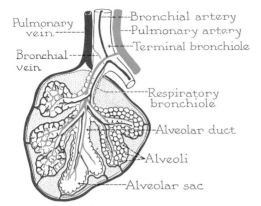

Figure 13.8 Structure of a lobule of the lung. (Modified from Spalteholz.)

sor of *surfactant* material (Fig. 13.10). The least numerous cells are *alveolar phagocytes* (dust cells). A delicate framework of elastic fibers holds the respiratory membrane in close proximity to freely anastomotic capillaries so that most of the capillary surface is available for gas exchange.

The lung surfactant acts as if it were an elastic tissue. As the diameter of the alveoli increases, the film increases surface tension. When the pressure within the alveoli decreases as the lung empties, the surfactant lowers surface tension to extremely low levels and thus aids in maintaining alveolar stability, i.e., protecting against collapse of the alveoli.

MECHANICS OF EXTERNAL RESPIRATION

While the respiratory membrane is in free communication with the outside air through the conducting passageways, the

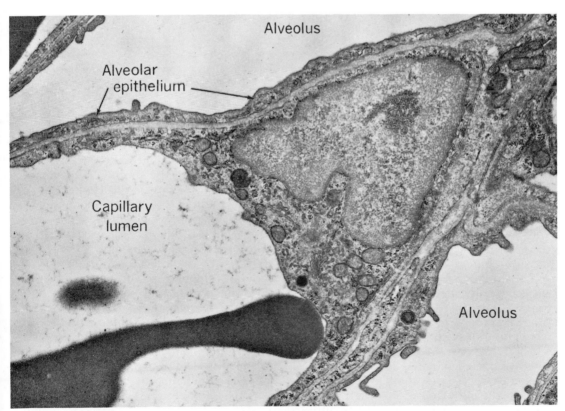

Figure 13.9 Electron micrograph of part of a capillary and adjacent alveoli, illustrating *(upper left)* the nature of the alveolocapillary membrane or blood-air barrier, which consists of three layers: the alveolar epithelium, an interstitial space occupied by a basement lamina, and the capillary endothelium. × 20,500. (Courtesy of E. R. Weibel. In Bloom and Fawcett: A Textbook of Histology, 9th ed., 1968.)

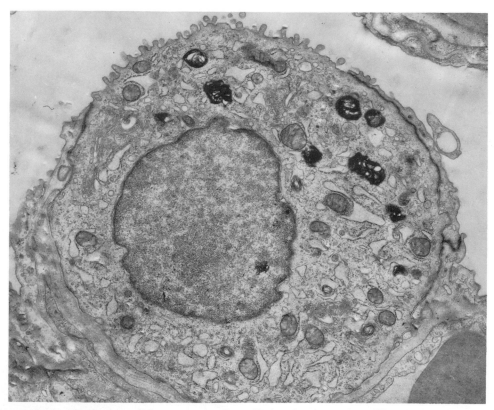

Figure 13.10 An alveolar cell from opossum lung. Notice the short microvilli on its free surface and its junctional complexes with the thin alveolar epithelial cells that partially cover its sides. A Golgi complex and numerous dilated cisternae of granular endoplasmic reticulum can be seen in its cytoplasm. (After S. Sorokin, J. Histochem. & Cytochem., *14*:834, 1966. In Bloom and Fawcett: A Textbook of Histology, 9th Ed., 1968.)

interchange of gases by diffusion alone is too slow a process to meet the bodily requirements of oxygen supply and carbon dioxide excretion. The exchange of gases is accelerated by the respiratory movements. The alternate inspiratory and expiratory phases of breathing replenish the oxygen and reduce the carbon dioxide content of the air in the alveoli.

The thorax constitutes a completely closed compartment surrounding the lungs, while the air passageways of the lungs communicate with the atmosphere. Both the thorax and lungs contain tissues which have elastic properties. These tissues are stretched by the action of respiratory muscles as the chest volume is increased during inspiration. The potential energy stored in the elastic tissues during inspiration acts to reduce chest volume during expiration. As the volumes of the thorax and lungs are increased, the pres-

sure within the lungs is decreased below that of the atmosphere and air flows into the lungs. When the volumes are reduced, the direction of flow is reversed.

The volume changes in the lung-thoracic cage system are associated with pressure changes. The pressure changes can also be related to air flow. There are static and dynamic measurements describing the pressure-volume-air flow relations in health and disease. The static measure, *compliance*, relates pressure and volume during breath-holding (or zero air flow) at different depths of inspiration. The usual units of measure are liters and centimeters of H_2O pressure, i.e., L./cm. H_2O. The dynamic measure, *resistance*, relates pressure change to air flow, i.e., cm. H_2O/L./sec.

A normal value for pulmonary compliance is 0.1 L./cm. H_2O when related to lung volume at the resting respiratory level.

Abnormal values may result from such conditions as changes in the tissues of the lungs and thorax, pulmonary edema, emphysema, and alteration in the surfactant lining of the pulmonary alveoli.

Thus far we have been considering the lung-thoracic cage system as a unit in discussing the effect of volume changes on transairway pressure differences and direction of air flow. Let us now consider how the force of contraction of the respiratory muscles acting on the chest wall is transmitted to the lungs so as to increase their volume and reduce pressure within the alveoli. The lungs with their pleural coverings are in apposition to the chest wall at all times. The 0.02 mm. layer of fluid between the two layers of pleura "links" the lungs to the chest wall. The force of the respiratory muscles is transmitted to the lungs through the linkage and the lung volume is increased as the chest volume is increased. At the same time this mechanism permits the lungs (lower lobes) to glide over the parietal pleura lining the inside of the chest (Fig. 13.7).

A simple experiment will serve to illustrate this type of linkage. Place a drop of water on a clean glass microscope slide, cover it with a second slide and press them together. The thin layer of water will hold the two slides firmly together, so that considerable force will be required to separate them, yet they can easily be moved back and forth over one another.

Acquaintance with the terminology used to describe pressure differences and pressures at various locations within the respiratory system is helpful in understanding the mechanisms of breathing.

Pressures:

Atmospheric	Outside pressure; standard atmosphere is 760 mm. Hg
Intrapleural	Within the potential pleural cavity between the parietal and visceral pleura
Intrathoracic	
Intrapulmonary	Within the lung, or specifically, within the alveoli
Alveolar	

Pressure differences:

Transthoracic	Between exterior of body and intrapulmonary pressure
Transpulmonary	Between intrapleural and intrapulmonary pressure
Transairway	Between mouth (atmospheric) and alveolar pressure

The pressure between the two layers of pleura is below atmospheric pressure (760 mm. of mercury), at all times in the adult. This can be more readily grasped by considering the relations of the lungs to the thoracic cavity at birth and during the initial period of growth. Before birth the lungs are collapsed, as are the alveoli and bronchial walls. The thoracic cavity is completely filled by the collapsed lungs, so that the pressure within the potential pleural cavity is equal to atmospheric pressure. When the thoracic cavity is enlarged during the first inspiration, the intrathoracic or intrapleural pressure decreases, the greater atmospheric pressure expands the collapsed conducting passageways, and air is brought into contact with the respiratory membrane. After having once expanded, the alveoli continue to retain some air even during expiration. Since the lungs are elastic structures, expansion is "resisted" by the tendency to return to the initial size and shape. After initial expansion of the thorax the elastic recoil is, however, limited by the fluid "linkage" between the pleurae. In the newborn, the intrapleural pressure is equal to atmospheric pressure at the end of expiration. During inspiration, when the elastic tissues of the lungs are stretched, the intrapleural pressure is about 755 mm. of mercury, or about 5 mm. less than atmospheric. As growth occurs and the thoracic content is decreased by the shrinking of the thymus gland and rapid growth of the chest, the volume of the thorax becomes progressively greater than that of the lungs. As a consequence, there is a progressive decrease in the intrapleural pressure that operates to stretch the lungs so that they continue to fill the thoracic cavity. In adults intrathoracic pressure during inspiration is between 4.5 and 9 mm. Hg below atmospheric pressure; during expiration it becomes 3 to 6 mm. Hg below the pressure of the outside air. Intrathoracic pressures are spoken of as negative pressures since they are always compared with atmospheric pressure; the values given above may be written as "−4.5 to −9 mm. Hg" during inspiration and "−3 to −6 mm. Hg" during expiration.

Inspiration. The size of the thorax is increased in all its diameters by the contraction of the muscles of respiration (Figs. 12.29 to 12.33). When the diaphragm contracts, it descends and increases the vertical diameter (Fig. 13.11). Contraction of the external intercostal muscles elevates the anterior extremities of the ribs so that they attain a more nearly horizontal position and the sternum becomes tilted about its upper articulation. This increases the anteroposterior diameter of the thorax. In addition, the lower ribs, whose axes are directed downward and outward, move outward as they are elevated. This, together with the eversion of the ribs as they are elevated, results in an increase in the lateral diameters of the thorax. The increase in the thoracic volume decreases the intrapulmonary pressure, so that atmospheric pressure causes air to enter the lungs and distend the alveoli until intrapulmonary pressure reaches that of the outside air.

Expiration. On relaxation of the diaphragm and the accessory inspiratory muscles the thoracic volume is decreased. This is accomplished by the rebound of the costal cartilages that have been placed under tension during inspiration, the return of the somewhat stretched abdominal wall

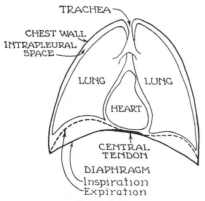

Figure 13.11 Relative position of diaphragm at end of normal inspiration and expiration. (From Ruch and Fulton: Medical Physiology and Biophysics. 18th ed. 1960.)

and the elastic recoil of the lungs; in addition, the force of gravity aids in restoring the chest to the expiratory position. It is now established that some muscular activity also is involved in the expiratory act. The muscles involved are the interosseous portions of the internal intercostals and, in some persons, the abdominal muscles, which show moderate contraction even during quiet respiration.

THE WORK OF BREATHING

Inspiration is an active process involving extensive muscular contraction. The energy of contraction overcomes (1) the elastic recoil of the lungs and thorax, (2) the frictional resistance of the lung tissues and tissues of the chest wall (including rib cage, diaphragm, abdominal contents, and abdominal wall), and (3) the airway resistance.

The work varies with the rate at which air is moved in and out of the lungs. During quiet breathing 0.5 kilogram meters work per minute (0.5 Kg. M./min.) is a normal value; this may be increased 500 times when a man is breathing maximally. Normal expiration under conditions of rest and moderate activity is largely a passive process and hence utilizes little of the total energy of breathing in a normal man. Pulmonary conditions, however, may reduce the rate of expiration and increase the energy requirement. Maximal breathing in healthy individuals also increases the work of exhaling. The total energy used for respiration during quiet breathing represents only a small proportion of the total body energy expended.

The resistance in the nose is the largest single component of airway resistance. This explains the practice of mouth breathing when respiration is markedly increased. Even with mouth breathing the upper airway resistance accounts for about one third of the total resistance at low flow rates. The airway resistance within the lungs decreases as lung volume increases.

The maximum volume of air that the lungs can contain may be divided into four portions. Together these represent the *total lung capacity.* Three of these portions can be controlled voluntarily and constitute *vital capacity*; this represents the maximum volume of air that can be expelled by a forced maximal expiration. A fourth portion represents the air volume that remains in the lungs as long as the thoracic cavity remains an air-tight compartment. This *residual volume* is about 1200 ml. in the adult. The lung capacity can be reduced to this volume only at the end of the most forcible expiration. When the lungs are collapsed as a result of opening the thoracic cavity, most of the residual air escapes.

Let us now consider the portions that can be exchanged. During rest or moderate activity an *expiratory reserve volume* can be expelled at the end of a quiet expiration; this amounts to about 1200 ml. Thus at the end of a quiet expiration there remains about 2400 ml. of air in the lungs — 1200 ml. residual volume and 1200 ml. of the expiratory reserve volume. This represents the *functional residual capacity.* The second volume of air that can be exchanged is *tidal volume.* This is the amount of air inspired or expired during each respiratory cycle. It is a variable volume which increases with increased body activity. In quiet respiration this volume may be 400 to 500 ml. During activity tidal volume is augmented by drawing upon expiratory and inspiratory reserve volumes. The third volume of air that can be exchanged is the *inspiratory reserve volume.* This is the maximal amount of air that can be inspired at the end of a quiet inspiration. Its contribution to vital capacity may amount to 3600 ml. The volumes

and capacities are summarized in relation to total lung capacity and vital capacity (Table 13.1). Although the amounts shown in the table are representative values, there are large variations with age, sex, and body size.

Types of Respiration. Normal quiet breathing is known as *eupnea.* Increase in depth of respiration is called *hyperpnea*; if the depth is increased and expiration is forcible, it is called *dyspnea.* Respiration that is characterized by a rapid rate is designated by the term *polypnea*; when exceedingly high rates are attained, it is known as *tachypnea.* Cessation of respiration for short intervals of time is known as *apnea.*

VENTILATION

Ventilation is customarily used to refer to the volume of gas *expired* per minute (somewhat less than inspiratory volume — see *Respiratory quotient,* p. 370). It is determined by the respiratory rate multiplied by the average tidal volume. Physiologically, ventilation is divided into two components. One is the dead space tidal volume, i.e., the portion remaining in the conducting passageways. The other is the alveolar ventilation, the portion of the total ventilation that participates in the gas exchange.

Dead Space. The anatomic dead space or total volume of the conducting airways varies with the degree of inflation of the lungs, the age, and sex. A representative value for dead space volume at the end of expiration is 150 ml.

TABLE 13.1 LUNG VOLUMES AND CAPACITIES (IN MILLILITERS)

	Residual Capacity	Functional Residual Capacity	Vital Capacity	Total Lung Capacity
Residual volume	1200	1200	—	1200
Expiratory reserve volume		1200	1200	1200
Tidal volume			+	
Inspiratory reserve volume			3600	3600
Total air volume	1200	2400	4800	6000

Alveolar Ventilation. Alveolar ventilation refers to the volume of fresh air entering the alveoli. It should be apparent that if the tidal expiration involves an exchange of only 500 ml. of air, and if the volume of air in the lungs is 3000 ml. at the end of a normal expiration, the exchange in the alveoli must be far from complete. The first portion of expiration is gas that has been lying within the dead space; its composition is that of inspired gas saturated with water vapor. The alveolar component emerges last. Correspondingly, only the first portion of the inspiratory tidal volume enters the alveoli. This portion is known as the *effective tidal volume*. Assuming a dead space of 150 ml. and a tidal inspiration of 500 ml., only 350 ml. remain to be mixed with the 3000 ml. in the alveoli. From these figures it may be calculated that slightly less than 12 per cent of the air is renewed in a quiet respiratory cycle. Table 13.2 shows the composition of inspired, expired, and alveolar air.

The degree of exchange of alveolar air is dependent upon (1) the tidal air and respiratory rate, (2) the capacity of the trachea, bronchi, and bronchioles constituting the dead air space, (3) the volume of air remaining in the lungs at the end of expiration, (4) the distribution of air ventilating the alveoli, (5) the pulmonary capillary blood flow, and (6) the diffusion characteristics of the alveolocapillary membrane.

Respiratory Rate. In adults during rest the normal range of respiratory rate is between 11 and 14 per minute, although rates of 2 to 30 per minute have been observed in normal persons. In children rates of 20 to 25 are normal; in infants breathing frequently the rate is even higher, e.g., up to 50 per minute.

TABLE 13.2 COMPOSITION OF AIR IN VOLUMES (PER CENT)

	Inspired Air	Expired Air	Alveolar Air
Oxygen	20.96	15.8	14.0
Carbon dioxide	0.04	4.0	5.3
Nitrogen	79.00	80.2	80.7

Minute Volume. The minute respiratory volume is the product of the tidal volume and the respiratory rate. It is a more significant index of pulmonary ventilation than either rate or depth alone since it is the product of these two that determines the supply of O_2 available for diffusion and the elimination of excess quantities of CO_2.

At rest and during light activity the composition of the alveolar air is maintained at physiological levels of CO_2 and O_2 by a relatively small percentage renewal of air. The initial adjustment to increased bodily activity is an increase in tidal volume through the contributions of the expiratory reserve, and inspiratory reserve air volumes. As bodily activity reaches a high level and there is a further demand for an increase in ventilation the respiratory rate is increased.

Distribution of Air. Differences in volume, distensibility, and resistance to flow among alveoli exist to some extent even in healthy young individuals. They occur to a greater extent among older people and also may be increased in disease. Such differences result in uneven ventilation of the alveoli. Uneven ventilation also results from moving from a supine to a lateral recumbent position.

Distribution of Capillary Blood Flow. Gas exchange in the alveoli is influenced by the pulmonary capillary blood flow. Even when an alveolus receives an unimpeded mass movement of air, the exchange of gas by diffusion will be reduced if the capillary blood flow is decreased or interrupted. The pulmonary capillary blood flow is not uniform even in normal healthy individuals when sitting or standing. In changing from a supine to an erect position, the differences in the partial pressures of CO_2 and O_2 between arterial blood and the alveoli increase by about 2 and 5 mm. respectively. This is equivalent to rendering about 6 per cent of the alveoli inactive through stopping the circulation. The lack of uniformity in distribution of the capillary circulation is due to the difference in the effects of gravity, i.e., hydrostatic pressure, on blood flow at the apices and bases of the lungs.

Diffusion of Gases Within the Lung.

In external respiration the process of diffusion (see p. 20) is responsible for mixing gases within the alveoli, exchange of gases across the alveolocapillary membrane, and exchange of gases between the blood plasma and the red blood cells within pulmonary capillaries. The exchange across the alveolocapillary membrane depends upon the difference in the partial pressure of gases between the alveoli and the blood plasma, the thickness and characteristics of the membrane, and the surface area available for diffusion. The exchange between the plasma and the interior of the red blood corpuscles depends upon the partial pressure of the gases, the characteristics of the cell membrane, and the chemical reactions of hemoglobin with O_2 and CO_2. Nitrogen does not enter into the formation of compounds with constituents of plasma or corpuscles. In consequence the amount of nitrogen in plasma is dependent only upon its solubility and partial pressure.

TRANSPORT OF BLOOD GASES

The exchange of gases between the alveoli and the blood (Fig. 13.8) takes place rapidly. The oxygen partial pressure (Po_2) in the alveoli is about 100 mm. Hg. The Po_2 in the blood as it enters the pulmonary capillary bed is about 40 mm. Hg. This is increased to a Po_2 of 100 mm. Hg by the time the blood leaves the pulmonary capillary some 0.75 seconds later. The amount of O_2 which is physically dissolved at this pressure at 38°C. is only 0.003 ml./ml. blood or 0.03 volumes per cent. The remainder of oxygen is carried in combination with the hemoglobin (HHb) within the erythrocytes. The combination of oxygen and hemoglobin is known as oxyhemoglobin ($HHbO_2$). When hemoglobin is exposed to Po_2 of 120 mm. Hg or more, 1 gram of HHb can combine with 1.38 ml. of O_2. Since there are normally about 15 mg. per 100 ml. of blood, we would expect the hemoglobin, under optimal conditions, to carry a little more than 20 ml. O_2 as oxyhemoglobin. Thus, the total oxygen-carrying capacity of the blood would be more than 20 volumes per cent as $HHbO_2$ and 0.03 volumes per cent as dissolved O_2. The total amount is referred to as the *oxygen capacity*. Since, however, the Po_2 in the blood is less than 120 mm. Hg, the *oxygen content* of the blood leaving the pulmonary veins (Fig. 13.8) is less than the oxygen capacity. The term *oxygen saturation* is used to describe the ratio of oxygen content to oxygen capacity. Blood leaving the pulmonary capillaries with a 97 per cent oxygen saturation is mixed with small amounts of venous blood from the bronchial circulation (Fig. 13.8). Before the oxygenated blood reaches the systemic arteries, blood from the smallest cardiac veins of the heart (p. 285) has been added. In consequence the blood in systemic arteries has a Po_2 of about 92 mm. Hg and an oxygen saturation of about 96 per cent.

Hemoglobin is well adapted to respiratory functions since it is 97 per cent saturated at oxygen partial pressures of 100 mm. of mercury and about 90 per cent saturated at 70 mm. Hg. This shows that it can take up a high per cent of its maximum load of oxygen at pressures that are lower than those normally occurring in alveolar air. Further, formation of oxyhemoglobin is favored by relatively low pressures of carbon dioxide. Dissociation of $HHbO_2$ is favored by low Po_2 and high CO_2 pressures (Pco_2) in the cells of the body tissues. These properties are illustrated in Figures 13.12 and 13.13.

The Po_2 of the mixed venous blood returning to the lungs is about 40 mm. Hg, and the Pco_2 is about 46 mm. Hg. These pressure gradients and the affinity of hemoglobin (HHb) for oxygen favor oxyhemoglobin formation ($HHbO_2$); since oxyhemoglobin is a stronger acid than hemoglobin and since there is a lower Pco_2 in the alveolar air than in the venous blood, the conditions are favorable for the release of carbon dioxide from the blood. During internal respiration, when Po_2 in the tissues may be 30 mm. Hg, or according to some observers considerably less, and the Pco_2 may be 50 to 60 mm. Hg, conditions are strongly in favor of the breakdown of oxyhemoglobin and the re-

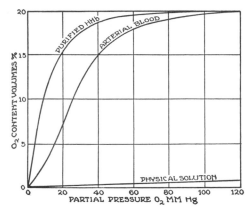

Figure 13.12 Oxygen contents of arterial blood and plasma (physical solution) and solution of purified hemoglobin at various partial pressures of oxygen. Note difference in shape of absorption curves of purified hemoglobin and arterial blood and small amount of oxygen carried in physical solution. (After Barcroft.)

lease of oxygen to the cells. Since the blood is in motion, there is not time for diffusion to continue until the oxygen pressures in the blood and tissues are equal. The venous blood upon returning to the heart shows average values of 14 ml. of oxygen per 100 ml. of blood. In some of the circulatory pathways, reduction of the oxygen content of the blood may be carried further, especially if the local tissues are active. In other circuits the venous blood may show values for oxygen that are almost equal to those of arterial blood; resting tissues and marked local vasodilatation usually minimize the percentage reduction in oxygen content.

Carbon Dioxide Carriage. The P_{CO_2} of the blood entering the systemic capillaries is about 40 mm. Hg. It is increased

to about 46 mm. Hg or more during the exchange with body tissues in which the P_{CO_2} may be 50 to 60 mm. Hg. In the lungs the alveolar P_{CO_2} is approximately 40 mm. Hg. The CO_2 diffuses through the pulmonary membrane more readily than does O_2, a fact which favors the rate and extent of exchange despite the low pressure gradient.

Some of the gas is carried as physically dissolved CO_2, or its hydrated form, H_2CO_3. By far the greater proportion is carried in chemical combination with base metals as bicarbonate, $NaHCO_3$ or $KHCO_3$, as carbamino CO_2 compounds of hemoglobin, $HbNHCOOH$, and other proteins, $RNHCOOH$.

The hydration and dehydration reactions in plasma, however, are so slow that they would seriously limit the exchange of CO_2 between tissues and the blood, and the lungs.

The erythrocytes are responsible for processes that not only increase the rate of exchange of CO_2 through action of the enzyme *carbonic anhydrase* but also increase the amount of CO_2 that is carried as bicarbonate in the plasma. The major chemical and physical changes are as follows:

I. *In the corpuscles:*

1. Carbon dioxide enters from the plasma. The hydration reaction is speeded up 600 times by the presence of carbonic anhydrase.

(*a*) $CO_2 + H_2O \xrightarrow{\text{carbonic}}_{\text{anhydrase}} H_2CO_3$

(*b*) $H_2CO_3 \rightleftarrows H^+ + HCO_3^-$

These ions interact with potassium hemo-

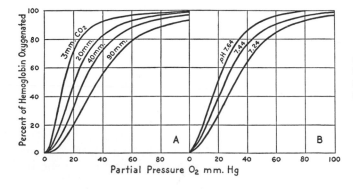

Figure 13.13 *A*, Effect of carbon dioxide on oxygen dissociation curve of whole blood. (After Bancroft.) *B*, Effect of acidity on oxygen dissociation curve of blood. (After Peters and Van Slyke.)

globinate, capturing the K^+ from the hemoglobin.

(c) K hemoglobinate + carbonic acid → K bicarbonate + acid hemoglobin; K Hb + H^+ + HCO_3^- ⟶ $KHCO_3$ + HHb.

Meanwhile, more HbO_2 is losing oxygen and becoming reduced hemoglobin, HHb, which is a weaker acid than HbO_2. In consequence, the reduced hemoglobin mops up H^+ more readily and so releases base more easily. This is one of the two ways in which hemoglobin plays a major role in the transport of CO_2 (p. 250).

(d) As the concentration of HCO_3^- rises, its concentration gradient across the red cell membrane increases. The cell membrane is freely permeable to HCO_3^- and Cl^-, but only slowly permeable to Na^+ and K^+. As HCO_3^- diffuses from the red cell to the plasma the electrical neutrality inside the cell tends to become upset by reduction of negative ions. This change, however, acts to draw Cl^- into the cell, and the Donnan equilibrium is maintained (see p. 26). The exchange of Cl^- is known as the *chloride shift*. By far the greater amount of CO_2 added in the tissues and carried as plasma bicarbonate results from the interchange of Cl^- and HCO_3^-.

2. About 20 per cent of CO_2 added by the tissues is carried by hemoglobin as a *carbamino compound*.

$$HHb\ NH_2 + CO_2 \longrightarrow HHbCOOH$$

This reaction proceeds rapidly; it does not require a special catalyst.

II. *In the plasma:*

1. Carbon dioxide is about 20 times more soluble than O_2 in plasma. About 5 per cent of the CO_2 carried by the blood is physically dissolved.

2. A small portion of dissolved CO_2 is hydrated in the plasma. This carbonic acid becomes dissociated, the HCO_3^- combining with Na^+ from the proteins and phosphates.

3. HCO_3^- diffuses out from the erythrocyte as Cl^- moves in the reverse direction. About 70 per cent of the CO_2 added by the tissues is carried as bicarbonate in plasma. HCO_3^- is derived from the erythrocyte.

In the lungs the processes are reversed, with carbon dioxide leaving the corpuscles and plasma and the Cl^- ion leaving the red blood corpuscles.

The degree of alkalinity of the blood is determined chiefly by the ratio of carbonic acid (physically dissolved carbon dioxide) to the bicarbonates (HCO_3^- in combination with Na^+ and K^+). Respiration tends to maintain the blood in a slightly alkaline state by keeping this ratio nearly constant even under widely varying degrees of bodily activity.

CENTRAL RESPIRATORY MECHANISMS

Breathing is controlled by the integrated action of neuronal structures known as the respiratory centers. Together these initiate respiration, respond to afferent impulses influencing ventilation and mediating protective reflexes, and coordinate the functions of the respiratory system with those of other systems of the body. The centers are the *inspiratory, expiratory,* and *special chemosensitive centers of the medulla;* the *apneustic* center in the middle or caudal level of the pons; and the *pneumotaxic center* in the rostral portion of the pons (Fig. 13.14).

Initiation of Respiration. The medullary centers possess inherent rhythmic activity which is retained even when the medulla is isolated from all other neuronal influence. They are not, however, solely responsible for rhythmicity. The apneustic center, acting from a higher level of the brain stem, facilitates inspiration. Its influence in stimulating respiration is sufficiently strong to interfere with rhythmic respiration unless counteracted by the pneumotaxic center or the vagal afferents from the lungs. When physiological function is interfered with, the dominance of the apneustic center can result in a gasping type of respiration or in *apneusis,* i.e., stopping breathing in the maximum inspiratory position. If, however, the pneumotaxic center, at a still higher level of the brain stem, is free to act, or afferent impulses from the lung act on the medullary centers, eupneic breathing results.

In addition to the pneumotaxic and the apneustic centers, the medullary centers are acted upon by a peripheral reflex

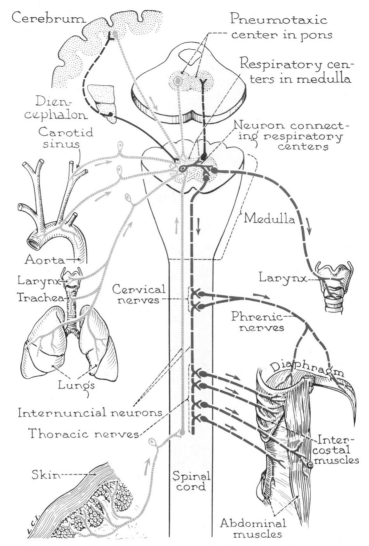

Figure 13.14 Diagram to illustrate the nervous control of respiration. Nerves on the left carry impulses to the respiratory centers; those on the right carry impulses from the respiratory centers to the muscles of respiration. The course of afferent impulses from the muscles is not shown.

mechanism. This is known as the *Hering-Breuer* reflex. As the lungs become inflated during inspiration, sensory nerve endings within the lung tissue are stimulated by stretching. This starts a series of inhibitory impulses in the afferent nerve fibers of the vagus traveling to the respiratory centers. The discharge of impulses occurs at a progressively increased rate as inflation proceeds until it reaches a critical level for inhibition of the inspiratory phase. Presumably this, together with the influence of the pneumotaxic center, tends

to terminate inspiration and supplement the influence of the neurons of the medullary expiratory center.

The separation of the inspiratory and expiratory centers of the medulla is based more on function than on anatomic sites. The population of neurons in the medullary centers is not sharply divided, with the inspiratory neurons in an inspiratory center, and the expiratory neurons in the expiratory center. There appears to be a predominance of expiratory neurons and a greater degree of activity of expiratory neurons in the expiratory center and a comparable representation and activity of the inspiratory neurons in the inspiratory center.

REGULATION OF VENTILATION

Ventilation is under chemical and nervous control (Fig. 13.14 and Table 13.3), which provides a wide range of adjustment of breathing. For example, when at rest a young man will use about 250 ml. O_2/min. and will exchange about 6 L.gas/min. At maximum level of bodily activity he may require over 5 L.O_2/min. and exchange about 100 L. gas/min.

Chemical control of rhythmic ventilation is exerted by P_{CO_2}, H^+ and P_{O_2} acting on chemosensitive areas of the brain and on the peripheral chemoreceptors whose influence is mediated through afferent nerves to the respiratory centers.

If the P_{CO_2} in arterial blood is increased by breath holding or by inhalation of CO_2, respiration is increased and excess CO_2 is blown off. If P_{CO_2} is increased through inhalation, or initially by reduction in ventilation, the acidity as well as P_{CO_2} increases. Experimentally it has been demonstrated that increased H^+ at constant P_{CO_2} increases respiration. Thus, while P_{CO_2} and H^+ can act independently, it would appear that the effects of both stimuli are added algebraically. We still cannot be sure of the location of the chemosensitive area or areas responsible for central chemical control. The P_{CO_2}

TABLE 13.3 FACTORS IN THE REGULATION OF RESPIRATION

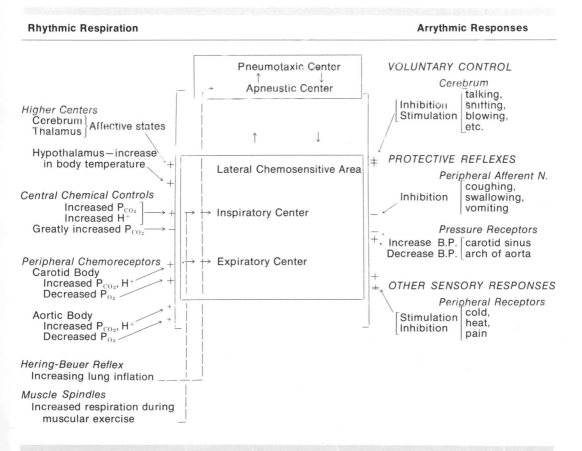

and H^+ may act on the respiratory centers in the medulla, or on chemoreceptors on its lateral surface.

If acting on the latter site, it has been hypothesized that CO_2, which is freely permeable, diffuses across the blood-brain barrier and alters the H^+ concentration of the cerebrospinal fluid. The increased H^+ in turn stimulates the medullary receptors.

The peripheral chemoreceptors are located in the carotid and aortic bodies (Fig. 13.14). They are responsive to increased Pco_2 and H^+, and decreased Po_2. It is probable that they act synergically with the central chemosensitive mechanism so that their combined effect is multiplicative rather than merely additive.

The hypothalamus and the cerebral cortex participate in the nervous control of rhythmic breathing through their influence on the respiratory centers. The influence of the hypothalamus is seen as changes in respiration occur with changes in body temperature. Affective or emotional states, such as a continuing fear, anxiety, or anger, also bring about changes in rate and depth of breathing; these are the result of the influence of the cerebral cortex and thalamus.

In exercise, increased ventilation results principally from afferent nerve impulses arising from propriorespiratory stimuli from muscles of the arms and legs. The response occurs rapidly — within a few seconds of the beginning of exercise. Under most circumstances arterial Pco_2 does not increase, nor does Po_2 decrease. A slight rise in H^+ may occur. Hyperventilation is reduced immediately upon cessation of exercise and gradually returns to resting levels.

Nervous control is also responsible for interruption of rhythmic breathing and may bring sharp inspiration, expiration, or inhibition. Breathing can be interrupted voluntarily as in talking, whistling, and blowing. Transient responses may result from fear, horror, and stimulation of end organs for cold, heat, and pain. In addition, there are protective reflexes involving respiration, i.e., coughing, sneezing, and inhibition of respiration when swallowing or vomiting.

An increase in blood pressure may result in a decrease in inhibition of breathing. Decreased blood pressure may stimulate inspiration. These effects are mediated through the carotid sinus, aortic arch baroreceptors, and afferent nerves.

THE ANOXIAS

The terms *anoxia* and *hypoxia* are used to describe conditions in which the oxygen supply is inadequate to meet the oxygen requirements for a particular level of body activity. The condition is relative. If a man while working receives an oxygen supply that is just adequate to maintain him while resting, he becomes anoxic. If the oxygen deficiency is accompanied by an excessive increase in carbon dioxide in the body, the condition is known as *asphyxia*.

Failure at any link in the chain of events in external or internal respiration may result in anoxia. If the supply of oxygen from the outside air is reduced or cut off, the condition is known as *anoxic anoxia*. This would occur if the trachea were closed either by a foreign body or by choking; it may also result from the decreased partial pressure of oxygen at high altitudes. The percentage of oxygen in the air remains constant with increasing altitude (i.e., 20.9 or roughly 1/5), but the partial pressure is reduced. For example, the total barometric pressure at 30,000 feet is 326 mm. of mercury; $1/5 \times 326 = 65.2$ mm. Hg oxygen partial pressure in outside air. This is insufficient to sustain life, so that consciousness is soon lost and death results if the inspired air is not enriched by the addition of pure oxygen within a short time. It is for this reason that transport aircraft pressurize their cabins.

If the transport of oxygen is interfered with by circulatory failure, the resulting condition is known as *stagnant anoxia*; if transport fails through stable chemical combination of carbon monoxide with hemoglobin which prevents the formation of oxyhemoglobin, or through a marked decrease in the amount of hemoglobin in the blood, the condition is known as *anemic anoxia*. Poisoning of the enzyme systems that catalyze the reactions in internal respiration results in *histotoxic anoxia*.

QUESTIONS FOR DISCUSSION

1. Explain the functions of the nasal fossae. How do the nasal conchae contribute to these functions?

2. Relate pulmonary and systemic circulations to the respiratory system.

3. Relate the anatomy of the respiratory system to the flow of air and the diffusion of gases. What is the significance of surfactant?

4. Describe what might occur in attempting to give fluids to an unconscious person.

5. Explain the functional adaptations of the epithelium along the respiratory tract.

6. What sequence of events might occur with the following: inhalation of ammonia, lodging of a fish bone in a piriform recess, aspiration of infected mucus from a paranasal sinus?

7. Review the function of the muscles of respiration.

8. Distinguish between intrapulmonary and intrathoracic pressures.

9. List all the factors that tend to decrease the thoracic volume in expiration.

10. Compare the amount of oxygen carried by blood plasma with the amount carried by the hemoglobin of the erythrocytes. Estimate approximately the number of milliliters of oxygen carried by the total blood volume of the body.

11. Give an example showing the close correlation of the respiratory mechanisms with bodily activity.

12. Describe the influence of eating and of talking on the respiratory pattern. Give illustrations of the influence of the cerebral cortex on respiration.

13. Discuss the influence of respiration on the carbon dioxide content and the acid-base balance of the blood.

14. Summarize the factors involved in regulation of ventilation in the following categories: regular respiratory responses and irregular responses; chemical factors; peripheral sensory factors; reflex mechanisms; central controls.

CIRCULATING BODY FLUIDS

CHAPTER
FOURTEEN

INTERSTITIAL FLUID AND LYMPH

In the exchanges that take place between the tissue cells and their environment all products must pass through an *interstitial fluid* that bathes the cells. Thus a gradient in the concentration of metabolites exists between the cells, the interstitial fluid, and ultimately the channels of transport or circulatory vessels (see Chapter 15). The gradients normally favor the passage of oxygen (Chapter 13) and food materials (Chapter 18) from arterial circulation to the cells and the passage of waste products (Chapters 13, 17, 19) of cellular metabolism in the reverse direction into veins and lymphatics.

The interchange of fluid between the tissues and circulation occurs continuously within the body. It is highly probable, however, that the exchange in any one area is intermittent. Fluid passes outward from circulation at a point where (or at a time when) the effective pressure within a minute vessel (p. 276) is greater than the total pressure of the interstitial fluid. Fluid from the tissue spaces passes back through the walls of the minute vessels when the pressure relations are reversed.

The outflow of fluid from circulation is governed by two physical forces: (1) the pressure of blood within the capillaries, the filtration pressure, which forces blood out through the capillary membrane; and (2) the protein osmotic pressure of the blood, which acts in the opposite direction. If we assume a pressure of 32 mm. Hg in the arterial end of a capillary and a protein osmotic pressure of 25 mm. Hg we have:

32 mm. Hg − 25 mm. Hg ⟶ 7 mm. Hg of force,

favoring formation of interstitial fluid. At the venous end of the capillary the blood pressure has fallen and protein osmotic pressure has risen slightly so we have:

12 mm. Hg − 27 mm. Hg ⟶ − 15 mm. Hg of force,

favoring an exchange of interstitial fluid into blood and lymph capillaries as shown in Figure 14.1.

Lymph flows from the tissues toward large lymphatic ducts (p. 281). The flow is maintained chiefly by the difference in pressure at the two ends of the system. The low pressure end is at the junction of the large lymphatic ducts with the brachiocephalic veins. At this point pressure may be zero or negative. Accessory factors aiding the flow of lymph are respiratory movements (pp. 246-247) and muscular contractions, particularly in the extremities (pp. 209-226). Inspiration aspirates lymph into transporting vessels of the chest. Alternate compression and release of lymphatic channels is accomplished by the contraction and relaxation of adjacent skeletal muscles. Since the lymph vessels are equipped with valves (Fig. 15.3) the direction of movement of lymph is always toward the chest cavity.

Composition of interstitial fluid, lymph, and blood plasma (Table 14.2) are very similar. Lymph collected from the liver contains somewhat higher concentrations of glucose and heparin, and lymph from the intestine is higher in fat content than interstitial fluids or blood plasma. Calcium, phosphorus, and protein composition of lymph is somewhat lower than corresponding plasma levels.

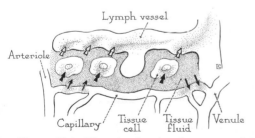

Figure 14.1 Diagram showing the course of the tissue fluid. Fluid passing out of the capillary may go into and out of tissue cells, may enter a lymph vessel, or may be resorbed into the capillary by osmosis.

Edema is the accumulation of interstitial fluid in abnormally large quantities. This tendency is more marked in dependent regions of the body. Inadequate lymphatic drainage of a region and increases in capillary permeability and pressure will contribute to formation of edema. A comparable mechanism may occur in the various fluid compartments, for example, pleural or pericardial effusion, ascites in the peritoneal cavity, or hydrocephalus in the ventricles of the brain. The accompanying increase in pressure upon adjacent tissues may be accompanied by limitation of function, pain, or even death of the compressed tissues.

BLOOD

The rapid movement of body fluids to and from the various fluid compartments or interstitial locations is accomplished by the organs of the circulatory system in the transportation of the blood. The major features of the regulatory mechanisms of the heart and blood circulation which facilitate transport and exchange are discussed in Chapters 15 and 16. In maintaining the cellular environment constant, the blood vascular system specifically subserves these functions:

Respiratory transport and exchange in conveying oxygen from the lungs to the cells and carbon dioxide from the cells to the lungs (Chapter 13).

Nutritive transport and exchange in carrying glucose, amino acids, lipids, inorganic salts, and vitamins from the digestive tract to the cells (Chapter 18).

Excretory transport and exchange of waste products of nitrogenous metabolism to organs of excretion (Chapter 17).

Regulatory transport and exchange of hormones of endocrine glands and tissues to the cells they affect (Chapter 9); of water, inorganic salts, and glucose to organs of excretion for adjustment to appropriate concentrations (Chapter 17); of heat to superficial blood vessels in the equalization of body temperature (Chapter 19).

Protective transport and exchange of immune substances and white blood cells in defense of body tissues against injurious substances (Chapter 14).

COMPOSITION OF THE BLOOD

Blood is a tissue that makes up about one-thirteenth of the total body weight. A man of average size, weighing 65 to 75 kilograms, would thus have 5 to 6 liters of blood. Direct observation of its gross characteristics may be carried out by withdrawing a sample of blood from a vessel and placing it in a test tube with a small amount of oxalate to prevent clotting. The color of a specimen may vary between the brilliant red of arterial blood and the dark red of venous blood, depending upon the amount of oxygen it contains. Determination of its specific gravity shows it to be about 1.05 to 1.06, with viscosity 5 to 6 times greater than that of water. Blood is slightly alkaline with a pH 7.37 to 7.44.

If the specimen is centrifuged or allowed to stand for a sufficient length of time (Fig. 14.2), the components of the blood separate so that either two or three distinct layers may be seen. At the top of the tube there will be a layer of clear straw-colored liquid, the plasma. If a graduated centrifuge tube is used, it may be seen that the plasma layer constitutes 50 to 60 per cent of the volume of whole blood. The formed elements, that is, the red and white blood cells and the blood platelets, settle out below the plasma. It is frequently possible to observe a thin layer of the white blood cells, or leukocytes, just below the layer of plasma. The red blood cells, or erythrocytes, and the blood platelets form the bottom layer, which makes up approximately 40 to 50 per cent (*hematocrit*) of the blood volume. Without centrifugation this separation will occur slowly as the formed elements settle to the bottom of a tube. The erythrocyte sedimentation rate (E.S.R.) has been recognized as a useful clinical diagnostic procedure. The sedimentation rate is measured by the depth in millimeters of clear plasma at the top of a vertical column of blood at the end of an hour (Wintrobe). Normal E.S.R. for men ranges from 1 to 3 mm. per hour and for women from 0 to 20 mm. per hour. Marked increases in E.S.R. will occur in certain infections.

Erythrocytes. (Fig. 14.3) The erythrocytes are biconcave discs that show a dumbbell outline when viewed from the side. The disc has no nucleus. The average diameter is about 7.2 microns.

The red blood cell consists mainly of hemoglobin and the supporting framework, called the stroma. The stroma is a combination of lipids (cephalin, lecithin, and cholesterol) and an insoluble albumin-like protein. A lipid-protein complex, *emelin*, contains the antigens associated with the *blood groups*.

Hemoglobin is composed of 4 per cent heme and 96 per cent globin. Hemes are iron-containing porphyrins. Similar compounds of porphyrin occur in myohemoglobin of muscle, cytochrome oxidative enzymes of most cells, and green and yellow chlorophyll pigments in plants. The globin portion of the hemoglobin molecule is comprised of two pairs of polypeptides. Normal adult hemoglobin is *hemoglobin A*. One pair of polypeptides, the α chain, contains 141 amino acids; the other pair, the β chain, contains 146 amino acids. Small

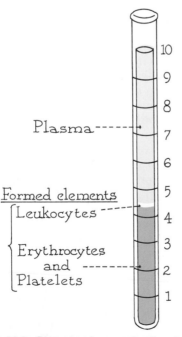

Figure 14.2 Diagram of a sample of centrifuged blood.

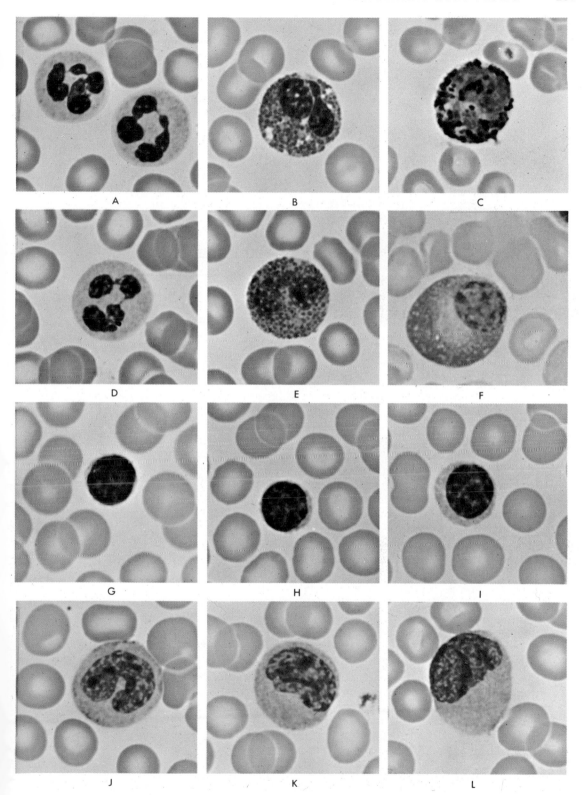

Figure 14.3 Human blood cells from a dry smear stained with Wright's stain. *A* and *D*, Neutrophilic leukocytes. *B* and *E*, Eosinophilic leukocytes. *C*, Basophilic leukocyte. *F*, Plasma cell. This is not a normal constituent of the peripheral blood but is included here for comparison with the mononuclear leukocytes. *G* and *H*, Small lymphocytes. *I*, Medium lymphocyte. *J, K,* and *L,* Monocytes. (In Bloom and Fawcett: A Textbook of Histology, 9th Ed., 1968.)

quantities of other hemoglobins are mixed with hemoglobin A under normal circumstances. Gamma chains are found in *fetal hemoglobin F* instead of beta chains. The fetal hemoglobin carries a higher oxygen content at a given Po_2 than does hemoglobin A. The amino acid sequences in the polypeptide chains of hemoglobin are genetically determined.

Many types of abnormal hemoglobin have been identified. These are usually designated by letter, for example, hemoglobins G, I, J, E, S, M, and so on. Hemoglobin S may cause an anemia by its insolubility to oxygen and distort the erythrocyte into a sickle cell shape. This same hemoglobin confers resistance to one type of malaria. An average hemoglobin value for males is 15.8 grams and for females 13.9 grams per 100 ml. of blood. A *hemoglobin determination* can be carried out rapidly by comparing a fresh drop of blood on filter paper with a standard set of colors representing different percentages of hemoglobin color intensity. A *color index* shows the amount of hemoglobin in proportion to the red blood cell count.

The red cells lead an active life of 120 days' duration or less. Their functions are to carry oxygen from the lungs to other cells of the body and to aid in the transport of carbon dioxide from those cells to the lungs. They assist in the maintenance of the pH balance and viscosity of the blood and influence its specific gravity.

The aging red blood cells are subject to constant mechanical injury in circulation and become more fragile than those cells just entering circulation. A *fragility* test can indicate this difference of resistance of the cell membrane by exposure of samples of blood to decreasing strengths of saline solution. Hemolysis (see pp. 22-23) of the cells normally begins at 0.45 per cent saline solution and is completed at 0.35 per cent solution. Final removal of the red cells from circulation is accomplished by cells of the reticuloendothelial system, particularly in liver, bone marrow, and spleen.

The cell-forming and cell-destroying activities, which proceed at a tremendous rate and in such widely separated organs,

appear to be remarkably well correlated, since under normal conditions the number of red cells in each cubic millimeter of circulating blood remains almost constant, between 3.8 to 5.8 million for women and 4.4 to 6.4 million for men. Daily variations, within these limits, of one half million cells are normal, and greater transient increases may occur during stress. Erythrocyte counts for the newborn and child are generally higher than adult values.

Leukocytes (Fig. 14.3). The white blood corpuscles, or leukocytes, are always nucleated and are capable of ameboid movement. The leukocytes are less numerous than the erythrocytes, a cubic millimeter of blood averaging between 5000 and 10,000 of these cells. Wide daily fluctuations occur with higher numbers present in the afternoon and during stress. There are several varieties of white blood cells, but they may be divided into two main groups: the nongranular leukocytes, or *agranulocytes*, which have few or no granules in their cytoplasm, and the granular leukocytes, or *granulocytes*, which have distinctive granules in their cytoplasm (Table 14.1).

The granulocytes have lobulated nuclei that show great diversity of form. The polymorphous nature of the nuclei is responsible for another name, *polymorphonuclear* leukocytes, often applied to this group. The granulocytes are classified in three groups according to the type of granules in the cytoplasm: eosinophil, basophil, or neutrophil. The nongranular leukocytes are the lymphocytes and monocytes.

Leukocytes have a variable life span. Granulocytes may survive for 2 to 14 days, while agranulocytes may survive in circulation for 100 to 200 days. Like erythrocytes, aging white blood cells are disposed of by the cells of the reticuloendothelial system, particularly of the liver and the spleen.

White blood cells function in protecting the body from substances that cause infection. Their capability to move through blood vessel walls by *diapedesis* enables them to reach a site of injury. Foreign particles, such as bacteria causing an infection, may be engulfed or *phagocytized*

TABLE 14.1   LEUKOCYTES (FIGS. 14.3)

Type	Per Cent of Total Count	Distinguishing Features (Wright's Stain)
Granular Leukocytes		
Eosinophil	2.5	About 12 microns in diameter; nucleus has 2 oval lobes; bright red granules
Basophil	0.5	About 10 microns in diameter; irregular S-shaped nucleus; large dark purple granules
Neutrophil	65-75	About 12 microns; polymorphic nucleus; fine, small orchid granules
Band forms	3-5	Single-lobed young nucleus
Segmented forms	51-67	2-5 lobes in nucleus, senile stage of nucleus has 5 lobes
Nongranular Leukocytes		
Monocyte	3-8	About 15 microns; eccentric kidney- or horseshoe-shaped nucleus; pale grayish blue cytoplasm, occasional purple granules
Large lymphocyte	2-3	About 12 microns; slightly indented spherical nucleus; pale grayish blue cytoplasm, occasional purple granules
Small lymphocyte	18-22	About 8 microns; thin layer of light blue cytoplasm

by the leukocytes; the neutrophils and monocytes are particularly active. The cytoplasmic granules disappear in the course of phagocytosis with the concomitant release of a bactericidal agent, phagocytin. The inflammatory reaction of tissue to disease depends upon this behavior of leukocytes.

Lymphocytes may transform into monocytes and macrophages and thus increase the phagocytizing potential at a particular site in the body. They are also capable of changing into tissue histiocytes and fibroblasts, which in turn are utilized at locations where repair of injured tissue occurs. Finally, lymphocytes can pass into bone marrow and form either hemocytoblasts or myeloblasts, leading to the formation of blood cells (pp. 159, 267).

The precise function of eosinophils is not known, although they increase in the presence of allergic reactions and parasitic infections. They decrease under stress and the influence of adrenocortical hormones. Basophils have the histologic features of mast cells (see p. 48) and are considered to be a source of intravascular heparin (see p. 265) and histamine (see p. 315).

Platelets.   The platelets are the smallest of the formed elements, ranging from 2 to 4 microns in diameter (Fig. 14.4). Their non-nucleated, disc-shaped bodies have a very fragile membrane and tend to adhere to uneven or damaged surfaces. The 250,000 to 500,000 per cubic millimeter of circulating platelets survive about eight days and are removed by cells of the reticuloendothelial system, particularly in the spleen.

Platelets participate in the control of bleeding *(hemostasis)* in several ways. When blood vessel walls are injured, the platelets adhere to the vessel wall in such a way as to form a mechanical plug. At the site of injury, the platelets release *serotonin* (5-hydroxytryptamine) which produces a local constriction of the blood vessel wall. Platelets liberate *thromboplastin* which is needed for the clotting of blood and adsorb a number of the plasma substances integral to this reaction. The final *retraction of the blood clot* is assisted by the ATP and actomyosin-like compounds in platelets.

These minute formed elements will aggregate around foreign matter and microorganisms, thus aiding in the defense of the body against infection. AB and O blood antigens and other types of antigens have been identified in platelets.

Plasma. The high water content of plasma provides the aqueous medium necessary for physiological processes.

The composition of the plasma may be considered from two standpoints: first, as a part of the vascular tissue and therefore containing constituents common to all protoplasm; second, as a vehicle of transportation and consequently containing materials in transit.

The plasma proteins make up 6 to 8 per cent of plasma. They are formed in the liver, spleen, bone marrow, and lymph nodes. Fibrinogen, albumins and globulins help to maintain pH, viscosity, and osmotic pressure of the blood and are important as nutrient substances. Fibrinogen is transformed into insoluble fibrin in the coagulation of blood. Immune substances, principally in the form of gamma globulins, aid in the protection of the body from foreign protein, essentially of bacterial origin.

Other nutrient substances are found in much smaller amounts in the plasma. Carbohydrates, utilized in energy-releasing reactions, circulate as glucose, lactic acid, and cerebrosides, ranging from 80 to 115 mg. per 100 ml., or about 0.1 per cent. Glucose remains remarkably constant, although the value does rise after meals when carbohydrates have been eaten. Lipids, consisting of fatty acids, cholesterol, phospholipids, and cerebrosides, are sources of energy and building materials in transit to cells or are for storage in fat depots. Amino acids are utilized in cellular construction much as are the plasma proteins.

Cholesterol is an essential constituent of the tissue cells and fluids, especially bile. Relatively large amounts of cholesterol are present in nerve tissue, adrenal glands, and testes and ovaries. Cholesterol is related to the formation of vitamin A and hormones of the adrenal glands, ovaries, and testes. Conduction of the nerve impulse, permeability of cell membranes, and the proper absorption and transfer of lipid

TABLE 14.2 COMPOSITION OF PLASMA

Organic Constituents 9%		Inorganic Salts 0.9%		Special Substances 90%	
	Gm. %		mEq./L.		Vol. %
Proteins* (6.7)	6-8	Sodium	142	Water	90
Albumin* (4)	5	Potassium	4	Blood gases	
Globulins* (2.3)	2	Calcium	5	Nitrogen	1
Alpha* (0.8)		Magnesium	2	Oxygen	0.3
Beta* (0.8)		Chlorides	103	Carbon dioxide	2.5
Gamma* (0.7)		Phosphates	3		
Fibrinogen* (0.4)	0.3	Sulfates	1	Enzymes	
		Bicarbonates	28	Transaminase	
				SGOT (aspartate)	5-100 I.U.†
Nutrients	mg. %			SGPT (alanine)	4-13 I.U.†
Glucose	80-115			Lactic dehydrogenase	60-250 I.U.†
Lactic acid	5-20	Iron 80-200 gm. %		Acid phosphatase	1.1 Bod. units‡
Cerebrosides	15	Iodine 0.5 gm. %		Alkaline phosphatase	4.0 Bod. units‡
Amino acids	5				
Fatty acids	370			Vitamins	
Phospholipids	6-13			Vitamin A	29-64 gm. %
Cholesterol	150-280				
				Hormones	
Nonprotein nitrogeneous	18-35 mg. %			Protein bound iodine	
waste (NPN)				(PBI)	3-8 gm. %
Urea (BUN)	8-25				
Uric acid	3-7				
Creatine	0.4				
Creatinine	1.2				
Ammonium salts	0.2				

*Electrophoretic separation of plasma proteins dependent upon migration in an electrical field. Values shown in gm./100 cc.
†International units.
‡Bodansky units.

substances are also dependent in part upon cholesterol. About 28 per cent of the blood cholesterol is present in the free form and cholesterol esters carried on the α and β globulins as lipoproteins account for the remaining 72 per cent.

About 18 to 35 mg. of nonprotein nitrogenous waste compounds are present in every 100 ml. of blood. Urea, uric acid, creatine, creatinine, and ammonium salts are breakdown products of protein metabolism. These are carried by the blood to the kidneys for excretion.

The inorganic salts comprise 0.9 per cent of the plasma. They represent a basic constituent of protoplasm found in all cells and necessary for life. They aid in maintaining osmotic pressure of the blood, in transporting carbon dioxide to the lungs, and in keeping the blood slightly alkaline. They consist chiefly of the chlorides, carbonates, bicarbonates, sulfates, phosphates, and iodides of sodium, potassium, calcium, magnesium, and iron. Sodium chloride constitutes the principal inorganic salt.

The high water content of the plasma provides the aqueous medium necessary for physiological processes. The blood gases — oxygen, carbon dioxide, and nitrogen — are slightly soluble in water and are therefore carried in small amounts dissolved in the plasma. Larger amounts of oxygen and carbon dioxide are carried in chemical combination.

Enzymes, vitamins, and hormones represent the numerous catalytic substances carried by the blood. A few examples are included in Table 14.2. When injury occurs to active cells the serum transaminase values rise. For example, serum glutamic oxaloacetic (aspartate) transaminase (SGOT) and serum glutamic pyruvic (alanine) transaminase (SGPT) values are elevated when the heart muscle cells are damaged. An elevation in the level of lactic dehydrogenase suggests a malignancy in the liver or pancreas. Malignancies involving the bone, liver, and urinary bladder may cause an elevation in the alkaline phosphatase. An upward shift of the range of acid phosphatase occurs during a malignancy of the prostate gland. Protein bound iodine reflects the presence

of thyroid hormones in circulation. A comparison of the values of the various components of plasma yields a great deal of information relative to the status of the physiological processes occurring throughout the body.

HEMOSTASIS

The control of hemorrhage is an adaptive mechanism necessary to the preservation of life. When a blood vessel is ruptured, several physiological changes ensue, resulting in the eventual formation of a clot that plugs the opening and prevents undue loss of blood. As blood flows over the cut edges of a blood vessel, platelets tend to adhere to the injured area. Spontaneous disintegration of the platelets releases serotonin, which has the local effect of constriction on the blood vessels, while its generalized action is that of reducing blood pressure. Both activities tend to impede hemorrhage as coagulation of the blood proceeds.

Control time or *bleeding time* is measured by puncturing the skin with a needle or a small lancet and observing the time span required for the bleeding to cease; normal bleeding time is approximately two and one-half minutes.

The *coagulation time* may be measured as the time which elapses between the drawing of blood into a capillary tube and the formation of a clot. It varies from three to ten minutes. The blood factors involved in formation of blood clot are listed in Table 14.3.

The significant process in coagulation of the blood is conversion of the soluble plasma protein, fibrinogen, into an insoluble protein, *fibrin* (Fig. 14.4). This reaction is catalyzed by the enzyme thrombin. Thrombin is produced by activation of its precursor, α globulin prothrombin. After the blood clot consisting of fibrin threads and formed elements has developed, it becomes firm and strong as it contracts and serum is compressed out of it. This *clot retraction* is dependent upon the presence of blood platelets and occurs approximately 30 to 60 minutes following coagulation. Within a few hours, and continuing over a period of several days and

TABLE 14.3 BLOOD COAGULATION FACTORS

Factor	Name (s)
I	Fibrinogen
II	Prothrombin
III	Thromboplastin, platelet factor
IV	Calcium ions
V	Proaccelerin, labile factor, AC globulin (AcG)
VII	Proconvertin, serum prothrombin conversion accelerator (SPGA), proconvertin, autoprothrombin I
VIII	Antihemophilic factor (AHF), antihemophilic globulin (AHG) antihemophilic factor A
IX	Plasma thromboplastin component (PTC), antihemophilic factor B, autoprothrombin II, Christmas factor
X	Stuart-Prower factor, autoprothrombin I_c
XI	Plasma thromboplastin antecedent, (PTA), antihemophilic factor C
XII	Hageman factor, glass factor, contact factor
XIII	Laki-Lorand factor, fibrin stabilizing factor, fibrinase

months, there occurs a fibrous organization of the clot as healing proceeds. New blood vessels may grow through the healed area to recanalize the old blood channel.

A number of theories have been advanced to explain the interaction of the blood coagulation factors listed in Table 14.3. The classic theory can be illustrated as follows:

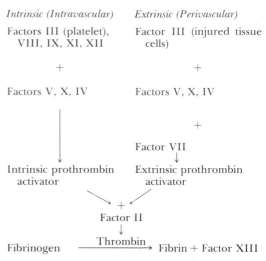

In another concept of the coagulation process prothrombin becomes the central element. At any time that extrinsic or intrinsic factor III comes in contact with blood, it initiates coagulation by enzymatic splitting of prothrombin to form thrombin and other degradation products. The thrombin and degradation products can

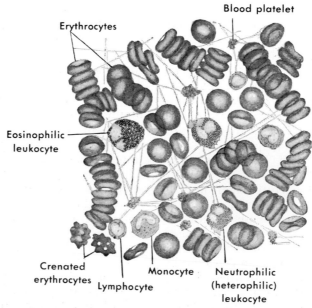

Figure 14.4 Fresh preparation of human blood. Note the strands of fibrin and rouleaux of erythrocytes. × 780. (After A. A. Maximow. In Bloom and Fawcett: A Textbook of Histology, 9th ed., 1968.)

act as enzymes to augment the quantity of prothrombin to thrombin conversion. In this concept, factors VII, IX, and X are degradation products of prothrombin. Thus their absence from the blood may be taken as evidence that the prothrombin molecule is genetically abnormal.

Factor III is a phospholipid present in tissue cells and platelets. Excluding factors III and IV, the remaining factors are plasma proteins. Factor II is an alpha globulin and most of the other factors belong to the beta globulin group. The plasma proteins are formed in the liver and lymphoid tissues. Vitamin K is necessary for the proper synthesis of the protein factors. Prolonged coagulation times may result from a deficiency of any of these components.

A measure of available prothrombin can be determined by *prothrombin time.* When plasma, oxalated to remove Ca^{++}, is combined with thromboplastin and calcium chloride, clotting occurs in 11 to 15 seconds when a normal amount of prothrombin is present. Such an evaluation may be valuable when anticoagulant drugs are used. Clotting of the blood is hastened by contact with injured tissue, contact with foreign surfaces, warming, and by stirring the blood. It can also be hastened by adding certain coagulants such as calcium; thromboplastins from extracts of brain, other tissues, or platelets; some diluted snake venoms which convert prothrombin to thrombin without factors III and IV; thrombin, fibrinogen, and fibrin.

Under usual conditions blood clots do not accumulate within undamaged blood vessels. There is a physiological mechanism for the continual lysis or dissolution of small amounts of fibrin as they occur within minute vessels and surrounding tissues. A beta globulin, profibrinolysin, is closely associated with fibrinogen. The *fibrinolytic* system may be indicated as follows:

$$\text{Profibrinolysin} \xrightarrow{\text{Fibrino-lysokinase}} \text{Fibrinolysin}$$
$$\text{(plasminogen)} \qquad\qquad \text{(plasmin)}$$

Fibrinolysin + Fibrin ⟶ Lysis of clot
$$\downarrow$$
Inactivation by antifibrinolysin in plasma

Epsilon amino caproic acid (EACA) will also inactivate fibrinolysin. An important feature of anticoagulation activity within the blood is the action of the alpha globulin *antithrombin.* Most of the thrombin formed in the course of coagulation is trapped within the mesh of fibrin threads and formed elements of the clot. That which is not trapped is inactivated within twenty minutes by antithrombin. *Heparin* is a sulfonated polysaccharide found in the cytoplasmic granules of many tissue cells. It is particularly abundant in the mast cells in pericapillary connective tissue and basophils. Mast cell concentrations occur in connective tissue in the lungs and liver. Heparin is active at several points in the coagulation process, by (1) preventing the formation of the intrinsic prothrombin activator, (2) inhibiting the action of thrombin on fibrinogen, (3) increasing the rapidity of combination of thrombin with antithrombin, and (4) increasing the amount of fibrin adsorbed. Anticoagulant drugs include heparin, bishydroxycoumarin (dicumarol), which antagonizes vitamin K to lower the blood factor II, and chelating agents which bind factor IV. Blood calcium levels low enough to interfere with coagulation are not compatible with life. Absence of any of the factors listed in Table 14.9 may cause a hemorrhagic disease.

BLOOD GROUPS

Mixture of a small amount of blood with the appropriate testing sera will indicate an individual's blood type. The clumping, or agglutination, of red blood cells follows definite patterns according to inherited blood characteristics. Erythrocytes and other cells contain *agglutinogens* (antigens), and plasma (and serum) may contain *agglutinins* (antibodies). The presence of an antigenic protein stimulates the body to produce neutralizing immune substances or antibodies.

In the international classification of blood types, the following patterns of *A* and *B* agglutinogens and Anti-*A* and Anti-*B* agglutinins prevail for the erythrocytes and plasma:

Type AB: Red cells contain type *A* and type *B* agglutinogens, plasma contains *no* agglutinins;

Type A: Red cells contain type *A* agglutinogens, plasma contains Anti-*B* agglutinins;

Type B: Red cells contain type *B* agglutinogens, plasma contains Anti-*A* agglutinins;

Type O: Red cells contain weak agglutinogens, plasma contains Anti-*A* and Anti-*B* agglutinins.

As can be seen in Figure 14.5, those red cells that have an *A* agglutinogen are agglutinated by serum containing Anti-*A* agglutinin. The blood types are named according to the agglutinogens carried by the respective erythrocytes. The pattern of agglutination reactions is *typed* by using two blood sera, one with agglutinin Anti-*A* and the other with agglutinin Anti-*B*. A few individuals have a variant of the *A* agglutinogen which can be typed as *A₂*. The *OAB* blood groups can be summarized as A_1B, A_2B, A_1, A_2, B and O.

The serologic typing of *O* blood suggests that it can be *donated* in blood transfusion to individuals of any other blood group. Similarly, type *AB* blood can *receive* from any of the other blood types because its plasma does not contain agglutinins. The donor plasma for a transfusion does not agglutinate the recipient's red cells because it is rapidly diluted in the recipient's plasma. If possible, it is desirable that a transfusion be made with blood of the recipient's own blood type.

As a further safeguard of the suitability of blood for transfusion, *crossmatching* may be done. Blood samples from both donor and recipient are centrifuged to separate the plasma from the formed elements. A small quantity of the donor's cells are mixed with the recipient's plasma and a similar amount of recipient's cells combined with the donor's plasma. If no agglutination of the red blood cells has occurred after 15 minutes at body temperature, the blood samples are considered to match each other. Mismatched blood will cause a transfusion reaction. Agglutination of the red blood cells occurs in small blood vessels and capillaries. Subsequent destruction of these clumps releases large quantities of hemoglobin, which become concentrated in the kidneys. This hemoglobin concentration may prevent normal function of the kidney in elimination of waste materials.

Our knowledge of other agglutinogen systems present in the red blood cell has brought the list of possible blood groups to a number exceeding 500 billion. A partial list of these systems includes M, N, S, s, P, Kell, Lewis, Duffy, Diego, and Lutheran groups. Since the antibodies (agglutinins) for these factors are seldom present in appreciable quantities in blood plasma, the factors do not constitute a hazard in blood transfusions. They may be utilized in legal medicine to ascertain probable familial relations.

The Rh–Hr blood factors may be strongly antigenic. This is a system made up of at least 13 agglutinogens. Those factors characteristic of Rh negative include rh, rh′, rh″ and rhᵧ. Rh positive factors are Rh_0, Rh_1, Rh_2, and Rh_z. It has been suggested that a reciprocally related Hr factor is present when Rh factor is absent. Agglutinins of the OAB system develop spontaneously whereas those of the Rh–Hr system seldom occur spontaneously. The individual must be exposed to some antigen of the system before he will

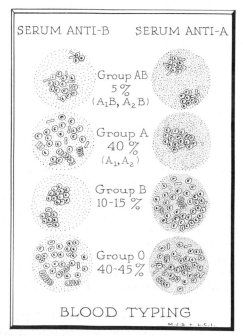

SERUM ANTI-B   SERUM ANTI-A

Group AB
5%
(A_1B, A_2B)

Group A
40%
(A_1, A_2)

Group B
10-15%

Group O
40-45%

BLOOD TYPING

Figure 14.5 Refer to text for description of blood typing.

develop a significant number of agglutinins in the plasma. Rh_0, Rh_1, Rh_2, and Rh_z are the most highly antigenic. A slow synthesis of Anti-Rh agglutinins in blood of the exposed individual will reach a peak of accumulated agglutinins in approximately two to four months. If a contact occurs between the blood of an Rh positive and an Rh negative individual, the latter will build up agglutinating antibodies. In subsequent contacts the Rh positive blood cells are agglutinated. Such contacts occur with blood transfusions of Rh positive blood into Rh negative persons, and in Rh negative mothers whose children are Rh positive. In the latter instance the child's blood cells are continually disintegrating, and Rh positive protein passes into the maternal circulation. Anti-Rh agglutinins formed by the mother are able to diffuse into the fetal circulation to cause hemolysis of fetal erythrocytes. Inheritance of the Rh-Hr factors is complex. Most individuals fall within six Rh positive groups that may be typed as are the standard blood groups.

HEMOPOIESIS

In the embryo the red corpuscles are formed in the yolk sac, liver, spleen, thymus, lymph nodes, and the bone marrow; but in the adult, *erythropoiesis* occurs only in the red bone marrow. Red bone marrow (p. 159) in adult is found in the sternum, ribs, scapulae, vertebrae, diploe of cranial bones, and proximal epiphyses of femur and humerus.

The erythrocyte develops from the common stem cell of the red bone marrow, the hemocytoblast. The cell in its immature stages has a nucleus but no hemoglobin. After mitotic divisions the nucleus is extruded. Hemoglobin accumulates in the cytoplasm, associated with a loss of ribonucleoprotein, mitochondria, Golgi complex, and endoplasmic reticulum.

Erythropoiesis is stimulated by hypoxia in the blood. The decrease in Po_2 results in the release of iron from its storage areas and in the secretion of a hormone composed of glycoprotein and alpha globulin. This hormone, *erythropoietin*, is produced by the kidney and other tissues. Erythropoietin initiates the change of undifferentiated hemocytoblasts to proerythroblasts in the bone marrow. At least two other factors are necessary for normal erythropoiesis. Vitamin B_{12} (cyanocobalamin) is essential for the synthesis of the DNA and RNA incorporated into the nucleoproteins of the mitotic cells. Proper absorption of B_{12} from the intestinal tract requires the presence of a factor in gastric juice manufactured by the chief cells of gastric mucosa (p. 345). An additional fraction of the vitamin B complex group, folic acid, is instrumental in the synthesis of DNA. Folic acid, or pteroylglutamic acid, is probably active in the form of folinic acid. Formation of the hemoglobin within the maturing erythrocyte is dependent upon the presence of its constituents of iron and the amino acids of the α and β polypeptide chains. Under the usual physiologic exchange, the required iron and amino acids are present in the body or supplied by dietary intake. Pyridoxine (vitamin B_6) facilitates the absorption of iron from the intestine. Minute amounts of copper, manganese, and cobalt are necessary for the enzymes responsible for hemoglobin synthesis. Hormones of gonads, thyroid, and adrenal cortex all play a part in maturation of the red cells.

It is probable that several factors are responsible for hemopoiesis of white blood cells. Disintegration products of aged leukocytes may be the physiological stimulus for *leukopoiesis*. Experiments show that protein fractions derived from such cells or from damaged tissues, or exudates from infected tissues cause an increase in the white cells in circulation. Adrenocortical hormones increase the numbers of neutrophils and, at the same time, decrease the numbers of eosinophils and lymphocytes in the blood.

White blood cells are manufactured in the embryo by the same blood-forming organs as are erythrocytes, namely the yolk sac, liver, spleen, thymus, lymph nodes, and the bone marrow. The stem cells, the hemocytoblasts, differentiate into myeloblasts and lymphoblasts. Myeloblasts in subsequent mitoses form eosinophils, basophils, and neutrophils.

Monoblasts and lymphoblasts are currently believed to be the same cell. The lymphoblasts develop into large and small lymphocytes. The large lymphocytes, which develop in a phagocytic direction, have the characteristics attributed to monocytes. In the adult the *myeloid tissue* of red bone marrow retains the ability to produce erythrocytes and granular leukocytes. Lymphocytes, including monocytes, develop in the *lymphatic tissues* of the adult.

The formation of platelets is by megakaryocytes of the red bone marrow, and blood-forming organs of the embryo. Megakaryocytes develop from hemocytoblasts, whose nuclei undergo peculiar divisions into daughter nuclei that fuse into a very large nucleus. The cytoplasm increases in amount without division. As the megakaryocyte matures, platelet demarcation membranes appear in the cytoplasm. Subsequent fragmentation of the cytoplasm along these demarcation lines produces the platelets.

LYMPHATIC TISSUE AND ORGANS

LYMPH NODULES AND AGGREGATES

Lymphatic tissue is found in the mucous membranes of the alimentary, respiratory, and genitourinary passageways. Some lymphatic tissue is present in the myeloid tissue of red bone marrow. The framework or stroma of lymphatic tissue is reticular connective tissue (Fig. 4.21, p. 50). Reticulocytes of the stroma may develop into fixed macrophages and lymphocytes and on occasion into myelocytes. The macrophage cells form the walls of the sinuses within the lymphatic tissue and have been called endothelial or reticuloendothelial cells. Within the reticulum are free cells, which include the large and small lymphocytes, and plasma cells (Fig. 14.3). Plasma cells have been shown to be the principal producer of antibodies carried by the gamma globulins of the blood plasma. *Lymphatic nodules* are a reflection of lymphocytopoietic activity at a focal point in lymphatic tissue. Dense accumulations of lymphocytes are embedded in a small amount of reticular tissue. The central portion, about 1 mm. in diameter, is generally an active germinal center with many mitotic figures surrounded by a peripheral corona of less active cells and reticular formation. New nodules of lymphatic tissue may develop in any loose connective tissue. These nodules occur frequently along the small intestine and collect into *aggregated nodules* (Peyer's patches Fig. 18.13). Larger aggregates of lymphatic nodules are found in the lingual, palatine, and pharyngeal *tonsils* (Figs. 13.6 and 14.6).

Lymph nodes (Figs. 14.6 and 14.7) are organized accumulations of lymphatic tissue, 1 to 25 mm. in diameter, located along the course of the lymphatic vessels (p. 280). The node is enclosed in a dense fibrous capsule. Septa or trabeculae from the capsule dip down into the substance of the gland and divide it into separate compartments. The substance of the node is arranged in an outer cortical and an inner medullary portion. In the cortex are the nodules of lymphoid tissue. Permeating the organ as a whole are irregular, tortuous channels, the lymphatic sinuses. As a lymph vessel approaches a node, it breaks up into a number of branches, the afferent lymphatics, which enter the gland from its convex surface. The lymph flowing in the vessels trickles through the sinuses of the node and into the efferent lymphatics, which leave the gland at the indentation or hilus.

Reticuloendothelial cells of the lymph nodes filter out solid particles, including bacteria, and prevent their entrance into the blood. Lymph nodes are very active leukopoietic sites for lymphocytes. Antibodies, or immune substances, and small amounts of plasma proteins are produced in the lymph nodes by plasma cells and fixed macrophages are added to the lymph as it percolates through the nodes. Immune substances that aid the body's defense against disease include those that dissolve (lysins), those that cause clumping (agglutinins), those that sensitize for white cell phagocytosis (opsonins), and those that neutralize poisons (antitoxins). These are usually attached to gamma globulins.

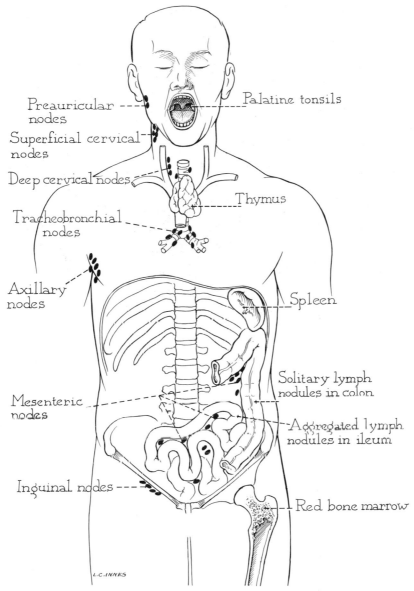

Figure 14.6 Locations of lymphatic tissues and organs.

The lymph nodes are usually distributed in groups (Fig. 14.6). Groups found in the *head* and *neck* are (1) submandibular nodes, just below the angle of the mandible, (2) pre-auricular nodes, just in front of the ear, (3) post-auricular nodes, behind the ear in the region of the mastoid process, (4) the superficial cervical nodes, at the side of the neck over the sternocleido-mastoid muscle, and (5) the deep cervical nodes, deep in the neck along the carotid artery and internal jugular vein. In general, each group drains the regions of the head and neck directly above it. The main group of the *upper extremity* is in the axilla. The axillary nodes receive the lymph from the arm, anterior and lateral walls of the chest, mammary gland, and scapular region. The most important glands of the *lower extremity* are the inguinal nodes, which lie in the groin. They receive the lymph from the leg and from the external

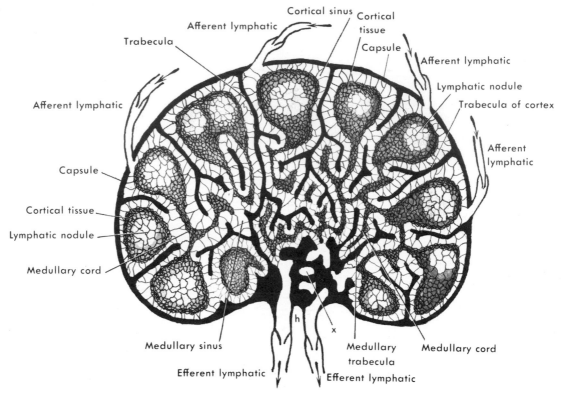

Figure 14.7 Diagram of lymph node, showing afferent and efferent lymphatic vessels with valves; arrows indicate the direction of lymph flow. The cortical trabeculae originate in the capsule and divide the cortex into ampullae. The medullary trabeculae are continuous with those in the cortex. *x*, Lymphatic vessels in the dense connective tissues in the hilus, *h*. The blood vessels are not shown. (In Bloom and Fawcett: A Textbook of Histology, 9th ed., 1968.)

genitalia. Important groups in the *thoracoabdominal* cavity are: tracheobronchial, mediastinal, gastric, mesenteric, and numerous glands along the main arterial trunks.

SPLEEN

The *spleen* (Figs. 14.6, 15.24, 18.17) is an ovoid organ about 12 cm. long, which is located on the left side of the upper abdominal cavity. Its lateral surface is convex and lies molded against the dome of the diaphragm. The medial surface is in contact with the stomach, the pancreas, and the left kidney.

The spleen is invested and held in place by a layer of peritoneum. Just beneath the peritoneal covering, a capsule of fibroelastic tissue, containing smooth muscle cells, encloses the organ and, turning inward at

the hilum, ramifies through the internal structure to partition it into spaces that are filled with splenic tissue. There are two types of splenic tissue. *White pulp* is typical lymphatic tissue with numerous nodules. It ensheathes the branches of the splenic artery. *Red pulp* is a looser lymphatic tissue filling the narrow spaces near large sinuses which are tributaries of the splenic vein. Red pulp is infiltrated by the formed elements of the blood. The erythrocytes are responsible for the characteristic color of the red pulp.

The spleen is placed in the course of the blood circulation through the splenic artery; in many respects it acts as a filter and a reservoir for the blood. Physiological changes in the vascular bed may speed up or slow down circulation of blood through the filtration mechanism of the organ. Large numbers of red blood cells stored in red pulp can be discharged into the splenic systemic circulation.

The spleen manufactures all types of blood cells during fetal life and for a short time after birth. In adult life this function is restricted to the formation of lymphocytes. Red blood cells are destroyed in the spleen; the iron from the hemoglobin is converted to its transport form of ferritin and routed to bone marrow for later utilization in the synthesis of new hemoglobin. Pigment is ultimately converted to bile pigments (see splenic, circulation, p. 290). The fixed macrophages of the spleen are active in destruction of microorganisms as well as of erythrocytes. Plasma cells of the spleen are important in the formation of antibodies.

THYMUS

The thymus is a lymphoepithelial organ in the anterior mediastinum dorsal to the sternum in close proximity to the pericardium at the base of the heart and great vessels and trachea (Fig. 14.6). Its two lobes meet in the midline. It is divided into a number of macroscopic lobules by septa of connective tissue extending inward from the capsule covering the organ. Each lobule contains a *cortex* in which the lymphoid tissue predominates and a *medulla* in which the epithelial cells predominate. Lymphatic tissue of the cortex follows the contours of the medulla and is uniform, without follicles so characteristic of other lymphatic tissues. Lymphocytes, macrophages, mast cells and reticular cells are found in the lymphatic tissue. The epithelial cells of the medulla are in contact with each other as a *cytoreticulum*, with numerous lymphocytes in the interspaces of the reticulum (Fig. 14.8). Concentric organizations of tightly wound epithelial cells or *thymic (Hassall's) corpuscles* are found throughout the medulla. Although their function is not known, these corpuscles contain high concentrations of gamma globulin.

The relative size of the thymus changes throughout life, as *age involution*. The thymus is largest during embryonic life and childhood up to puberty. Adipose and fibrous tissue replaces the parenchyma of the thymus from cortex toward medulla.

The thymus carries out the same hemopoietic functions found in other lymphatic tissues in formation of lymphocytes. There is some evidence to suggest that lymphocytes which emigrate from the thymus move to the spleen and lymph nodes where they persist and multiply. There are few plasma cells in the thymus and it does not appear to produce significant amounts of antibodies. However, the thymus does have some role in inducing the development of the immunologic competence of lymphocytes produced in

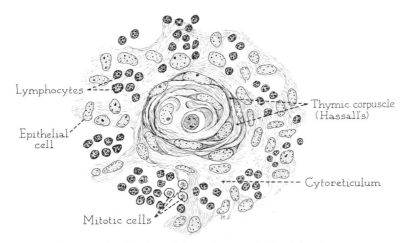

Figure 14.8 Section of tissue from medulla of the thymus.

other lymphatic tissues. A cell-free extract of the thymus will stimulate a lymphocytosis in lymphatic tissues. This is taken as evidence of hormonal function of the thymus. Some abnormality of thymic mechanism is apparently involved in the diseases in which a rejection type of reaction occurs against the body's own tissues. An increase in the size of the thymus is present with these *auto-immune diseases*, such as myasthenia gravis, rheumatoid arthritis, and thyroiditis.

QUESTIONS FOR DISCUSSION

1. What factors are responsible for maintaining the formed elements of the blood?

2. How are the constituents of plasma maintained at relatively constant values?

3. How is blood typing related to antigen-antibody reactions?

4. Explain how a blood clot might form within a blood vessel.

5. How might the following be related to erythropoiesis: iron deficiency, hemorrhage, lack of dietary protein, genetic variation in hemoglobin formation, vitamin B_{12}, removal of the stomach?

6. How are these circumstances related to coagulation: Absence of vitamin K in diet, extracts of lung and liver tissues, snake bite, decrease in blood platelets, absence of each of the factors I to XIII?

7. What first aid measures might be taken to promote hemostasis? Explain how these are related to the coagulation mechanism.

8. What might occur in blood transfusion of an Rh negative person with Rh positive blood at the first transfusion? At the fifth transfusion?

9. What might occur in the fetal circulation of blood of the third Rh positive baby of an Rh negative mother?

10. What might be the result of abnormal activity of myeloid tissues? Of lymphoid tissues?

11. What is the functional significance of the arrangement and location of lymphatic vessels and nodes?

12. Compare functions of the following: lymphatic tissues, bone marrow, lymph nodes, spleen, thymus, tonsils.

13. Relate the formation of lymph to the minute vessels of the capillary bed.

14. What physical principles and processes are involved in formation of lymph?

CIRCULATION

CHAPTER FIFTEEN

CIRCULATORY SYSTEM

The circulatory system with its organs of blood vessels, lymphatics, and heart serves a significant role in the mechanics of exchange and transport of blood and lymph and provides for the metabolic requirements of all the tissues of the body over a wide range of physiologic needs. In the body at rest this burden is at a minimum. Increased activity of any cell, tissue, or organ results in utilization of more oxygen and nutrient materials and the formation of greater quantities of carbon dioxide and waste products. The circulatory system meets these additional burdens and maintains the internal environment within physiologic limits by increased blood flow to the local area of greater activity or by widespread increase in the blood flow if the body as a whole is involved.

STRUCTURE AND ORGANIZATION OF CIRCULATORY VESSELS

The circulatory vessels of the body fall into three principal classes, each of which is characterized by functional and structural differences. There is a system of minute vessels, the capillaries, through which substances are exchanged between blood and lymph and the tissues. There is a low pressure collecting system, made up of lymphatic vessels and veins, which returns blood to the heart. Finally, there is a high pressure distributing system made up of arteries which carries arterialized blood and nutrient substances to all regions of the body.

Blood and lymph *capillaries* (Fig. 15.1) are formed by a single layer of flattened endothelial cells. Although the caliber of

273

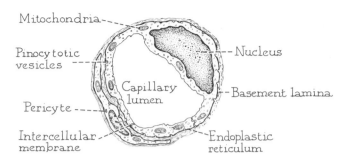

Figure 15.1 Fine structure of a capillary.

the capillaries varies in different parts of the body, the average diameter, at 8 microns, is related to the size of a red blood cell. The lymphatic capillaries begin as blind ends and are farther away from the surface of the skin or mucous membranes than are blood capillaries. The blood capillaries are interposed between distributing and collecting vessels. Pericytes are common along the wall of the blood capillaries and comprise a portion of the diffusion surface involved in capillary exchange. The endothelium of the capillaries rests upon a basal lamina. The nature of the lymphatic basement membrane allows greater permeability to macromolecules than does that of the blood capillary. The exchange of materials between blood and lymph and tissues appears to occur with the capillary acting as a porous membrane at fenestrae and intercellular junctions and by micropinocytosis (p. 27). A variety of structurally adapted capillaries are present in regions of the body which have particular physiological requirements. Some of these vessels are listed in Table 15.1. *Sinusoids* are an unusual variation of the capillary. Their wide (5 to 30 microns) irregular laminae are lined by phagocytes of the reticuloendothelial system (p. 51). These vessels are similar to fenestrated capillaries with deficient basement laminae. These structural variations offer little impediment to the passage of large molecules into perivascular space at the same time that injurious materials are removed by the phagocytes.

In the walls of *lymphatics*, *veins*, and *arteries* three layers of tissues can be distinguished (Fig. 15.2). The structural detail varies from vessel to vessel dependent upon size and physiologic demands

upon the vessel. In general, veins and lymphatics have thinner and less elastic walls than arteries. The caliber of a vein is greater than that of a corresponding artery.

The *tunica intima* is composed of a smooth lining of endothelial cells continuous into the capillaries and into the heart. The fibroelastic connective tissue elements are oriented longitudinally. An internal elastic membrane is prominent in medium-sized arteries at the junction of tunica media and tunica intima.

The *tunica media* consists mainly of circularly oriented smooth muscle and elastic tissue. In the arteries, an external elastic membrane separates tunica media from tunica adventitia. Tunica media is poorly developed in medium and large venous and lymphatic vessels in which collagenous fibers are mixed with the smooth muscle. Small veins over 45 microns begin to have a continuous layer of smooth muscle in their tunica media.

Tunica adventitia is formed by a loose arrangement of fibroelastic connective tissue oriented longitudinally. This coat is very well developed in medium and large veins with a shift toward the elastic component and the addition of smooth muscle fibers.

Valves (Fig. 15.3) are found in lymphatic vessels and in veins of medium size, in which the position of the vessels and hydrostatic pressure do not favor the flow of their contents against the force of gravity. The valves appear as semilunar pockets, or intimal folds on the inner surface of the collecting vessel with free edges lying centrally in the direction of the circulatory flow. This arrangement

TABLE 15.1 TYPES AND LOCATIONS OF CIRCULATORY VESSELS

Capillaries (4 to 12μ)	Collecting Vessels (Fig. 15.5)	Distributing Vessels (Fig. 15.6)
1. *Lymph capillaries:* skin, mucous and serous membranes; absent in central nervous system, bone marrow, eye, liver lobule, and spleen.	1. *Venules* (20-50μ): throughout the body.	1. *Arterioles* (20μ-0.3 mm.): throughout the body.
2. *Continuous capillaries:* muscle tissues, central nervous system.	2. *Small veins and lymphatics* (50μ-2 mm.): throughout the body.	2. *Small arteries* (0.3 mm.-0.5 mm.): throughout the body.
3. *Fenestrated capillaries:* renal glomeruli; endocrine glands, intestinal villi.	3. *Medium veins and lymphatic ducts* (2-9 mm.): extremities, cutaneous surfaces; thoracic duct and right lymphatic duct.	3. *Medium (muscular) arteries* (0.5 mm.-1 cm.): majority of named arteries in the body.
4. *Sinusoids:* liver, bone marrow, spleen, adrenal, and pituitary glands.	4. *Large veins* (> 1 cm.): venae cavae and junctional vessels.	4. *Large (elastic) arteries* (> 1 cm.): aorta, brachiocephalic, common carotid, pulmonary.
5. *Variants* a. — b. — c. — d. Portal system (Fig. 18.18 A, B): hepatic portal system, pituitary portal system.	5. *Variants* a. Increased smooth muscle in tunica intima: iliac, femoral, popliteal, saphenous, cephalic, basilic, umbilical veins. b. Reduced tunica media: pia mater veins, sinuses of the dura mater, cerebral veins, erectile tissue. c. See *Distributing Vessels,* 5c. d. See *Capillaries,* 5d.	5. *Variants* a. Thin-walled cerebral vessels. b. Reduced tunica intima and increased smooth muscular tunica media in umbilical arteries. c. *Arteriovenous anastomoses* (arteriole-venule): fingers, toes, ears, skeletal muscle. d. See *Capillaries,* 5d.

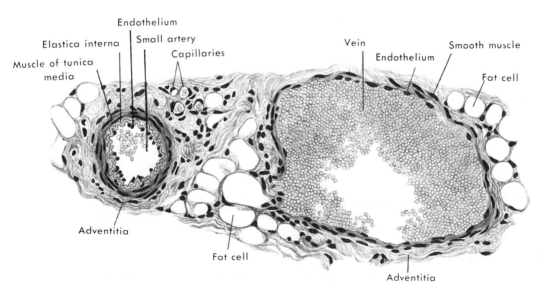

Figure 15.2 Cross section through a small artery and its accompanying vein from the submucosa of a human intestine. × 187. (After A. A. Maximow. In Bloom and Fawcett: A Textbook of Histology 9th ed., 1968.)

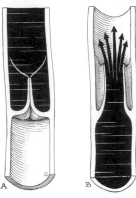

Figure 15.3 Valves of a vein. *A*, Valve closed, cups are filled with blood. *B*, Valve open, blood is passing through.

produces little interference with flow toward the heart, but is effective in preventing a reversal of the direction of flow. Valves are numerous in vessels of the extremities. They are absent in the venae cavae, veins of the intestine, vertebral veins, and in the sinuses of the dura mater.

Minute Vessels of Exchange. The distal portions of the arterial tree are made up of arterioles that lead into a system of minute vessels. These minute vessels, which display several types of structural design, are spoken of collectively as capillaries, and the system of vessels as capillary beds. They constitute the functional units of the circulatory system for distribution and exchange of substances between the blood and the tissue fluid and body cells. Blood flows along rapidly in the arteries and veins, but in the tremendously expanded vascular bed provided by the capillary areas, where it flows into a multitude of minute tubes, it is slowed down so that the fluid passes more slowly through the network of vessels. This allows time for the exchange of material to occur.

In skeletal muscle, and in the gastrointestinal tract, where the level of activity is subject to wide variations, many of the units of minute blood vessels follow the same general architectural organization. There are two more or less parallel routes, one direct and one indirect, between the most distal portions of the distributing system and the collecting system. The direct route, formed by a continuation of the arteriole, is the preferential or *thoroughfare channel*; the proximal portion of this thoroughfare channel is called a *metarteriole*. The less direct route consists of a precapillary sphincteric offshoot, called a *precapillary*, which may branch either directly from an arteriole or from a metarteriole, to lead into an interanastomosing network of *true capillaries*; a *postcapillary*, which collects the blood from the network of true capillaries, may connect with either the venous end of the thoroughfare channel or directly with a *venule* (Fig. 15.4).

The thoroughfare channels, in the units supplying skeletal muscle and the gastrointestinal tract, may be structurally differentiated only in the region of the metarteriole, or throughout their length. They show a distinct though not well developed muscular element, the muscular coat of the arterial portion being more prominent. The precapillaries are characterized by sphincteric muscular elements. The true capillaries are formed by a single layer of pavement-like endothelial cells. The

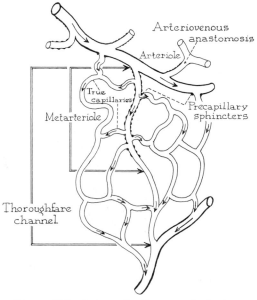

Figure 15.4 Schematic diagram of minute vessels of exchange. (After Chambers and Zweifach.)

musculature of the arterioles, metarterioles, and precapillaries allows for adjustment and progressive restriction of blood flow through the minute vessels of the vascular bed. When the tissues are relatively inactive, the blood flow may be directed chiefly to the thoroughfare channels. As activity is increased, more frequent relaxation of the precapillaries increases the flow through the network of true capillaries, thus providing for a greatly enlarged area and a higher rate of metabolic exchange. Continuation of flow through the thoroughfare channels, even when the blood flow through the true capillaries is greatly increased, may be an important factor in maintaining the pressure relations, or pressure gradient, between the arterial and venous sides of the circulatory system.

In tissues that maintain a relatively constant level of activity the organization of units of the minute vessels is less well defined; in fact, there appears to be no discernible pattern.

SYSTEMIC CIRCUITS

Systemic arteries (Fig. 15.5) are branches from the aorta beginning at the left ventricular chamber of the heart. The location of the larger vessels in the trunk and limbs affords them protection from injury. For example, arteries to extremities pass to the medial and flexor aspects of the limb. The great majority of arteries communicate with adjacent arteries to form anastomoses. In the distribution of blood to the intestine by *arterial arcades* and to the brain by the *circulus arteriosus*, the anastomoses, occurring among vessels of medium size, provide an even distribution of blood to a part by distributing vessels from several sources. Smaller anastomoses around the articulations of the extremities or in the walls of the heart are capable of opening up a *collateral circulation* if an injury occurs to the major distributing artery. *End arteries* without anastomoses before entry into the capillary bed are found in the retina, kidney, spleen, and central nervous system. Occlusion of the end

artery may cause death to the tissue it supplies.

Systemic veins are tributaries of the superior and inferior venae cavae and coronary sinus (Figs. 15.6, 15.15) which terminate in the right atrial chamber of the heart. Veins are more numerous than arteries. In many parts of the body extensive *venous plexuses* composed of anastomotic networks of small veins may be found, such as those around the vertebral column and pelvic organs. The blood in the pterygoid plexus deep to the muscles of mastication contributes to the contour of the face. *Superficial veins* in the skin and subcutaneous tissues anastomose freely with each other and with deeper veins. Such veins are prominent in the extremities (Figs. 15.21 and 15.22) and may not accompany arteries. *Deep veins* occur in anastomotic pairs (venae comitantes) around the medium and small arteries which they accompany.

Systemic veins are assisted in their role in transport and exchange by the lymphatic vessels. These vessels are interrupted in course by the lymph nodes (p. 269). *Superficial lymphatic vessels* lie in skin and connective tissues close to the superficial veins and join deep lymphatic vessels at specific points. *Deep lymphatic vessels* tend to accompany the blood vessels of a particular region and unite into lymphatic trunks and ducts (Figs. 15.7 and 15.8).

The growth of most mammalian embryos, including man, is dependent upon the placenta as the source of nutrition and arterialized blood. The unusual arrangement of *fetal circulation* (Fig. 15.25) to serve this requirement reverses the conducting and distributing role of the *umbilical arteries and veins*. Accommodation of the increased volume of blood in the liver not necessitating sinusoidal circulation is made by the *ductus venosus*. Adjustment to the lack of respiratory function of the lungs is provided by bypassing the pulmonary circulation from right atrium to left atrium of the heart through the *foramen ovale*, or from the pulmonary artery to the aorta through the *ductus arteriosus*.

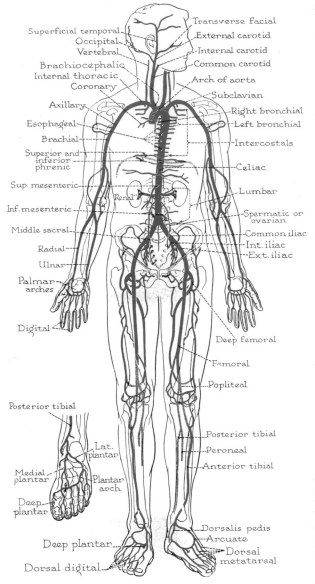

Figure 15.5 Diagram of the arterial system.

When the lungs begin to function, some of the fetal vessels and passages fall into disuse. The old channels are abandoned suddenly, but the structural occlusion is a gradual process of fibrosis that proceeds slowly in the months after birth.

With the first few breaths of the newborn infant, the ductus arteriosus closes and the blood previously shunted to the aorta now goes to the active lungs. The increase in the flow of blood to the lungs augments the volume of blood returned to the left atrium by the pulmonary veins. With increase in the pulmonary return, the compensating flow through the foramen ovale decreases and finally ceases altogether. Closure of the foramen ovale then follows as the atrial intakes are equalized. The ligation of the umbilical cord stops the flow of blood in the umbilical vessels, which are gradually obliterated by fibrous invasion. The proximal portion of

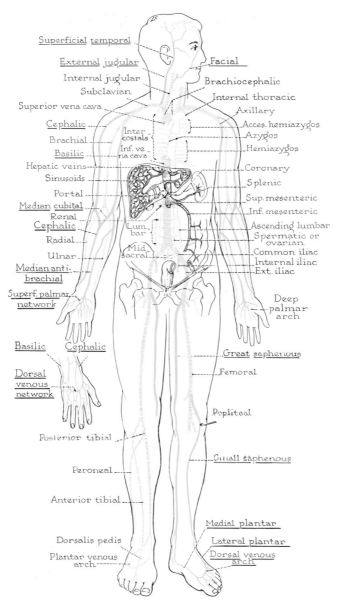

Superficial temporal
External jugular
Internal jugular
Subclavian
Superior vena cava
Cephalic
Inter costals
Brachial
Basilic
Inf. vena cava
Hepatic veins
Sinusoids
Portal
Median cubital
Renal
Cephalic
Lumbar
Radial
Mid sacral
Ulnar
Median antibrachial
Superf. palmar network
Basilic   Cephalic
Dorsal venous network
Posterior tibial
Peroneal
Anterior tibial
Dorsalis pedis
Plantar venous arch

Facial
Brachiocephalic
Internal thoracic
Axillary
Acces. hemiazygos
Azygos
Hemiazygos
Coronary
Splenic
Sup. mesenteric
Inf. mesenteric
Ascending lumbar
Spermatic or ovarian
Common iliac
Internal iliac
Ext. iliac
Deep palmar arch
Great saphenous
Femoral
Popliteal
Small saphenous
Medial plantar
Lateral plantar
Dorsal venous arch

Figure 15.6 Diagram of the venous system. Deep veins are cut across, superficial veins are in solid blue. The labels of the superficial veins are underlined. Vessels of the portal system are black.

the umbilical arteries remains as the functional internal iliac arteries; the distal or obliterated portions form the umbilical ligaments, extending from the bladder to the umbilicus beneath the peritoneum. The course of the umbilical vein is represented by a fibrous cord and is called the round ligament of the liver (see Fig. 18.17, p. 351). The remains of the ductus venosus appear as a fibrous band on the inferior surface of the liver.

In summarizing, it may be pointed out (1) that the placenta serves as a respiratory, nutritive, and excretory mechanism for the fetus; (2) that the liver receives blood directly from the placenta by way of the umbilical vein—hence the large size of this organ during fetal life and at birth; and (3) that blood distributed to the head and upper extremities is less contaminated than that passing to the lower half of the body.

(Text continues on page 292)

LYMPHATIC CIRCULATION

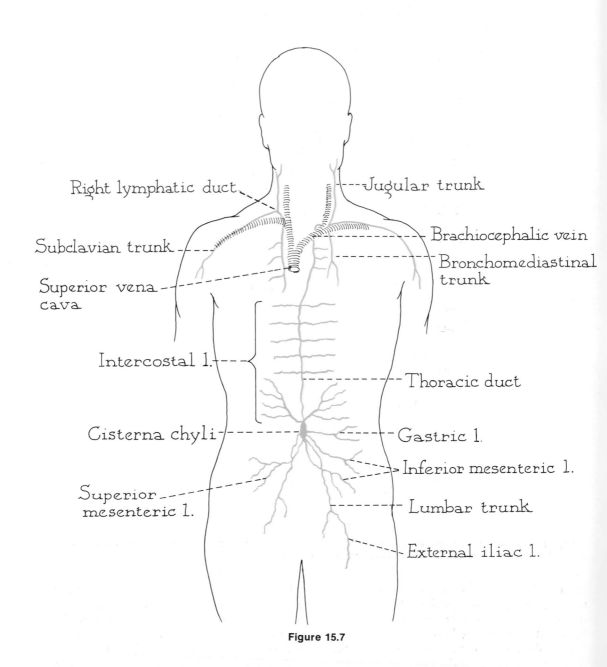

Figure 15.7

LYMPHATIC CIRCULATION

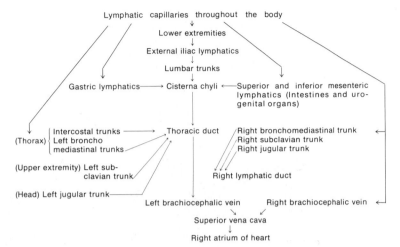

Lymphatic capillaries throughout the body
↓
Lower extremities
↓
External iliac lymphatics
↓
Lumbar trunks
↓
Gastric lymphatics ⟶ Cisterna chyli ⟵ Superior and inferior mesenteric lymphatics (Intestines and uro-genital organs)

(Thorax) { Intercostal trunks ⟶ Thoracic duct
Left broncho mediastinal trunks

Right bronchomediastinal trunk
Right subclavian trunk
Right jugular trunk

(Upper extremity) Left sub-clavian trunk

Right lymphatic duct

(Head) Left jugular trunk

Left brachiocephalic vein   Right brachiocephalic vein
↓
Superior vena cava
↓
Right atrium of heart

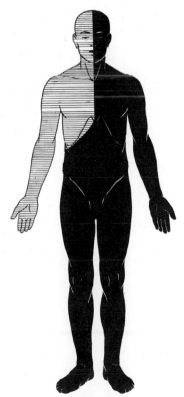

Figure 15.8

CIRCULATION TO THE BRAIN

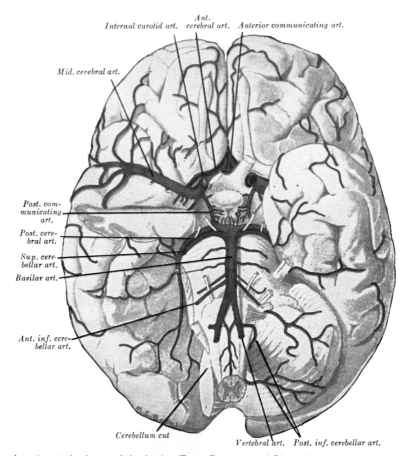

Figure 15.9 Arteries at the base of the brain. (From Ranson and Clark: Anatomy of the Nervous System.)

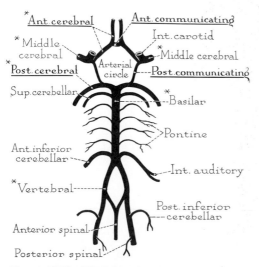

Figure 15.10 Diagram of arteries at the base of the brain. Labels of the arteries forming the arterial circle are underlined.

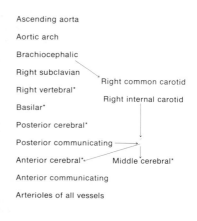

Ascending aorta

Aortic arch

Brachiocephalic

Right subclavian

Right vertebral*

Basilar*

Posterior cerebral*

Posterior communicating

Anterior cerebral*

Anterior communicating

Arterioles of all vessels

Right common carotid

Right internal carotid

Middle cerebral*

*Major feeding vessels to brain stem and cerebrum.

CIRCULATION TO THE BRAIN

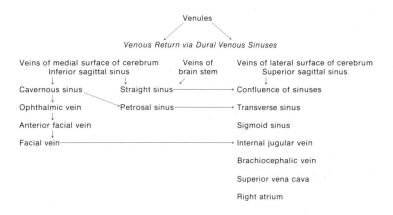

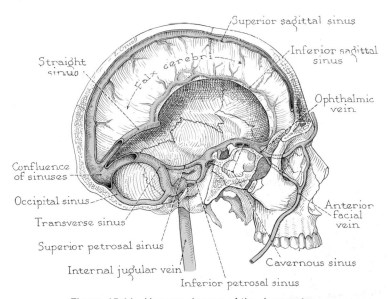

Figure 15.11 Venous sinuses of the dura mater.

CIRCULATION TO SCALP AND FACE

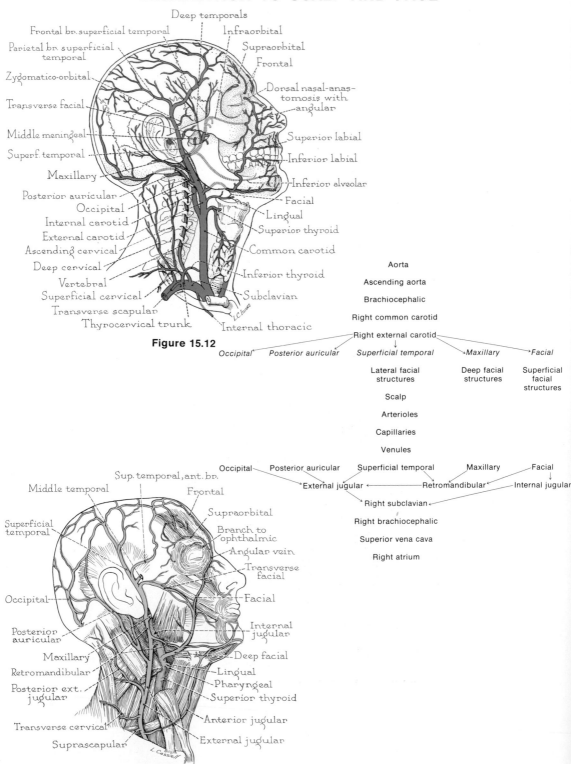

Figure 15.12

Figure 15.13

CIRCULATION TO THE HEART

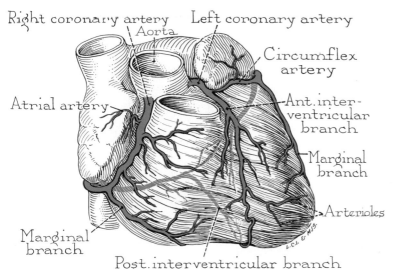

Right coronary artery   Left coronary artery

Aorta

Circumflex artery

Atrial artery

Ant. inter-ventricular branch

Marginal branch

Arterioles

Marginal branch

Post. interventricular branch

Figure 15.14

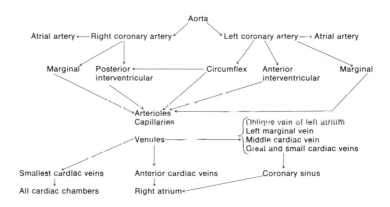

Aorta

Atrial artery ← Right coronary artery   Left coronary artery → Atrial artery

Marginal   Posterior interventricular ← Circumflex   Anterior interventricular   Marginal

Arterioles
Capillaries

Oblique vein of left atrium
Left marginal vein
Venules   Middle cardiac vein
Great and small cardiac veins

Smallest cardiac veins   Anterior cardiac veins   Coronary sinus

All cardiac chambers   Right atrium ←

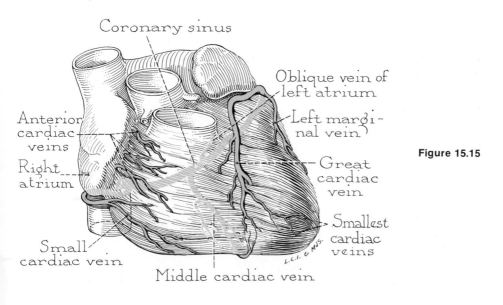

Coronary sinus

Oblique vein of left atrium

Anterior cardiac veins

Left margi-nal vein

Right atrium

Great cardiac vein

Smallest cardiac veins

Small cardiac vein

Middle cardiac vein

Figure 15.15

CIRCULATION TO RIGHT UPPER EXTREMITY*

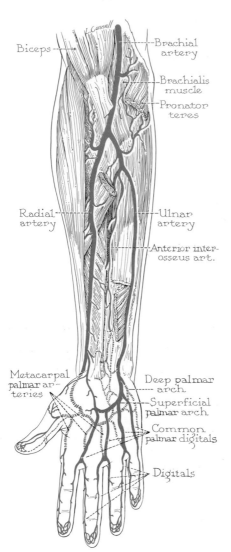

Biceps

Brachial artery

Brachialis muscle

Pronator teres

Radial artery

Ulnar artery

Anterior interosseus art.

Metacarpal palmar arteries

Deep palmar arch

Superficial palmar arch

Common palmar digitals

Digitals

Figure 15.16 Arteries of the forearm and hand. (Modified from Cunningham.)

Ascending aorta
Aortic arch
Brachiocephalic artery
Subclavian artery
Axillary artery
Brachial artery

Radial and Ulnar arteries

Superficial and deep palmar arterial arches

Digital arteries
Arterioles
Capillaries
Venules
Digital veins

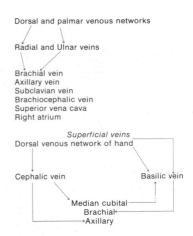

Dorsal and palmar venous networks

Radial and Ulnar veins

Brachial vein
Axillary vein
Subclavian vein
Brachiocephalic vein
Superior vena cava
Right atrium

Superficial veins
Dorsal venous network of hand

Cephalic vein

Basilic vein

Median cubital
Brachial
Axillary

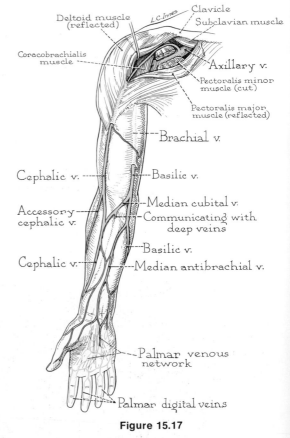

Deltoid muscle (reflected)

Clavicle

Subclavian muscle

Coracobrachialis muscle

Axillary v.

Pectoralis minor muscle (cut)

Pectoralis major muscle (reflected)

Brachial v.

Cephalic v.

Basilic v.

Accessory cephalic v.

Median cubital v.

Communicating with deep veins

Basilic v.

Cephalic v.

Median antibrachial v.

Palmar venous network

Palmar digital veins

Figure 15.17

*Refer to Figures 15.5, 15.6 and 15.23.

CIRCULATION TO LOWER EXTREMITY*

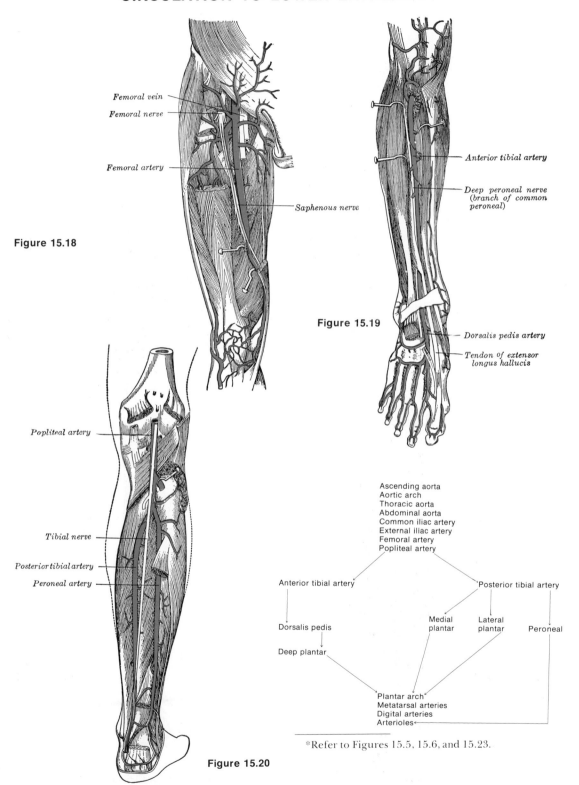

Femoral vein
Femoral nerve

Femoral artery

Saphenous nerve

Figure 15.18

Anterior tibial artery

Deep peroneal nerve
(branch of common
peroneal)

Figure 15.19

Dorsalis pedis artery

Tendon of extensor
longus hallucis

Popliteal artery

Tibial nerve

Posterior tibial artery

Peroneal artery

Figure 15.20

Ascending aorta
Aortic arch
Thoracic aorta
Abdominal aorta
Common iliac artery
External iliac artery
Femoral artery
Popliteal artery

Anterior tibial artery

Posterior tibial artery

Dorsalis pedis

Medial
plantar

Lateral
plantar

Peroneal

Deep plantar

Plantar arch
Metatarsal arteries
Digital arteries
Arterioles

*Refer to Figures 15.5, 15.6, and 15.23.

CIRCULATION TO LOWER EXTREMITY*

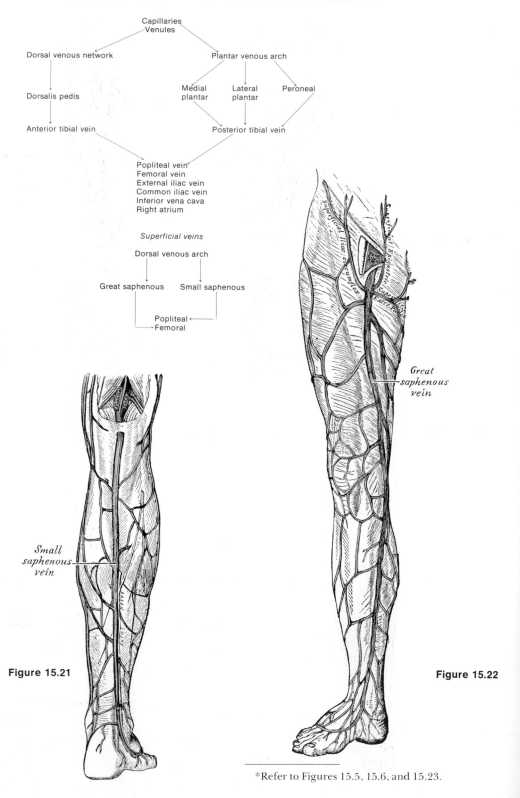

Capillaries
Venules

Dorsal venous network

Plantar venous arch

Dorsalis pedis

Medial plantar | Lateral plantar | Peroneal

Anterior tibial vein

Posterior tibial vein

Popliteal vein
Femoral vein
External iliac vein
Common iliac vein
Inferior vena cava
Right atrium

Superficial veins

Dorsal venous arch

Great saphenous   Small saphenous

Popliteal
Femoral

Small saphenous vein

Figure 15.21

Great saphenous vein

Figure 15.22

*Refer to Figures 15.5, 15.6, and 15.23.

CIRCULATION TO THE GASTROINTESTINAL TRACT

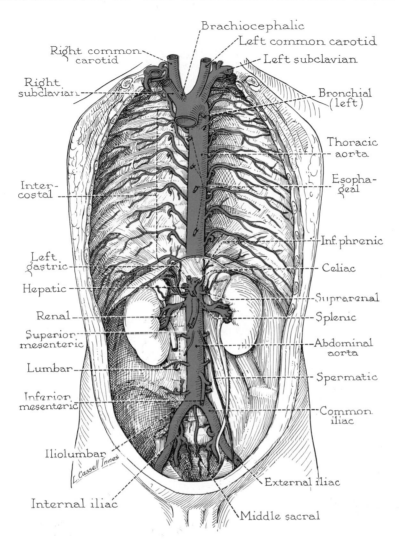

Figure 15.23 The aorta and its branches.

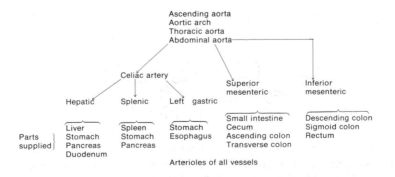

CIRCULATION TO THE GASTROINTESTINAL TRACT

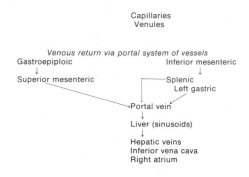

Capillaries
Venules

Venous return via portal system of vessels
Gastroepiploic   Inferior mesenteric
Superior mesenteric   Splenic
                                                           Left gastric
                                    Portal vein
                                    Liver (sinusoids)
                                    Hepatic veins
                                    Inferior vena cava
                                    Right atrium

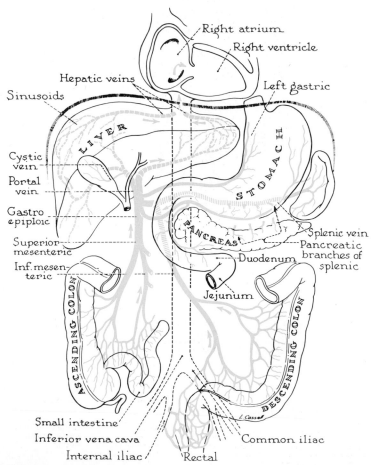

Figure 15.24 The portal system of veins. The transverse colon and small intestine have been partially removed and the organs separated in order to show the vessels.

FETAL CIRCULATION

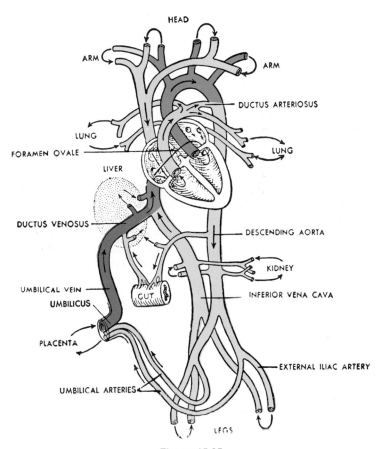

Figure 15.25

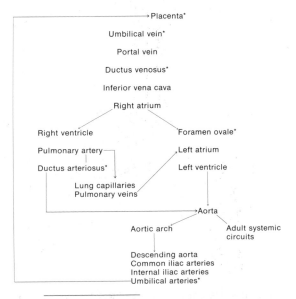

---

*Cease function at birth or shortly after.

HEART AND PULMONARY CIRCUIT

LOCATION AND STRUCTURE OF THE HEART

The heart furnishes the power needed to maintain the circulation of the blood. It expels blood into distributing vessels at a pressure sufficient to drive it through the extensive vascular circuits. The heart is located obliquely in the chest behind the sternum and the costal cartilages (Fig. 15.26). Approximately two-thirds of the heart lies to the left of the median plane; the base is directed upward and to the right, the apex downward and to the left. The apex of the heart moves toward the anterior chest wall during contraction, and its beats may be felt in the fifth intercostal space just inside the nipple line about 8 cm. to the left of the midsternal plane. Age, body build, and position will alter the relationships of the heart to the chest wall. The heart is situated between the lungs; below it is the diaphragm, and above it are the great vessels.

The heart is surrounded in the middle mediastinum by a fibroserous sac of *pericardium*. Its relations may be visualized by thinking of a ball pushed into a slightly inflated balloon. The layer which is next to the heart and adherent to it is the visceral pericardium, or epicardium. The layer forming the outer wall of the balloon is the parietal pericardium (Fig. 15.27). This is reinforced and strengthened on the outside by a layer of white fibrous tissue that is continuous with the fibers of the central tendon of the diaphragm and reflected onto the great vessels. The heart and the beginnings of the great vessels completely fill the pericardial cavity, and under normal conditions the visceral pericardium is in contact with the parietal layer. The smooth serous surfaces are lubricated by a small amount of serum.

The heart is a hollow muscular organ, roughly cone-shaped, about the size of the fist. It is completely divided by a *septum* into right and left halves. Physiologically, it functions as two pumps, the right side forcing blood through the pulmonary circulation for exchange of gases in the lungs, while the more muscular left side pumps blood through the systemic circulation. Each half of the heart is divided into an upper chamber, the *atrium*, and a lower

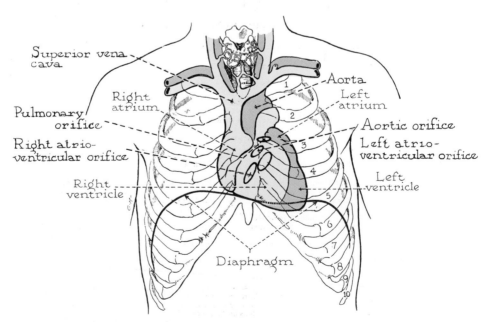

Figure 15.26 Position of heart in the chest. (From Eycleshymer and Jones: Hand Atlas of Clinical Anatomy, Lea & Febiger.)

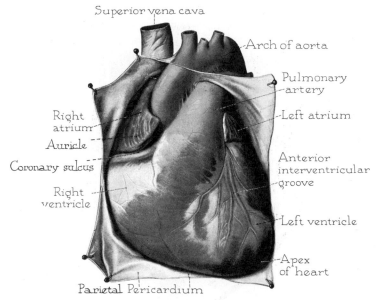

Superior vena cava

Arch of aorta

Pulmonary artery

Left atrium

Right atrium

Auricle

Coronary sulcus

Right ventricle

Anterior interventricular groove

Left ventricle

Apex of heart

Parietal Pericardium

Figure 15.27 The heart in the pericardium. The pericardium is opened from in front. (From Sobotta and McMurrich.)

chamber, the *ventricle*. The division of the heart into four chambers is indicated on the external surface by *sulci*, or grooves. The atria are separated from the ventricles by an encircling constriction, the coronary (atrioventricular) sulcus. The ventricles are separated by two grooves, the anterior and posterior (inferior) interventricular sulci. Internally, the atria are separated by the interatrial wall, which is marked by a depression, the fossa ovalis (see *fetal circulation*, p. 291). The right and left ventricles are separated by the interventricular septum (Fig. 15.28).

The walls of the heart in both atria and ventricles consist of three layers, an inner, the endocardium; a middle, the myocardium; and an outer, the epicardium or visceral pericardium. These walls are believed to be homologous with the three tunics of the blood vessels.

Endocardium is lined by endothelium continuous with that of the blood vessels which enter and leave the heart. A delicate connective tissue, the subendothelial layer, unites the endothelium with the larger portion of endocardium which is composed of elastic elements and smooth muscle fibers. The subendothelial fibroelastic

connective tissue layer contains the branches of the conduction system of the heart (Fig. 15.30). In several regions the collagenous fibers are unusually dense and form a *cardiac skeleton* to support some of the structures of the heart. The orifices of pulmonary artery and aorta and valves between atria and ventricles (Fig. 15.26) are surrounded by supporting tissue of the cardiac skeleton. The membranous portion of the interventricular septum is reinforced by elements of the cardiac skeleton.

Myocardium consists of layers and bands of cardiac muscle fibers (Fig. 11.5) wound around the atria and ventricles in complex spirals and interwoven by elastic and reticular fibers. Most portions of the atrial walls are thin and smooth. Distensible columns of pectinate muscles can be found in the auricles (Fig. 15.28). Trabeculae carneae are a comparable arrangement of muscle fibers in the thick walls of the ventricles. Such an architecture is appropriate since the burden of pumping the blood falls upon the ventricular chambers of the heart. The walls of the left ventricle

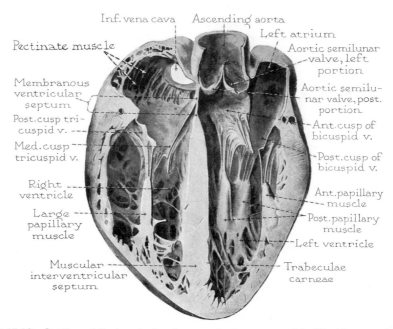

Figure 15.28 Section of the heart, showing ventricular septum. (Modified from Spalteholz.)

are three times the thickness of the walls of the right ventricle (Fig. 15.28). Left ventricular pumping maintains the systemic circuits of the body at relatively high pressures and against the considerable resistance to blood flow which is offered by the friction of the extensive network of blood vessels. Right ventricular pumping maintains circulation through the pulmonary circuit at relatively low pressures and at considerably less peripheral resistance.

The *epicardium* or visceral pericardium consists of a single layer of mesothelial cells supported by a small amount of connective tissue. Extrinsic nerves to the heart (p. 311) and coronary blood vessels are found here.

The orifices between the atria and ventricles and between ventricles and aorta are guarded by heart valves that permit the passage of blood in one direction only. If the heart is to function effectively as a pump, valves are necessary at these points or energy will be wasted in pumping blood in the wrong direction. The valves consist of membranous leaflets with a cover of chondroid tissue that are opened or closed

by the pressure of the blood. The *right* (tricuspid) and *left* (bicuspid) *atrioventricular valves* are prevented from turning back into the atrium by tough collagenous *chordae tendinae*, which pass from the edges of the leaflets to the *papillary muscles* projecting from the walls of the ventricle (Figs. 15.28, 15.29). When the ventricle becomes filled with blood and begins to contract, these leaflets are floated into position and forced shut by the increased pressure. *Pulmonary semilunar valves* between right ventricle and pulmonary artery and *aortic semilunar valves* between left ventricle and aorta permit blood flow from the ventricles into the large arteries during the contraction of the heart. When the ventricles relax the three membranous leaflets of each valve are floated shut and prevent the back flow of blood from the pulmonary artery and aorta into the heart. The single membranous flap of the valve of the foramen ovale between right atrium and left atrium of the fetal heart opens with blood flow provided by the placenta and closes with contraction of the heart. Equalization of blood flow into both atria occurs as the newborn infant begins to use his pulmonary circuit and the valve of the

PULMONARY CIRCULATION

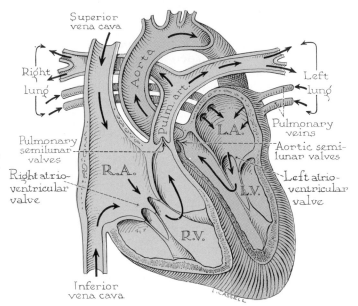

Figure 15.29 Diagram of the heart, showing the direction of blood flow.

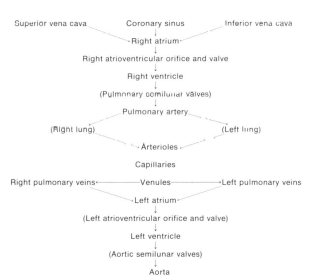

foramen ovale closes permanently to become the *fossa ovalis*.

The orifices of the collecting vessels are not guarded by valves. Systemic circulation returns to the right atrium through the superior and inferior venae cavae and coronary sinus. Pulmonary circulation returns to the left atrium of the heart through the four pulmonary veins. Details of the respiratory exchange in the pulmonary circuit have been discussed in Chapter 13. The relationships of pas-

sage of venous blood from the collecting point in right atrium through the heart into the arterializing capillary networks of the lungs and back to the collecting point in the left atrium for passage into systemic circulation are shown in summary in the pictorial and word diagram. This summary will also serve to reemphasize the following features of cardiac function:

1. The heart plays the role of a compound pump placed between and connecting two circulations. The

right side of the heart acts as the pump to the pulmonary circuit and the left side of the heart to the systemic circuits.

2. The right side of the heart contains "venous" blood laden with carbon dioxide and deficient in oxygen. The left side of the heart contains "arterialized" blood with high Po_2 and low Pco_2.

3. The atria are receiving chambers for the collecting vessels, and the ventricles are discharging chambers for the distributing vessels.

ORIGIN AND PROPAGATION OF THE HEART BEAT

Cardiac muscle has the properties common to all types of muscle, and in addition shares with smooth muscle the property of inherent rhythmicity (see pacemaker potentials, p. 67). Hearts that have been severed from all nervous connections or removed from the body will continue to beat for some time if cared for properly. Those of cold-blooded animals continue to beat for relatively long periods of time; they serve well for studies of the properties of the heart.

The turtle heart, which is structurally different from the mammalian heart, has a sinus venosus, two atria, and a single ventricle. If these three parts are divided into two parts by cutting between the sinus and the atria, both portions will begin to beat after a short period. The sinus will beat first, and then after a short period the atria and ventricle will start. The sinus beats at a faster rate than the lower portions of the heart. If a second cut is now made between the atria and the ventricle, the atria continue to beat and usually the ventricle recovers its rhythmic contractions, but at a slower rate than that of the atria. From this experiment it may be seen that the property of inherent rhythmicity is common to all chambers of the heart, but that the rate of contraction is highest for the sinus, slower for the atria, and slowest for the ventricle. In the intact turtle heart the sinus is called the pacemaker of the heart, since, because it

shows the most rapid rhythm, it sets the pace for the atria and ventricle.

In the mammalian heart there is a small mass of specialized tissue, the *sino-atrial* (S-A) *node*, located in the right atrium near the superior vena cava; this area serves as the pacemaker under normal conditions. The same gradient of rhythmicity between pacemaker, atria, and ventricles is evident in the mammalian heart. The mechanism underlying rhythmicity is still obscure.

The wave of excitation or depolarization (Fig. 15.30) spreads throughout the right and left atria, the impulse traveling in the muscular tissue of their walls and causing the contraction of these chambers. On the lower part of the inner wall of the right atrium there is a second mass of specialized tissue, the *atrioventricular* (A-V) *node*. Continuing from the atrioventricular node, a bundle of conducting fibers, the *atrioventricular bundle* (bundle of His), passes down to the upper border of the interventricular septum, where it divides into a right and left branch. Each of these *bundle branches* passes to the corresponding ventricle, subdividing to form an interlacing *subendocardial network*, (Purkinje fibers), ending in the papillary muscles and the ventricular tissue generally. The atrioventricular node acts as a relay station that picks up impulses that pass from the region of the sino-atrial node, and after a brief delay transmits them to the ventricles through the atrioventricular bundle. Impulses reach both ventricles at approximately the same time and cause them to contract. To summarize: the wave of contraction in the mammalian heart is initiated at or close to the sino-atrial node, radiates throughout the muscular wall of the atria, perhaps preferentially through an intra-atrial band between the atria, and by the most direct route to the atrioventricular node; impulses excite the atrioventricular nodal tissue and after a slight delay are transmitted to the ventricles through the atrioventricular bundle.

In certain abnormal conditions the region of the sino-atrial node does not act as a pacemaker. For example, the common bundle may fail to conduct, as occurs in heart-block. If this occurs, the beat may

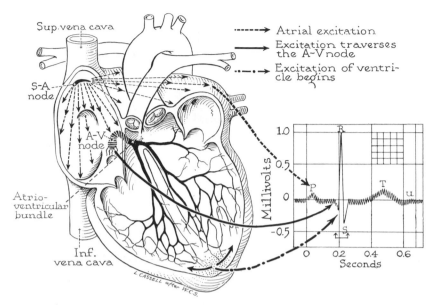

Figure 15.30 Correlation of the electrocardiogram with the spread of the excitation wave.

originate in the center having the next highest rate of rhythmic discharge. Thus either the atrioventricular node or the atria may act as pacemaker, or, when conduction is blocked, the ventricles may beat at their own inherent rhythm.

The rate of discharge of the pacemaker which determines heart rate is normally modified by changes in its chemical environment, by temperature and by influence of the cardiac nerves. The control of heart rate is discussed in Chapter 16.

CARDIAC CYCLE

In a single beat of the heart the atria and ventricles go through a succession of events that are repeated at each beat. The sequence of events during one heart beat is spoken of as a "cardiac cycle" (Figs. 15.31 and 15.32). During a cardiac cycle the term *systole* is given to the contraction phase and *diastole* to the relaxation phase. We use the terms "atrial systole" and "atrial diastole," "ventricular systole" and "ventricular diastole" to indicate the state of activity of the heart chambers.

In a single cardiac cycle, atrial systole is followed closely by ventricular systole. Atrial systole is completed and the atria enter the diastolic phase as ventricular systole begins. Ventricular systole is followed by diastole of the ventricles. For a short time the entire mass of cardiac tissue is relaxed, since a part of the diastolic phases of the atria and ventricles overlaps. Atrial systole is again initiated as a second cardiac cycle begins.

The absolute duration of the phases of the cardiac cycle varies with the heart rate, the length of both the diastolic and systolic phases shortening as the heart rate increases. With a fast heart rate the diastolic phase shortens proportionately more than the systolic phase. When the heart is beating at a rate of 70 per minute, the duration of a cardiac cycle is about 0.8 second. Atrial systole lasts 0.1 second, atrial diastole 0.7 second; ventricular systole 0.3 second, diastole 0.5 second. The relationship of atrial and ventricular cycles is shown in Figures 15.31 and 15.32. The diastolic periods of the two chambers overlap for 0.4 second, during which brief period the entire heart is quiescent.

Two audible sounds occur during each heart beat. They may be detected by placing an ear against the chest wall or by listening with a stethoscope. The sounds can be described by the syllables *lubb-dupp*. The first sound is low-pitched and of relatively long duration. This sound

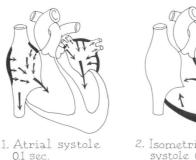
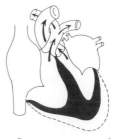
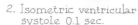

1. Atrial systole 0.1 sec.

2. Isometric ventricular systole 0.1 sec.

3. Isotonic ventricular systole 0.2 sec.

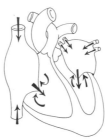

4. Isometric ventricular diastole 0.05 sec.

5. Late diastole 0.35 sec.

Figure 15.31 Relation of time to the contraction phases of the cardiac cycle.

is best distinguished at the left fifth interspace of the ribs at the apex region of the heart (Fig. 15.26). It is caused by closure of the atrioventricular valves and the contraction of ventricular muscle. The second sound is short, sharp, high-pitched, and audible at right or left sternal borders and the second interspace of the ribs. It is produced by the closure of the semilunar valves at the beginning of ventricular diastole.

It is possible to arrange a series of records showing the changes in the ventricular volume and ventricular pressure, atrial pressure, aortic pressure, heart sounds, and an electrocardiogram, so that simultaneous events in the cardiac cycle become apparent. The pulse and pressure changes are discussed in Chapter 16; the electrocardiogram and heart sounds are dealt with in the following paragraphs. It has been necessary to redraw the records to a common scale so that the characteristic tracing of events in each record can be compared at any moment in the cardiac cycle. The phases of the cardiac cycle and valve action are indicated on the diagram.

Diligent analysis and study of the simultaneous curves in Figure 15.32 will well repay the student for his effort, for such a chart unfolds the story of related circulatory events.

ELECTROCARDIOGRAMS (EKG)

Myocardial fibers have a resting electrical potential of −80 mv. Depolarization occurs in the heart, with myocardial fibers acting as a syncytium (p. 193). The ion exchanges are similar to those of skeletal muscle, although the slow repolarization may be due to a delay in increased potassium permeability. Body fluids are good conductors and the body as a whole constitutes a volume conductor. The differences in the electrical potential from various regions of the heart at any moment can be measured at the body surface through electrodes placed on the extremities and on the chest. These *manifest potential differences* from moment to moment during the cardiac cycle can be re-

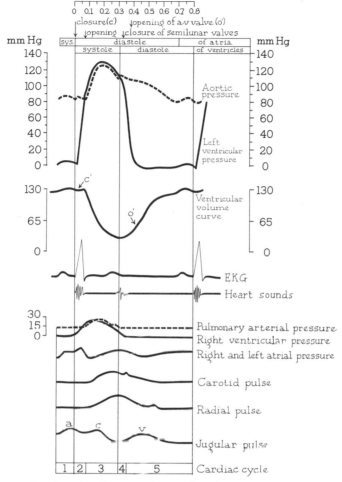

Figure 15.32 Curves showing simultaneous changes in volumes, pressures, pulses, heart sounds, and electrocardiogram.

corded by an electrocardiograph, i.e., a recording galvanometer and transistor amplifiers, on a strip of moving paper or magnetic tape.

There are three standard bipolar leads from electrodes placed upon the right arm, left arm, and left leg. These can be visualized as a triangle paralleling the frontal axes of the heart. Lead I, between right arm and left arm, constitutes the base of the triangle lying along the base of the heart and measures the potential differences between the right and left sides. Lead II, between right arm and left leg, is the right side of the triangle and measures potential differences between

the right side of the base of the heart and the apex. Lead III forms the left side of the triangle between the left arm and left leg. The bipolar leads are used to record heart action as viewed from the frontal plane. Nine unipolar chest and limb leads are also customarily employed to register the cardiac activity in the area of the heart under the positive electrode along various cardiac axes. The unipolar leads are used for locating more precisely any areas of dysfunction that may exist.

During periods when all the cardiac fibers contributing to the record are simultaneously active or when all are relaxed, no potential differences exist and the electrocardiogram does not show any deflections; the record shows an isoelectric base line. By convention the upward deflections indicate positive potentials and downward deflections demonstrate negative potentials from the isoelectric base line. Figures 15.30 and 15.32 show normal electrocardiograms. The P wave is produced by atrial depolarization; QRS complex occurs with ventricular depolarization and the ST segment and T wave represent ventricular repolarization. The potentials of atrial repolarization are buried in the QRS complex. The U wave is not a consistent finding and is thought to indicate a repolarization in the papillary muscles. PR interval of 0.18 seconds occurs with depolarization of the atria and conduction of the potentials through the atrioventricular (A-V) node. QT interval of 0.4 seconds represents depolarization and repolarization, and the T wave ventricular repolarization.

The records are important physiologically and clinically, because they not only indicate normal activity but also reveal abnormalities in the sequence of events in the cardiac cycle, in heart rhythm, and in conduction of the muscle fibers. For example, if the intervals between successive QRS waves are equal, we know the heart is beating regularly. If the PR interval is of normal value, we know that the conduction between the sino-atrial node and ventricles is unimpaired. The electrocardiogram will reveal cardiac arrhythmias when the heart beat originates from an abnormal or ectopic site in the conducting mechanism or follows an abnormal path or time interval through the conducting mechanisms. Injury to cardiac muscle following impairment of the blood supply in the coronary circuit commonly appears as an elevation in the ST segment. Changes in blood plasma levels of calcium and potassium will produce severe cardiac abnormalities. Thus, deviations from the well-defined characteristics of normal electrocardiograms reveal abnormal conditions of the heart.

QUESTIONS FOR DISCUSSION

1. How do arteries differ from veins in structure and function?

2. Discuss the value of the following circulatory structures: (a) minute vessels; (b) sinusoids; (c) foramen ovale; (d) arterial circle; (e) portal circuits; (f) dural sinuses; (g) arteriovenous anastomoses; (h) superficial and deep veins.

3. What are the structural and functional differences of lymphatic and blood capillaries and sinusoids? Compare the location of fenestrated and nonfenestrated capillaries and formulate a general concept of their relative value in location.

4. What adaptations have occurred in fetal circulation? What happens to these structures in neonatal life?

5. Relate the functional loss in the nervous system to injury of the following arteries: middle cerebral, posterior cerebral, vertebral, basilar.

6. How are the coronary and pulmonary circuits related?

7. Retrace the pulmonary and bronchial circuits in the light of systemic respiratory exchange to lung tissue and arterialization of blood of the pulmonary artery.

8. In the electrocardiogram, what conditions of cardiac muscle are indicated by an isoelectric line? How are the P, QRS, and T waves associated with the action of the heart?

9. How does the activity of the heart compare with that of skeletal muscle?

10. What might be responsible for an acceleration of heart beat in the course of a fever?

11. Describe the changes in valves and chambers that occur in the cardiac cycle. Why does ventricular volume build up in diastole?

12. If the EKG reveals a PR interval of 0.34 seconds and normal P, QRS, and T waves, what may have occurred?

13. How are heart sounds related to the EKG?

MAINTENANCE AND REGULATION OF BLOOD PRESSURE

CHAPTER SIXTEEN

SYSTEMIC CIRCUIT

Observations on Blood Pressure. If a small artery is cut, blood will spurt from the point of injury to a considerable height. The column of blood will rise and fall, reaching its maximum height during cardiac systole and its minimum during diastole. This demonstrates that the blood within the arteries is under pressure and that the pressure varies with the phase of the cardiac cycle. The peak, which occurs during ventricular systole, is called *systolic pressure*; the minimum value, which occurs during ventricular diastole, is known as *diastolic pressure*. The arithmetic difference between systolic and diastolic pressures is called the *pulse pressure. Mean arterial pressure* represents the simple average between the peak and low points, that is, between the systolic and diastolic pressures in the continuous pressure change. Since mean arterial pressure does not take into account the variation of pressure with time during a cardiac cycle, it is not a good index of the effective force driving the blood through the vessels.

Blood pressure is measured in terms of

the height of the column of mercury, expressed as mm. Hg, that it is capable of supporting. The significance of the values may be more readily grasped if the pressures are related to the height to which they would raise a column of blood. This was demonstrated by an animal experiment first performed in 1773 by Reverend Stephen Hale. An artery is connected to a vertical glass tube that extends 5 feet above the level of the heart. If we assume a normal adult systolic pressure of 120 mm. Hg and a diastolic pressure of 80 mm.Hg, blood will flow over the top of the tube during systole (120 mm. Hg is equivalent to 5 feet 1½ inches of water pressure) and during diastole it would form a column nearly 3 feet 5 inches high within the tube.

Hemodynamic Pressures. In the heart chemical energy is converted to mechanical energy, which in turn is transformed into blood pressure and blood flow. There are two major components of hemodynamic pressure—*driving pressure* and *transmural pressure*. Driving pressure, the pressure difference at any two points in the vascular system, is responsible for blood flow. Transmural pressure is the result of the elastic stretch of the blood vessels; it affects the size of the vessels and hence influences resistance to flow. The role of these two components will be discussed further in a later section (page 308).

The pumping action of the heart ejects blood—a somewhat viscous fluid—against the volume of blood already contained in a closed system of elastic vessels. Since, during ventricular systole, blood is forced into the highly elastic arterial system faster than it can escape into the capillaries and veins, the arteries are stretched to greater capacity. As blood is continually leaving the arterial system and passing into the capillaries and then to the veins, the blood pressure begins to fall at the end of ventricular systole when the inflow into the arteries stops. The elastic recoil of the arterial walls presses upon the blood within and forces it onward through the vessels at a constantly decreasing pressure until the arteries regain the presystolic caliber. The energy that was stored up during the stretching of the elastic tissue is expended between heart beats. As a result, the flow of blood through the broad bed of the capillary system and the veins is continuous rather than pulsatile.

The driving pressure is used in performing the work necessary for moving blood throughout the circulatory system (and, in the capillaries, in supplying filtration pressure); that part of this energy utilized in overcoming friction is transformed into heat. Blood pressure measured at any point in the circulatory system represents the amount of energy that remains to force the blood through the vessels.

In the passage of blood through the larger arteries relatively little energy is lost as heat, so that in general the blood pressure in these arteries would be nearly the same as that in the proximal aorta. However, as the blood flows into the smaller arteries and arterioles, resistance becomes an important factor and considerable quantities of energy are used up in overcoming friction, so that the energy that remains to move the blood along decreases rapidly. This results in a rapid fall in pressure as the blood passes through the arterioles into the capillaries. The capillaries are extremely small and might be expected to offer a high resistance to flow of blood, with a consequent rapid fall of pressure in the capillary system. However, the frictional resistance is to some extent minimized by the low velocity and the lesser viscosity of the blood in the capillaries. Still, a significant pressure drop does occur in the capillaries, since work is expended in the transport of blood through this system. Further decreases in pressure result from the passage of blood through the venules and the veins, so that venous pressures measured at the level of the heart may show zero or even subatmospheric pressure.

The gradation of pressure from the mean arterial pressure of about 100 mm. Hg to the arteriolar pressures of 70 to 30 mm. Hg, the capillary pressures of 35 to 15 mm. and the venous pressure of 15 to less than zero mm. Hg is called the *pressure gradient* of the circulatory system. Figure 16.1 illustrates pressure gradients in different divisions of the systemic circuit.

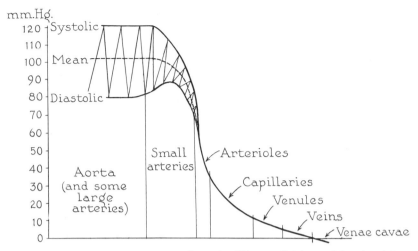

Figure 16.1 Diagram showing pressure gradients in different divisions of the circulatory system.

Velocity of Blood Flow. Blood flows rapidly through the arterial system, slows down as it passes through the capillaries, and speeds up again as it passes into the veins. The variations in velocity are related to the difference in the cross-section areas of the vascular bed, blood velocity decreasing as the total cross-section area increases (Table 16.1).

Approximate values for velocity and relative values for cross-section area in the various divisions of the circulatory system are shown in Table 16.1. The values are only illustrative, since wide variations exist.

The velocities in the circulatory bed may be illustrated by the more familiar example of a stream passing from a narrow channel into a pond that is drained by another relatively narrow stream. It must be borne in mind that in any given time the same amount of water passes each section along the way. When the stream bed is narrow, the water flows rapidly; in the pond the same quantity of water per unit of time will pass any point on the shore, but because of the increased width of the channel the velocity of flow is reduced. Occasionally measurements are made of the time it would take a particular portion or drop of blood to be transmitted from one point in circulation to another; these are known as *circulation times*. A number of factors, including differences in form and length of blood vessels, pulse rate, and size of the individual cause variations of these values. Circulation time from a vein of the arm to the tongue would be from nine to sixteen seconds.

Arterial Pulse. If we place a fingertip over a superficial artery, we feel an impact or pulse that appears to coincide closely with the beat of the heart. If we were equipped to make sufficiently precise observations of the time relations, we would find that the pulse occurred shortly after the beginning of systolic ejection and that the interval between these two events was greater in the more peripheral arteries such as the radial and femoral arteries than in the more central vessels such as the subclavian and carotid arteries.

The pulse is the result of the sudden pressure variations that occur as blood is forced out of the heart against the column of blood already filling the arterial system at a time when the vessels are only moderately stretched and are capable of con-

TABLE 16.1 VELOCITY OF BLOOD FLOW

Division	Relative Area of Total Cross Section	Blood Velocity
Arterial (aorta)	1	22 cm. per sec.
Venous (venae cavae)	2	11 cm. per sec.
Capillaries	600-800	0.1 to 0.05 cm. per sec.

siderable further elastic expansion. The expansion and the elastic recoil of the arteries set up vibrations in the arterial wall which are transmitted peripherally. These vibrations in the arterial wall will travel faster than the column of blood that has been ejected from the heart. The pulse may travel at a rate of 5 to 10 meters a second, while the blood travels only about 0.2 to 0.6 meter per second.

The pulse may be taken wherever an artery approaches the surface of the body. It is felt in the radial artery at the wrist, the common carotid artery in the neck, the superficial temporal artery in front of the ear over the zygomatic arch, the popliteal artery under the knee, and the dorsalis pedis in the foot.

Palpation of the pulse is a convenient way of determining heart rate; it is of value in detecting abnormal cardiac rhythms and variations in pulse pressure. The character of the pulse may differ with variations in the factors which affect and maintain blood pressure (see outline on p. 314).

Measurement of Blood Pressure: Direct Methods. Direct methods of measuring pressure in arteries, veins, or capillaries are usually limited to experimental animals since they involve a certain amount of operative procedure. Venous pressure can be measured directly in man, however, using an apparatus known as a phlebomanometer. A needle containing citrate, and connected to a calibrated glass tube and a sensitive manometer, is inserted into a superficial vein. Blood enters and forces back the level of saline in the glass tube (the meniscus); counter pressure is applied until the meniscus is forced back to its original position, and the pressure registered on the manometer is noted. Pressure varies in the median basilic vein from 40 to 140 mm. of water pressure. Venous pressure is elevated when the heart does not contract efficiently to maintain pulmonary circulation.

Arterial pressures can be measured directly in animal experiments by inserting a needle or cannula into an artery and connecting it with a strain gauge manometer and recorder which, when used properly, register accurate pressure curves. If only mean arterial pressure is to be measured a mercury manometer will suffice.

The contours of the arterial pressure curve will vary somewhat, depending upon the artery selected. A record taken from the aorta or a proximal artery usually shows *(a)* an abrupt rise of pressure corresponding with the beginning of ejection of blood from the ventricles, *(b)* a fall in pressure as the ejection of blood falls off, *(c)* the dicrotic notch, which signals the closure of the aortic semilunar valves, and *(d)* a gradual drop in pressure during diastole (Fig. 15.32).

Measurement of Arterial Blood Pressure in Man (Fig. 16-2). Clinically, blood pressure is measured with a sphygmomanometer by an indirect method. The principle of the method is to balance the pressures in the artery with an externally applied air pressure and to observe the air pressure by means of a mercury or aneroid (air-pressure gauge type) manometer.

The sphygmomanometer consists of (1) a rubber bag covered with an unyielding material that extends to a length convenient for wrapping the bag around the arm, (2) a hand bulb for inflating the cuff connected to the cavity of the bag by a rubber tube, (3) an escape valve (usually made as part of inflating bulb) that permits release of air at various rates, and (4) a manometer connected to the pressure bag by a length of rubber tubing.

The *brachial artery* is usually chosen as the site of measurement. Pressure is applied over the artery at a value *(a)* that just permits the passage of blood under the cuff at the systolic peak—this value is taken as systolic—or at a value *(b)* that permits the passage of blood under the cuff through the entire cardiac cycle—diastolic pressure. In determination of systolic pressure the passage of blood under the cuff is noted by the auscultatory method, in which the observer listens for characteristic sounds with a stethoscope placed over the artery, or the palpatory method, in which the observer feels the radial pulse.

Normal Values. Blood pressure is routinely measured without attempting to control the subject's activity before the

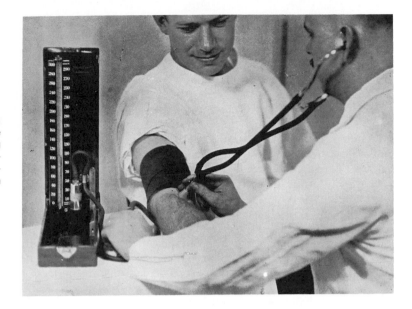

Figure 16.2 Determining the blood pressure by the auscultatory method, using a mercury type of sphygmomanometer. (From Crandall: Introduction to Human Physiology.)

rest period that generally precedes the measurement, or the time that has elapsed since his last meal. If the results of the measurements may influence his future activities, as when he is being examined for service in the armed forces or for life insurance, the subject's eagerness, fear, or anxiety may increase his blood pressure readings. For these and other reasons it is doubtful whether indirect readings may be relied upon to give results that are nearer than 10 mm. Hg above or below the resting physiologic value. Since this is generally known by those experienced in making and interpreting the measurements, they are guided accordingly in distinguishing between normal and abnormal or pathologic values. Normal values, then, represent an order of magnitude rather than a precise figure. Most of the reference values apply to measurements taken under everyday routine conditions. These are, however, adequate to show variations with age, weight, and sex.

Though we do not have results from acceptable studies on all age groups, it has been established that normally there is an increase in the systolic and diastolic pressures up to the age of about sixty-two years and a more rapid increase from sixty-two to eighty-five years, after which they may decrease. Blood pressure of newborn infants has been reported as 80/46 mm. Hg,

with the standard deviations of 8.1 and 8.2 mm., respectively, for systolic and diastolic pressures (results of *direct* measurement). No significant differences in blood pressures between boys and girls have been reported up to the age of ten to twelve years, at which time the systolic pressure in girls is slightly higher. After puberty, when adult levels have been attained, the blood pressures in young men exceed those in women. The pressures for male adults are given as 110/70 mm. Hg at twenty years of age to 140/90 mm. Hg at sixty-five years of age. After menopause, the systolic pressure of women may exceed that of males in a corresponding age group. Heavy people show somewhat higher values than persons of normal weight.

If the subjects have been resting in bed, and have not eaten for three to five hours, systolic pressures may decrease by 15 to 30 mm. Hg and diastolic from 5 to 10 mm. Similar values are also observed in normal, quiet sleep.

PULMONARY CIRCUIT

The pulmonary circuit is the vascular bed between the right and left sides of the heart. It is an elaborate system for perfusing the lungs for exchange of respiratory gases. Also, because of its location between the two sides of the heart, it is in a position to serve three mechanical functions. It can act as a reservoir of blood for the left ventricle, control the left ventricular output by varying venous return, and the small vessels in the pulmonary arterial system can filter out systemic venous particles.

When the heart and circulation are normal, the output of the right and left sides of the heart are virtually identical. Although the pulmonary circulation receives the same blood flow as the systemic circulation, the right heart ejects the blood into a highly distensible low resistance system. Pulmonary arterial pressure is only about one fifth to one sixth that of systemic blood pressure. Systolic pulmonary pressure is in the range of 20 to 30 mm. Hg; during diastole this drops off to about 7 to 12 mm. Hg. Two characteristics of the pulmonary circulation have marked influence on pulmonary blood pressure. The first, the marked distensibility of the arterial tree, prevents a sharp rise in pressure during systolic ejection. The second is the rapid run-off of blood from the arterial tree during systole because of the low vascular resistance. The pressure drop over the vascular bed is in the order of one tenth of that of the systemic circuit. Pulse velocity is relatively slow in the pulmonary artery and its branches, i.e., 0.2 to 0.28 m/sec.

FACTORS INFLUENCING BLOOD PRESSURE

The relatively narrow range of blood pressures that are maintained during rest and light activity may be extended by a variety of circumstances encountered in everyday living. The upper range for systolic pressure may be increased to 180 to 200 mm. Hg and diastolic pressure to 100 to 110 mm. Hg under conditions of maximum exercise or extreme emotion. Other circumstances involving emotional reactions, such as particularly distressing or distasteful situations, may result in so great a fall of blood pressure as to cause fainting or unconsciousness. For the most part, however, extreme variations are prevented or minimized by compensatory reactions, and blood pressure is nicely adjusted to the state of bodily activity. Blood supply, locally and throughout the body, is regulated to the degree of activity. The mechanisms of these adjustments are discussed in the following sections.

Cardiac Output. Blood pressure and blood flow are intimately dependent upon the amount of blood pumped by the heart. The principal factors determining cardiac output are the amount of blood entering the heart during diastole, i.e., diastolic filling; force of the heart beat; degree of emptying during diastole; and heart rate.

The amount of blood entering the heart is influenced by the venous return; the duration of diastole; the impedance to inflow which depends on the amount of blood remaining at the end of systole and on the distensibility of the ventricles; and the pressure and rate of flow of the blood returning through the veins, including the contribution of atrial contraction at the end of diastole.

The state of the blood vessels that determines the flow through the capillary bed and the condition of the capillaries themselves influence venous return. These determine the run-off from the arterial system and the volume capacity of the capillary bed. If any extensive area of capillary dilation occurs, the capacity of the circulatory system is increased so that the rate of flow of venous blood into the right atrium is decreased.

Venous return to the heart is increased during exercise by the contraction of the skeletal muscles, which tend to force the blood toward the heart by compressing the thin-walled veins, since veins have valves that prevent blood flow in the opposite direction. The deep and rapid breathing that occurs during exercise also aids venous return, since deep inspirations lower the pressure within the chest, aspirating the blood toward the heart. The descent of the diaphragm compresses the abdominal viscera, forcing blood from the veins in this area.

Gravity also has its influence, since blood below the heart level must return against the force of gravity, while the flow of blood from areas above the heart level is aided by gravity. This effect may be easily demonstrated by observing the veins of the hand when the arm is allowed to hang by the side of the body and then raised above the head. Standing quite still for a relatively short period of time may cause fainting, since the venous return is reduced by (a) the effects of gravity and (b) by lack of the muscular movements that normally aid the flow of blood in the veins.

The force of the heart beat is affected by diastolic filling. The size of the heart is increased with increased filling. As a result, there is a greater initial length and tension of the cardiac muscle fibers at the beginning of systole. The cardiac fibers behave like skeletal muscle fibers in that, within physiological limits, the strength of a contraction increases with initial length and tension. The distensibility depends upon the condition of the ventricular muscle and is affected by its chemical environment, e.g., metabolites, epinephrine, and norepinephrine.

Chemical stimuli, particularly epinephrine, affect the *contractility* of the heart. Contractility is a term employed to include physiological adaptations in pressure, flow, and size of the heart. Increased contractility is related to such things as increases in pressure, the rate at which pressure develops, the rate at which size of the heart diminishes in systole, the rate of ejection, and perhaps in rate conduction and repolarization of cell membranes. Although it is broad and somewhat loosely defined, it is a convenient general term to describe the numerous interrelated factors that enable the heart to meet varying blood pressure and flow requirements of the body.

There is also a physical factor relating to the pressure developed by the heart. As the dimensions of the heart increase, the tension within the walls must be increased actively by the ventricular muscles to develop the same pressure within the ventricle. Here the heart is following the law of Laplace, a law of physics which relates the principal curvatures of a hollow, distensible sphere such as a soap bubble, the tension within the walls, and the pressure within the sphere, i.e., *transmural pressure*.* Transmural pressure is the difference in pressure inside and outside the sphere. As the curvatures of the heart decrease and the walls of the ventricle "flatten out" upon distension, the "mechanical advantage" of the muscular ventricular walls is reduced. Interaction between the physiological and physical factors affecting contractility can be summarized as follows: the energy of contraction at any level of contractility of the heart muscle is a function of length of the cardiac muscle fiber. As the size of the heart is increased, the strength of contraction must be increased to develop the pressure necessary for ejection of blood from the heart. Thus, while the strength of contraction is directly proportional to the initial length and tension of fiber, the overall level of performance of the heart will vary with its physiological condition and its dimensions.

The volume of blood ejected per beat is known as *stroke volume*. This volume depends upon diastolic filling, or the volume of blood contained in the heart at the end of diastole, and upon the degree of emptying of the heart during systole. When a man is lying down at rest his heart is at or near its maximum size because of the duration of diastole and diastolic filling, and because of the distensibility of the ventricles. Not all of the contained blood is ejected during systole. There remains in the heart a *residual volume* which cannot be ejected even during a maximal contraction, and a *systolic reserve volume* which can be ejected when a man's level of activity is increased, or if he is startled or emotionally disturbed (Fig. 16.3). The residual volume and the systolic reserve volume are called the *systolic reserve capacity*. The reserve systolic capacity is decreased upon changing from a supine, or resting, to a standing position. If the diastolic filling increases with standing or with increased activity, the ventricle may eject

---

*The law of Laplace is expressed by the equation $P = T\left(\dfrac{1}{R_1} + \dfrac{1}{R_2}\right)$, in which P is transmural pressure, T is tension of wall, and R_1 and R_2 are principal radii of curvature of the surface area of the wall under tension T.

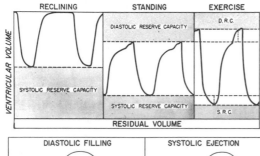

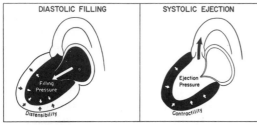

Figure 16.3 The diastolic dimensions, the systolic and diastolic reserve capacity, and stroke volume reclining, standing, and exercising. (From Ruch and Fulton: Medical Physiology and Biophysics. 18th ed.)

an extra volume of blood in addition to the resting stroke volume; this increment is called the *diastolic reserve volume*. The amount, i.e., the volumes of blood that are in the ventricles at the end of diastole, is called *diastolic capacity* (note the analogy to lung volumes, p. 247). In trained athletes, change in stroke volume plays a part in the physiological adjustment to strenuous exercise; it does not appear to play a consistent or important role in nonathletes.

The frequency of the heart beat influences the output of the heart per minute. *Minute volume* or *cardiac output* is determined by stroke volume and number of beats per minute. It is the heart rate rather than stroke volume that plays the principal role in adjustment of cardiac output to increased activity in nonathletes. The heart rate is influenced by chemical and nervous stimuli. Those stimuli that increase heart rate also reduce the duration of systole, but increase the force of contraction and the rate of systolic ejection. As a result the stroke volume may be maintained relatively constant—that is, without reduction—at increased heart rate.

Cardiac output for a man at rest is about 5 to 6 liters per minute—a reported mean value is 6.6 liters per minute with a range of 4.4 to 8.9 liters per minute. At a heart rate of 70 beats per minute this would mean a stroke volume of from 63 to 128 ml. Under conditions of extreme exercise athletes may attain an output as high as 20 or even 27 liters per minute at heart rates of 170 to 180 per minute. As would be expected, cardiac output varies with the size of the man. It has been shown to be related to body surface area and is reported as *cardiac index*. A normal resting cardiac index is about 3 to 3.5 liters per minute per square meter of body surface.

Resistance to Flow. *Resistance* to the flow of the blood ejected from the heart is determined by the caliber of the vessels and the viscosity of the blood. The caliber may vary because of the type of vessel, e.g., the aorta, small artery, arteriole, or capillary, or because of change in the diameter of the same vessel under differing pressure and degree of vasomotor activity. For example, the radius of the aorta measures approximately 13 mm., that of a small artery 2 mm., an arteriole 150 to 60 microns, and a capillary 4 microns.

The caliber of any type or size depends upon the transmural pressure, the distensibility of the vessel, and, in the case of the smaller vessels such as the arterioles and capillaries, the influence of the vasomotor nerves and the chemical environment. As pressure is increased the walls of a vessel are stretched, but by successively small increments. Its walls do not act as "perfect elastic material." Different vessels have different degrees of distensibility depending upon their architecture, i.e., the amount of endothelium, elastic fibers, collagenous fibers, and smooth muscle (see Table 15.1, p. 275). The elastin and collagen are primarily responsible for elastic stretch and for maintaining the tension of the walls of the vessels. The smooth muscle produces active tension, which reduces the diameter of the lumen but contributes little to maintenance of tension—it provides for adjustment of the size or condition of the vessels upon which the elastic stretch factor is superimposed.

LaPlace's law applies to blood vessels as well as to the heart, but in blood vessels only a single radius of curvature need be considered—the circumferential radius (see p. 307). Hence, the transmural pressure is equal to the tension divided by the circumferential radius:

$$P = \frac{T}{R}$$

This tells us two things. First, as the radius decreases, the tension of the vessel wall increases for any given pressure. This favors constriction of the vessel and increase in resistance to flow. When the lumen of an arteriole or precapillary sphincter is narrowed by action of its smooth muscle, so that the value of R is decreased, the vessel becomes unstable. If transmural pressure P drops, the vessel may collapse and add to the resistance to flow offered by the vascular bed. The pressure that can no longer overcome the tension in the walls of a vessel is known as *critical closing pressure*. The law also tells us the reason that very minute vessels with their extremely thin walls of endothelium can withstand pressures of 20 to 30 mm. Hg — their radius of curvature is so small that the tension, or ability to withstand stretch, yielding, and bursting, becomes great.

Resistance to flow can be expressed as the ratio of driving force to the resulting flow of blood, i.e.,

$$R \propto \frac{\text{driving pressure}}{\text{blood flow}}$$

Flow is directly proportional to the ratio of driving pressure to resistance, i.e.,

$$F \propto \frac{\text{driving pressure}}{\text{resistance}}$$

In rigid tubes with nonturbulent flow this relationship is linear. In elastic vessels, the relationship is complex and is influenced by the "geometry" or length and diameter of the vessels. Total peripheral resistance is influenced by the geometry of all the vessels of the vascular bed and the output of the heart.

An increase in the lumen of a blood vessel reduces resistance to flow, a decrease in lumen decreases flow. This is expressed as Poiseuille's law as it applies to blood vessels (where viscosity is approximately the same in all the vessels) — *resistance between two points P1 and P2 is proportional to one*

divided by the fourth power of the radius of the vessel. Shown as a mathematical expression this is: $R \propto 1/r^4$. The equation demonstrates the marked effect of the size of the vessel. For example, if the radius of a vessel A is 2 (arbitrary units) and the radius of vessel B is 1, the resistance of vessel B is 16 times as great as that of A.

The arterioles contribute about 40 per cent and capillaries nearly 30 per cent of the resistance to blood flow. The venules and veins contribute only about 7 per cent and the remainder is due to the aorta and arteries.

Capacity of the Closed Vascular Bed. The pressure in the closed elastic system is dependent upon the total volume capacity of vessels, and upon the quantity of fluid that they contain. The capacity of the system is increased by a volume equal to stroke volume during each systole and decreased during the diastolic run-off and diastolic filling. These changes due to the elasticity of the vessels are evidenced by the pulse. Widespread changes in capacity of the system may occur by constriction or closure of some vessels. The minute vessels, because of their tremendous total cross-sectional area, exert a considerable influence on the capacity-volume-pressure relations within the circulatory system. The systemic capillaries may accommodate as much as 10 per cent of the total blood volume under normal physiological conditions. Dilation of the capillaries may so increase the capillary capacity that a marked fall in blood pressure may occur, resulting in *syncope* or fainting.

If considerable loss of blood occurs, as in hemorrhage, there is some compensatory reduction of the capacity of the vascular bed, so that no noticeable change in blood pressure may occur. At some point however, hemorrhage will result in such a disparity between the content and the capacity of the system that blood pressure will fall until the blood volume is restored.

The pulmonary capillaries can accommodate about 2 per cent of the total blood volume. Based upon the approximate estimates of distribution of blood between the pulmonary and systemic circuits, the total capacity of the pulmonary circuit may be about 35 to 40 per cent of the capacity of the systemic circuit under normal physiological conditions.

As people become older the change in the capacity of the blood vascular system with each heart beat is reduced because of some loss in the elasticity of the blood vessels. This is compensated for, in some degree by an increase in the caliber of the vessels, so that they receive the systolic output with a lesser rise in pressure than would otherwise occur. If the vessels became increasingly inelastic and no change in presystolic capacity occurred, enormously high systolic pressures would result. If on the other hand, the arterial tree were extensible but inelastic, like a paper bag before it is blown up, the blood pressure would fall to zero between heart beats.

Blood Volume. The blood volume undergoes relatively small changes under physiological conditions in spite of wide variations in fluid intake and fluid excretion. This is the result of the finely adjusted balance between the fluid component of the blood that leaves the blood system at the arterial end of the capillary bed to form tissue fluid and lymph, and the return of fluid to the blood system from the tissue spaces at the venous end of the capillary bed.

The kidneys constitute another such mechanism for regulation; there large quantities of plasma are filtered out into the renal tubules (see Fig. 17.5, p. 325), but much of the fluid is reabsorbed into the blood stream. There appears to be a nervous control mechanism in which afferent vagal fibers are stimulated by distention of the right atrium; these impulses are believed to decrease the secretion of the antidiuretic hormone (ADH) and increase water loss through the kidney (see p. 329). In the case of reduced plasma volume, such as might occur in hemorrhage, greater quantities of the interstitial tissue fluids are reabsorbed, restoring or tending to restore blood volume. Secretion of ADH and a decrease in diuresis occurs in the presence of the diminished plasma volume and reduced stimulation of the atrial receptors (see p. 311).

Normally, man has 70 to 100 ml. of blood per kilogram of body weight, or roughly 6 liters of blood for an average person. Hemorrhage, exercise, or various conditions that modify water balance will cause some variations from these values.

Viscosity of the Blood. The more viscous a fluid, the greater is the force required to set it in motion. Blood is about five times as viscous as water, so that it aids in maintaining blood pressure by its resistance to movement. Viscosity is an expression of the friction that results from the sliding of molecules past one another in a moving fluid. The blood corpuscles and the plasma proteins are the main factors determining blood viscosity.

Summary of Factors Influencing Blood Pressure. In summary, given constant conditions so far as blood volume, blood viscosity, and arterial elasticity are concerned, blood pressure is the result of two simple factors: cardiac output, and resistance to flow. That is, given a closed system of constant size and a circulating fluid with constant volume and viscosity, the pressure within any segment of the system depends only upon the rate at which fluid enters that segment and the rate at which it leaves. If the rate at which fluid enters the segment remains constant while the rate at which fluid leaves it decreases, the pressure within the segment will increase. If input is decreased and output is constant, the pressure will fall. Compensatory changes in arterial pressure are intimately related to control of cardiac output, which sets the rate at which blood enters the aorta, and to the control of the caliber of the arterioles, which sets the rate at which blood leaves the arterial tree. The mechanisms of these controls will be discussed in the following sections.

NERVOUS AND CHEMICAL CONTROL OF BLOOD PRESSURE

Regulation of the Heart Rate. The heart rate is regulated through integration of nervous and chemical stimuli acting upon cardiac centers in the medulla and discharge from these centers through efferent pathways to the heart. Let us first consider the action of the cardiac nerves. The heart is innervated by the *vagus nerves*, which belong to the parasympathetic (craniosacral) division of the autonomic nervous system, and the *accelerator nerves*, which are postganglionic fibers of the sympathetic (thoracolumbar) division of the autonomic nervous system (Fig. 16.4). The vagi act as inhibitory or depressor fibers to slow the heart rate and to modify the rate of conduction and the strength of atrial contractions. Efferent vagal impulses depress conduction so that the interval between atrial and ventricular systole is increased. The right vagus is primarily responsible for slowing the heart rate. When the level of activity of the left vagus is high, it may also slow the atria as well as diminish the strength of their contractions. Strong stimulation results in cardiac inhibition. Section of the vagi results in an increase in heart rate. The vagus nerves exert their inhibitory action through liberation of a chemical substance, *acetylcholine*, at the nerve endings, which acts on the pacemaker cells of the S-A node and atrial muscle fibers. This substance is rapidly destroyed, so that, unless the vagus continues to discharge, the heart rate will increase.

The accelerator nerves act as pressor fibers having a *chronotropic effect* tending to increase heart rate and an *inotropic effect* increasing the strength of cardiac contraction. Like the vagus, the accelerator nerves act by a *neurohumoral mechanism;* i.e., they liberate a chemical substance. This substance, norepinephrine, is a synaptic activator substance that causes a depolarization, or excitation, of the membrane at the sympathetic nerve endings. The cardiovascular pressor reflexes are usually associated with a widespread sympathetic outflow with stimulation of the adrenal glands and secretion of epinephrine. This outflow also acts to increase the strength of heart beat and the rate of conduction.

The cardioinhibitory center and cardio-accelerator center of the medulla have reciprocal action as a result of their interconnections—the influence of the cardiac accelerator center increases as that of the cardioinhibitory center decreases and vice versa. Sensory nerves from other parts of the body influence these centers, so that either the vagus influence is increased and the heart slowed, or the accelerator nerves are acted upon to increase heart rate. These centers may be acted upon from the higher brain centers; emotions such as anger or excitement may increase heart rate, while sudden shocks may slow it. Stimulation of any somatic nerve may either hasten or retard the rate. In addition, sensory nerve endings located in the circulatory system, which are stimulated by changes in blood pressure or by changes in the chemical environment, have their effects on the heart rate. The chief circulatory receptors that give rise to cardiac reflexes are located in:

1. The aortic arch;
2. The carotid sinus and carotid body (see Fig. 16.5);
3. The right atrium and neighboring segments of the great veins.

These reflexes are brought about by stimulation of sensory nerve endings that are sensitive to stretch or tension. Such endings are called *pressure receptors* or *baroreceptors*. Increases in pressure within the blood vessels or in the right atrium stretch the walls of these structures to stimulate

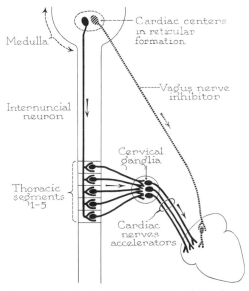

Figure 16.4 The efferent nerves of the heart.

the pressure receptors; decreases in pressure diminish the tension and reduce the stimulating effect.

The pressure receptors located in the region of the aortic arch (Fig. 16.5) respond to a rise in blood pressure by increasing the influence of the vagus and slowing the heart rate; a drop in blood pressure reduces vagus influence and the heart beats more rapidly. These responses are reinforced by similar pressure receptors of the carotid sinuses located at the bifurcation of the common carotid arteries where they divide into the internal and external carotid arteries.

Stimulation of the sensory nerve endings in the right atrium and great veins may cause an increase in heart rate (Bainbridge reflex) or a decrease, depending upon the existing rate at the time. The increase occurs when the great veins and atrium become distended by the increased venous return and the heart rate is below its maximum for increasing cardiac output.

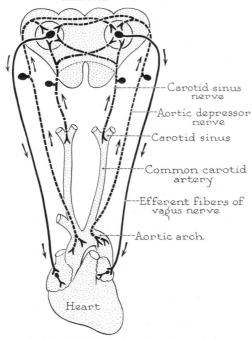

Cardiac inhibitory centers in medulla

Carotid sinus nerve

Aortic depressor nerve

Carotid sinus

Common carotid artery

Efferent fibers of vagus nerve

Aortic arch

Heart

Figure 16.5 Diagram showing reflex action of aortic depressor and carotid sinus nerves upon the heart rate.

In addition to pressure receptors, there are *chemoreceptors* in the region of the carotid sinus (in the carotid body) and the aortic arch, which are sensitive to lack of oxygen, increases in carbon dioxide, and an increase of the hydrogen ion concentration of the blood. All these chemical changes cause reflex increase in heart rate, either directly or through the influence of the respiratory centers on the cardioaccelerator center. Decrease in oxygen to the cardiac centers depresses their activity.

Control of Resistance. It has been stated that the arterioles constitute the chief factor in determining resistance to blood flow. Changes in the caliber of these vessels have a marked effect on blood pressure. The efferent nerves that bring about changes in the diameter of the vessels are called *vasomotor nerves*. There are two types: the vasoconstrictor nerves, which are distributed chiefly to the arterioles of the skin and viscera, and to a lesser extent to the arterioles of the muscles and mucous membranes; and the vasodilator nerves, supplying the arterioles of the salivary glands, tonsils, pharynx, and erectile tissues of the penis and the clitoris.

The arterioles are regulated by the activities of the *vasomotor centers* in the medulla oblongata. The *vasoconstrictor center* acts to decrease the caliber of the vessels, and the *vasodilator center* acts to increase their caliber. The balance of the two activities determines the state of the arterioles. The vasoconstrictor center is tonically active; that is, it is constantly sending out vasoconstrictor impulses. The activity of the vasodilator center is intermittent. Impulses from the vasodilator center act by inhibiting the efferent discharge from the vasoconstrictor center. Both centers are influenced by afferent nerve stimuli; their physiological state is influenced by their chemical environment.

The baroreceptors in the carotid sinus, aortic arch, the right atrium, and the great veins are the chief circulatory receptors for the vasomotor centers as well as the cardiac centers. They are pressure receptors that are stimulated in the same manner as the pressure receptors affecting heart rate. A rise in blood pressure in the aortic arch and carotid sinus stimulates the receptors and increases the rate of discharge of inhibitory impulses that reach the vasoconstrictor center, decreases its activity, and so causes a relaxation of the arteries; decreases in blood pressure result in vasoconstriction. A decrease in the pressure in the right atrium and great veins causes a vasoconstriction.

The vasomotor centers are affected by impulses from the higher centers, so that emotional stress or excitement may cause constriction of the arterioles, while disagreeable or shocking experiences may cause dilatation of the arterioles, a fall in blood pressure, and fainting. The respiratory center, which is near the vasomotor center, causes an increase in vasoconstrictor tone during inspiration. Cold decreases and heat increases the size of the vessels by acting on the centers.

Stimulation of a somatic sensory nerve may cause a decrease or an increase in the caliber of the vessels, depending upon the nature of the stimulus. The vasomotor centers are affected both directly and reflexly by changes in the chemical environment. An adequate concentration of carbon dioxide is necessary for efficient functioning of the centers, while excess carbon dioxide and lack of oxygen act directly to depress them. Moderate increases of carbon dioxide or the lack of oxygen stimulates the chemoreceptors in the aortic and carotid bodies and causes vasoconstriction.

Epinephrine acts as a constrictor to arterioles of the skin and kidneys but in physiologic concentrations causes vasodilation of the arterioles of the muscle and liver, and of the coronary vessels. Norepinephrine causes constriction of all except the coronary vessels. Local metabolites, excesses of carbon dioxide and oxygen lack may act directly on the vessels to cause dilatation. Cold decreases and heat increases the size of the vessels by acting locally.

Control of Capillary Flow. Since the capillaries lie between the arterioles and the collecting venules, capillary flow is to a great extent regulated by the reactions of these vessels. Capillary flow can be reduced either by arteriolar constriction, which decreases the amount of blood entering the capillary bed, or by constriction of the collecting venules, which reduces the outflow from the capillaries. Dilatation of the arterioles and the venules, on the other hand, increases the capillary flow. The metarterioles and precapillary sphincteric muscular elements serve to alter local flow through the capillary beds. The responses of the minute vessels are controlled principally by chemical agents (see summary, p. 315).

The chief evidence for *independent activity* in the capillary vessels in man is found in the reaction of the cutaneous vessels. If the skin of an area that is not commonly exposed (such as the back or the forearm) is stroked lightly with a smooth blunt instrument, a sharply defined white line appears. This is known as the "white reaction." As the color of the skin is due to the blood in the capillaries and subcapillary venous plexus, the reaction is interpreted as being the result of capillary constriction in response to a stretch stimulus. A white reaction is also caused by pricking a drop of epinephrine into the skin.

Capillaries may be dilated by almost any type of injury to the surrounding tissues. If a rubber band is snapped against the skin or if a blunt instrument is drawn forcibly across an area, the underlying tissues are subjected to mechanical injury. A sharply defined red mark appears. This is known as the "red reaction." Heat, exposure to sunlight or ultraviolet light, and an injection of foreign substances cause the red reaction. It has been interpreted as the action of a substance liberated by tissue destruction. When the stimulus has been vigorous, an arteriolar dilatation or flare results; edema or swelling resulting from the passage of increased amounts of fluid from the capillaries to the surrounding tissues may also occur.

External pressure influences the blood flow through the capillaries. Constricting clothing, bandages, pressure from lying in bed, or standing decrease the capillary flow. When external pressures are relieved, the previously constricted area becomes flushed, indicating an increased flow through the dilated capillaries. Examples of this phenomenon may be seen by observing the feet on removing shoes or in other areas that have been subjected to compression. Long-continued external pressures may cause more marked tissue injury such as is seen in skin irritation after long confinement in bed.

SUMMARY: MAINTENANCE AND REGULATION OF BLOOD PRESSURE

Factors in the Regulation of Blood Pressure and Circulation

Blood pressure depends upon:

I. Cardiac output
  A. Venous return and diastolic filling
    1. Increased by contractions of skeletal muscle (increased activity)
    2. Increased by deep respirations
    3. Increased by gravity by the effect of blood above the heart level
    4. Increased with increased duration of diastole
    5. Increased with increasing distensibility of ventricular chambers
    6. Decreased by gravity by the effect of blood below the heart level
    7. Decreased when there is dilation of blood vessels over a wide area
  B. Force of heart beat
    1. Increased by initial length and tension of cardiac muscle fibers at beginning of systole.
    2. Increased with increased contractility
    3. Increased with decrease in size of heart (for any given degree of tension of the heart muscle)
    4. Increased with norepinephrine and epinephrine.
    5. Maintained by adequate coronary circulation for proper nutrition of the heart
  C. Heart rate
    1. Regulated by cardiac nerves
      a. Accelerator nerves increase rate; cardioaccelerator center is in the medulla oblongata
      b. Vagus nerves decrease rate; cardioinhibitory center is in the medulla oblongata
    2. Impulses from higher centers may cause acceleration or inhibition through their effect on the cardioregulatory centers
    3. Cardiac reflexes
      a. From pressure receptors
        (1) Aortic arch and carotid sinus: increase in rate results from a fall in blood pressure; decrease in rate results from a rise in blood pressure
        (2) Right atrium and great veins: rise in venous pressure causes an increase in rate
      b. Other sensory nerve stimulation may cause a decrease or an increase in heart rate
    4. Great excesses of carbon dioxide or marked oxygen lack depresses the excitability of the heart muscle and the cardiac centers in the medulla
    5. Rise in body temperature causes increase in heart rate
    6. Epinephrine causes increased rate; norepinephrine has an accelerator effect, but reflex reduction from pressure effect is usual response

II. Peripheral resistance
  A. Caliber of arterioles and capillaries
    1. Nervous control of these vessels
      a. Vasoconstrictor nerves
        (1) Sympathetic nerves constitute the majority of constrictor fibers
        (2) Vagus fibers to coronary arteries
      b. Vasodilator nerves
        (1) Parasympathetic nerves
        (2) Some sympathetic dilators
        (3) Posterior root dilators
    2. Nervous control may be influenced by:
      a. Impulses from the higher centers
      b. Impulses from the respiratory center

c. Vasomotor reflexes
  (1) From pressure receptors
    (a) Carotid sinus
    (b) Aortic arch
    (c) Right atrium and great veins
  (2) From chemoreceptors
    (a) Carotid body
    (b) Aortic arch
d. Action directly on the vaso-motor center
  (1) Carbon dioxide in moderate excess causes vasoconstriction
  (2) Carbon dioxide lack causes vasodilatation
  (3) Great excess of carbon dioxide causes vasodilatation
  (4) Marked oxygen lack causes vasodilatation
e. Changes in temperature (central action)
  (1) Rise in temperature causes vasodilatation
  (2) Fall in temperature causes vasoconstriction

3. Chemical and thermal control of vessels
a. Action on arterioles
  (1) Metabolites
    Carbon dioxide excess causes vasodilatation
    Oxygen lack causes vasodilatation
  (2) Hormones
    Epinephrine causes dilation of coronary vessels and vessels in muscles and liver and

constriction in vessels of skin and kidney
Norepinephrine causes generalized vasoconstriction
  (3) Histamine causes vasoconstriction

b. Action on capillaries
  (1) Metabolites
    Carbon dioxide lack causes capillary constriction
    Carbon dioxide excess causes capillary dilatation
    Oxygen lack causes capillary dilatation
  (2) Hormones' local action on injection
    Epinephrine causes capillary constriction
    Norepinephrine causes capillary constriction
  (3) Histamine causes capillary dilatation
  (4) Temperature, local action
    Rise causes capillary dilatation
    Moderate fall causes capillary dilatation
    Marked fall causes capillary constriction

Factors that remain relatively constant in normal healthy man ⎱
  III. Capacity of the closed vascular bed
  IV. Elasticity of the blood vessels
   V. Blood volume
  VI. Viscosity of the blood

QUESTIONS FOR DISCUSSION

1. Explain the meaning of systolic and diastolic pressures in terms of the work of the heart.

2. What is the relation of the pulse to *(a)* the sounds heard in taking blood pressure by the auscultatory method; *(b)* the velocity of blood flow; and *(c)* circulation time?

3. How are the numerous factors that control the heart integrated?

4. Explain the differences in the effects of carbon dioxide excess on the vasomotor centers of the brain and upon the capillaries.

5. Discuss the physiology of hemorrhage.

6. Relate changes in skin color to circulation.

CONSTANCY IN COMPOSITION OF BODY FLUIDS

CHAPTER SEVENTEEN

EXCRETION

We have observed in the biology of cells (Chapter 2) that fluid serves as a medium for the chemical processes of metabolism. The interstitial fluid provides the immediate or internal environment for the body cells. It facilitates the transfer of nutrient and essential substances from the plasma to the cell, and of waste products from the cell to the plasma. The plasma (Chapter 14) provides the link between the external and internal environments of the body cells by transporting a wide variety of substances from the intestinal tract (Chapter 18) and oxygen from the lungs (Chapter 13) to the interstitial fluid, and transporting waste products to the kidneys (Chapter 17), lungs, skin (Chapter 3), and in-

testinal tract, through which they leave the body and pass to the outside. In these ways, *excretion* plays a vital role in maintaining the constancy in composition of body fluids.

DISTRIBUTION AND EXCHANGE OF FLUID

Location of Body Fluids. The water and dissolved substances lying within the cells are *intracellular fluid*. *Extracellular fluid* is composed chiefly of plasma, lymph, and interstitial fluid. In addition, extracellular cavity fluids include cerebrospinal fluid, intraocular fluids, and those small quantities of fluid found in the potential

317

spaces of the pleural, peritoneal, and synovial cavities throughout the body.

Physiological extracellular water is the *plasma* that is in the vascular compartment and the *interstitial* fluid, including lymph, in the interstitial space. The morphologic boundaries of the extracellular fluid cannot be definitely defined or its volume precisely measured, since no ideal chemical has been found that will mix only with physiological extracellular water. Allowing for the inaccuracies of measurement and variable quantity, the extracellular fluid volume is known to constitute approximately 25 per cent of total body weight, of which 6 per cent is plasma and about 15 per cent interstitial fluid. *Intracellular* fluid makes up about 45 to 50 per cent of the body weight (Fig. 17.1).

Water Balance. Total body water can be measured satisfactorily by determining the dilution of a small measured quantity of heavy water (deuterium oxide) that, when injected into the blood, mixes with body water in about one hour. The results by this indirect method agree closely with direct measurement of weight loss of the bodies of small experimental animals following desiccation. The per cent of lean body weight (fat-free body mass) appears to be fairly constant from one normal individual to another. The total water re-

presents 60 to 70 per cent of total body weight.

Total body water and the amounts of it in various tissues and locations are not constant, but vary over a limited range under normal physiological conditions. The limited extent of the range and the overall constancy is shown by determination of the water balance. Water is consumed in liquid form and in food. Water derived from food may be a component of it, be mixed with it, or may result from its oxidation; carbon dioxide and water are the principal end-products from the oxidation of all types of foodstuffs. Water is lost from the body by vaporization, by excretion in the stool, and as urine. A characteristic daily exchange of water that has been balanced shows the approximate quantities taken in from various sources and lost by various routes under conditions of moderate ambient temperature and humidity, and moderate bodily activity. These are:

Water Intake

SOURCE	AMOUNT (ML.)
Drink	1200
Food	
(a) Mixed with or constituent of	1000
(b) From oxidation	350
Total	2550

Water Output

LOSS	AMOUNT (ML.)
Urine	1350
Stool	150
Vaporization	
(a) Lungs	300
(b) Skin	750
Total	2550

The ranges of the amounts of the separate losses are not great for moderately active people in moderate weather. For the most part, variations in water intake are balanced by differences in the amount of urine secreted, i.e., between 1 and 1.5 liters. Fifty to 200 ml. may be lost through the intestine in the feces. The losses from the lungs usually fall within the relatively narrow limits of 250 to 300 ml. per day. Loss from insensible perspiration, so called

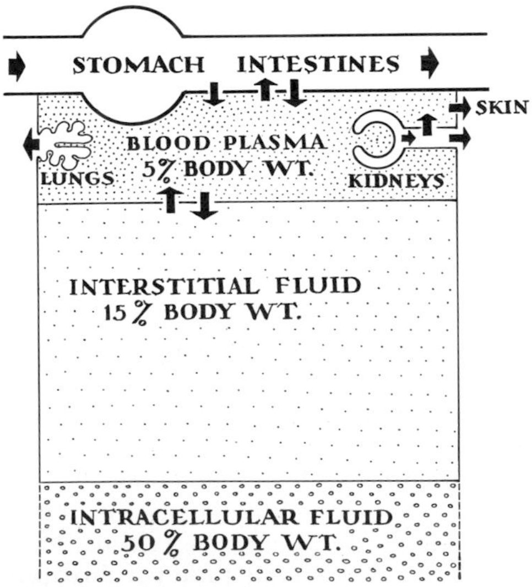

Figure 17.1 Diagram of body fluid distribution. (After Gamble.)

because it is evaporated as fast as it is formed, is influenced to a great degree by the temperature, humidity, and air movement of the surrounding environment. It may vary from about 0.5 to 1 liter.

Water intake increases with increased activity and increased temperature, both separately and in combination; it may reach as high as 13 to 14 liters per day for men doing heavy labor in a hot, dry climate. Water output is greatly increased under similar conditions by the skin secreting sweat in copious quantities that are lost by evaporation or by dripping from the body.

The distribution of water and electrolytes in the various compartments are dynamic processes. Disturbances in water metabolism may occur, however. Perhaps the most familiar of these conditions are dehydration and retention of excess water, which may be distributed throughout the body or localized in certain areas, with a resulting swelling or *edema*.

Dehydration may occur as the result of water deprivation or from excessive water losses. If the loss amounts to approximately 10 per cent of body weight, the disturbance becomes serious; if approximately 20 per cent of body weight is lost through dehydration, fatal consequences may be expected. Water deprivation may occur among survivors at sea when they are forced to exist in rafts or small boats for extended periods, and among soldiers under rigorous combat conditions; occasionally prisoners who go on "hunger strikes" will refuse water. Excessive water losses may be associated with diarrhea, vomiting, profuse sweating, salt deficiency, and various types of disease. Water and salt disturbances occur in diabetes and in adrenal cortex insufficiency.

Hydration, or increased water retention, may occur in kidney disease, in certain conditions associated with pregnancy, and upon administration of antidiuretic hormone. Where the increased fluid volume occurs without a corresponding salt retention, "water intoxication" may result. Where salt and water are shifted in excessive quantities to intracellular spaces, the swelling or puffiness characteristic of edema may be seen. Edema may result from many causes; strictly local swelling, as in a bruise, is caused chiefly by changes in the permeability of the walls of the capillaries.

REGULATION OF WATER BALANCE

Continuous exchange takes place between the plasma and the interstitial fluid and between the interstitial fluid and intercellular fluid as the result of differences in hydrostatic pressures and osmotic pressures. Although individual ions and molecules change, the amounts of the substances remain remarkably constant. A comparison of the composition of cells and serum in Table 17.1 illustrates ionic and osmolar "balance." In such dynamic equilibria, we must use approximate values rather than an absolute value for individual substances; further, we do not know the values for all constituents. In consequence, "balance" does not imply identical totals.

A portion of regulation of water loss from the body is vested in the *osmoreceptor–antidiuretic hormone system*. An increase in the osmolarity of the intracellular fluids excites the osmoreceptor cells in the anterior portion of the hypothalamus (p. 97). The neuronal discharge from hypothalamic neurons promotes the release of antidiuretic hormone. ADH (p. 98), by the neurohypophysis. Action of ADH upon the renal tubules of the kidney (p. 329) causes a marked reabsorption of water. *Aldosterone's* (p. 143) effect upon the reabsorption of sodium and chlorine and excretion of potassium from renal tubules results in a net increase in electrolytes of extracellular fluids, an effect which stimulates the hypothalamic antidiuretic hormone system also.

A conscious desire or *thirst* for water is important in regulating the intake of water for body fluids. Electrical stimulation of nerve cells of the hypothalamus close to those concerned with the release of ADH will cause an experimental animal to begin drinking water. The animal continues to drink until the stimulation ceases. Various explanations have been offered of the physiological stimulus for thirst. It is probable that all the effects in engendering

TABLE 17.1 CHEMICAL COMPOSITION OF HUMAN SERUM OR PLASMA AND CELLS
(Representative values in milliosmols and milliequivalents)

Constituent	Serum or Plasma		Cells	
	mOsm.	mEq.	mOsm.	mEq.
Nonelectrolytes				
Urea	7		7	
Glucose	4		4	
Other	?		?	
Bases				
Na$^+$	142	142	6	6
K$^+$	4	4	112	112
Ca^{++}	2.4	5	0.4	1
Mg^{++}	0.9	1.7	1.8	2.2
Acids				
Cl$^-$	103	103	78	78
H$_2$CO$_3^-$	27	27	13	13
Inorgan. HPO$_4^-$	3.7	3.7	2.5	2.5
Organ. Phos.	trace	?	12.0	?
Protein	1	18	7	62

thirst are dependent upon intracellular dehydration.

ACID-BASE BALANCE

Slight changes in the hydrogen ion concentration will have marked effects upon the chemical reactions of the cells in the body. pH of intracellular fluids has never been measured although it is estimated to be between 7.0 and 7.2. Extracellular fluid pH is 7.4, or about 4×10^{-8} mEq./ liter. Arterial blood pH is 7.4, and venous blood is 7.35. *Acidosis* describes the condition of the body when arterial blood pH is below 7.4. *Alkalosis* connotes the condition of the body when pH rises above 7.4. The limits, beyond which the individual can live no more than a few minutes, are pH 7.0 and 7.8. *Coma* occurs with acidosis and *convulsions* with alkalosis. The significant feature in regulation of the acid-base balance in the body is the control of the value of the hydrogen ion concentration. Although twenty-four hours may be required for acid-base regulation by the kidneys, they constitute the most effective means of maintaining the pH of body fluids at normal levels. The adjustment of hydrogen ion concentration by the respira-

tory system has been presented in detail in Chapter 13 and should be reviewed at this time. Approximately one to three minutes are required in the adjustment of carbon dioxide levels, and hence the pH, in the blood when the hydrogen ion causes the respiratory center to alter the rate of pulmonary ventilation.

All body fluids are supplied with *buffer systems* which can act within fractions of a second to control excessive alterations in the hydrogen ion concentration. The buffer systems include two or more chemical compounds which resist a shift in pH when either an acid or a base is introduced into the solution. Each of the three major buffer systems of body fluids acts under slightly different conditions. The *protein buffer system* is the most plentiful. The numerous proteins of cells and plasma, with their amino acids, can act as either acids or bases as shown:

1. $-COOH \rightarrow -COO^- + H^+$ (acid)
2. $-NH_3OH \rightarrow -NH_3^+ + OH^-$ (base)

The *phosphate buffer system* is particularly important in intracellular fluids. Approximately 75 per cent of the chemical buffering occurs within the tissue cells. The reactions of the NaH_2PO_4 and Na_2HPO_4 tend to shift strong acids and bases into weaker acids and bases with very little alteration in the total pH of the fluid environment.

3. $HCl + Na_2HPO_4 \rightarrow NaH_2PO_4 + NaCl$
4. $NaOH + NaH_2PO_4 \rightarrow Na_2HPO_4 + H_2O$

Despite the fact that the *carbonate buffer system* is not chemically powerful, it is the most important of the three major buffer systems. The mixture of carbonic acid and bicarbonate salts is labile to regulation by the respiratory and urinary systems.

5. $HCl + NaHCO_3 \rightarrow H_2CO_3 + NaCl$
6. $NaOH + H_2CO_3 \rightarrow NaHCO_3 + H_2O$

Alterations in hydrogen ion concentration in body fluids tend to activate all the buffer systems.

ROLE OF THE URINARY SYSTEM

ORGANS

The organs of the urinary system (Fig. 17.2) are the kidneys, which secrete the urine; the ureters, or tubes that convey urine to the urinary bladder, where it is temporarily stored; and the urethra, through which urine is discharged from the body.

The Kidneys The kidneys perform regulatory and excretory functions. They play a principal role in regulation of the volume, the ionic concentration, and osmotic pressure of the internal fluid environment. This involves water balance, acid-base balance and constancy of normal physiological constituents of the body fluids. The excretion of waste products of metabolism, i.e., the excretory function, is a consequence of the regulatory mechanisms that are responsible for keeping the internal environment within physiological limits. The kidneys are paired organs lying on the posterior abdominal wall on either side of the vertebral column and behind the peritoneum (Fig. 17.2). They are somewhat bean-shaped, having a convex lateral border and a concave medial border. The surface of the kidney is smooth and is covered by a thin fibrous

membranous *capsule*. Each kidney is surrounded by a considerable quantity of perirenal fat and connective tissue that, together with the peritoneum, support the organ. The notch on the medial border of the kidney is the *hilus*; here the ureters, nerves, and blood vessels enter and leave the organ. The upper portion of the ureter expands to form the funnel-shaped renal pelvis with its subdivisions, numerous small funnels called *calyces*.

A longitudinal section of the kidney shows an outer part, the *cortex*, and an inner part, the *medulla* (Fig. 17.2). The medulla consists of 8 to 18 *pyramids*, the bases of which border on the cortex, while their apices constitute the *papillae* that project into the calyces. The cut surface of a pyramid shows striations that represent the large collecting tubules or ducts. *Outer* and *inner zones* of the medulla can also be recognized. The cortical substance forms the peripheral layer and penetrates for some distance between the pyramids to form the *renal columns*.

The minute structure of the kidney is organized as the *nephron*. Each nephron consists of a renal corpuscle and its subjoined tubule (Fig. 17.3). The renal corpuscle is an elaborate series of parallel fenestrated blood capillaries (*glomerulus*) surrounded by Bowman's capsule, the invaginated blind end of the uriniferous tubule. Subjoined to Bowman's capsule are (1) *convoluted* and (2) *straight portions* of the *proximal tubule*, (3) a *thin segment*, (4) *straight* and (5) *convoluted* portions of the *distal tubule*, and (6) the *arched tubule*, which connects the nephron to the collecting ducts of the kidney medulla.

The microscopic plan of the cortex and medulla brings epithelial surfaces into contact with capillary networks at several sites which are important in the process of ultrafiltration, reabsorption, secretion, and concentration involved in the formation of urine (pp. 326-329). The parietal layer of squamous cells of Bowman's capsule forms the capsular boundary and the inner visceral layer is intimately applied to the loops of the glomerular capillaries. Cells of the visceral layers are modified into *podocytes* (Figs. 17.3 and 17.4) whose

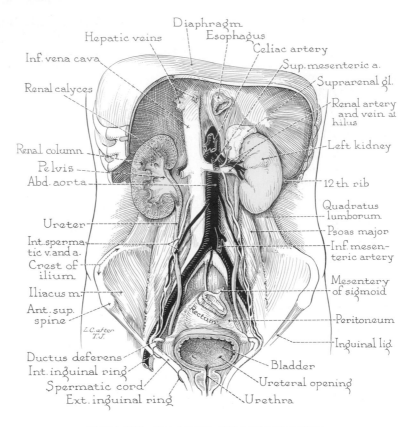

Figure 17.2 The organs of the urinary system.

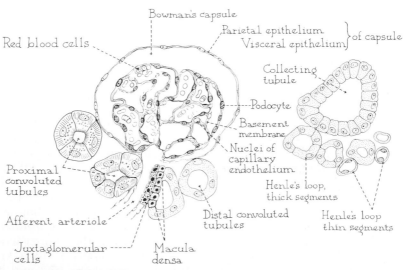

Figure 17.3 Renal corpuscle with convoluted tubules from cortex of the kidney are shown at the left and Henle's loop and connecting tubule from medulla of kidney are shown on the right.

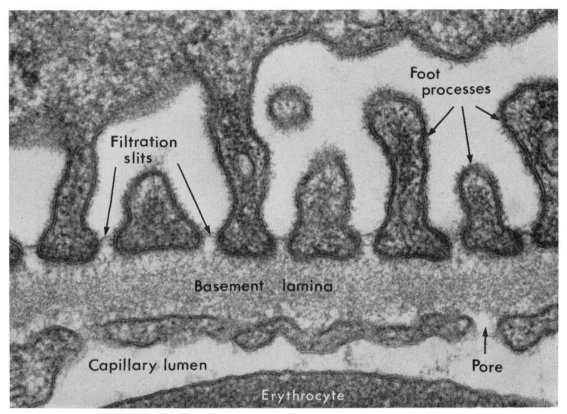

Figure 17.4 Electron micrograph of a portion of the wall of a glomerular capillary, showing pores in the extremely attenuated endothelium. On the outer surface of the basement lamina are the foot processes of the podocytes with the narrow filtration slits between them. × 70,000. (Courtesy of D. Friend. In Bloom and Fawcett: A Textbook of Histology 9th ed., 1968.)

small cell bodies stand away from the basement membrane between the glomerular and visceral epithelium by means of pedicels. Adjacent pedicels are separated by slit pores 250 Å wide which have delicate diaphragmatic coverings and a differential permeability which holds back substances exceeding 90,000 molecular weight. The fenestrations in the glomerular capillaries are 500 Å in diameter. The basement membrane between these two perforated epithelial surfaces is a homogeneous matrix of connective tissue fibrils 0.1 to 0.15 microns thick. It constitutes the *principal filtration membrane* for ultrafiltration in the renal corpuscle. Maintenance and continuity of this basement membrane is provided by the podocytes and occasional connective tissue cells in the renal corpuscle.

Proximal convoluted and straight tubules make up the bulk of the kidney cortex. The cuboid cells of these tubules with diameters of 60 microns have brush borders of tightly packed microvilli projecting into their narrow lumen. Their numerous mitochondria are oriented at the base of the cells and suggest striations. The apical region is filled with canaliculi and vacuoles. All these cellular structures suggest that the proximal tubules are well adapted for absorption and concentration of protein and other substances from glomerular filtrate.

The thin segment of the subjoined tubule, about 15 microns in diameter, is composed of a few squamous epithelial cells which are in close contact with capillary loops of the medulla. The thin segment is combined with a descending portion of the proximal straight tubule and an ascending portion of the distal straight tubule to form a U-shaped *Henle's loop.* The role of Henle's loop in concentration of urine is discussed on page 329.

The straight and convoluted parts of the distal tubule have a tubular diameter of 50 microns and a larger lumen than the proximal tubule. The base of cuboidal cells in the distal tubule is invaded by membranes of the peritubular capillary network. Such an arrangement facilitates the reabsorption and secretion which occur in the distal tubule.

An arched tubule connects the nephron to the collecting ducts of the kidney medulla (Fig. 17.5). This marks the embryonic union of structures which have developed at separate sites and fused secondarily in the formation of the kidney.

Among the smooth muscle cells of the afferent arteriole at its point of entrance into the glomerulus are cells which possess cytoplasmic granules rich in a vasopressor substance, *renin.* (See Chapter 9 for further discussion of renin in regulation of aldosterone secretion.) These are the juxtaglomerular cells. The base of juxtaglomerular cells contacts a group of cells modified into the macula densa from the lumen of the distal straight tubule. These two specialized cellular regions comprise the *juxtaglomerular apparatus* (Fig. 17.3).

BLOOD SUPPLY. The kidneys, which clear the blood of waste products accumulated throughout the body, each receive 1200 to 1300 ml. of blood per minute. Renal circulation varies in the different parts of the kidney, the cortex receiving the highest volume of blood per minute, the outer medulla a lesser amount, and the inner medulla the least quantity. It has become apparent from injuries which involved shock and subsequent renal failure that blood is circulating in two routes simultaneously. One serves predominantly renal corpuscles and tubules in the cortex and the other provides circulation to renal corpuscles and tubules in juxtamedullary and medullary areas (Fig. 17.5). The arteriolae rectae and venulae rectae are particularly important as *countercurrent exchangers* for diffusible substances in the

loop of Henle (see *Concentration of Urine,* p. 328).

Renal circulation may be traced through the structures illustrated in Figures 17.3 and 17.5 as follows:

aorta → renal arteries
↓
interlobar artery
↓
arcuate artery
↓
interlobular artery
↓
afferent arterioles
↓
glomerulus
↓
efferent arterioles
↓
secondary capillary network
↓
interlobular vein
↓
arcurate vein
↓
interlobar vein
↓
renal vein → inferior vena cava

The Ureters. The ureters are musculomembranous tubes about 27 cm. long, connecting the renal pelves with the urinary bladder. They descend beneath the peritoneum on the posterior abdominal wall and cross the pelvic floor to reach the urinary bladder. The wall of a ureter is composed of three layers: an inner or mucous coat covered with transitional epithelium, a middle coat of smooth muscle with inner longitudinal and outer circular layers, and an outer fibrous coat. Peristaltic contractions of the ureters aid in transporting urine to the bladder.

The Urinary Bladder. The bladder is a muscular sac lying in the pelvis behind the symphysis pubis, in front of the rectum in the male and in front of the vagina and uterus in the female. The relationships of organs of the pelvis are illustrated on pages 390 and 397. It serves as a reservoir in which urine is retained until it is eliminated from the body. There are three openings on the floor of the bladder—one anteriorly for the urethra and two laterally for the ureters. These orifices outline a

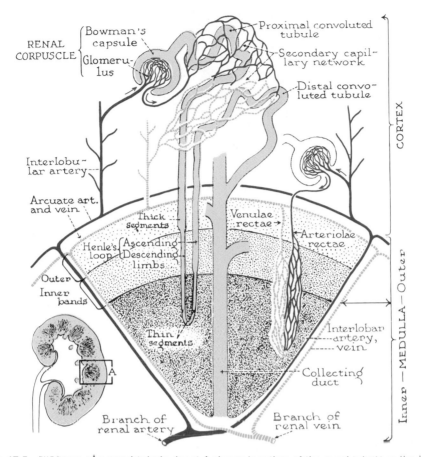

Figure 17.5 Diagram of a renal tubule. Inset *A* shows location of the renal tubule in the kidney.

smooth, fixed triangular area called the *trigone*.

The *wall* of the bladder is composed of four coats: (1) An inner mucous coat, which is thrown into folds when the organ is empty. The epithelium is of a special type called transitional epithelium. It is highly elastic; in the contracted state it consists of several layers of polygonal cells, but when stretched in extreme distention only two layers can be seen, a deep row of cuboidal cells and a surface row of large squamous cells. Small folds of mucosa cover the ureteral orifices and prevent the backflow of the urine accumulating in the bladder. (2) A submucous coat of loose areolar tissue that allows free movement between mucous and muscular layers. (3) A strong muscular coat arranged in three layers of smooth muscle, consisting of a middle circular layer between an inner and an outer longitudinal layer. The cir-

cular fibers of the middle layer are thickened in the region of the trigone to form the internal sphincter. (4) An outer coat of peritoneum that covers the superior surface.

THE URETHRA. The urethra is the passageway passing from the bladder to the exterior. Its character differs in the two sexes. The female urethra is about 2.5 to 3.0 cm. long. At the junction of the urethra with the bladder the circular muscle layer forms the internal sphincter, while at the periphery skeletal muscle forms the external sphincter. The urethral orifice is in the vestibule just above and anterior to the vaginal orifice (Fig. 20.5, p. 393).

The male urethra is about 20 cm. long and is composed of three portions (Fig. 17.6). The *prostatic urethra* extends from the bladder to the pelvic floor. It is about 2.5 cm. long and is surrounded by the

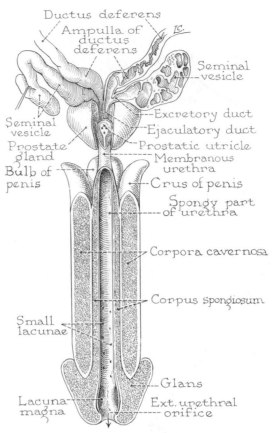

Figure 17.6 The male urethra laid open on its anterior (upper) surface.

prostate gland. The *membranous urethra* pierces the pelvic wall. It is about 2 cm. in length, and is surrounded by an external sphincter of skeletal muscle. The *cavernous urethra* extends through the penis, terminating at the urethral orifice. This portion is about 15 cm. long and passes through the corpus spongiosum of the urethra.

COMPOSITION OF URINE

Urine is a liquid, colored by the presence of bile pigments. The range of pH of urine is from 4.5 to 9.0, depending principally upon diet, general health, and environment. The specific gravity varies between 1.015 and 1.025. The quantity of urine excreted in twenty-four hours normally varies between 1000 and 1800 ml. The amount may be markedly decreased by an increase in water loss

through the sweat glands. The amount of urine secreted during the day is two to four times greater than the amount secreted during the night.

Water makes up 95 per cent of the urine. Analysis of 1000 ml. of urine yields from 40 to 50 gm. of total solids, with urea constituting one-half of this amount. The solids of the urine consist of inorganic and organic substances. The inorganic compounds are sodium chloride and the sulfates and phosphates of sodium, potassium, magnesium, and calcium. The chief organic compounds in the urine are urea, uric acid, creatinine, and ammonium salts.

FORMATION OF URINE

The three mechanisms of kidney function responsible for maintenance of the constancy of the internal environment are: (1) ultrafiltration, (2) reabsorption and

(3) secretion. By virtue of the three mechanisms, blood plasma is filtered through the glomeruli, some substances are reabsorbed from the ultrafiltrate of the plasma, and other substances are added to the fluid which is ultimately excreted as urine.

Ultrafiltration. Ultrafiltration is the first step in the formation of urine. Capillary blood passing through the glomerulus is filtered so that red blood cells, platelets, lipids, and almost all plasma proteins are retained in the blood vessels. Water and crystalloids are passed through the glomerular membranes into the urinary spaces in Bowman's capsule (p. 322).

The energy for filtration is supplied from the heart beat through the glomerular capillary pressure. This pressure is opposed by the intracapsular or back pressure on the other side of the membrane and the colloid osmotic pressures of the capillary blood. The glomerular capillary pressure is approximately 70 mm. Hg; the opposing intracapsular and colloid osmotic pressures are 15 mm. Hg and 30 mm. Hg respectively. Thus the energy remaining for forcing the ultrafiltrate through the glomerular membrane is about 25 mm. Hg.

About one quarter or one fifth of the total cardiac output passes through the kidney. If we assume that under conditions of rest or light activity the heart pumps 6 liters per minute, the kidneys would receive 1200 ml. of whole blood per minute. If the hematocrit shows 45 per cent red blood cells and 55 per cent plasma, the plasma flow would be about 660 ml./min. The volume of plasma filtered per minute is called the *glomerular filtration rate*. The rate varies with sex, age, and surface area of the body. It is expressed in ml./min./1.73M² body surface area (see p. 328). The average glomerular filtration rate is about 125 ml./min. for men and about 110 ml./min. for women. Since plasma is about 93 per cent water, the volume of *glomerular filtrate* obtained in one minute would be 116 ml. or 7 per cent less than the amount implied by the glomerular filtration rate.

Glomerular filtration rate can be measured directly in experimental animals by inserting a micropipet into the urinary space in Bowman's capsule and collecting the filtrate for a given period of time. In man, however, it must be measured indirectly. This can be done by injecting into the blood a substance which is neither removed from nor added to the glomerular filtrate, and determining the amount found in the urine in a given period of time. For example if, after injection, plasma contains 1 mg./ml. of *inulin* and 125 ml. of inulin passes into the tubules each minute, we know that the glomerular filtration rate is 125 ml./min. Inulin has special properties which make it the substance of choice for quantitative measurement of the glomerular filtration rate in man. It can be measured quantitatively in plasma and in urine; it passes freely through the glomerular membrane; it is neither reabsorbed nor secreted by the renal tubules; and it is nontoxic and does not modify renal function.

Clearance is the degree to which a substance is removed from plasma and excreted into the urine. It is expressed in the volume of plasma which would have to be completely cleared to account for the amount of the substance found in urine in a unit of time. If you think about this, you will realize that if not all the material is cleared in a single passage of blood through the glomeruli, the clearance value will be less than the true glomerular filtration rate. Because inulin clearance gives the highest value (125 ml./min.) and because of other evidence, inulin clearance rate is taken as a standard measure of glomerular filtration rate in man.

Glomerular Filtrate and Mechanisms for Its Modifications. About 180 liters of glomerular filtrate are produced in 24 hours. Its composition is the same as that of plasma except for the proteins. It contains water, small amounts of albumin, nutrients, nitrogenous waste, inorganic salts, enzymes, vitamins, and hormones. About 99 per cent of the water, Na^+, and Cl^- and 100 per cent of the glucose and albumin of the filtrate is ultimately recovered, and retained by the body. Most of the normal constituents are retained to at least some extent. When the constituents such as water and inorganic salts are in excess of body needs they are excreted in the amounts necessary to maintain the constancy of the internal environment. Waste products of metabolism, e.g., urea and uric acid, are kept down to levels consistent with normal physiological function. Substances foreign to the body, such as dyes, penicillin, and organic acids, are excreted.

As glomerular filtrate moves through the renal tubules its volume and composition are modified by *reabsorption* and *secretion*. Reabsorption is the movement of material from the lumen of the tubules to the tissue fluid surrounding the tubules, i.e., the *peritubular fluid*. Secretion is the mechanism through which materials are moved from the peritubular fluid into the lumen of the tubules.

Both reabsorption and secretion involve passive and active transport mechanisms. Passive transport is the diffusion of substances down a chemical activity gradient and an electrical potential gradient (pp. 25, 26). Active transport involves the expenditure of energy by the participating cells; work is performed on the substances being transported.

One type of active transport which participates in both reabsorption and secretion is referred to as the *transport maxima mechanisms (Tm)*. These mechanisms have a maximum capacity in handling materials. When the amount of material presented to them per unit of time is less than their maximum capacity, all the substance is transported. When presented in amounts greater than maximum capacity per unit of time, the substance being reabsorbed continues to be transported up to the maximum capacity and the excess is excreted in the urine. For example, a normal value for glucose is 100 mg. per 100 ml. of plasma. The Tm_G or transport maxima for glucose for men is 375 mg./min./1.73M² surface area. In consequence, normally all glucose will be reabsorbed—none will be excreted in the urine. If large quantities of sugar are ingested, 375 mg./min. will continue to be reabsorbed but *digestive glycosuria*, or the appearance of glucose in the urine, will result.

A second type of active transport in reabsorption and secretion is the *gradient-time* mechanism. Here, the limitation in transport is the gradient of concentration which is established between the glomerular filtrate and the peritubular fluid during the time the fluid is in contact with the epithelium. For example, the amount of Na^+ transported is determined by the rate it is filtered through the glomerular membrane. Approximately 80 per cent of the Na^+ in the filtrate is reabsorbed. Thus reabsorption is increased if the Na^+ concentration in the filtrate is high, or if the Na^+ concentration is unchanged and the glomerular filtration rate is increased.

Principal Mechanisms for Transport of Some Constituents of Glomerular Filtrate and Urine. Passive transport mechanisms in reabsorption are responsible for exchange of water, urea, and chlorides. These exchanges are, however, controlled principally by the active reabsorption of Na^+, which increases the concentration gradient for diffusion of water; urea follows water in accordance with the activity gradient. Chloride is reabsorbed down the electropotential gradient due to Na^+ reabsorption.

Passive mechanisms in secretion are responsible for transport of ammonia, weak acids and bases, chlorides and bicarbonates from the peritubular fluid.

Transport maxima mechanisms of reabsorption are responsible for transfer of glucose, phosphate, sulphate, amino acids, lactate, and (small amounts) albumin from the lumen of the tubules to the peritubular fluid. Organic acids and bases and creatine are secreted into the filtrate by Tm mechanisms.

Gradient-time mechanisms are responsible for reabsorption of Na^+, some chloride and bicarbonate. These mechanisms, acting in the opposite direction, are responsible for secretion of K^+ and H^+.

Concentration of Tubular Urine. The glomerular filtrate is eventually reduced to a small percentage of its original volume by a series of exchanges of water and salts between the tubular urine and the peritubular fluid. This process can be visualized as occurring in five stages:

1. Isosmolar fluid is reabsorbed (Fig. 17.5) in the thick segment of the proximal tubule.

2. The osmolarity is markedly increased by reabsorption of water from and secretion of Na^+ into the tubular urine in the descending thin segment of Henle's loop.

3. The osmolarity is decreased in the ascending thin segment of Henle's loop through active reabsorption of Na^+ and retention of water.

4. The fluid becomes isosmolar in the distal segment of the convoluted tubules. Water and salt pass outward to peritubular fluid, further reducing the volume of the tubular urine.

5. In the collecting tubule Na^+ is reabsorbed and K^+ and H^+ are secreted; NH_3 diffuses into the tubular fluid.

Let us consider the mechanisms by which the exchanges take place. The isosmolar glomerular filtrate (300 mOsm.) is reabsorbed into the peritubular fluid of the cortex, and is carried away by the capillary circulation. The tubular isosmolar urine, which has been reduced to about 20 per cent of its original volume, passes into the descending thin segment of Henle's loop. The thin segments lie in the medullary tissue of the kidneys. Now the extracellular fluid of the medullary interstitium is hypertonic as a result of active secretion of Na^+ from the tubular urine in the thin segment of the ascending limb of the nephron; this segment is normally impermeable to water, so that water does not accompany the Na^+ and other ions excreted. This hypertonicity of the extracellular fluid of the medullary layers results in the continuing reabsorption of water from the thin segment of the descending limbs of Henle's loops. The increased Na^+ within the medullary tissues and the activity of the Na^+-pump secretory mechanisms favors transport of Na^+ into the modified filtrate within the descending thin segment of the loop of Henle. Thus, the osmolarity of the tubular urine increases during its passage down the descending portion of the thin segment. Since Na^+ is being reabsorbed and H_2O retained, the osmolarity of the fluid in the thin segment of the ascending limb of Henle's loop is decreased. As a result, the tubular urine passing into the thick segment of the distal tubule is hypotonic. Thick segments of distal tubules lie within the cortical interstitium where the peritubular fluid is isotonic. The distal tubule is permeable to water and Na^+. Water is reabsorbed until the fluid becomes isosmotic, then reabsorption of Na^+ accompanied by water occurs. The tubular urine flows into the collecting tubules which lie within the medullary layers (Fig. 17.5). The volume of the fluid is further decreased by reabsorption of water into the hypertonic medullary interstitium, and the osmolarity is decreased by secretion of K^+, H^+, and NH_4^+ (from NH_3) into the tubular lumen and reabsorption of Na^+ into the interstitium.

Sites of Reabsorption and Secretion. Substances reabsorbed in the proximal convoluted tubules include Na^+, K^+, glucose, amino acids, protein, phosphate, bicarbonate, water, Cl^-, and urea. In the proximal portion of the thin segment water is reabsorbed, and sodium excreted; in the distal portion Na^+ is reabsorbed. In the distal convoluted tubules Na^+, H_2O, and urea are reabsorbed. In the collecting tubules Na^+, Cl^- and urea are reabsorbed; H^+, K^+, and NH_4^+ are secreted.

The permeability of the distal tubules and the collecting tubules is influenced by the hormone ADH (p. 141); a high titer of ADH increases the tubular permeability to water, and absence of ADH decreases tubular permeability. (See also *water balance*, p. 319.) ADH may also stimulate Na^+-pump transport mechanisms in the loops of Henle.

The role of the kidney in the regulation of acid-base balance is discussed in another section (see p. 320).

MICTURITION

From the distal convoluted tubules the urine passes into arched and collecting tubules through the calices into the renal pelvis to form the ureters. The ureters (one from each kidney) carry the urine to the urinary bladder (Fig. 17.2).

The smooth muscle (detrusor muscle) of the bladder wall maintains just enough tone at all times to accommodate additional amounts of urine with only a slight rise in pressure within the bladder. In man when the bladder contains about 150 ml. of urine, the pressure rises enough to stimulate sensory receptors in the bladder wall and bring the matter to the level of consciousness. The average adult becomes uncomfortably aware of bladder distention with a bladder volume of around 400 ml. These pain sensations are transmitted from the dome of the bladder by the upper lumbar nerves in the hypogastric plexus, from detrusor muscle by pelvic splanchnic nerves, and from the urethra by the pudendal nerves (Figs. 17.7 and 17.8). The probable route to conscious awareness of discomfort is through the lateral spinothalamic tract and thalamus to cerebral cortex.

Emptying of the bladder is brought about by the *micturition reflex*, which occurs spontaneously as the tension in the bladder wall reaches the threshold level at 150 ml. of urine. Parasympathetic autonomic innervation brings about rhythmic contrac-

tions of the detrusor muscle, relaxation and opening of the internal and external urinary sphincters, and evacuation of the bladder. The micturition reflex in the spinal cord can be facilitated or made more powerful by nerve centers in the pons, midbrain, and hypothalamus. This reflex may be inhibited or made less powerful by centers in the cerebral cortex and sympathetic autonomic reflexes in the spinal cord so that the bladder fills until volitional urination occurs. At this time the cortical centers facilitate the micturition reflex and inhibit or relax the external urinary sphincter so that urination can occur. Cerebral control of the micturition reflex is mediated through the corticospinal tract. The lack of bladder control in infants is related particularly to the maturation of the lateral corticospinal tract. Injury to the brain, the corticospinal tract, or spinal cord may cause a diminution in voluntary control of urination in later life.

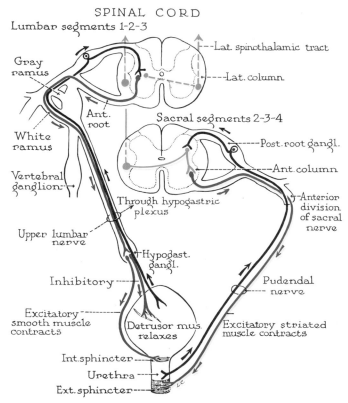

Figure 17.7 Diagram of nervous mechanisms controlling the bladder and sphincters in retention of urine (filling the bladder). Reflexes involve the sympathetic division of the autonomic nervous system.

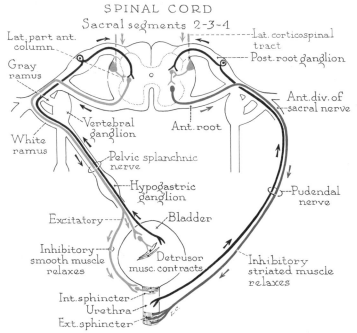

SPINAL CORD
Sacral segments 2-3-4

Figure 17.8 Diagram of nervous mechanisms controlling the bladder and sphincters in micturition; reflexes involve the parasympathetic division of the autonomic nervous system.

QUESTIONS FOR DISCUSSION

1. How is excretion related to the exchange and transport of materials within the body?

2. List the excretory mechanisms and the materials which each mechanism controls.

3. At what locations in the kidney might diuretic drugs be active?

4. What might be the effect of the following upon regulation of extracellular fluid: fever, craving for salt, hemorrhage, dryness of mouth, injury to the posterior pituitary gland, disease of the adrenal cortex?

5. Discuss the factors which control pH in the body.

6. How might the acid-base balance of the body be altered by: diarrhea, vomiting, diabetes mellitus, kidney disease?

7. What is the role of the renal corpuscle in the formation of urine? What is the function of the tubules? What physiological processes are involved in the formation of urine?

8. What part does the urinary system play in maintaining a constant composition in the internal environment?

9. Explain micturition in terms of nerve control.

10. How might micturition be brought about after injury to the thoracic spinal cord?

UNIT 5

METABOLISM

18. DIGESTION 19. UTILIZATION OF FOOT AND REGULATION OF BODY TEMPERATURE

Unit Five deals with the details of the structures and the physiological processes that maintain the balance between energy intake and energy expenditure, and prepare nutrient material for use in the construction of protoplasm for growth and repair in the body.

DIGESTION

CHAPTER
EIGHTEEN

STRUCTURES AND FUNCTIONS OF THE DIGESTIVE SYSTEM

Digestive Activities. Pressure gradients are responsible for movement of food from the oral to the anal of the digestive tract. The upper portion of the tract prepares food for absorption into the blood. This involves both chemical and mechanical activities. The structures involved in the chemical and mechanical processes in the mouth are under the voluntary and involuntary control of the central nervous system (pp. 113-116). In the remainder of the alimentary tract these activities are under the control of the autonomic system or chemical mechanisms, so that we are not normally aware of their occurrence. Final elimination of food residues by defecation is normally under voluntary control in that it may be consciously inhibited or facilitated.

The Alimentary Canal. The digestive system (Fig. 18.1) consists of the alimentary canal, a tube that is about 4.5 to 5 meters in length from mouth to anus as measured in the living, and a number of related portions, the accessory organs. The canal is formed by mouth, pharynx, esophagus, stomach, small intestine, large intestine (colon), and rectum. Associated with the canal are the accessory structures,

335

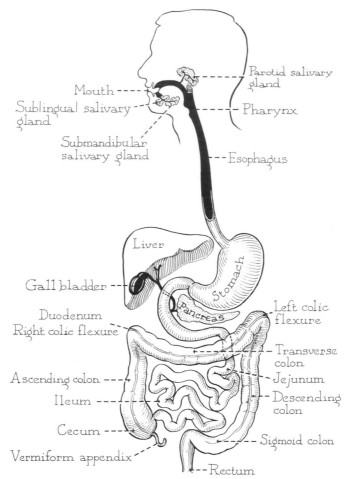

Mouth

Sublingual salivary
gland

Submandibular
salivary gland

Parotid salivary
gland

Pharynx

Esophagus

Liver

Stomach

Gallbladder

Duodenum
Right colic flexure

Pancreas

Left colic
flexure

Transverse
colon

Ascending colon

Jejunum

Ileum

Descending
colon

Cecum

Sigmoid colon

Vermiform appendix

Rectum

Figure 18.1 Diagram of the alimentary tract.

salivary glands, liver, gallbladder, and pancreas.

The distal portion of the esophagus and the remaining portion of the alimentary canal are contained in the abdomen. The abdominal cavity proper is bounded above by the diaphragm, below by the rim of the true pelvis, behind by the vertebral column, quadratus lumborum and psoas muscles, and in front and at the sides by the abdominal and iliacus muscles. The upper boundary formed by the dome of the diaphragm extends high into the thorax and lies well under the shelter of the ribs.

In order to locate the organs of the abdominal cavity proper, the anterior surface of the abdomen is divided by two horizontal and two vertical planes into nine regions (Fig. 18.2). The upper horizontal plane passes through the body at the lowest point of the tenth costal cartilages; the lower horizontal plane passes through the anterior superior iliac spines. The longitudinal planes coincide with the lateral margins of the rectus muscles extending from the costal borders to the pubic tubercle. The central regions from superior to inferior are epigastric, umbilical, and hypogastric. On either side in the same order are the right and left hypochondriac, the right and left abdominal or lumbar, and right and left inguinal or iliac regions (see also Figure 18.9).

Though the different regions of the alimentary tract have individual and special features, the tube conforms to a definite structural plan from the esophagus to the

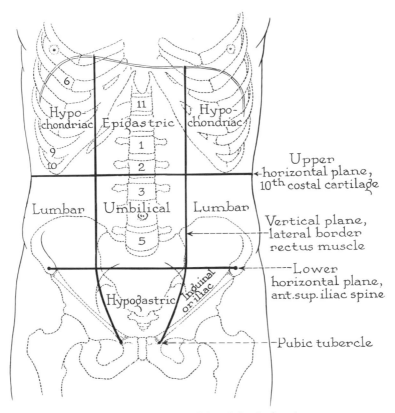

Figure 18.2 Diagram of the abdominal regions.

rectum. From within outward there are the following layers: mucous, submucous, muscular, and serous (Fig. 18.3).

The *mucous layer* is composed of a superficial epithelium, an underlying supporting connective tissue (lamina propria), and a relatively thin arrangement of smooth muscle fibers, or muscularis mucosae. In the esophagus, the epithelium is of the stratified squamous type, but the stomach and intestine have a simple columnar epithelium. The cells of the mucosa secrete digestive juices, mucus, and gastrointestinal hormones. Glands formed by the lining epithelium extend into the lamina propria or submucosa, or even outside the tube proper. The entire mucosa may project into the lumen of the tube as folds *(rugae or plicae)* or fingers *(villi)*. Both invaginations and evaginations of the mucous membrane increase the total active surface area of the alimentary tract. The lymphatic tissue of the tract contains an abundance of plasma cells. The organization of the lymphatic tissue runs from diffuse lymphoid tissue, to solitary nodules and aggregated nodules. Such tissue is located primarily in the lamina propria. Sensory nerve fibers extend up to the epithelium of the mucosa.

The *submucous layer* is composed of fibroelastic tissue that connects the mucous and muscular coats and provides an adjustable basis for movements and changes in size of the tube. This layer supports numerous lymphatics, blood vessels, and nerves. Sympathetic nerve endings from cells in the celiac, superior, and inferior mesenteric ganglia are found around the blood vessels. An autonomic plexus of nerves lies between the submucous and muscular coats. This is known as the *submucous (Meissner's) plexus*; its ganglion cells synapse with the parasympathetic endings from vagal and sacral nerves.

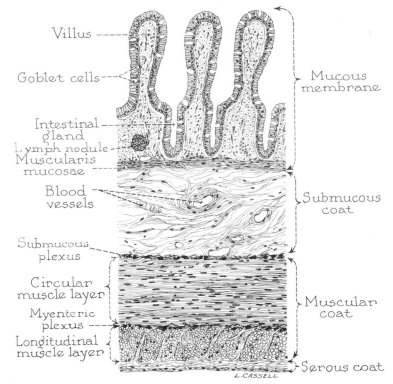

Figure 18.3 Diagrammatic cross section of the small intestine, showing the four coats which form a conspicuous structural feature throughout the gastrointestinal tract.

The *muscular coat* consists of smooth muscle arranged in two layers: an inner circular one surrounding the tube, and an outer longitudinal one whose fibers run parallel with the long axis. Contraction of the circular layer narrows the lumen of the tube, and contraction of the longitudinal layer shortens the tube. At several points along the canal the circular layer is thickened to form sphincters, or valves, which are closed by contraction of these muscle fibers. Another autonomic plexus of nerves, the *myenteric (Auerbach's) plexus* is located between the inner circular and outer longitudinal layers of the muscular coat. It is comparable to the submucous plexus, with the ganglion cells synapsing with parasympathetic vagal and sacral nerves. Sympathetic nerve fibers are intermingled with the fibers of the submucous and myenteric plexuses.

In the esophagus the *serous* layer is lacking and the outer coat (adventitia) is fibrous in nature. The portions of the alimentary tract lying in the abdomen are covered with the outer serous layer, the peritoneum.

The alimentary tract is richly supplied with lymphatic vessels arising as blind capillaries in the mucosa. In the small intestine the close association of blood and lymphatic vessels (Fig. 18.4) facilitates absorption. The dilated lymph capillary within the villus is a *lacteal*. Lymphatic vessels from these lacteals possess a muscular wall and are able to propel their contents toward the cisterna chyli (p. 280).

The *peritoneum* has two distributions: a parietal layer, which completely lines the abdominal cavity, and a visceral layer, which is reflected over the organs contained within the cavity (Fig. 18.5). The spaces that may exist between the parietal and visceral layers of the peritoneum comprise the *peritoneal cavity*. Certain folds of the visceral layer receive special names. The portion that passes from the inferior surface of the liver to the lesser curvature

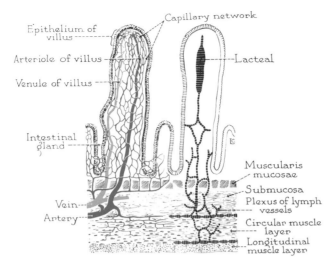

Epithelium of villus

Capillary network

Arteriole of villus

Lacteal

Venule of villus

Intestinal gland

Muscularis mucosae

Submucosa

Plexus of lymph vessels

Vein

Artery

Circular muscle layer

Longitudinal muscle layer

Figure 18.4 Diagrammatic cross section of human small intestine, villus at the left shown with blood vessels only, that at the right with lacteal only, but both occur in all villi. (After F. P. Mall.)

of the stomach is the *lesser omentum*; the fold extending from the greater curvature of the stomach to the transverse colon is the *greater omentum*. This fold is the most conspicuous of all and spreads out like an apron over the anterior surface of the intestines. From the transverse colon the peritoneum is carried backward to the posterior abdominal wall as the *transverse mesocolon*. A fan-shaped membrane, the *mesentery*, attaches the small intestine to the posterior abdominal wall. The peritoneum is arranged in such a manner that two cavities are formed; the greater or main cavity, and the lesser cavity or *omental bursa* (Fig. 18.5). The omental bursa lies posterior to the stomach; its walls are formed principally by the lesser omentum, the greater omentum, and the transverse mesocolon. A connection between the two cavities is provided by the epiploic foramen.

MOUTH. The mouth is the first division of the alimentary tract. Its function in digestion is largely mechanical. The food is broken up by the teeth, ground into small particles, and moistened and softened by saliva. When moistened the food can be rolled into a plastic mass; the saliva provides it with a lubricating coat which facilitates swallowing. The lips form the anterior boundary of the oral cavity and the glossopalatine arch the posterior limit, at which point it leads into the pharynx.

The roof is formed by the palate, the floor by the tongue, and the lateral walls by the cheeks. It houses the teeth, which are embedded in the upper and lower jaws. The vestibule of the oral cavity lies between the cheeks and jaws and the oral cavity proper is internal to the jaws. It is lined with stratified squamous epithelium that is continuous with that of the pharynx. The large salivary glands empty their secretions into the mouth. Numerous small glands opening into the vestibule, floor of the oral cavity, and surface of the tongue or palate also contribute their secretions to saliva.

The *tongue* is a muscular organ. The mucous membrane covering the upper surface shows numerous elevations, the *papillae* and *lingual tonsils*. There are three varieties of papillae: filiform, fungiform, and vallate (Fig. 18.6). The filiform and fungiform papillae are scattered over the anterior two-thirds of the tongue; the latter, less numerous, appear as red points chiefly near the edges. The vallate papillae, numbering ten to twelve, are arranged in the form of a **V** on the posterior part of the tongue. The apex of the **V** is directed toward the pharynx. The end organs of taste, the taste buds, are distributed over the surface of the tongue, but are most conspicuous on the sides of the vallate papillae. Extrinsic and intrinsic muscles form the muscular substance of the tongue. These skeletal muscles are arranged

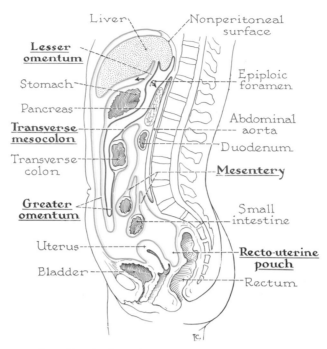

Figure 18.5 Diagrammatic midsagittal section of female body to show peritoneal reflections. The greater sac of the peritoneum is shown in green; the omental bursa in red.

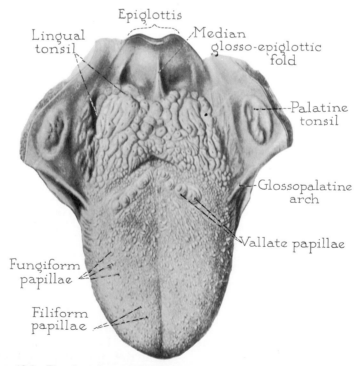

Figure 18.6 The dorsal surface of the tongue. (From Sobotta and McMurrich.)

parallel to and at right angles to the long axis of the tongue. Lingual musculature is also divided into right and left halves by a median fibrous septum. Paralysis of the muscle can cause the tongue to draw toward the paralyzed side or fall backward into the pharynx and obstruct the airway. The tongue is innervated through the cranial nerves (p. 115) concerned with taste, general sensation, speech, mastication, and swallowing.

Teeth. The teeth begin to form early in embryonic life, about the seventh week. They develop from the oral mucosa, but do not begin to erupt until the infant is about six or seven months old.

There are two sets of teeth: the first to develop are the deciduous or milk teeth; later the permanent teeth appear. The *deciduous teeth* are twenty in number, ten in each jaw. Beginning at the center in each half jaw there are two incisors, one canine and two molars. Their eruptions begin about the sixth or seventh month and end usually at two and one half years. The *permanent teeth* (Figs. 18.7) are thirty-two in number, sixteen in each jaw. Beginning at the center in each half jaw there are two incisors, one canine, two premolars, and three molars. The permanent teeth begin to erupt about the sixth year, and the full complement may not be attained until the twenty-fifth year. The incisors have sharp, chisel-like edges for biting and tearing; the canines have pointed tips for piercing; the premolars and molars have flattened, irregular surfaces for grinding. The third molars are called the "wisdom teeth."

The structure of a tooth consists of an exposed portion protruding from the gums, called the *crown*, a portion embedded in the socket, or alveolus, of the jaw bone, called the *root*, and a portion connecting the crown and root, known as the *neck*. The neck is covered by the gum.

Examination of a vertical section of a tooth (Fig. 18.8) shows it to be composed of a solid outer portion and a central pulp cavity. The solid portion consists of an ivory substance, dentine, which forms the main body of the tooth, and an adamant substance, enamel, which covers the crown. The enamel is the hardest substance in the body. The root of the tooth is covered by a thin layer of hard material, the substantia ossea or cement. The tooth socket is lined with periosteum that supplies nourishment and serves to attach the tooth to the socket. The pulp cavity extends lengthwise through the center of the tooth; blood vessels and nerves enter it through openings in the root tip.

PHARYNX. The structure of the pharynx has been described on page 237. The *palatine tonsils* are on the lateral walls of the oral pharynx between the glossopalatine and pharyngopalatine arches. The oral and laryngeal portions of the pharynx serve as a channel for the passage of both food and air; food is conducted through it from the mouth to the esophagus, and air from the nasal pharynx to the larynx. When swallowing occurs, the soft palate is pushed backward against the posterior pharyngeal wall, closing the passage to the nose; the larynx is elevated, and its superior aperture is protected by a projecting ledge formed by the epiglottis.

ESOPHAGUS. The esophagus is a musculomembranous tube about 23 to 25 cm. long which conveys food from the pharynx to the stomach. It passes through the thorax, pierces the *esophageal hiatus* of the diaphragm, and joins the cardia of the stomach, which begins about 1 to 2 cm. below the hiatus (Fig. 18.10). In the thorax it lies in the mediastinum posterior to the trachea and heart and anterior to the vertebrae. In the lower part of its course it sweeps in front of the aorta, passing through the diaphragm at the left of the median line to end in the stomach. Its walls conform to the general plan described earlier in this chapter.

In the upper third of the esophagus, the muscular wall is formed by skeletal muscle with an outer layer of longitudinal bundles of fibers and an inner layer of circular bundles of fibers. The second third is a transitional segment between the striated muscle above and smooth muscle below; the lower third contains smooth muscle only. There are two sphincters, one at each end of the esophagus. The superior end is guarded by the *pharyngoesophageal sphincter*—a thickening of the circular muscle wall. The muscles in this

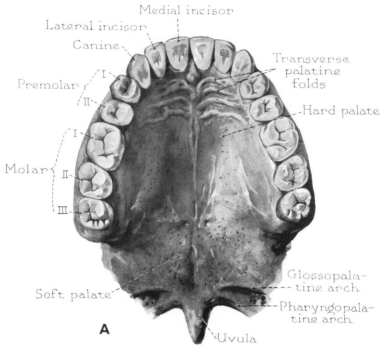

Figure 18.7*A*   The palate with superior dental arch seen from below. (Modified from Spalteholz.)

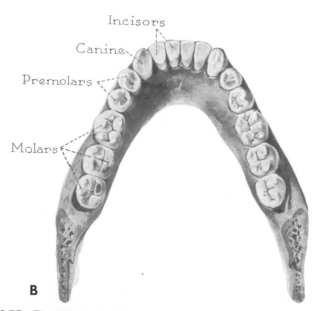

Figure 18.7*B*   The inferior dental arch from above. (Modified from Spalteholz.)

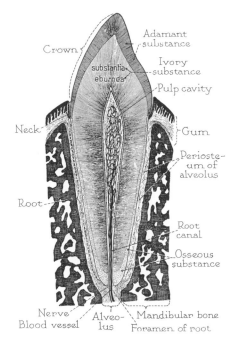

Crown

Adamant substance

substantia eburnea

Ivory substance

Pulp cavity

Neck

Gum

Periosteum of alveolus

Root

Root canal

Osseous substance

Nerve
Blood vessel

Alveolus

Mandibular bone

Foramen of root

Figure 18.8 Longitudinal section of a tooth in its alveolus (diagrammatic). (From Sobotta and McMurrich.)

vomitus from the esophagus. At the inferior end the *gastroesophageal sphincter* extends from the cardia to a few centimeters above the hiatus. The thickened circular muscle is reinforced by the interlaced muscle fibers of the right crus of the diaphragm.

STOMACH. The stomach is a dilated portion of the alimentary canal lying in the left hypochondriac and epigastric abdominal regions (Figs. 18.9 and 18.10). It may be thought of as a retaining and mixing reservoir in which the chemical phases of digestion begin. The opening into the esophagus is called the *cardiac orifice*, since it is just below the heart; and the opening into the small intestine is the *pyloric orifice*. The two borders of the stomach pass between these orifices. The right border or lesser curvature is short and somewhat concave; the left border or greater curvature is long and convex. To the left side of the midline, the stomach can be divided into a *cardiac portion, fundus,* and *body*. The *pyloric antrum* and *pyloric canal* are found in the pyloric portion of the stomach, on the right side of the midline. These parts are shown in Figure 18.10.

The shape and position of the stomach show great variations, not only among

segment are normally contracted, closing off the esophagus from the pharynx, except for a very brief period during swallowing and also during expulsion of

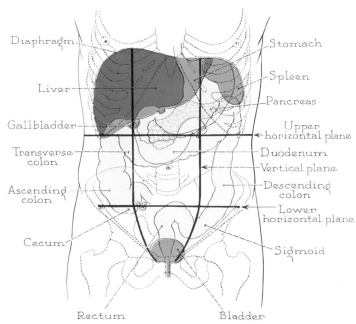

Diaphragm

Stomach

Liver

Spleen

Pancreas

Gallbladder

Upper horizontal plane

Transverse colon

Duodenum

Vertical plane

Ascending colon

Descending colon

Lower horizontal plane

Cecum

Sigmoid

Rectum

Bladder

Figure 18.9 Surface projection of the abdominal viscera.

different individuals, but also in the same person at different times. Frequently, especially when distended, it extends into the umbilical and right hypochondriac regions. X-rays taken of man standing erect show that when the stomach is filled with food it assumes an almost vertical position and has a tubular shape. Because of the sharp angle formed at the junction of body and pylorus, its shape has been likened to the letter **J**. The mucous membrane is smooth when the organ is full, but is thrown into folds, called *rugae*, when empty (Fig. 18.10).

The mucous membrane contains the secreting cells of the stomach, which are arranged in small tubular units to form the gastric glands. The glands of the fundus (Fig. 18.11) and body are most important in the secretion of gastric juice. There are four types of cells in the glands (Fig. 18-11); mucous neck cells, argentaffin cells, chief or zymogenic cells, and parietal or oxyntic cells. Mucous neck cells as well as the mucous cells of the surface epithelium secrete the mucus, which forms a protective layer against autodigestion of gastric mucosa. *Argentaffin* (enterochromaffin) *cells* synthesize and store serotonin (5-hydroxytryptamine). *Chief* or *zymogenic cells* are cuboidal or low columnar cells whose zymogen granules contain the inactive proteolytic enzyme, pepsinogen.

Chief cells are also believed to secrete the intrinsic antianemic factor (p. 267). *Parietal* or *oxyntic cells* are the source of hydrochloric acid. A fluid rich in sodium chloride is secreted into the canaliculus of the parietal cell (Fig. 18.12). Interaction with carbonic acid in the lumen of the stomach accompanied by rapid resorption of sodium is presumed to produce the hydrochloric acid of gastric juice.

The muscular wall of the body of the stomach is thin, whereas that of the antrum is thick. The muscular coat, in addition to circular and longitudinal layers, has an inner layer in which the fibers run obliquely. The circular layer is thickened at the cardiac and pyloric orifices to form sphincters.

SMALL INTESTINE. The small intestine plays the principal role in the digestion and absorption of food and delivers the residue to the large intestine. The small intestine consists of a thin-walled musculomembranous tube about $2\frac{1}{2}$ to $3\frac{1}{2}$ meters long. It is divided into three parts: the *duodenum*, the *jejunum*, and the *ileum*. The duodenum, which is about 20 cm. long, is attached to the posterior abdominal wall and arranged in a horseshoe shape to enclose the head of the pancreas. The bile and pancreatic ducts open into the duodenum at the junction of its middle and lower third. The portion between the py-

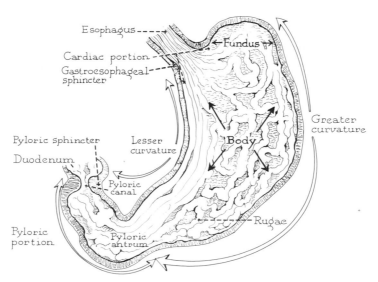

Figure 18.10 Stomach showing external features, parts, and mucosal contours.

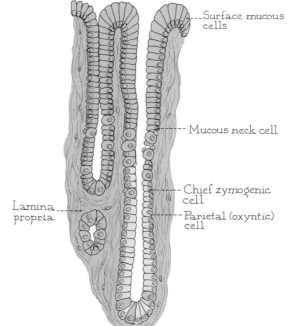

Figure 18.11 Cytology of gastric glands.

Surface mucous cells

Mucous neck cell

Chief zymogenic cell

Parietal (oxyntic) cell

Lamina propria

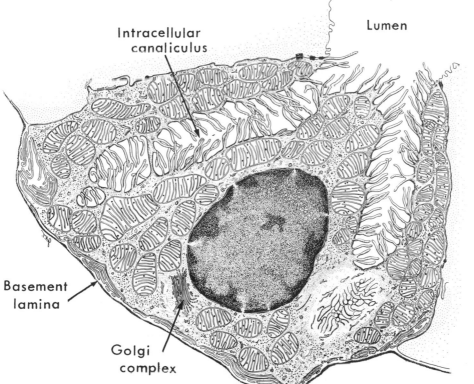

Intracellular canaliculus

Lumen

Basement lamina

Golgi complex

Figure 18.12 Diagram of the ultrastructure of a gastric parietal cell, illustrating its abundant mito-chondria, sparse reticulum, and prominent "intracellular" canaliculus. (After S. Ito and R. J. Winchester, J. Cell Biol., *16*:541, 1963. In Bloom and Fawcett: Textbook of Histology, 9th Ed., 1968.)

loric sphincter and the entrance of the ducts is called the duodenal cap; its physiological behavior differs somewhat from the parts of the small intestine below. The jejunum continues from the duodenum and thence into the ileum, which connects with the large intestine at the cecum. There is little anatomic differentiation other than in blood supply and in contours of the villi between these two segments of the small intestine, but the jejunum is commonly considered to constitute the upper $2/5$ and the ileum the lower $3/5$ of the jejunoileum. These two portions of the small intestine are suspended from the posterior abdominal wall in the fanlike fold of peritoneum, the mesentery (Fig. 18.5).

Although the three portions differ slightly, their structural principle is the same throughout. The four coats of the alimentary canal previously described are typically represented in the small intestine. Certain features of special interest are the villi, the circular folds and the glands. The circular folds and the villi of the mucous layer are structural devices which increase the surface enormously. Beginning a short distance from the pylorus, the circular folds (Fig. 18.13) are numerous and high in the duodenum and first portion of the jejunum, but from this point on they gradually become less numerous and smaller

and fade out completely about the middle of the ileum. They are permanent structures and do not disappear when the wall is distended. The presence of about 5,000,000 villi in the intestine provides an absorbing surface of some 10 square meters. The tall columnar cells of the villi are covered on their free surfaces by microvilli which further increase the cellular surface area available to intestinal contents. Higher concentrations of certain digestive enzymes are present in the microvillus border than in free digestive juice. Sucrase, maltase, aminopeptidase, and alkaline phosphatase are among the enzymes that have been identified. Their location strongly suggests that this is a site of active transport and digestion as well as of absorption.

The *intestinal glands* (crypts of Lieberkühn) are found throughout the small and large intestines. They have the form of a simple tube. In the small intestine they are placed between the villi and secrete the intestinal juice containing the digestive enzymes. The bottom of the crypt is lined with *Paneth* (zymogenic) *cells* and argentaffin cells.

The *duodenal glands* (of Brunner) are found only in the duodenum. They are tortuous and branching submucosal glands; their secretion is alkaline and contains mucus.

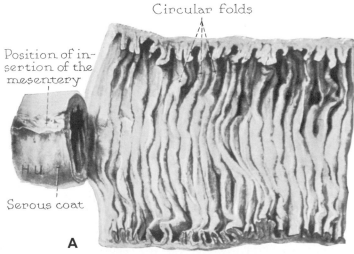

A

Figure 18.13*A* Circular folds of small intestine as seen in a portion of the jejunum. (Modified from Spalteholz.)

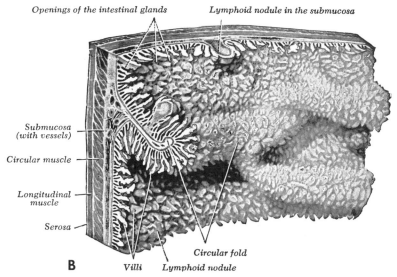

Figure 18.13*B* Portion of wall of small intestine, showing villi and a circular fold. (From Maximow and Bloom, after Braus.)

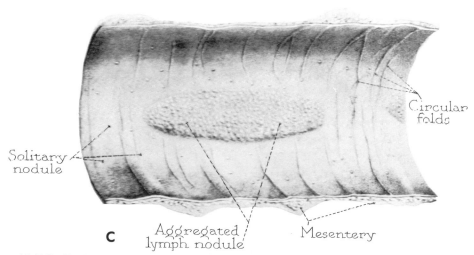

Figure 18.13*C* Portion of lower ileum opened along its entire length, showing an aggregated lymph nodule. (From Sobotta and McMurrich.)

Lymphoid tissue is present in the form of nodules throughout the small intestine. The nodules may appear singly as the *solitary nodules* or may be massed together as the *aggregated nodules* (Peyer's patches) (Fig. 18.13). Aggregated nodules are found chiefly in the ileum (see also pp. 268-270).

LARGE INTESTINE. The remaining portion of the alimentary canal is the large intestine (Fig. 18.9). It is a little over 1 meter long and is divided into cecum, colon, rectum, and anal canal. The digestive functions performed by the large intestine are absorption of water and partial dehydration of the chyme; some bacterial digestion of residues, chiefly those from vegetables; some absorption of vitamins; the excretion of certain elements, and transport of feces to the rectum.

Contrary to popular belief, there is no evidence of absorption of toxic products from the colon into the systemic circulation, even during the state of constipation. The symptoms of constipation result from the distention of the descending colon and rectum rather than from autointoxication from colonic contents.

The *cecum* is that part of the large intestine below the attachment of the ileum. It is a blind pouch from the lower portion of which projects the appendix. At the opening of the ileum into the cecum is the *ileocecal valve,* a true sphincter, which controls the passage of the intestinal contents into the cecum.

The *colon* is divided into ascending, transverse, descending, and sigmoid portions. The ascending colon passes upward on the right of the abdomen from the cecum to the inferior surface of the liver, where it bends to become the transverse colon. This bend is called the right colic flexure. The transverse colon sweeps across the abdominal cavity from right to left below the stomach. It is attached to the posterior abdominal wall by a peritoneal fold, the transverse mescolon (Fig. 18.5). At the spleen it bends downward to become the descending colon. This is the left colic flexure. The descending colon

extends downward along the left side of the abdomen to the brim of the pelvis. From this point the colon courses in a curve like the letter **S** as far as the third segment of the sacrum, where it becomes the rectum. The **S**-shaped curve is called the sigmoid colon.

The walls of the large intestine (Fig. 18.14) conform to the general structural plan and have the usual four layers. The mucous layer is like that of the small intestine, but there are no villi and no circular folds. The intestinal glands are present, but they secrete chiefly mucus. The cells at the bottom of the crypt are undifferentiated columnar cells and argentaffin cells. Lymphoid tissue is present in solitary nodules, but there are no aggregated nodules. The muscular layer shows a striking difference; the longitudinal layer does not completely surround the intestine, but is confined to three narrow bands called *teniae,* placed at nearly equal distances from each other. The teniae shirr the tube into sacculations known as *haustra.* The inner aspect presents semilunar folds between the haustra that correspond to the creases on the outer surface. The serous coat is marked by little pouches of

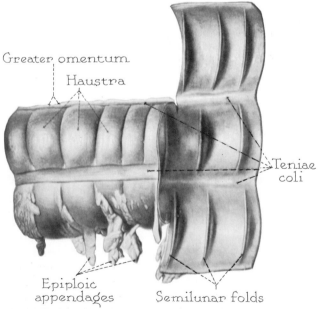

Figure 18.14 A portion of the transverse colon from in front and below. The right end is opened up. (From Sobotta and McMurrich.)

peritoneum containing fat. These are the *epiploic appendages*.

Rectum and Anal Canal. The *rectum* continues from the sigmoid colon, at about the third sacral vertebra, down to the pelvic diaphragm (p. 391), in front of the coccyx. Its length is 12 cm. Three *transverse rectal folds* are found in the side-to-side dimension of the tube. These folds include the mucosa, the submucosa, and the circular portion of the muscular layer. Externally there is no visceral peritoneum and the haustra have disappeared as the teniae coli spread out to form a more complete longitudinal muscular coat.

The *anal canal*, about 3 cm. in length, is the portion of the large intestine below the pelvic cavity communicating through the anus to the exterior of the body (Fig. 18.15). It receives feces from the descending colon. Feces may either be discharged through the anal canal or stored until a voluntary act of defecation occurs. Below the pelvic diaphragm the anal canal is surrounded by the skeletal muscle of the *external anal sphincter*. In this same region the longitudinal muscular layer disappears as the circular muscular layer thickens to become the *internal anal sphincter*. In the upper half of the anal canal the mucous membrane is thrown into five to ten vertical *anal columns*. Each column contains the terminal branches of the rectal artery and vein. The columns are connected by small folds of mucous membrane, the *anal valves*, under which passes a plexus of communicating valveless veins. The transition from mucosa to skin occurs in this region.

Accessory Digestive Organs. The glandular accessory digestive organs develop in the embryo as epithelial evaginations from the endoderm layer. They retain their connection with the alimentary

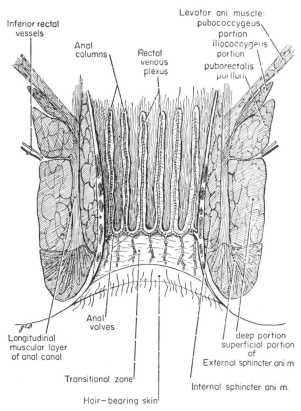

Figure 18.15 The anal canal as seen in semischematic vertical section. (From Woodburne: Essentials of Human Anatomy, 4th Ed., New York, Oxford University Press, 1969.)

canal through their ducts. These organs are the salivary glands, liver, gallbladder, and pancreas. The accessory digestive organs perform a variety of functions, principally secretion, storage, modification, and delivery of digestive juices. The liver is active in additional digestive functions concerned with metabolism and in the storage of nutrients; the pancreas also carries on a major metabolic function.

SALIVARY GLANDS. The large salivary glands consist of the parotid, in front of and below the ear, the submandibular, below the mandible, and the sublingual, in the floor of the mouth under the tongue (Fig. 18.16). Ducts from the three pairs of glands open into the mouth. The glands are classified according to the type of their secreting cells into mucous, serous, and mixed glands. The mixed glands contain both serous (zymogenic) and mucus-secreting cells. The parotid gland is a serous gland; the submandibular and sublingual glands are mixed glands. Saliva is a mixture of the secretions of these large salivary glands and of the numerous small salivary glands in the oral cavity. Saliva contains water, inorganic salts, salivary proteins, and enzymes. The principal digestive enzyme is amylase. As the serous cells secrete they also release the enzyme *kallikrein*,

which acts upon plasma protein to produce *bradykinin*. The local vasodilation caused by bradykinin augments the circulation to the actively secreting salivary glands.

THE LIVER. The liver is the largest gland of the body, weighing 1.5 kilograms in men and somewhat less in women. It is a soft, plastic organ, which is molded by surrounding structures (Fig. 18.17). It occupies chiefly the upper right hypochondriac and epigastric regions directly beneath the diaphragm. There are two principal *lobes*, the right and the left. The right lobe consists of the right lobe proper, with the small quadrate lobe on the inferior surface and the caudate lobe on the posterior surface. The line of demarcation between the right and left lobes is indicated on the anterior and superior surfaces by the falciform ligament, which passes from the liver to the diaphragm and the anterior abdominal wall. The ligament is a remnant of the anterior mesentery and conveys on its free border a fibrous cord, the occluded umbilical vein, now the *round ligament*. The surface of the liver is covered with peritoneum with the exception of a small area on its posterior surface that is attached directly to the diaphragm. Beneath the peritoneum is a dense connective tissue layer called the capsule of Glis-

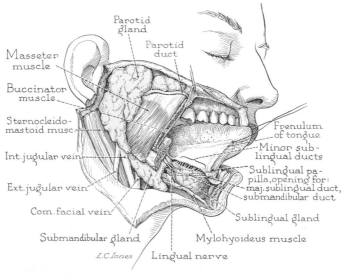

Figure 18.16 The salivary glands on the right side of the face.

son, which covers the entire surface of the organ, and at the hilum or porta is continued into the liver substance, forming a framework for the branches of the portal vein, hepatic artery, and bile ducts.

Microscopic Structure. The cells of the liver are arranged in tridimensional units: the *classic lobule*, the *portal lobule*, and the *acinus*. The architecture of the lobule is shown in Figure 18.18. Running lengthwise through the center of the lobule is a central vein. Encircling the periphery are interlobular branches of the portal vein, hepatic bile ducts, and hepatic ar-

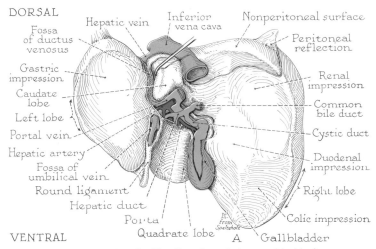

Figure 18.17A The liver from below and behind.

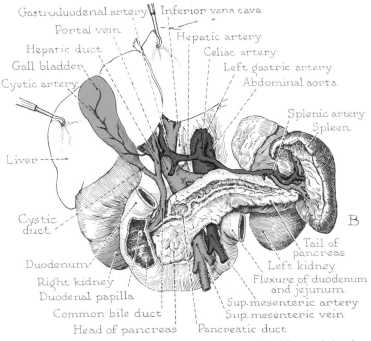

Figure 18.17B Relative positions of liver, spleen, pancreas, gallbladder, and duodenum. (Eycleshymer and Jones: Hand Atlas of Clinical Anatomy. Lea & Febiger.)

tery. The parenchyma is arranged in radiating layers of liver cells and sinusoids. The portal lobule takes the portal vein branch as its central focus and the "central" veins as peripheral boundary marks. In the acinus the parenchyma associated with an axis composed of an "interlobular" vein, artery, and bile duct is considered to be a functional unit. All three concepts are useful considerations of the hemodynamics and multiple functions of the liver.

The polyhedral parenchymal cells have six or more surfaces (Fig. 18.18). The differently adapted surfaces can be seen as perisinusoidal, arranged toward a bile canaliculus, and toward an adjacent liver cell. The perivascular *space of Disse* is a large interstitial space in which active exchange of metabolites between the blood stream and microvilli of the liver cells occurs. Liver cells produce a large amount of lymph with high plasma protein content synthesized in the endoplasmic reticulum. Lymph moves through the space of Disse toward the lymph capillaries accompanying the branches of the portal vein. The lumen of the bile canaliculus appears as an expansion of the intercellular surfaces of adjacent hepatic cells. *Bile* secreted in relation to the Golgi complex and lysomes is transmitted by an intricate network of the canaliculi into the hepatic biliary duct system. About 500 ml. of bile are secreted by the liver cells in twenty-four hours. The main constituents of bile are water (97 per cent), bile salts (0.7 per cent), bile pigments (0.2 per cent), and inorganic salts (0.7 per cent). Small amounts of cholesterol, fatty acids, fat, and lecithin are also present in bile. Glucuronides of biliverdin and bilirubin produced by the liver cells from the breakdown products of hemoglobin give the yellow color to bile. Bile salts, sodium and potassium glycocholate and taurocholate, are responsible for the alkaline reaction of hepatic bile at pH 8.0. The appearance of the cytoplasm in the liver cells varies according to the functional state of the cell and its peripheral or central location in the acinus. Stored carbohydrate glycogen and fat are more prominent at the periphery of the acinus where hepatic cells are in a relatively anoxic zone in relation to the hepatic artery.

The liver sinusoids are irregular blood channels formed by a discontinuous layer of endothelial cells (Kupffer cells) which have taken on a phagocytic function (Fig. 18.18). Destruction of leukocytes and erythrocytes and storage of iron are included in the phagocytosis by the Kupffer cells. *Microcirculation* (Fig. 18.18) of blood in the liver lobules emphasizes the position of the liver between the gastrointestinal por-

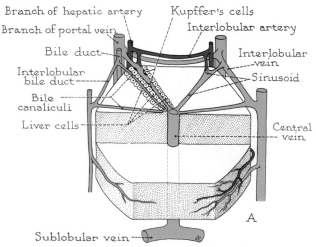

Figure 18.18A Diagram of a liver lobule, showing the hepatic circulation and the relation of liver cells to sinusoids and bile canaliculi.

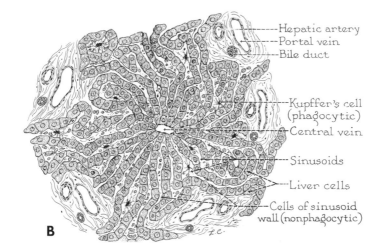

Figure 18.18*B* Cross section of a liver lobule, semidiagrammatic.

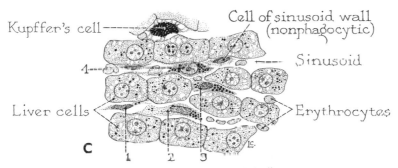

Figure 18.18*C* Liver of a rabbit injected intravenously with India ink. Kupffer's cells (histiocytes) have engulfed granules of India ink. Kupffer's cell at top is packed with granules; cells (1 to 4) in sinusoids below are in transitional stages. (Redrawn from Bloom and Fawcett.)

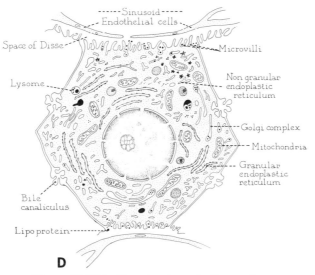

Figure 18.18*D* Fine structure of a liver cell.

tion of the alimentary tract and the systemic circulation. The conducting vessels of the portal circuit have been discussed (p. 289 to 290). The mixture of arterialized blood from interlobular branches of the hepatic artery along with nutrients from the interlobular branches of the portal vein circulates slowly through the sinusoids with access to the liver cells through the spaces of Disse. The central vein of the lobule transmits the systemic venous return to the tributaries of the hepatic veins. Interlobular veins are highly contractile and control the character of the blood flow through the lobule as well as the *blood reservoir* of the entire portal venous network.

Functions. The functions of the liver are summarized to describe the extent and versatility of the activities of this important gland. They include:

1. Formation of bile (p. 352)
2. Activity of reticuloendothelial tissues (Chapter 14)
   Hemopoiesis in the embryo
   Production of plasma proteins and antibodies
   Destruction of red blood cells
   Phagocytosis (Kupffer cells) (p. 352)
3. Metabolism of carbohydrates, lipids, and proteins preparatory to use or excretion (Chapter 19)
   Glycogenesis, glycogenolysis, and gluconeogenesis to maintain normal blood sugar
   Desaturation of fats and conversion to phospholipids
   Synthesis of amino acids.
   Formation of serum albumin, serum globulin, antibodies, heparin, fibrinogen, and prothrombin (p. 265)
   Deamination of amino acids
   Conversion of protein to carbohydrate and fat
   Formation of urea and uric acid; destruction of uric acid
4. Storage depot (pp. 371, 374, 271)
   Glycogen
   Amino acids
   Fats
   Vitamins A, D, B complex
   Iron and Copper

5. Blood reservoir (p. 290)
6. Heat production (p. 279)
7. Detoxication
   Indol, skatol, phenol
   Morphine, strychnine, nicotine
   Steroid hormones
8. Formation of lymph (p. 252)

More detailed treatment of most of these functions is given as indicated.

GALLBLADDER. The gallbladder is a pear-shaped hollow sac attached to the under surface of the liver (Fig. 18.17). It serves as a reservoir for storage and concentration of bile. The capacity of the gallbladder varies among individuals; commonly the capacity is about 30 ml., but it may be from one half to twice that value. It ends in the cystic duct, which joins with hepatic ducts to form the *common bile duct*. The bile, which is being secreted continuously by the liver, may not immediately enter the intestines, but, after passing down the hepatic duct, may turn into the cystic duct and enter the gallbladder. Blood vessels and lymphatics absorb water and inorganic salts removed by mucosal epithelial cells from the bile. Consequently gallbladder bile may be about ten times more concentrated than that collected from the hepatic duct which has a pH of 7.0.

At intervals during digestion the gallbladder contracts and forces the bile down the cystic duct and into the common bile duct, which opens into the duodenum about 10 cm. below the pylorus. The common bile duct pierces the duodenal wall obliquely and joins with the pancreatic duct to form the *ampulla of Vater*, which opens into the duodenum through a small elevation called the duodenal papilla (Fig. 18.17, *B*). The orifice on the summit of the papilla is surrounded by muscle fibers that form a sphincter.

PANCREAS. The pancreas is a long, slender, vascular organ with its head lying to the right in the loop of the duodenum, its body posterior to the stomach and its tail touching the spleen on the left (Fig. 18.17). The portion of the pancreas that secretes pancreatic juice is a compound alveolar gland similar in structure to the large salivary glands. Endocrine cells of

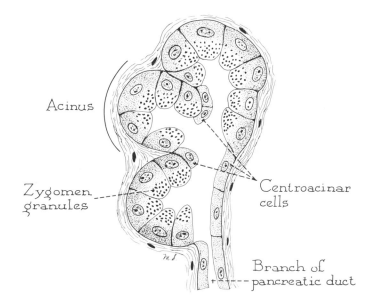

Figure 18.19

Acinus

Zygomen granules

Centroacinar cells

Branch of pancreatic duct

the pancreas have been discussed on page 147. The exocrine pancreatic acinar cells are generally similar to the zymogenic cells of the salivary glands and to gastric parietal cells (Fig. 18.19). Enzymes formed by ribosomes are probably transferred by the Golgi complex into endoplasmic reticulum in which the granules are concentrated and stored at the apex of the cell. Proteolytic enzymes *(trypsinogen, chymotrypsinogen, carboxypeptidase), amylase,* and *lipase* are the principal digestive enzymes which have been demonstrated in the zymogen granules. Formation of bradykinin occurs under the same circumstances of cellular activity and with the same result of local vasodilation as found in the salivary glands. Ducts from the lobules collect into a long *pancreatic duct* extending transversely from the tail to the head. At this point the pancreatic duct is usually joined by an *accessory pancreatic duct* draining the head of the gland. The pancreatic duct empties into the duodenum with the common bile duct at the ampulla of Vater as described previously (Fig. 18.17, *B*).

REGULATION OF FOOD INTAKE

Ingestion of food and water is essential for maintenance of the energy balance and the constancy of the internal environment of the body. Hunger, appetite, and satiety, which regulate food intake, are properly considered as functions of the central nervous system, or more specifically of areas in the hypothalamus. These areas are influenced by the cerebrum and exert both a facilitatory and an inhibitory influence over the lower, more basic reflex centers in the brain stem and spinal cord.

According to a current hypothesis, the feeding centers and possibly the higher cerebral centers, following abstinence from food, become active and food is sought. Subsequently the concentration of nutrient materials, particularly glucose, activates the satiety mechanism and feeding behavior is terminated until the ingested substances are reduced by their utilization for work and heat production.

Hunger, which is a familiar complex sensation evoked by depletion of nutrient stores, involves a vague, diffuse feeling that cannot be localized, with or without the hunger pains that are referred to the epigastric region. Appetite may be defined as a desire for food, and frequently for specific foods. The latter may involve the higher centers, which are more discriminating than the calorie-metering satiety center. Satiety is an affective state in repletion; it induces a desire not to eat.

In general, the energy expended for work and heat production is balanced by the energy derived from food intake so that body weight remains fairly constant over extended periods of time. Long-term regulation of food intake is, however, neither an accurate nor sensitive mechanism, so that appetite may result in increased caloric intake and adiposity. Increased food intake, i.e., *hyperphagia* and obesity, also occurs following injury or destruction of the satiety center. *Aphagia*, failure to eat, as well as *adipsia*, failure to drink, take place following lesions of lateral hypothalamic areas. Partial recovery may eventually occur under special experimental conditions when the lower center takes over the feeding function.

MECHANICAL FACTORS IN DIGESTION

The mechanical factors of digestion are those that (1) have direct action in breaking up the ingested foods; (2) are effective in causing a mixing of the foodstuffs with the digestive secretions; (3) effect a renewal of the surfaces of the nutrient material presented to the absorbing surfaces of the gut; (4) serve to hasten or retard the progress of foodstuffs through the gastrointestinal tract; (5) effect the evacuation of the exogenous and endogenous residues, through defecation.

The muscular tissues of the alimentary canal consist largely of smooth muscle; the exceptions are the striated muscles in the mouth, pharynx, upper part of the esophagus, and the external sphincter of the rectum. Smooth muscle contracts slowly, has greater extensibility, is able to sustain contraction at varying lengths with small expenditure of energy, has the power of rhythmic contraction, and is especially sensitive to the mechanical stimulus of stretching. (See pages 201-202.)

Mastication and Deglutition. The incisors can exert considerable force in biting off a mouthful of food. Even greater force can be applied by the molars in chewing, i.e., mastication. Particles of food in contact with the gums constitute tactile stimuli bringing about the chewing reflex, in which the muscles closing the jaw are alternately inhibited and stimulated to contraction. The tongue, cheeks, and hard palate as well as the teeth participate in the process. Voluntary control determines the pattern of mastication, depending upon the food and habits with respect to duration and extent. Customarily we reduce our food to particles of a few cubic millimeters.

Deglutition or swallowing involves the use of both smooth and striated muscles (Fig. 18.20). The first movement brings the bolus of food on the tongue, which is then moved backward so that the bolus is pushed through the glossopalatine arches into the pharynx. Up to this point the act is under voluntary control. Once the food enters the pharynx, reflexes are set up the propel the food into the esophagus and prevent its entrance into the respiratory passages. The nasal cavity is blocked off by the raising of the soft palate. The entrance to the mouth is closed by elevation of the tongue to the hard palate and contraction of the palatine arches. Muscular contraction elevates the larynx and places it under the shelter of the base of the tongue and the epiglottis, which acts as a protecting shelf to deflect food from entrance into the trachea. The approximation of the vocal cords closes the glottis. Just before swallowing, a slight inspiration is taken, followed by inhibition of respiration for about five seconds. The pressure in the pharynx rises to about 100 mm. Hg for a very brief time. During the third stage of swallowing the pharyngoesophageal sphincter relaxes, the food enters the esophagus, the sphincter closes, and the pharyngeal pressure drops to ambient pressure. The time required for its passage will vary with the composition of the food; liquids travel more rapidly than solids (Table 18.1). Powerful contractions of the striated muscle in the upper part of the esophagus insure the rapid movement of food through the region lying immediately posterior to the trachea. Smooth muscle then takes over the task of propelling the food by a series of peristaltic waves (Fig. 18.21). A *peristaltic wave* is a band of constriction, involving the circular muscles, which travels along the esophagus and other parts of the digestive tube for varying distances. This wave is sometimes preceded by a wave of relaxation. Food

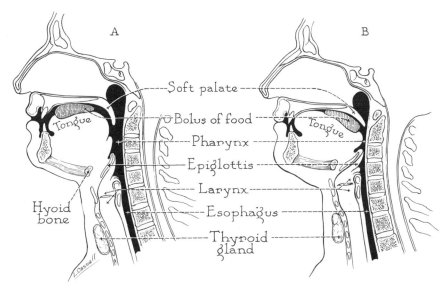

Figure 18.20 Deglutition. *A*, Before swallowing begins; parts in normal position. *B*, Nose closed off, larynx raised, tip of tongue pressed against the roof of mouth.

may be passed through the cardiac sphincter of the stomach by the peristaltic wave, or it may be delayed until the arrival of a succeeding wave. During a meal there is less and less tendency for the cardia to close between swallows.

The intraesophageal pressures at various levels are of physiological significance. The high pressure at the level of the pharyngoesophageal junction prevents entrance of food except during the coordinated swallowing reflexes. This pressure prevents regurgitation into the pharynx during peristaltic contraction of the esophagus. When at rest, the intraesophageal pressure equals intrathoracic pressure as the esophagus traverses the thorax, thus creating a large gradient that assists in expeditious passage of food though that segment. Below the dia-

phragm the intraesophageal pressure is normally 5 to 10 mm. above intragastric pressure and thus prevents regurgitation from the stomach into the esophagus.

Movements of the Stomach. The normal stomach has a remarkable ability to adapt its capacity to the volume of food with little change in intragastric pressure. This pressure amounts to about 5 to 10 mm. Hg, rising another 5 mm. Hg as the diaphragm descends.

In considering movements of the stomach it becomes necessary to state the condition of gastric filling. When a small amount of food enters the stomach it passes at once to the pyloric region. Liquid may pass directly through the pyloric sphincter into the duodenum without being propelled by gastric contractions. When the stomach is empty its volume is

TABLE 18-1. TIME RANGE FOR DIGESTION AFTER SWALLOWING

	Arrival in Stomach	Arrival in Small Intestine	Arrival in Large Intestine	Excretion of Residues from G.I. Tract
From	6 sec. (liquids)	5 min.	4-5 hrs.	24-72 hours
To	30-60 sec. or more (solids)	4 hrs.	12-15 hrs.	

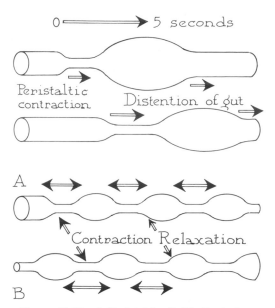

Figure 18.21 *A*, Peristalsis. *B*, Rhythmical segmentation in alimentary tract.

small and the muscles of the wall are relaxed. Some weak contractions occur. Hunger, however, causes strong contractions which begin near the cardia. When the lower end of the esophagus, i.e., the esophagogastric sphincter, and the cardia relax to admit food, the muscular wall of the fundus may relax, but motility of the antrum is unaffected. As the stomach fills, the tone of the muscle of the fundus and body increases, and the body diminishes in size. Peristaltic waves arise from constricted rings at the pacemaker located near the cardia and travel over the body and antrum. As digestion proceeds, the waves become deeper and encroach on the main mass of food in the fundus. Marked constriction of the pyloric portion occurs but does not obliterate the lumen of the pylorus. The strength of the contraction in the different portions of the stomach is influenced by the thickness of the musculature. Thus, the waves of contraction are weaker and shallower in the fundus and the body, and stronger and deeper in the antrum. As the peristaltic wave moves distally some portion of the gastric content is passed into the duodenum, another portion remains in the antrum, and the largest portion is forced back into the proximal antrum. The musc-

ular contractions perform two functions—mixing of the food with digestive juices, and moving the food along for further digestion and absorption.

EMPTYING OF THE STOMACH. The emptying of the stomach depends upon two fundamental factors: (1) the existence of an opening between the stomach and the duodenum and (2) the existence of a higher pressure in the stomach than in the duodenum at the time of the passage of stomach contents. The pylorus is open when the antrum is relaxed and between peristaltic waves during strong gastric activity. Thus the first condition for emptying exists at these times. When the stomach contains food, the sequential contraction of the fundus, body, and antrum increases the intragastric pressure above the pressure in the duodenum. The second condition is satisfied during this period and emptying occurs until the wave of contraction involves the pylorus. The contraction of the pylorus outlasts that of the antrum and prevents regurgitation of the *chyme* (semifluid material resulting from gastric digestion) back into the stomach when the duodenum contracts. It is established that emptying of the stomach requires some time, that it is emptied in small portions, and that the transport of these portions is the result of vigorous peristaltic waves. If the observations of prominent investigators in this field are combined, the mechanism may be summarized by the following description:

Liquid passes directly through the pyloric sphincter, which is either open or exhibiting low tone at the beginning of the filling of the stomach. If, because of its consistency and chemical composition, it fails to excite the myenteric reflex, no closure of the pyloric valve results and emptying continues. Food or liquids that cause mechanical or chemical stimulation of the mucosa when entering the duodenum may cause constriction of the pyloric sphincter lying immediately above by eliciting the myenteric reflex. The *myenteric reflex* may be described as the constriction of circular muscles of a valve or of the digestive tube at any point immediately above the site of stimulation of the intestine. Emptying would then cease until the chyme was moved out of the first portion of the duodenum and the intragastric pressure increased over that of the intestine. Chyme in the duodenum may delay emptying, not only through the myenteric reflex, but by elaboration of *enterogastrone*, which inhibits gastric motility. Thus as successive portions pass through the pyloric valve they may cause closure of the valve and a decrease in motility (and hence a decrease in intragastric pressure); as the chyme is passed along these influences are removed and further emptying of the stomach takes place. This may account for the delays in emptying caused by large particles of food in the chyme (myenteric reflex) and the presence of fats in the stomach (enterogastrone).

The closure of the sphincter precedes and lasts throughout contraction of the duodenum so that regurgitation is normally prevented.

VOMITING. There is another method of emptying the stomach. Vomiting, or *emesis*, is the forceful expulsion of the gastric contents through the mouth. In man, vomiting is frequently associated with a complicated sensory phenomenon called *nausea*.

Vomiting is a neuromuscular event that involves the digestive and respiratory systems. The process begins with a quick, deep inspiration that is followed by: (1) closure of the glottis, which seals off the trachea, (2) elevation of the soft palate, partially sealing off the nasopharynx, and (3) simultaneous contraction of the diaphragm and abdominal muscles with relaxation of the stomach musculature, including the cardiac sphincter. The rise in intragastric pressure brought about by the powerful, sudden contraction of the diaphragm and abdominal muscles expels the gastric contents through the relaxed esophagus.

The complex neuromuscular coordination is controlled by a vomiting center located in the medulla oblongata. This center has many afferent connections, including those from the stomach and intestines, from the posterior surface of the tongue, from the pharynx, and from the semicircular canals. There is also a chemoreceptor center located nearby (area postrema), which sends afferents to the vomiting center. This receptor center is activated by emetic agents, such as apomorphine and copper sulfate. It in turn activates the vomiting center.

Movements of the Small Intestine. Two main kinds of movement are observed in the small intestine: peristaltic waves, which carry the chyme onward, and rhythmical segmentation, which churns and mixes it with digestive juices.

Peristaltic movements appear as traveling waves of constriction that when sufficiently strong "strip" the tube and transfer the contents onward (Fig. 18.21). The waves pass for varying distances along the intestine and then fade out. Rhythmical segmentation consists of alternate rings of compression regularly spaced so that they divide the intestinal contents into numerous small segments. When the constriction rings of circular muscle relax, new rings appear in the middle of the previously formed segments. The halves of adjacent segments so divided flow together to form new segments (Fig. 18.21). As the process is repeated over and over again, the chyme is mixed with digestive secretions and exposed to the absorptive surface of the mucosa.

These churning or segmenting movements continue in a part of the small intestine for a time and are followed by a peristaltic wave that moves the materials onward into the next portion, in which churning movements are repeated.

It seems probable that the existence of an intestinal gradient of activity is responsible for the fact that food passes down the intestine rather than in the opposite direction. The duodenum normally shows the highest rate of muscular contraction with the gradient of motility progressively decreasing from the level of the jejunum to the ileum. The duodenum might be described as the pacemaker of the intestine. Since it exhibits a higher rate of rhythmicity, waves pass aborally; contractions initiated at lower levels would be more likely to encounter refractory periods or states in the musculature above. Since muscle cannot be excited during the refractory period, the wave is interrupted. Waves passing aborally to the regions of lesser activity are more likely to encounter resting muscle, which would favor its propagation in that direction. Under certain pathological conditions the gradient may be reserved.

Another type of activity taking place in the small intestine is the movement of the villi. By exposing the intestinal mucosa of a living animal and examining it under low power magnification, the villi can be seen swaying from side to side and lashing to and fro. Their movements stir the fluids in contact with their surfaces and undoubtedly aid both digestion and absorption.

The ileocecal valve opens at intervals, permitting the passage of the contents from the intestine into the cecum. Swallowing of food causes an initial reflex opening of the sphincter. The ileocolic valve delays the emptying of the intestine, allowing time for digestion and absorption, and aids in preventing regurgitation from the colon into the ileum.

Movements of the Large Intestine. Mixing of alimentary tract contents and movement through the absorbing surfaces of the large intestine are accomplished by contractions of the haustra. These movements resemble the rhythmic segmentations found in the small intestine. Peristaltic movement in the large intestine have been called mass movements or mass peristalsis. The waves appear from time to time and carry the contents for a distance along the tube. They are frequently preceded by peristaltic waves in the small intestine. Mass movements occur only at long intervals, usually two or three times in twenty-four hours. They often follow the taking of food into the stomach. This reaction is known as the *gastrocolic reflex.*

The pelvic colon, which serves as a storehouse for feces, becomes filled from below upward, the rectum remaining empty until just before defecation. Entrance of feces into the rectum may follow mass movements or may result simply from overloading the pelvic colon. The emptying of the rectum, or defecation, involves a strong contraction of rectal walls and a relaxation of the anal sphincter. This mechanism is usually reinforced by the contraction of abdominal muscles and diaphragm.

CHEMICAL FACTORS IN DIGESTION

The chemical phase of digestion consists in the breaking down of large nondiffusible molecules into small diffusible molecules that are able to pass through the cells of the digestive tract. Hydrolysis, which is the principal type of chemical reaction involved, is a decomposition reaction in which a substance combines chemically with water to form simpler substances with smaller molecules:

$$\underset{C_{12}H_{22}O_{11}}{\text{Maltose}} + \underset{HOH}{\text{Water}} \rightleftarrows \underset{C_6H_{12}O_6 + C_6H_{12}O_6}{\text{Glucose and Glucose}}$$

The steps in the hydrolysis of the three principal food materials, carbohydrates, fats (lipids), and proteins, are:

Carbohydrates:
1. Starch, a polysaccharide that must be changed to a monosaccharide before absorption can occur
   Starch → dextrin → maltose → glucose
2. Disaccharides, which are hydrolyzed to monosaccharides
   Maltose → glucose and glucose
   Sucrose → fructose and glucose
   Lactose → galactose and glucose.

Fats:
   Fats → glycerol and fatty acid.

Proteins:
   Protein → polypeptides
   peptides → amino acids.

For the most part digestive enzymes follow the system of classification of adding the suffix *-ase* to the name of the substance acted upon; thus a starch-splitting enzyme is called an *amylase,* a fat-splitting enzyme is a *lipase,* and a protein-splitting enzyme is a *protease.* Usually another name is included to indicate the source of the enzyme, as, for example, *pancreatic lipase.* However, the older names ptyalin, pepsin, and trypsin continue to be used.

Table 18.2 includes the more important digestive enzymes. A study of the table shows some duplication and overlapping of enzyme action. For example, four enzymes act in breaking down protein: pepsin, trypsin, chymotrypsin, and carboxypolypeptidase. Pepsin in the gastric juice starts protein digestion by changing it to

TABLE 18.2. DIGESTIVE ENZYMES

Digestive Fluid	Enzyme	Substance Acted Upon	Products Formed
Saliva	Salivary amylase	Boiled starch and dextrins	Dextrins and maltose
Gastric juice	Pepsin	Protein	Polypeptides and clotted milk
	Gastric lipase	Emulsified fat	Fatty acids and glycerol
Pancreatic juice	Trypsin	Proteins Chymotrypsinogen	Polypeptides Chymotrypsin
	Chymotrypsin	Proteins	Polypeptides
	Carboxypolypeptidase	Polypeptides	Peptides and amino acids
	Pancreatic amylase	Starch and dextrins	Maltose
	Pancreatic lipase	Fat	Fatty acids and glycerol
Succus entericus	Enterokinase	Trypsinogen	Trypsin

polypeptides; trypsin and chymotrypsin from the pancreas change proteins to polypeptides; carboxypolypeptidase changes polypeptides and peptides to amino acids.

Sufficient time must be allowed in each of the divisions of the digestive tract for chemical actions in digestion to take place and for absorption to occur. Table 18.1 shows the range of times after swallowing for arrival of ingested food in the different regions of the digestive tract.

REGIONAL DIGESTION

In the Mouth. Human saliva is slightly acid, generally having a pH of 6.35 to 6.85. It consists of 99.5 per cent water and 0.5 per cent total solids. Its chief constituents are water, inorganic salts, mucin, serum albumin and serum globulin, and salivary amylase (ptyalin). The composition of saliva, like that of most digestive juices, may vary with the rate and duration of secretion. After the secretions have been extruded into the ducts, their compositions may be modified through exchange of substances with the plasma of adjacent capillaries and by activity of the ducts' cells. One chemical change is effected by salivary amylase, which acts on the boiled starch, changing it to dextrin and possibly to maltose. It is unlikely that this change

occurs to any extent while the food is in the mouth, but the ptyalin may continue to act on the starch within the bolus of food for some time after it has entered the stomach.

Salivary digestion is important in preparing the food for the changes to follow. Saliva dissolves some of the solid substances so that they are brought in contact with the taste buds; thus they stimulate appetite and result in a series of reflexes that increase the flow of gastric juice and augment salivary secretion.

In the Stomach. The food that reaches the stomach is mixed with saliva and is semisolid in consistency. It accumulates in the fundus, and the mass thus formed is not penetrated to any extent by the gastric juice, so that salivary digestion can continue for some time. Gradually, however, owing to muscular movements, the food is mixed with the gastric juice and the acidity so increased that the action of the ptyalin ceases. The reaction of the gastric juice is acid, pH 0.9 to 1.5. The more important constituents are hydrochloric acid, mucin, pepsin, gastric lipase, and the intrinsic factor, which is essential for absorption of an extrinsic antianemic factor (Vitamin B_{12}) (see p. 267).

The first step in gastric digestion is the action of hydrochloric acid upon protein. The acid causes the protein to swell to a gelatinous mass that goes rapidly into solution in the acid gastric secretions. This process is called denaturation of protein, i.e., change in its physical and chemical properties. Pepsin then hydrolyzes denatured proteins into *polypeptides*; these are a mixture of substances called proteoses and peptones, which are intermediate in molecular weight between the proteins and the smaller *peptides*. The peptides are compounds of two or more amino acids. Protein digestion, which does not go beyond the polypeptide stage in the stomach, is completed in the intestine. In man pepsin has a strong milk clotting activity comparable to that of the enzyme rennin found in the gastric juice of calves.

Pepsin is secreted in the form of a precursor *pepsinogen*; the precursor is activated into pepsin by acid and by other pepsin which may be present.

Gastric lipase is a weak enzyme of little importance in fat digestion. It acts only on emulsified fats such as milk and egg yolk. There is no carbohydrate enzyme in the gastric juice, but some of the cane sugar (sucrose) is hydrolyzed by the hydrochloric acid.

As a result of muscular movements that mix the food with the gastric juice, and of the various chemical changes caused by the gastric enzymes, the gastric contents are reduced to a semifluid, more or less homogeneous, creamy mass i.e., chyme. At intervals, portions of the chyme pass through the pylorus into the duodenum.

In the Small Intestine. Before discussing digestion in this part of the alimentary canal, let us consider the condition in which we find the various food substances of the chyme as it enters the duodenum. Much of the protein has been reduced to polypeptides, carbohydrate digestion has barely begun, some of the starch is converted to dextrin and small amounts as far as maltose, disaccharides are in solution, but not digested except for hydrolysis of a portion of sucrose by hydrochloric acid in the stomach. Fats are melted and emulsified fats hydrolyzed to some extent. Much remains to be done.

As the acid chyme enters the duodenum, the secretions from the liver and the pancreas mix with it, and it also comes in contact with the *succus entericus* or intestinal juice, secreted by the intestinal glands. Intestinal juice is alkaline in reaction because of the presence of sodium carbonate and bicarbonate. Mucus and the enzyme enterokinase, which activates trypsinogen, are secreted by the intestinal glands. Other enzymes found in succus entericus are believed to be derived from cellular debris rather than from secretion in the intestine.

The pancreas contributes an alkaline fluid in which there are three important enzymes, trypsin, amylase, and lipase. Trypsin, or pancreatic protease, is secreted in an inactive form known as trypsinogen. It is changed to the powerful proteolytic trypsin by enterokinase. Trypsin and its related factors hydrolyze proteins and polypeptides to peptides. Pancreatic amylase changes starch, glycogen, and dextrin to maltose. Pancreatic amylase, unlike salivary amylase, is capable of digesting unboiled starch. Lipase acts upon the fat molecule, reducing it to fatty acid and glycerol. Some of the fatty acids made soluble in the presence of bile react with the alkali in the intestinal fluid to form soaps. Bile salts and the soaps thus formed lower surface tension and have important effects in the emulsification of fats. Lowering the surface tension facilitates the division of fat into small globules and, by increasing the total surface area exposed to the action of the enzyme, correspondingly enhances the effect. Bile contains no digestive enzymes. The function of the bile salts in the absorption of fats is discussed on page 373.

In the Large Intestine. The large intestine contains the feces, which are composed of bacteria, material secreted through the wall of the intestine and the bile, leukocytes, epithelial cells, and food residues. The contents of the ileum are fluid in consistency, but as they pass through the large intestine, water is absorbed, so that under normal conditions the feces are solid or semisolid. The glands of the large intestine secrete mucus, but no enzymes. The mucus helps to hold the feces together and facilitates evacuation.

The large intestine serves as a channel of excretion for calcium, magnesium, iron, and phosphate. Substantial amounts of calcium, magnesium, and phosphate are also eliminated in the urine, but practically all iron is excreted in the large intestine and appears in the feces as iron sulfide.

CONTROL OF DIGESTIVE JUICES

The glands of the gastrointestinal tract that are responsible for elaboration of digestive secretions are controlled by nervous and chemical action. The flow of digestive secretions is frequently started by reflexes initiated by the sight or smell of food. As soon as food enters the mouth or stomach, additional reflex secretion results from mechanical or chemical stimulation of sensory nerve endings in the alimentary tract. This secretion of the "ignition" juices (the juices responsible for starting digestion and secretion) is for the most part of too short duration to insure complete chemical breakdown of the foodstuffs. Action of these "ignition" juices does, however, result in some digestion of the food with the liberation of substances called secretagogues. *Secretagogues are products of digestion of food that act to cause secretion of digestive juices by chemical stimulation.* It seems highly probable that the initial digestive juices, together with the secretagogues or digestive products of the foods, are responsible for bringing into play the chemical mechanism that insures the continuance of the secretions of the glands of the stomach and small intestine, and accessory digestive glands until digestion is complete. The ignition juices and the secretagogues play an important role in the elaboration of the digestive hormones. These hormones are chemical messengers which are formed in various parts of the digestive system, absorbed into the blood stream and carried to various parts of the gastrointestinal tract, where they stimulate secretion and influence mechanical activity. Secretory correlations are summarized in Table 18.3.

Salivary Secretion. The rate of salivary secretion is variable; it may vary from a basal rate of 0.5 ml. per minute to over 7.0 ml. per minute when awake. Secretion practically ceases during sleep. The total output of saliva is between one and two liters per day.

The salivary glands are entirely under nervous control (Fig. 18.22). Salivary flow is increased over basal rate by chemical and mechanical stimulation of receptors in the mouth and pharynx and by chemical stimulation of the olfactory area. The parasympathetic and sympathetic nerves provide the efferent innervation. The parasympathetic nerves exert the principal control on secretory function, producing a copious flow of saliva and an increase in blood flow of the salivary gland. Sympathetic nerve activity causes reduction or inhibition of flow and vasoconstriction.

Conditioned reflexes (Chapter 7) probably play a minor, if any, role in salivary secretion in man. The sensation of mouth watering upon thinking about food has been thought probably to result from becoming more aware of the saliva already in the mouth.

In addition, mechanical and chemical stimulation by the presence of food in the esophagus and in the stomach causes salivary secretion; these reactions are known as the esophagosalivary and gastrosalivary reflexes, respectively. The former is of value when particles and incompletely masticated food become temporarily lodged in the esophagus.

Gastric Secretion. In the resting state the secretions of the stomach are neutral or slightly alkaline. The alkaline fluid is absorbed by the thick adherent coat of mucus which forms a protective covering of the mucosa. Upon preparing to take food and on taking food there is a copious secretion of gastric juice high in acid and pepsin. The secretion of gastric juice has three phases: (1) the cephalic phase, (2) the gastric phase, and (3) the intestinal phase. We now know that these phases occur at the same time rather than sequentially.

The *cephalic* or *vagal* phase of gastric secretion is initiated by afferent reception in the head. The vagus nerves constitute the final common pathway for impulses arising from chemical stimulation of receptors in the mouth and pharynx, from

TABLE 18.3. SECRETORY CORRELATIONS

Secretion	Initial Secretions	Continued Secretions	Further Relations of Secretions
Saliva	Conditioned reflexes	Unconditioned reflexes: (a) chemical and mechanical stimuli from mouth (b) esophago-salivary (c) gastrosalivary	
Gastric juice	Cephalic phase: (a) conditioned reflexes (b) chemical and mechanical stimuli from mouth	Gastric and intestinal phases: (a) distention of stomach (b) initial gastric secretions aiding in elaboration of: (1) secretagogues (2) gastrin (3) intestinal gastrin (4) inhibitory effects of enterogastrone	Initial and conditioned gastric juice + secretagogues + partially digested food pass into intestine to stimulate or aid in the elaboration of cholecystokinin secretin pancreozymin enterogastrone intestinal gastrin
Pancreatic juice	Nervous control: conditioned? unconditioned?	→ Secretin → Pancreozymin	Pancreatic juice — water and bicarbonate + Pancreatic juice containing trypsinogen → trypsin
Bile formation	Nervous control	→ Secretin Bile salts ←	→ Bile salts	Aid in elaboration and absorption of secretin
Emptying of gallbladder	Nervous control	Cholecystokinin ←	Release of bile which aids in elaboration and absorption of secretin
Succus entericus		→ Secretin Trypsin ← Mechanical stimulation	Enterokinase in succus entericus activates trypsinogen of pancreatic juice to trypsin

the olfactory nerves, and from other receptors which may have connections with the vagal nucleus. Thus there may be a psychic component of the cephalic phase in which the sight and smell of appetizing food or the sound of its preparation may bring about a flow of gastric juice even before food is taken into the mouth. There is considerable variation in conditioned gastric secretion reflex in man. *Hypoglycemia* or low blood sugar also results in stimulation of the flow of gastric juice through pathways converging on the vagal nucleus. The cephalic phase of gastric secretions is completely abolished by bilateral section of the vagi.

The *gastric* phase is excited by distension of the pylorus. Distension results in the elaboration and liberation of the hormone *gastrin*. This hormone is formed by the pyloric (non-acid-secreting) portion of the stomach; gastrin when absorbed into the blood stimulates secretion of pepsin by the chief cells and HCl by the oxyntic cells in the body and fundus of the stomach. The release of gastrin and the resulting secretion of gastric juice take place independently of vagal influence. This has been demonstrated by experimental studies in which portions of the stomach were denervated, separated from the stomach, and transplanted elsewhere. A denervated pyloric pouch, i.e., a transplanted portion of the pylorus, will secrete gastrin upon distention. The hormone, carried by the blood stream, will cause secretion of gastric juice in a denervated fundic pouch. Acetylcholine stimulates gastric secretion; thus the response to distention of the pylorus may be mediated by stimulation of postsynaptic cholinergic fibers.

In the normal physiologic response the influence of the vagi appears to contribute to the release of gastrin from pyloric distention. Further, the cephalic phase of gastric secretion continues long after ingestion of food. Currently the "unitarian" concept is widely accepted by physiologists: the secretory response to a meal is considered to result from close interaction of vagal activity and gastrin. A feedback mechanism serves to regulate the release of gastrin and hence the pH of the chyme discharged into the intestine. The secretion of gastrin is completely inhibited if the pH of the pyloric content falls to 2.0, and the secretion is reduced at pH 3.0 and somewhat higher levels.

The *intestinal phase* is important in that it may either excite or inhibit gastric secretions. The presence of food, secretagogues or even nonabsorbable or poorly absorbable substances in the intestine will cause elaboration of the hormone *intestinal gastrin*. The presence of fat in the intestine has an inhibitory influence on gastric secretion (and also on gastric motility). This is due to enterogastrone, which is elaborated from the duodenal mucosa. The intestinal phase proceeds throughout the whole period of digestion. Gastrin acts with other hormones of the upper duodenum and influences pancreatic and biliary secretions. In turn other enzymes—secretin, cholecystokinin, and enterogastrone—influence gastric secretion.

Pancreatic Secretion. Experiments indicate that pancreatic secretion is a continuous process, but that the rate of secretion is increased two or three minutes after a meal and rises to a maximum in two or three hours. The initial augmentation appears long before digestion could have released secretagogues for hormone formation, so that it must be ascribed to nervous control. The secretion is continued by hormones liberated from the duodenal mucosa. When gastric juice, chyme, bile, or certain other substances enter the duodenum, two hormones are secreted. One of these, *secretin*, controls the secretion of water and bicarbonate by the small centroacinar cells associated with the ducts of the exocrine pancreas. Secretin also excites the secretion and flow of bile and possibly the formation of intestinal juices. The other hormone, *pancreozymin*, stimulates enzyme secretion by the exocrine pancreas acinar cells. The proteolytic enzymes of the pancreatic juices are secreted in an inactive form—principally *trypsinogen*, *chymotrypsin*, and *carboxypolypeptidase*. Enterokinase of the succus entericus activates trypsinogen to form trypsin. Trypsin, once present, activates all the inactive precursors of the proteolytic enzymes.

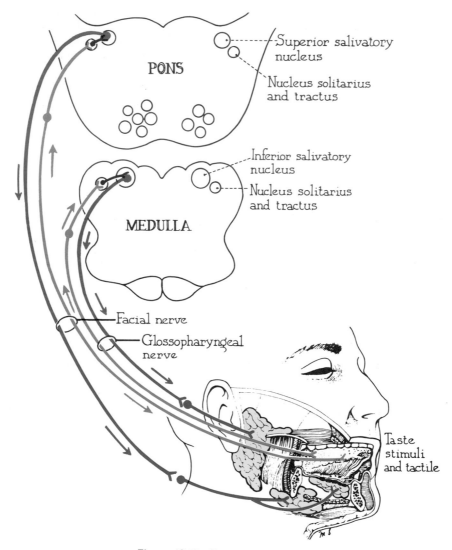

Figure 18.22 Nervous control of salivation.

Bile Formation and Excretion. In considering the role of bile in digestion it must be borne in mind that there are two components in its mobilization for use: (1) formation and (2) release into the gastrointestinal tract.

Bile formation may be affected by nervous influences to a minor degree. By far the most effective stimulus, however, is bile salts. Bile is being continuously secreted, but, if it is drained out of the body, secretion soon stops; nerve stimulation is without effect, but intravenous injection serves to reestablish the flow. Secretin is probably a normal factor in stimulating bile formation.

The emptying of the gallbladder is primarily under chemical control. The hormone, *cholecystokinin*, which is released when proteins, fats or fatty acids, hydrochloric acid, or other substances enter the duodenum, is specific for the contraction of the gallbladder.

Intestinal Secretion. Secretion of the succus entericus may be largely the result of mechanical stimulation of the intestinal mucosa by intestinal contents. However, trypsin appears to be an excellent excitant; secretin may also stimulate secretion.

The glands of the large intestine respond chiefly to mechanical stimulation.

QUESTIONS FOR DISCUSSION

1. At this point in the text all reticulo-endothelial tissues have been mentioned in their locations in the body. Where are they and what functions do they perform?

2. Relate the circulatory supply of the liver to its functions.

3. What similarities exist in the organization of the tissues of the salivary glands, liver, and pancreas?

4. Contrast the functional anatomy of the respiratory system with respect to the transfer of gases to the functional anatomy of the digestive system with respect to its transfer of liquids and solids.

5. Contrast the action of the inspiratory centers in respiration with the "hunger" and "satiety" centers in regulation of food intake.

6. Test your knowledge of enzyme activity by describing the digestion of a piece of buttered toast and an egg.

7. In this chapter many correlations in time between the secretion of digestive juices and the mechanical phases of digestion are considered. Discuss such time relationships for the three phases of gastric secretion and for the secretion of pancreatic juice.

UTILIZATION OF FOOD AND REGULATION OF BODY TEMPERATURE

CHAPTER NINETEEN

PRECIS

The digestive processes change food to simple materials that can be used by the cells. But until the digestion products, salts, water, and vitamins have passed into the blood vessels and lymphatics and become part of the internal environment, they are not available for use by the tissue cells. This passage of digested food material through the wall of the alimentary canal is called absorption. Practically all absorption of food products, water, salts, and vitamins occurs in the small intestine; water and salts are also absorbed in the colon. Absorption involves the selective permeability of the cells as well as the physical processes of diffusion and osmosis. The epithelial cells of the villi actively take up substances from the intestinal contents and pass them into the blood and lymph. The epithelium does not merely act as a passive membrane, but also performs cellular work with the expenditure of energy.

Once the food has entered the internal environment the metabolic processes begin, involving the maintenance of an equilibrium or balance between catabolic and anabolic processes. Materials taken into the body through the digestive tract and those derived from the tissues of the body form *metabolic pools*, e.g., amino acid pools, glucose pools. These products of intermediary metabolism are used in catabolic and anabolic processes. They are broken down to supply energy. They are also used to build tissues and to maintain the constancy of the internal environment with respect to body fluids, acid-base and electrolyte balance, and osmotic pressures.

Although it has been possible to trace the material from the metabolic pools through various pathways to materials releasing high energy or to the formation of precursor substances or substances essential for structural or physiologic requirements, we know little about the priorities for the multitude of alternate pathways and how they are established. There is, however, a common pathway for the aerobic catabolic processes for fragments of carbohydrate, fat, and protein metabolism—the tricarboxylic acid cycle (also known as the citric acid cycle or Krebs cycle). The student is directed to a biochemistry text for a description of the major pathways.

ENERGY METABOLISM

The source of energy is the chemical energy of the food materials, which is transformed by oxidation into heat and mechanical energy, i.e., work. It is possible to reduce all other forms of energy to heat. The term *energy metabolism* is used to denote the total energy input and output of the body. The energy of a food is expressed in terms of the heat it produces. The unit of heat, the *Calorie*, is defined as the amount of heat required to raise 1 kilogram of water 1 degree centigrade. The amount of heat liberated by complete combustion of the three types of food has been determined by burning them outside the body. One gram of carbohydrate yields 4 Calories; 1 gm. of fat, 9 Calories; and 1 gm. of protein, 5 Calories. The same values are found for combustion of carbohydrates and fats within the body. However, only part of the protein can be oxidized in the body, since the nitrogenous portion is incombustible; hence the physiological oxidation of 1 gm. of protein yields only 4 Calories.

Metabolic Rate, Basal Metabolism, and Respiratory Quotient. The caloric value of food ingested for twenty-four hours must equal the energy utilized by the individual during the same period; otherwise body tissues will be consumed for fuel. The dietary requirements range from 2400 Calories per day for a person leading a relatively sedentary life to 7000 Calories in a lumberman working in winter. In estimating the caloric requirements, it is customary to determine the basal metabolic rate first and then add to this the extra calories required for the particular grade of muscular activity.

Basal metabolism is the energy expenditure of a subject who is lying down at complete muscular and mental rest, some twelve to fourteen hours after taking food, and in a room with temperature at about 20° C. Figure 19.1 shows one type of apparatus used to measure metabolism.

Under these basal conditions the three factors that are most powerful in stimulating metabolism—physical exercise, ingestion of food, and environmental temperature—have been eliminated. The heat generated under such conditions is due mainly to the activity of heart, blood vessels, alimentary canal, glands, and respiratory movements, and indicates the energy required to maintain vital processes. It represents the minimum level of cellular activity. The basal metabolism is proportionate to the surface area of the individual and is expressed in terms of Calories per square meter of body surface per hour. On this basis the average metabolism for normal men between twenty and fifty years is from 38 to 40 Calories, and for women between the same ages 36 to 38 Calories. Values 10 per cent above or below these figures are considered within the normal range. In the usual clinical determination of metabolic rate the heat production is computed indirectly on the basis of the oxygen consumed. Knowledge of the volume of oxygen used and carbon dioxide formed is the basis for another valuable determination—the *respiratory quotient*. This is the ratio of the volume of

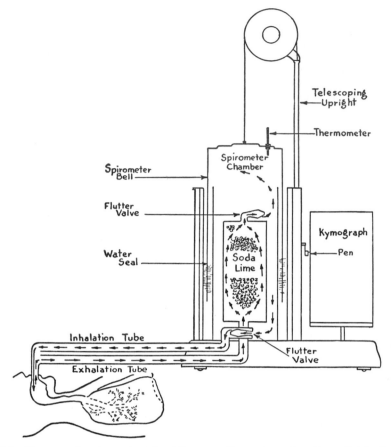

Figure 19.1 Diagram showing principle of the recording spirometer. (Benedict-Roth principle.)

carbon dioxide given off to the volume of oxygen consumed, thus:

$$\frac{\text{Vol. of } CO_2 \text{ given off}}{\text{Vol. of } O_2 \text{ used}} = \text{Respiratory quotient, or R. Q.}$$

The value of the respiratory quotient lies in its being a useful indication of the type of food being burned. Since the three food materials differ in the relative amounts of oxygen and carbon in the molecule, the volumes of oxygen used and carbon dioxide produced during the metabolism of each food material also vary. When a person is burning a carbohydrate such as glucose, all the oxygen consumed goes to form carbon dioxide, so that for every molecule of oxygen, 1 molecule of carbon dioxide results. The following equation shows this:

$$C_6H_{12}O_6 + 6\ O_2 \rightarrow 6\ CO_2 + 6\ H_2O$$

$$\text{R. Q.} = \frac{6 \text{ mol. (6 vol.) } CO_2}{6 \text{ mol. (6 vol.) } O_2} = 1$$

When fat is oxidized, some of the oxygen goes to form water and the respiratory quotient is as follows:

Tripalmitin:
$$C_{51}H_{98}O_6 + 72.5\ O_2 \rightarrow 51\ CO_2 + 49\ H_2O$$

$$\text{R. Q.} = \frac{51 \text{ mol. } CO_2}{72.5 \text{ mol. } O_2} = 0.703$$

Fats vary somewhat in composition, and the average respiratory quotient is about 0.7, while that of protein is 0.8. When the respiratory quotient is close to 1, the assumption is that diet is chiefly carbohydrate; when it is around 0.7, that it is mainly fat. On a mixed diet the respiratory quotient is about 0.85.

Metabolism of Carbohydrates. Carbohydrates may be ingested as starch or sugar or they may be formed in the body from noncarbohydrate food substances. Physiologically the most important polysaccharide is glycogen, and the most important monosaccharides are the hexoses, e.g., glucose, fructose, and galactose. The monosaccharides also include the pentose, *ribose*, which in combination with adenylic acid and phosphate forms ATP and ADP. The polysaccharides and disaccharides are hydrolyzed by the digestive enzymes to monosaccharides and are absorbed from the intestine into the portal blood by diffusion and active transport (p. 26). A small amount of monosaccharide may enter the thoracic duct. By far the major portion is carried by the portal circulation to the liver. Following a high carbohydrate meal, i.e., over 50 per cent carbohydrate, the monosaccharide level may rise to between 130 and 150 mg. per 100 ml. of blood.

The liver mechanisms perform four functions in the intermediary metabolism of carbohydrate. These are (1) uptake and conversion of fructose and galactose into glucose, (2) oxidation of glucose to CO_2 and H_2O, providing a primary source of energy to meet body requirements during the absorptive state, (3) conversion of glucose to glycogen for storage in the liver, and (4) conversion of glucose to fatty acids and certain glucogenic amino acids. As a result of these mechanisms the blood sugar is lowered. The value of 100 mg. per 100 ml., which is frequently given as normal for blood sugar determined by routine clinical tests, represents both glucose and other reducing substances in the blood. The concentration of glucose in the blood is about 60 to 80 mg. per 100 ml. The level is held remarkably constant except during the absorptive state and under certain conditions that will be considered in the discussion of the regulation of blood sugar. It is not reduced beyond the normal postabsorptive range even in prolonged fasting.

There are two phases of carbohydrate metabolism which occur in sequence

anaerobic and aerobic. The anaerobic phase involves (1) phosphorylation, or generation of a high energy phosphate, (2) the formation of glycogen, (3) conversion into trioses; and (4) formation of pyruvic or lactic acid.

Glucose from the blood stream enters the cells by a transfer mechanism stimulated by insulin (see p. 148). Here *phosphorylation*, i.e., the generation of a high energy phosphate, occurs, forming glucose-6-phosphate. This initial step in the metabolism of glucose, and other sugars as well, is catalyzed, irreversibly, by the phosphokinases or hexoses:

$$\text{Glucose} + \text{ATP} \xrightarrow[\text{Mg}^{++}]{\text{phosphokinase}} \text{glucose-6-phosphate}$$

In the anaerobic pathways, part of the glucose-6-phosphate is broken down into pyruvic acid and then to lactic acid. Here, the first step is conversion to fructose-6-phosphate, which is phosphorylated by ATP to *fructose-1,6 diphosphate*; the hexose is then split into trioses, and then to pyruvic and lactic acid. Another portion is synthesized into glycogen, first by transformation of glucose-6-phosphate to glucose-1-phosphate. Following further reactions, the glucose moieties of an intermediate compound, in the presence of a *glycogen transferase*, are attached to a pre-existing polysaccharide chain. The liver cells are the primary sites of formation of glycogen, but it can also be formed by the cells of other tissues. The process of the formation of glycogen from glucose is called *glycogenesis*. Muscle glycogen formation follows the same metabolic pathways as liver glycogen formation. The principal path of aerobic metabolism is the same as in anaerobic metabolism, through the formation of pyruvic acid. In aerobic metabolism lactic acid is not formed or, if it is, it is reoxidized locally back into pyruvic acid. Finally the pyruvic acid of both the anaerobic and aerobic phases, and also lactic acid when formed, is further broken down into CO_2 and water.

In addition to immediate utilization and storage, the blood sugars can be transformed into fatty acids and some amino acids. The conversion of carbohydrates to fatty acids appears to be a rapid, continuous process. If the rate of formation exceeds the rate of oxidation, *triglyceride* is formed and stored in the adipose tissue. The formation of the triglyceride, or neutral fat, takes place in the adipose tissue as well as in the liver. The amino acids formed from carbohydrates are "non-essential." Thus while they contribute to energy metabolism and to the formation and repair of tissues, the conversions cannot provide the essential amino acids contained in the complete proteins. (See protein metabolism.)

In the postabsorptive state the utilization of blood sugar for supplying energy is reduced through increased utilization of fatty acids. However, the brain and entire nervous system consume glucose during the postabsorptive as well as during the absorptive state. This consumption, together with the postabsorptive level of utilization by other tissues, would result in a continuous decrease in blood sugar level if the glucose were not constantly being replaced. However, the liver performs functions which provide for the maintenance of physiologic levels of blood sugar. These are (1) conversion of fructose and galactose to glucose, (2) conversion of glycogen to glucose and its release into the blood stream, and (3) formation of glucose from protein moieties. Thus there is a balance between glycogenesis and glyconeogenesis and the reverse process, glycogenolysis. Glycogenolysis and glycogenesis in muscle have been discussed in connection with muscular contraction (Chapter 11).

The formation, storage, release, and consumption of carbohydrates are regulated by hormones secreted in a coordinated, balanced system of endocrine control. Addition and removal of glucose from the plasma are regulated principally by the anterior lobe of the hypophysis, the islet cells of the pancreas, and the cortex and medulla of the adrenal glands. Insulin acts to limit the amount of glucose by increasing the rate of its utilization, by controlling glyconeogenesis, and by increasing the formation of muscle glycogen and the conversion of carbohydrate to fat. Large doses of insulin cause a marked reduction in blood sugar, a condition known as hypoglycemia. The anterior hypophysis appears to act both directly and through its influence on the adrenals, in a manner that is antagonistic to that of insulin. Epinephrine, the sympathomimetic hormone of the adrenal medulla, stimulates glycogenolysis, and so tends to prevent a marked lowering of the blood sugar level. The *glucocorticoids*, e.g., *cortisol* and *cortisone*, secreted by the adrenal cortex, stimulate glycogenesis and glyconeogenesis, reduce tissue utilization of carbohydrate, and promote the conversion of carbohydrate to fat. (See also section on endocrines for discussion of blood sugar.)

If the blood sugar rises excessively in spite of these mechanisms or as the result of diabetes, glucose is lost through the urine. The kidney tubules are capable of reabsorbing normal and even large quantities of glucose from the glomerular filtrate, but at some point after excessive ingestion of carbohydrate, these tubules may become overloaded even in normal individuals so that not all of it is reabsorbed, and *glucosuria* results.

Metabolism of Lipids. A broad definition is necessary to define the term lipids. We commonly think and speak of them as fats, which, while correct, is apt to provide an inadequate concept of these substances. The biochemist Bloor has defined lipids as "a group of naturally occurring substances consisting of the higher fatty acids, their naturally occurring compounds and substances found naturally in chemical association with them." Others have defined lipids in terms of their solubility. Most lipids are insoluble in water but soluble in ether, chloroform, and fat solvents.

The roles they play in the body further emphasize the diversity and physiologic importance of these substances. Lipids are light in weight, they can be stored in large quantities in the body, and they serve as a source of high energy fuel, having approximately twice the calorific value of carbohydrates. They provide structural materials as constituents of cell membranes, protective coverage of nervous tissues, and thermal insulation of the body. The lipids are also important for their relation to the fat-soluble vitamins; the association may be chemical, or the lipids may facilitate the absorption of such vitamins. Certain fatty acids are essential to physiologic function. Lipids can be divided into four groups on the basis of their chemical characteristics:

1. Simple lipids include the natural fats and oils that are esters of fatty acids and glycerol, and waxes that are esters of fatty acids and higher alcohols other than glycerol.
2. Compound lipids include *phospholipids*, which are compounds of fatty acids, glycerol, phosphoric acids, and a nitrogenous substance; *glycolipids*, which may contain a hexose or a disaccharide; and *lipoproteins*, which are lipids combined with proteins. Lecithin and cephalin are important phospholipids. Glycolipids are present in high concentration in the nervous tissue, especially in the myelin of the central and peripheral nervous systems. Thromboplastic protein and rhodopsin, a combination of vitamin A and proteins, are classified as lipoproteins (see pp. 121, 264).
3. Derived proteins include saturated and unsaturated fatty acids; alcohols, such as sterols of provitamin D; hydrocarbons, such as the carotenoids, which are precursors of vitamin A.
4. Substances associated with lipids in nature include the steroids and fat-soluble vitamins, i.e., A, D, E, and K. The steroids include hormones, bile acids, precursors of vitamins, and cholesterol. The association with lipids is based upon like solubilities and metabolic relationships.

The most common lipids of the diet are the neutral fats or triglycerides, which are made up of glycerol esterified with three fatty acids. Other dietary constituents include small quantities of phospholipids, cholesterol, and cholesterol esters. These exogenous fats are emulsified into minute fat droplets in the intestine by bile and by other lipids including fatty acids, glycerides, cholesterol, and lecithin. The fine emulsification prepares the fats for digestion and absorption. Pancreatic lipase is the principal lypolytic agent. Lipase hydrolyzes the triglyceride in three stages. The first fatty acid is removed leaving a *diglyceride*. Removal of the second fatty acid leaves a *monoglyceride*. In the third stage the monoglyceride is hydrolyzed to fatty acid and glycerol. About a third to one-half of the triglyceride is completely hydrolyzed in the intestine. Forty to 50 per cent of the triglyceride is broken down only to the monoglyceride. Further hydrolysis of the monoglyceride occurs in the mucosal cells of the intestine. The fatty acids form complexes with bile and thus become water-soluble. This *hydrotropic action* aids in the transfer of fatty acids through the intestinal membrane. It is probable that bile also acts on cholesterol and the fat-soluble vitamins in this way. Short chain fatty acids, i.e., those containing up to 12 carbon atoms, are absorbed into the portal blood as free fatty acid (FFA). Long chain fatty acids and glycerol are re-esterified to triglyceride in the mucosal cells. Both long chain fatty acids (such as palmitic, stearic, oleic, and linoleic acids) and triglycerides are absorbed into the lymph, moving from the mucosal cells into the lacteals, through the deeper lymphatics, to the thoracic duct, and then to the blood stream (p. 338).

As fat is absorbed and passes through the lacteals (see Figure 18.4), the lymph vessels of the mesentery take on a milklike appearance as the result of the great number of fat droplets, called chylomicrons, in the lymph; they may also be seen in the blood stream (Fig. 19.2). The chylomicrons are rapidly removed from the blood, principally by the liver and by the fat cells of the adipose tissues. The dietary fat is then oxidized or is stored in the fat depots as neutral fat. After the fat enters the cells, the first step in its oxidation is its breakdown into glycerol and fatty acids. This oxidation takes place in the mitochondria. The fatty acids are broken down into acetyl-CoA, following pathways which are also

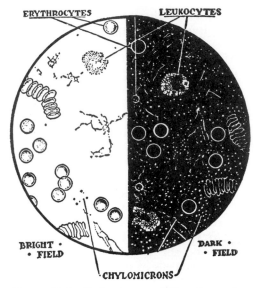

Figure 19.2 Chylomicrons. (After Gage; from Best and Taylor: Physiological Basis of Medical Practice. 6th ed. Baltimore, The Williams & Wilkins Co., 1955.)

common to carbohydrate and amino acid moieties (citric acid cycle). Glycerol is ultimately broken down into CO_2 and H_2O.

Fats can be resynthesized from acetyl-CoA — a reaction that probably takes place in the microsomes. Adipose tissue and the liver are the major sites of synthesis of fats. The stored fat is a product of the metabolism of lipids, and also of carbohydrate and protein material which has been converted from fat. The fat deposits in the depots are not static; the breakdown and resynthesis of the neutral fats proceed continuously. The metabolism of the endogenous fats in oxidation and resynthesis is the same as that of ingested fats. Three fatty acids which cannot be synthesized in the body, and are thus called *essential fats*, are the polyunsaturated fatty acids: linoleic, linolenic, and arachidonic. These fatty acids appear to be necessary for proper growth in children.

Liver fat storage appears to be controlled by the interaction of certain substances. Important among these are choline and chemically related substances, and methionine and proteins containing it, which act to prevent excess fat storage,

i.e., fatty liver. This action is opposed by cholesterol, cystine, thiamine, and other substances that favor fat storage, and which if taken in large doses may result in excessive fatty infiltration.

Before oxidation occurs, neutral fats are hydrolyzed to glycerol and fatty acid. Apparently, the fatty acids are desaturated in the liver and burned two carbon atoms at a time. Oxidation may be complete or ketone bodies may be formed. The ketone bodies, which are formed only by the liver, are normally oxidized by other body tissues to the final end products, CO_2 and water. When the rate of fat metabolism is greatly increased by lack of adequate carbohydrate, or when a high fat diet is taken, or from other causes, an excess of ketone bodies accumulates and ketosis develops. This may lead to severe acidosis, coma, and death.

Metabolism of Proteins. Protein contains carbon, oxygen, hydrogen, nitrogen, sulfur, and sometimes phosphorus. The first three constituents are also in carbohydrates and fats; the fourth, nitrogen, is the principal chemical characteristic of protein.

Not all proteins have equal dietary importance. There are eight amino acids considered necessary for growth and repair. These essential amino acids are not synthesized within the body at rates sufficient to meet body requirements. Other amino acids can be converted or synthesized. Proteins having the essential amino acids are called *complete proteins*. Protein not only serves as a source of energy for the body, but acts to increase the release of energy above and beyond the amount that can be derived from the portion of the protein ingested. This response is spoken of as the *specific dynamic action* of protein. For example, if we eat an amount of protein that contains a chemical source of energy approximately equivalent to the basal metabolic rate, the energy derived from the resulting metabolic activities is approximately 30 per cent in excess of that which could be derived from the ingested protein. The additional heat results from simultaneous oxidation of other foodstuffs already in the body.

Protein is hydrolyzed into amino acids

by the proteases during the digestive process. These are absorbed through the small intestine into the portal circulation. Amino acids are also derived from the breakdown of tissues within the body; this breakdown process is catalyzed by intracellular proteolytic enzymes, the *cathepsins*. The exogenous and endogenous amino acids form an amino acid pool. Amino acids from this pool are (1) used to build new protoplasm as it is needed for growth and repair, (2) oxidized to carbon dioxide, water, and urea, (3) converted to carbohydrate or fat, and (4) transformed into protein derivatives including creatine, glutathione, epinephrine, and compounds with carbohydrates and fats.

PROTEIN SYNTHESIS. The synthesis of proteins takes place in the ribosomes of the cells of the various tissues. Each of the tissues synthesizes its characteristic proteins. Most of these proteins remain within their cell of origin. Other proteins are synthesized within certain groups of cells and then released. The liver, for example, synthesizes the plasma proteins as well as the proteins within its own cells. Enzymes and hormones are also examples of proteins which are formed intracellularly and then released into the body fluids.

The reaction common in the synthesis of all proteins is the formation of a peptide linkage between two amino acids. This union occurs between the carboxyl group of one amino acid and the amino group of the other amino acid. The reaction requires energy. This requirement is met by activation of the carboxyl member of the linkage. Activation involves the development of a complex of an amino acid, ATP and an activating enzyme, *amino-acid-adenyl transferase*, which is present in all tissues. Each activating enzyme is specific for an amino acid. The activated amino acid then combines with a specific molecule

of transfer or soluble RNA ($sRNA_1-sRNA_n$) (see p. 403). The $sRNA-amino-acid-adenylate$ complex is attached to the messenger RNA (mRNA) which is the template for formation of the specific protein. RNA is present in greatest amounts in cells that are highly active in the process of protein synthesis.

Protein synthesis is influenced by hormones—the growth hormone of the hypophysis and testosterone—which decrease the breakdown of amino acids and increase their storage. Insulin also affects protein synthesis indirectly by favoring glycolysis and providing energy for peptide linkage. The absorption of amino acids after a meal also stimulates protein synthesis, reduces breakdown, and utilizes more ribosomes. When amino acid influx is reduced the processes are reversed and the breakdown of protein and RNA in the cell is accelerated.

PROTEIN DEAMINIZATION, TRANSAMINATION, AND AMINATION. *Deaminization* is the removal of the amino group, NH_2, from amino acid. The amino acids not used for protein synthesis are deaminized in the liver and kidney. In oxidative deaminization the amino acids, acted upon by a dehydrogenase, break down into a keto acid and ammonia. The equation shown at the bottom of the page shows the oxidative deamination of the amino acid, glycine.

In *transamination* the amino group may be transferred without being released in a free state. It can be transferred to a keto acid forming a new amino acid and keto acid. The keto acid, which constitutes the non-nitrogenous portion following deamization of amino acid, may be oxidized directly to carbon dioxide and water to yield energy; or it may be synthesized to glucose and subsequently stored as glycogen or fat. A third reaction, as just indicated, is the formation of a new amino acid by union with the amino group of another acid. *Amination* is the combining of NH_3 and amino acid to form an amine. The NH_3 can be excreted as ammonium salts, used in transamination and amination, or utilized in the formation of urea. Urea, which is formed in the liver, is one of the principal end products of protein metabolism.

The synthesis involves the combination of the amino acid *ornithine* with NH_3 and CO_2 from carrier molecules, whose formation requires ATP, to form citrulline. Citrulline is then converted to arginine. Urea is split off from arginine with the re-formation of ornithine. The process is cyclical as shown below:

1. Ornithine + NH_3 + CO_2 → arginine
2. Arginine + water + arginase (in liver) → urea + ornithine

The relation between the amount of nitrogen in the protein of the diet and the amount excreted in the urine is known as the *nitrogen balance*. This does not imply that the exchange goes on a constant level. Protein utilization and protein excretion do not proceed at a constant rate, but may vary considerably with age, activity, and

state of health. The term nitrogen balance does, however, describe the extent to which a balance has been attained. If the nitrogen intake exceeds the total nitrogen excreted, the balance is positive; if the amount excreted is the greater, the balance is said to be negative. The positive balance is associated with growth, pregnancy, muscular exercise, and convalescence; a negative balance may occur in starvation, following trauma, and in certain wasting diseases. The nitrogen excreted in the urine as urea, and other nitrogen-containing waste products—uric acid, creatinine, and ammonium salts—constitute the nonprotein nitrogen, NPN, of the urine.

REGULATION OF BODY TEMPERATURE

Poikilothermic and Homothermic Animals. Animals may be divided into two classes with respect to body temperature, those of variable body temperature, the *poikilotherms*, and those of relatively constant body temperature, the *homotherms* (Fig. 19.3). Poikilothermic ("cold-blooded")

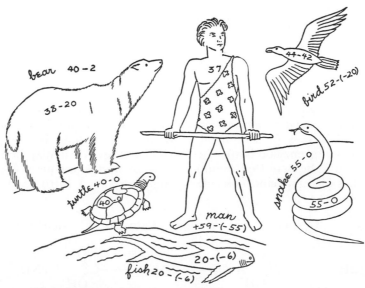

Figure 19.3 Homothermic and poikilothermic animals. Body temperature is compared with range of temperature of the environment. The temperatures are given in the centigrade scale. (Lemon: From Galileo to Cosmic Rays. University of Chicago Press.)

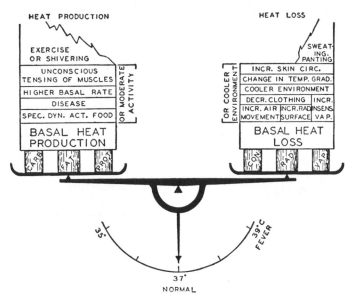

FACTORS INCREASING

Figure 19.4 Scheme showing balance between factors of changing heat production and heat loss. (Wiggers, by Courtesy of DuBois: Ann. Int. Med.)

animals, such as the amphibians and reptiles, have body temperatures that are dependent upon environment. In hot weather, their bodies gain heat by transfer from surrounding objects having higher temperatures. As the body temperature rises, the speed of its metabolic reactions is increased and heat production in the body is accelerated.* In cold weather, the poikilotherms lose heat to surrounding colder objects, their metabolic processes are slowed, and their movements become sluggish. Homothermic animals, such as mammals and birds, are able to maintain a fairly constant body temperature range in spite of changes in environmental temperature. Like the cold-blooded species, they lose heat to surrounding colder objects. The body temperature of homothermic animals, however, represents a continuously regulated balance between heat production and heat loss (Fig. 19.4).

Normal Temperatures of the Human Body. Normal body temperatures rep-

resent ranges rather than single values, as do the other physiological constants encountered in our study (Fig. 19.5). An oral temperature of 98.6° F. (37° C.) is considered a normal reference value. Actual temperatures vary slightly above or below this for different persons and for the same person at different times. The normal temperature range for the mouth is about 98° to 99° F., compared to 99° to 100° F. for the rectum. The temperature readings undergo a rhythmic change of two or more degrees Fahrenheit each day, known as the *diurnal variation.* Temperature is commonly lowest (97.7° F.) about six or seven o'clock in the morning; it reaches a high point of about 99.6° F. close to six or seven in the evening, and then decreases gradually throughout the night. There are, however, various individual patterns. Diurnal rhythm appears to be related to eating and activity habits.

The temperature of the body surface is far more variable than that of the deeper tissues. In parts of the body such as the fingers, toes, and ears, where the surface area is great in proportion to the mass of tissues, extreme and often painful tem-

---

*The rate of a chemical reaction is usually doubled for each 10° C. rise in temperature.

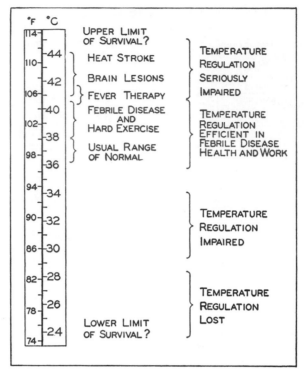

Figure 19.5 Extremes of human body temperatures and estimated ranges of temperature variations. (From DuBois, E. F.: Fever and the Regulation of Body Temperature. American Lecture Series, No. 13. Springfield, Ill., Charles C Thomas, 1948.)

perature changes may result upon exposure to cold. When the body is adequately clothed and under less extreme environmental conditions, the temperature of the skin of the trunk is close to 95° F. (35° C.), and that of the forehead about 91.5 ° F.

Temperature Regulation. Body temperature regulation may be defined as the maintenance of body temperatures within prescribed limits under varying thermal loads. The thermal loads are those arising from the external environment and from metabolic processes of the body itself. Temperature regulation affords an excellent example of homeostasis, permitting the maintenance of a constant internal environment through a wide range both of external temperatures and of bodily activity (Fig. 19.5). Relatively stable internal conditions favor the completion of chemical processes, such as enzyme reactions that are especially sensitive to temperature change, and protect against injury to or impairment of the functioning of the cells.

There is a *neutral zone* of temperature ranges in which man neither loses nor gains heat. It has been experimentally determined that this condition exists for a nude man at rest, in a basal state, at an environmental temperature of 86° F. Deviation from the condition of *thermal neutrality*, as a result of heat loss or gain from either external or internal causes or both, brings about compensatory changes in body temperature. The mechanisms for automatic temperature regulation are the metabolic rate, the peripheral blood flow, and the heat loss from the skin and lungs by evaporation. These are discussed in relation to the physiological response of the body to heat and cold, and to the thermo-regulatory control mechanisms.

Physiological Response to Cold. Increased heat production is one of the major mechanisms for maintenance of body temperature in a cold environment, or *cold zone*. The cold zone denotes a relative range, depending not only on air temperature, but also upon air movement, the temperature of surrounding objects, and body posture and clothing. Under customary living conditions, indoor temperatures below 68° F. may be considered to be in the cold zone.

Heat is produced by oxidation occurring in the tissues. It may be increased by ingestion of food, by shivering, by exercise, or by hormonal effects. Since the highest rate of chemical activity under basal conditions occurs in the liver, this organ generates a significant portion of the heat in a body at rest. The proteins, through their specific dynamic action, have a stimulating effect upon the tissue cells, which increases their rate of metabolism (see p. 374). Fat also constitutes a valuable food in cold environments, as it has a high calorific value (9 Calories per gram of fat).

Skeletal muscle contributes to heat production in amounts varying with the degree of bodily activity and the type of work. Approximately 70 to 80 per cent of the energy released in muscular contraction is liberated as heat (see p. 196). Mere tensing of the muscles results in a small but significant increase in heat production. Exercise may increase calorific output five or six times during heavy work. It is a highly effective voluntary response to cold.

The heat production of a man shivering at a maximal rate but otherwise "at rest" may be in excess of 200 Calories per square meter of body surface area per hour, written as 200 Cal./m.²/hr. This is comparable to heat production during strenuous work. Further, shivering may be nearly twice as efficient in raising body temperature as exercise, since it does not involve the air movement across the skin that results from vigorous exercise of the body and its extremities.

The endocrine system plays a role in the metabolic response to cold. It has been established that the activity of the thyroid gland increases almost immediately upon exposure of the body to cold, and may continue to maintain a high level of activity over an extended period. This effect may be mediated through the action of the central nervous system (see hypothalamus, p. 98) and the anterior pituitary gland, although the mechanism of this process is not well understood. Norepinephrine may also be one of the important mediators of the metabolic response to cold.

Heat conservation is a very important factor in the physiological response of the body to cold. It has been noted above that the temperature of the body surface is normally lower than its internal temperature. It is convenient, then, to think of the body as a core with a shell formed by the more superficial layers of tissue. This shell serves two functions in heat exchange: it acts as a layer of insulation between cold external environment and the core, and it serves as a reservoir in which heat may be stored, and from which heat may be given off with relatively little effect on internal body temperature. The insulation provided is relatively constant in neutral and cold zones; this limits heat loss to about 6 to 9 Cal./m.²/hr. for each degree centigrade of difference between internal temperature and the environment. Heat stored in the superficial layers is reduced rapidly when the environmental temperature is much lower than that of the body surface, and more slowly as the surface temperature declines. This mechanism, which permits the outer layers to cool with little effect on the core temperatures, is quite effective in reducing the heat loss of the body. Man is, however, less well insulated by his superficial tissues than, for example, seals, whose deep layer of fat protects them from extreme heat loss in the icy waters of the Arctic region.

Another insulating layer is provided by an air envelope, or "private climate," which surrounds the body at rest under conditions of still air or low-velocity air movement. Roughness of the skin and pilomotor activity, or "gooseflesh," increases the insulation value. This insulation is approximately equal to that provided by a business suit. It would give reasonable comfort to a nude man indoors at rest at approximately 82° F.; the additional insulation of a suit would provide equal comfort under the same conditions at 70° F. The air envelope of man gives far less protection than do those of animals, whose thick fur coats are more effective in trapping air. Man's comfort in cold environments depends upon clothing and other types of artificial insulation.

There is another mechanism of heat conservation that is very important in maintaining the temperature of the hands and feet. Upon exposure to cold, the temperature of these extremities may drop to low values, as a result of their high ratios of surface area to mass. Heat exchange occurs between the deep arteries and the veins supplying the extremities. Venous blood is warmed by the neighboring arterial blood flow, so that some body heat is returned to the core by a "short circuit" route. The arterial blood is proportionally cooled, so that less heat loss occurs between it and the cold toes or fingers and their colder external environment. Thus there are two temperature gradients—the transverse gradient between the core and shell, and the axial or longitudinal temperature gradient along the extremities.

Heat Exchange. The body loses heat in the following ways:

1. By convection, conduction, and radiation;
2. By vaporization, or evaporation of water from the lungs and skin;
3. By raising the temperature of inspired air to that of the body;
4. By liberation of carbon dioxide from the blood as it passes through the lungs;
5. By elimination of urine and feces;
6. By the ingestion of food, which may cause either a loss or a gain of some heat.

Over 80 per cent of the heat loss of the body is brought about by convection, conduction, and radiation, and by evaporation from the skin.

Convection is the transfer of heat from one body to another by a circulating medium, either a liquid or a gas. The transfer of heat from the interior of the body to the body surface, which is a convective transfer, is an important homeostatic function of the circulatory system. It is an essential first step in reducing the heat load on the body, since heat exchange takes place principally at the body surface, though some exchange occurs in the lungs and the countercurrents at the extremities. Convection also accomplishes the heat exchange between the air envelope and the outer environment by movement of air over the surface of the body.

Conduction and radiation also are physical phenomena involving the transmission of heat. Unlike convection, which requires movement of blood or respired gases and the air of the air envelope, heat exchange by conduction and radiation takes place without any medium of transmission. *Conduction* is simply the passage of heat energy between two objects of different temperature, accomplished through molecular vibration. Thus a body loses heat when immersed in a cold bath or when in contact with objects below its own temperature. *Radiation* is the transfer of infra red waves through space; it occurs through either air or vacuum. In this respect the body acts much as does the heating element in an electric heater or in an infra red lamp.

Vaporization, or evaporation of water from the skin and lungs, requires the absorption of about 0.6 Calorie for each gram of water vaporized at 37° C. Water is lost from the skin by insensible perspiration even when there is no apparent sweating. When sweating occurs and the sweat evaporates, the skin surface cools as the result of the heat absorbed in the process of evaporation.

Under normal conditions at room temperatures, about 25 per cent of the heat loss of the body results from vaporization, of which half or less occurs in the lungs. A small amount of heat also is lost when the carbon dioxide of the blood passing through the lungs comes out of solution. About 15 per cent or less of the heat loss is by conduction to the air of the air envelope, causing convection currents in which the warmed gases rise, moving away from the body surface, and are replaced by cooler air. Approximately 60 per cent is lost through radiation. These proportions vary greatly under different environmental conditions.

Physiological Response to Heat. The insulation value of the superficial tissues is relatively constant in the neutral and cold zones. Below environmental temperatures near neutrality (28° to 30° C.) the vasomotor system is in a state of full constriction insofar as heat exchange with the outside environment is concerned. Within this temperature range, in which body temperature is maintained at physiological levels without either increased metabolism or sweating, small increases and decreases in blood flow through the skin cause minor changes in conductance and so constitute a "fine adjustment" in body heat exchange. The *neutral temperature zone* is also spoken of as the zone of *vasomotor regulation*.

In the *hot zone*, above 30° C., heat exchange is effected by dilatation of the superficial blood vessels and increased blood flow in the skin, and by sweating. When the heat load on the body is increased as the result of high environmental temperatures, exercise, or both, marked vasodilation of the superficial vessels occurs. This may result in an increase in blood flow through the skin, with a resulting sixfold reduction in the insulating value of the superficial tissues in a resting man. A twentyfold reduction in insulation may occur during exercise.

As the conductance of peripheral tissues increases, the difference between internal body temperature and skin temperature decreases. Thus the gradient becomes less steep. Transfer of the heat from the body surface is effected by radiation only as long as skin temperature is higher than that of the objects in the surrounding environment. When internal body temperature rises as the result of a reduction in heat exchange or of increased heat production through work, sweating occurs. Under extreme conditions of heat and work, sweating rates in excess of 2 liters per hour have been observed; rates of 4 liters per hour may occur for brief periods of time.

There are also environmental limits to heat exchange by vaporization. The amount of water vapor in the air depends upon the air temperature and upon a source of water for evaporation. Maximum water vapor content is achieved at 100 per cent relative humidity. The evaporation of water from the body depends upon the wetted area of the skin, skin temperature, air temperature, air velocity and the relative humidity, and body characteristics influencing the flow of convection currents. The greater the air movement and the lower the relative humidity, the greater the rate of evaporation. When conditions are such that heat can no longer be given off, the body temperature rises and extreme discomfort, heat exhaustion, or death may result.

Temperature Regulating Mechanisms. Body temperature is a regulated variable in which the internal temperatures have a more limited physiological range than those of the superficial tissues. Body temperature is regulated by nervous and hormonal mechanisms. Temperature-sensitive nuclei of the hypothalamus and temperature receptors of the skin and other body areas participate in this regulation.

The central temperature control nuclei, or "thermostatic" neurons, are located in the hypothalamus (see p. 98). They are sensitive to blood temperature, and react to the difference between the "thermostatic setting" and the temperature of the body as reflected by the temperature of the blood supplying the hypothalamus. Nerve cells in the anterior part of the hypothalamus are concerned with control of the mechanisms of heat loss, which are vasodilation and sweating. Heat production and heat conservation are mediated by neurons located in the caudal region, while the lateral hypothalamic neurons appear to be concerned with shivering. Regulation of body temperatures in the hot zone and during activity is thought to be primarily under the control of the hypothalamus, as is the physiological mechanism of fever.

The peripheral receptors, located deep in as well as near the surface of the more superficial tissues, are stimulated by changes in the outer shell temperature. They are advantageously located for early detection and measurement of the rate of loss or gain of the body heat. The peripheral receptors play a major role in regulation of body temperature in the cold and neutral temperature zones.

The hypothalamus and peripheral receptors participate in stimulation of the anterior pituitary gland in response to cold; this gland in turn stimulates the thyroid and adrenal glands. Together, then, the thermoregulatory mechanisms of the body are influenced by the magnitude of the temperature variation as well as by the rate of such temperature change.

The responses to any heat load upon the body are proportional both to the change in body temperature and to the rate at which such a change occurs. If the heat load is increased by a given amount, the mechanisms for cooling the body react to a corresponding degree. If this were the only type of regulatory response, marked changes in heat load might require a long period for readjustment, while small changes might result in too rapid or too great a reaction with a succession of increases and decreases in heat exchange before settling at a proper level. The regulatory characteristic of responding rapidly to the rate of change and, after a brief lag, to the degree of change provides for a more uniform body temperature, and protects against the injurious and even fatal results of prolonged hyperthermia or hypothermia. Of the two, overheating constitutes the more serious threat.

Fever. Fever is a manifestation of a disturbance in the thermoregulatory apparatus. Ordinarily "fever" means a significant rise in body temperature occurring in a man at rest in a normal environmental temperature. Fever may come as the result of drug action, of the injection of foreign materials, of brain injury, or as the accompaniment of disease or infection. Relatively little is known about the way in which these various factors act. In recent years, however, a considerable amount of evidence has been developed to support the hypothesis that the fever accompanying bacterial disease and infection is caused by a pyrogenic (*pyro*, fire; *gennan*, to produce) material release from the injured cells of the body. The common response to many diseases appears to be the release of such an *endogenous pyrogen*.

In fever, the initial reactions are those normally observed in a man exposed to cold: shivering, vasoconstriction, and gooseflesh. This is the type of response expected when the body temperature is below the "thermostatic" setting. The present concept visualizes fever as a condition in which the thermostat is advanced to a higher than normal level. The posterior portion of the hypothalamus is involved in this process, but by what means is not known. The increased heat production and the reduction in heat loss that follow result in a rise in body temperature until the level of the new setting is reached. Heart rate, respiration, and other bodily processes are accelerated at this higher temperature. Upon recovery, that is, resetting of the thermostat at a more normal physiological level, the body responds as it would to a hot environment or to vigorous exercise, and its heat loss mechanisms are brought into play.

QUESTIONS FOR DISCUSSION

1. Describe the absorption of fats. What are lipids? FFA?

2. To what substances are carbohydrates reduced for absorption? In what form are they transported in the blood? In what forms are they stored?

3. What part does the liver play in the metabolism of carbohydrates and fats?

4. How is basal metabolism measured? How is it regulated?

5. What is the role of the following in intermediate and energy metabolism: mitochondria, lysosomes, ribosomes, phosphokinase, cathepsins, ATP, sRNA, mRNA?

6. Explain the fate of the amino acids that are not used by the cells in the construction of protoplasm.

7. Discuss the importance of a constant, normal range of internal body temperature for the physiological processes of the body.

8. Explain the meaning of conduction,

convection, and radiation in relation to heat loss from the body.

9. Discuss the response to fever and the return to normal temperature in relation to the physiological mechanisms of temperature regulation.

10. How are metabolism and temperature regulation interrelated?

UNIT 6

REPRODUCTION OF THE HUMAN BEING

20. THE REPRODUCTIVE SYSTEMS 21. DEVELOPMENT OF THE HUMAN BODY

This unit considers the origin and development of the human body. The reproductive structures of the male and female are described, and the reproductive process explained. A portion of the continuum of growth and development is presented.

THE REPRODUCTIVE SYSTEMS

CHAPTER TWENTY

THE FEMALE REPRODUCTIVE SYSTEM

The female reproductive organs consist of the ovaries, in which sex cells develop; the uterine tubes, through which the sex cells pass; the uterus, in which the embryo develops; the vagina, a canal that connects the uterus to the exterior; and the external genitalia; the mammary glands are accessory organs. The ovaries, uterine tubes, and uterus are shown in Figure 20.1.

Ovaries

LOCATION AND STRUCTURE. The ovaries are flattened, oval bodies about 2.5 cm. long, which lie on the sides of the pelvis, attached to the posterior surface of broad ligament and supported laterally by the suspensory ligament of the ovary. These ligaments are folds of peritoneum. A fibromuscular cord, the ovarian ligament, attaches the ovary to the lateral wall of the uterus below the uterine tube.

The ovary consists of a connective tissue, or *stroma* covered with a single layer of cuboidal epithelium. In the central medullary portion the connective tissue is loose and blood vessels are numerous. The denser outer cortical portion contains

387

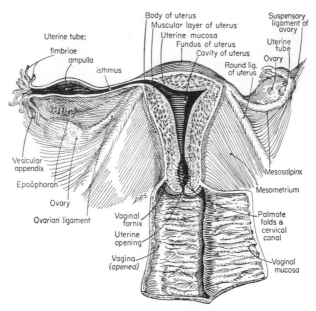

Figure 20.1 The internal genital organs in the female, partly in frontal section. (From Woodburne: Essentials of Human Anatomy. New York, Oxford University Press, 1969.)

many follicles in which the egg cells (oocytes) are contained.

Three types of follicles are found in the ovaries: primary, growing, and mature or vesicular follicles (Fig. 20.2). The *primary follicles* are the most numerous. They consist of the ovum surrounded by a few small follicular cells. Some of the primary follicles become *growing follicles* and show marked increase in size of the ovum and in the number of the follicle cells. Soon spaces filled with fluid appear among the cells; the spaces coalesce to form a single cavity that increases so much in size that the ovum is pushed to one side. With growth of the follicle the connective tissue cells form a capsule around it called the *theca*. The inner layer of the theca is highly vascular, but the outer layer is fibrous in character. The growing follicle has matured into a *vesicular follicle*, and is seen bulging from the surface of the ovary. The

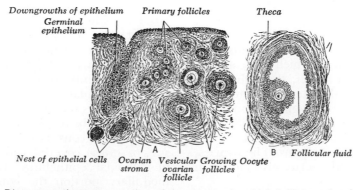

Figure 20.2 *A*, Diagrammatic representation of the manner in which follicles arise during development of the ovum. *B*, Diagram illustrating the structure of a ripe vesicular follicle. (From Cunningham: Textbook of Anatomy. Oxford University Press.)

vesicular follicle either ruptures or undergoes involution. Follicles may degenerate at any stage of development. With rupture of the follicle the follicular fluid and ovum pass into the abdominal cavity, constituting *ovulation*. This usually occurs every twenty-eight days from puberty to menopause.

After ovulation the thecal and follicular cells change rapidly into large cells that contain a yellow pigment. The body formed in this way is called the *corpus luteum*. Corpus luteum is rich in pigment and lipids. If the ovum is not fertilized on its way to the uterus, menstruation follows in about fourteen days and this structure becomes the corpus luteum of menstruation. If the ovum is fertilized, menstruation ceases during the period of pregnancy. The corpus luteum of pregnancy continues to develop for five to six months and increases greatly in size. Both types of corpora lutea undergo involution and are reduced to small scars.

In the two ovaries of the newborn infant there are about 400,000 follicles. Primordial ova arise from epithelial tissue of the embryonic intestinal tract, migrating to the developing ovary by ameboid motion. It has been estimated that not more than 400 of these follicles mature and discharge their ova during the period of sexual activity of the human female. The rest of the 400,000 follicles gradually degenerate and disappear as they undergo *atresia*. This process proceeds at a rapid rate up to the time of puberty, after which it continues more slowly and is completed after the menopause.

OVARIAN HORMONES. The estrogens are steroids formed principally by the vascular theca interna of the ovarian follicle. During pregnancy the placenta produces large amounts of estrogens. Small amounts are secreted by the adrenal cortex and probably by the corpus luteum, although this has not been established for man. The principal estrogens are *estradiol-17β*, *estrone*, and a metabolic product, *estriol*. Estradiol is the principal and most powerful estrogen.

Estrogens are considered to be "feminizing hormones," which produce the bodily changes that occur in girls at puberty. These changes comprise *secondary sex characteristics*. The estrogens stimulate growth and development of the reproductive passageways and their cyclic changes following puberty. The deposition of fat in the external genitals, breasts, buttocks, thighs, and hypodermis of the skin is influenced by estrogens. This influence tends to produce narrow shoulders, broad hips, thighs that converge and arms that diverge in a wide *carrying angle*. The larynx retains its prepubertal cartilaginous proportions and voice production remains relatively high-pitched. Body hair develops and thickens in the axillae, over the external genitals, and on the head. The skin becomes more vascular and of a softer texture than in males.

Osteoblastic activity, rapid growth, and union of the epiphyses with the diaphyses are stimulated by the estrogens. The changes in the innominate bone that result in a pelvis typical of the female (p. 183) are the result of estrogenic influence. Water retention and protein anabolism in the body are increased by estrogens. These hormones participate in reproductive physiology. It is believed that they aid in development of the ovarian follicle and may increase the tone and contractions of the muscle in the nonpregnant uterus.

The corpus luteum and the placenta secrete *progesterone* which is concerned with the preparation of the uterus for receiving the fertilized ovum and its maintenance during pregnancy. A large part of the preparation of the mammary glands for lactation is controlled by progesterone. This hormone stimulates respiration, and alveolar P_{CO_2} is lower during times that significant amounts of progesterone are in the circulation.

The corpus luteum also forms *relaxin* or *uterine relaxing factor* (URF), which reaches its highest circulatory blood level during the terminal stages of pregnancy. Relaxin, which is not chemically related to steroid estrogens and progesterone, effects a marked pelvic relaxation, providing for separation of the symphysis pubis and dilation of the cervix of the uterus during labor and delivery of the baby.

The biosynthetic pathway of estrogens and progesterone involves *androgens* or male sex hormones. The androgen steroids are associated with the development of masculine secondary sex characteristics. Small amounts of androgens are secreted by the ovary.

Reproductive Passageways

UTERINE TUBES. The uterine tubes are musculomembranous channels about 10 cm. long, lying in the fold of the broad ligament along the superior border. Medially the *isthmus* connects with the uterus; laterally it opens into the abdominal cavity. The lateral end of the tube widens out into a funnel-shaped *infundibulum*, the margins of which are frayed into irregular fringes called *fimbriae*. The *ampulla* is the somewhat dilated portion of the tube adjoining the infundibulum. Epithelium of the mucosa of the uterine tube is composed of simple ciliated and nonciliated columnar cells. Smooth muscle in the wall of the tube is arranged in circular and longitudinal layers. Peritoneum forms the serous covering of the tube. Important events occurring in the tube are fertilization, segmentation, and early differentiation of the blastocyst. The mechanism by which the ovum is transported from the ruptured follicle into the uterine tube is unknown. Vascular changes in the blood vessels of the fimbriae, together with contraction of

smooth muscle tissue in these structures, probably effect the transfer. Peristaltic movements of the smooth muscle in the walls of the tube forward the ovum toward the uterus.

UTERUS. The uterus is a hollow organ with thick muscular walls (Fig. 20.3). It is here that the ovum, if fertilized, undergoes its development into the embryo and fetus. The uterus resembles a pear in shape, but is flattened in the anteroposterior direction. It lies in the pelvic cavity between the bladder and the rectum, and is about 7 cm. long, 5 cm. wide, and 2.5 cm. thick. The rounded upper part of the uterus above the entrance of the tubes is the *fundus*. The *body* of the uterus narrows from the fundus to the *isthmus*, or lower uterine segment. The *cervix* continues this tapering as it projects into the upper part of the vagina.

The wall of the uterus is composed of three layers: an inner mucosa, a middle muscular layer, and an outer serous covering. The mucosa lining the uterus is the *endometrium*. It consists of one layer of ciliated columnar cells and loose connective tissue. The glands, which are simple tubular in type, branch in their deeper portions. The muscular layer, or *myo-*

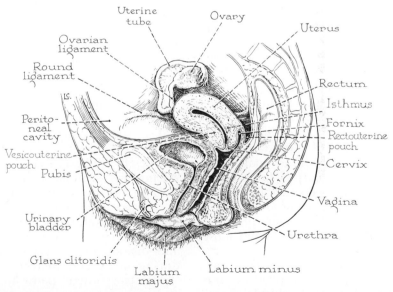

Figure 20.3 Diagrammatic sagittal section of female pelvis, showing the genital organs and their relation to the bladder and urethra. (From Turner: General Endocrinology.)

metrium, of the uterine wall is made up of smooth muscle fibers that run in many directions. Numerous branches of uterine arteries and veins penetrate the muscle layers. Peritoneum, or *perimetrium*, forms the serosa covering the uterus.

The peritoneum lining the abdominal wall continues into the pelvis and is reflected over the viscera. It covers the anterior and lateral surfaces of the rectum and is reflected over the uterus, forming the folds of the broad ligament. From the anterior surface of the uterus it passes over the bladder and on to the anterior abdominal wall. Figure 20.3 shows the *recto-uterine* and *vesicouterine pouches* which are formed by peritoneal reflections from rectum to uterus and from bladder to uterus.

Support of the Uterus. The adult uterus is anteverted from the vagina at an angle of 90 degrees. Support of the uterus is provided by vaginal attachment into the muscles of the pelvic floor and indirect fixation to adjacent structures by way of ligaments. The position of the uterus varies in pregnancy or in distention of the bladder

or intestine. The *broad ligament* of the uterus is a wide peritoneal fold that passes from the lateral margin of the uterus to the side wall of the pelvis. Enclosed between its layers are the uterine tubes, round ligaments, vessels, and nerves. The *round ligaments* are attached to the lateral angles of the uterus below the entrance of the uterine tubes. They run outward in the broad ligament to the sides of the pelvis, at which point they enter the inguinal canals to terminate in the tissues of the labia majora. *Uterosacral ligaments* connect the cervix to the sacrum by folds of fibrous connective tissue and smooth muscle. The *lateral cervical ligaments* are fibromuscular cords arising lateral to the cervix and inserting in the fascia of the muscles of the lateral pelvic wall. These attachments maintain the anteflexion of the uterus. Most of the uterine support is provided by the muscles of the pelvic floor.

The paired levator ani and coccygeus muscle close the outlet of the pelvis and form a diaphragm supporting the pelvic viscera (Fig. 20.4). The *levator ani* muscle arises from the pubis, the spine of the

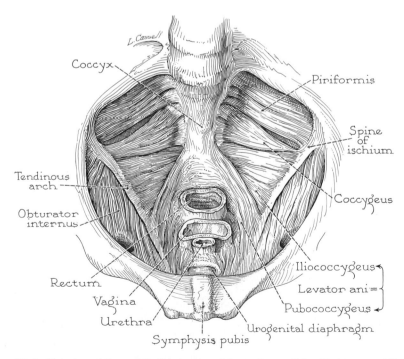

Figure 20.4 Muscles of the pelvic floor, viewed from above. (After T. Jones and F. Netter.)

ischium, and a tendinous arch, connecting these two points along the lateral pelvic wall. Two portions of the muscle are often described, the one arising from the pubis and called the pubococcygeus, and the other arising from the tendinous arch and called the iliococcygeus. The fibers of both portions pass downward, backward, and medialward. The most posterior fibers insert on the coccyx, while the anterior ones unite in the midline with those from the opposite side. The urethra, vagina, and rectum lie in the interval between the two muscles anteriorly, and some of the fibers are inserted into the sides of the rectum and vagina. The *coccygeus* muscle completes the pelvic floor posteriorly. It arises from the spine of the ischium and is inserted along the side of the sacrum and coccyx.

Both muscles support and elevate the pelvic organs. The coccygei draw the coccyx forward after it has been pressed back during defecation or parturition. The levator ani muscles constrict the lower end of the rectum and vagina, and draw the rectum forward and upward. The strength of the pelvic floor is dependent upon the intact *central perineal tendon* (perineal body) which is present between the anal and vaginal orifices. This structure is the reason for the restricted use of the term perineum. It is generally understood that the perineum includes the entire pelvic outlet from the symphysis pubis to the coccyx.

VAGINA. The vagina is a flattened musculomembranous tube about 7.5 cm. long, extending from the uterus to the vulva. It is posterior to the bladder and urethra, and anterior to the rectum. The cervix projects funnel-like into the upper end of the vagina, forming a circular recess between the vaginal wall and the cervix called the *fornix*. The posterior fornix is deeper and more conspicuous than the anterior fornix. The mucous membrane is arranged in transverse folds of *vaginal rugae*. The epithelium of the membrane is stratified squamous. The vaginal orifice is partially closed by a semilunar or annular fold of mucous membrane called the hymen. Longitudinally oriented smooth muscle fibers constitute the muscular coat of the vagina. The outer coat is fibroelastic connective tissue continuous with the fascia of the muscles of the floor of the pelvis.

The vagina is the organ of copulation in the female. It also forms an important part of the birth canal and an excretory passage for the menstrual discharge.

External Genitalia. The external genital organs, referred to collectively as the vulva, comprise the mons pubis, labia majora, labia minora, clitoris, vestibule, vestibular glands, and the bulb of the vestibule (Fig. 20.5).

The mons pubis is the rounded eminence in front of the symphysis pubis. It is composed of fibrous and adipose tissue enclosed by skin, and after puberty is covered with hair. The labia majora are two longitudinal folds of skin covering the adipose tissue and the round ligament. They extend downward from the mons pubis toward the anus. Between the labia majora are two smaller folds, the labia minora. They meet above to form the prepuce of the *clitoris*; below, they fuse with the hymen. The clitoris is the homologue of the penis in the male. It consists of two small, cavernous, erectile bodies. The cleft between the labia minora is the *vestibule*. The urethral and vaginal orifices are in the vestibule. A pair of elongated masses of erectile tissue lie on either side of the vaginal orifice as the bulb of the vestibule. The *greater vestibular glands* are two glands on either side of the vagina. They correspond to the bulbourethral glands in the male. Their ducts open into the vestibule between the hymen and the labia minora. Between the urethral and vaginal orifices are numerous minute openings for the mucous secretion of the *lesser vestibular glands*.

Mammary Glands. The breasts, or mammary glands, resemble sweat glands of the skin in structure. Their function places them as accessory organs of the female reproductive system. Figure 20.6 shows the structure of the glands and their relation to the pectoralis major muscle of the chest wall.

Each mammary gland is composed of fifteen to twenty-five compound alveolar glands, or lobes, that radiate from the nipple into the surrounding stroma much as

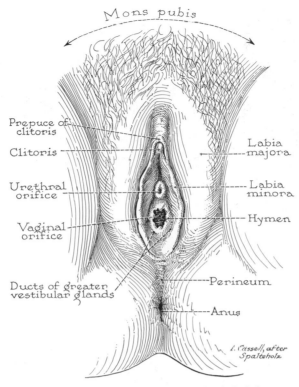

Figure 20.5 The vulva. (After Spalteholz.)

spokes radiate from the hub of a wheel. The supporting tissue or stroma consists of connective tissue and much adipose tissue. The *nipple* contains circular smooth muscle and sebaceous glands. It is surrounded by a pigmented circular area of skin called the *areola*. The areola also has circular smooth muscle, sebaceous and sweat glands, and a rich supply of nerve endings. Under the areola, each glandular duct enlarges to form a *lactiferous sinus*, and constricts again as it enters the nipple. Each duct has its separate opening on the summit of the nipple. Preparatory to lactation during pregnancy the glandular tissue shows very active growth.

The numerous *lymphatics* of the breast originate as a network in the interspaces of the glands. They join axillary, sternal, subclavicular, and deep cervical lymph nodes (Fig. 14.6). Lymphatics of one breast cross the median plane to anastomose with those of the opposite breast.

Reproductive Physiology. The period of growth in the female between ten and fourteen years of age is known as *puberty*. It is marked by changes in the ovaries in the maturation of follicles, the growth of the uterus, uterine tubes, vagina, and mammary glands, the appearance of pubic and axillary hair, and an adult type of body contour determined by musculoskeletal growth and distribution of fat.

Only small amounts of gonadotrophic hormones of the pituitary are found in the urine of prepubertal females. It may be assumed that only a little secretion is being elaborated. However, secretions of ovarian hormones increase gradually in girls from about 7 to 10 years old, indicating an increase in circulating gonadotrophins or increasing response on the part of the ovary. We do not know what causes the beginning of gonad stimulation by the pituitary. It may be caused by hypothalamic mechanism of nervous control or by the cessation of the inhibitory action of the

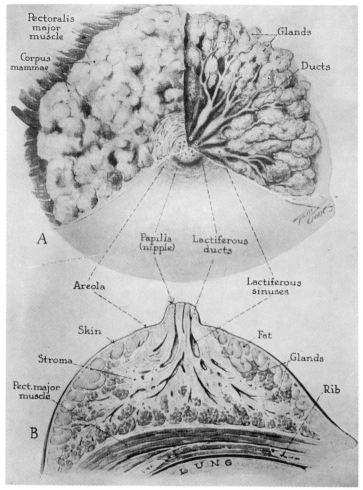

Figure 20.6 The breast. *A*, Dissection of lactating breast. *B*, Relation of breast to chest wall. (Courtesy of S. H. Camp Co.)

low concentration of female sex hormones acting on a highly sensitive pituitary. At puberty, however, urinary concentration of the gonadotrophins increases rapidly, approaching levels found in the adult, indicating a rapid rise in their rate of secretion. Puberty terminates with the onset of *menstruation*.

A series of parasympathetic neuronal reflexes is responsible for physiological preparation for the female sexual act. Psychic factors and adrenocortical and ovarian hormones, together with local stimulation of the perineal region, initiate the vascular changes which cause erection of the clitoris and bulb of the vestibule and

the secretion of the vaginal and vestibular glands. The combination of sensory and motor events constitutes *orgasm*.

After approximately thirty years of menstrual cycles, ovarian function declines in the female *climacteric*, and ceases entirely after *menopause*. In menopause there is a regression and general atrophy of the structures of the reproductive system. Vasomotor changes (hot flashes) frequently accompany menopause, particularly affecting the skin of the head, neck, and upper trunk. Alterations in personality, such as intense depression, may also accompany these changes. Changes that occur in the endometrium during the menstrual cycle are directly related to ovarian changes and to activity of the adenohypophysis (Fig. 20.7).

The increase in estrogens produced by the growing and vesicular follicles is believed to limit the secretion of FSH and prepare the pituitary to secrete LH, i.e., the luteinizing hormone. FSH and LH together are concerned with the final maturation and rupture of the follicle with resulting ovulation and formation of corpus luteum. During the luteal phase the action of progesterone leads to the development of a secretory endometrium and stimulates cyclic changes in the breast.

Oral contraceptives act to prevent ovulation. Estrogen in the form of mestranol (ethinylestradiol) inhibits the secretion of FSH, and the continued action of progesterone inhibits the release of LH. The estrogen is the principal factor in the secretion of pituitary gonadotrophins. Progesterone, which has an additive effect, is included in the regimen of medication

to provide for prompt withdrawal bleeding that follows the physiological pattern.

CYCLIC CHANGES IN THE ENDOMETRIUM. The endometrium of the nonpregnant woman undergoes partial destruction about every twenty-eight days. The stroma of the endometrium contains capillaries, arterioles, venules, and arteriovenous anastomoses. The mucosa is so arranged that it has a fixed basal portion that does not participate in cyclic changes and a functional portion that does. The two possess independent blood supplies. The destruction of the epithelium is accompanied by a discharge of blood and secretion that constitutes the menstrual flow. The average duration of the flow in the *menstrual phase* is from three to five days, during which approximately 50 ml. of blood are discharged.

The first day of menstruation is considered the first day of the cycle. As the flow ceases, which is usually about the fifth day, a follicle begins to increase in size rapidly

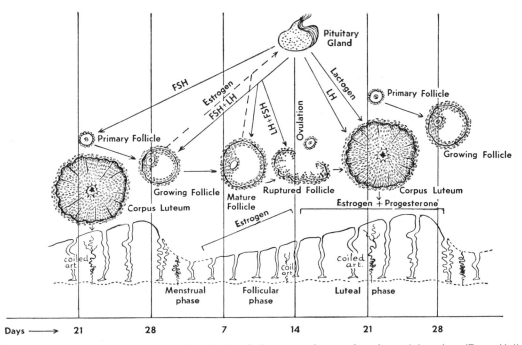

Figure 20.7 Schematic representation of the pituitary, ovarian, and endometrial cycles. (From Hall: Functions of the Endocrine Glands.)

and to produce estrogens. This growth of the follicle is accompanied by marked proliferation of the epithelial cells of the uterine mucosa, and the formation in the glands of a mucoid secretion. The *follicular phase* ends with rupture of the follicle, which occurs sometime between the tenth and sixteenth days. After ovulation, the more active premenstrual changes develop progressively for the approximate two weeks of the *luteal phase* under the stimulus of progesterone from the corpus luteum. The mucous membrane increases in thickness, and the epithelial cells cease dividing, but increase in size and begin to secrete. The glands grow and become tortuous; the arterioles become tightly coiled and the venous capillaries are engorged with blood. The endometrium is now ready to receive the fertilized ovum. If the ovum is not fertilized, menstruation occurs. The distended capillaries burst; the blood and disintegrating epithelium together with secretion of glands are eliminated. Menstruation results from cessation or marked diminution of the secretion of estrogens and progesterone.

CYCLIC CHANGES IN THE BREAST. With the onset of regular menstruation the breast undergoes cyclic activity coordinated with the events of the ovarian cycle. In the *proliferative phase*, from the tenth day of the menstrual cycle until the beginning of the next cycle, the lobes develop and expand to acquire acini. Decline in lobular development and the disappearance of the acini occur in the *regressive phase*, the first nine days of the menstrual cycle. Estrogens cause an increase in the length of the lactiferous ducts and an increase in the size of the areola and nipple. Progesterone stimulates the development of the acini, but requires the prior action of estrogens for this effect. In order that both ovarian hormones may exert their effect the adenohypophysis must be normally active. The specific actions of prolactin and oxytocin in initiation and maintenance of lactation were explained in Chapter 9. Continuation of lactation appears to require the presence of adenohypophysial STH, ACTH, TSH, and LH, adrenal glucocorticoids, and thyroxin, together with the appropriate nutrient substances.

THE MALE REPRODUCTIVE SYSTEM

The male reproductive system consists of the testes, which produce both the male hormones and the male germ cells, called *spermatozoa*, a system of ducts for transporting the spermatozoa, a number of auxiliary glands, and the penis (Fig. 20.8).

Testes

LOCATION AND STRUCTURE. The testes are two ovoid bodies that lie in the scrotum. In the embryo the testes develop on the ventral border of the kidneys, and just before birth or soon afterward they descend beneath the peritoneum and pass through the inguinal canal into the scrotum. The *scrotum* is to be thought of as an extension of the abdominal cavity, although in the adult it is closed off and no connection exists. The temperature within the scrotum is somewhat lower than in the abdomen. The dartos muscle of the scrotum contracts in response to cold and brings the testes closer to the abdomen; heat, or the other hand, relaxes the dartos muscle. In this way the testes are maintained within a relatively narrow temperature range, but below that of internal body temperature, which is too high for the process of spermatogenesis to occur.

Each testis is a compound tubular gland, enclosed in a firm fibrous capsule (Fig. 20.9). Fibrous extensions from the capsule divide the gland into numerous lobules. Within each lobule are found the terminal portions of the *seminiferous tubules* (Fig. 20.10). These tubules unite to form a network from which efferent ducts arise to enter the head of the epididymis. The cells lining the seminiferous tubules are of two types: sustentacular cells, and spermatogenic or germinal cells. The *sustentacular cells* serve nutrient and supporting functions. They are elongated, pillar-like cells attached to the basement membrane of the tubule. Like pylons, they give support to the centrally placed spermatogenic elements. The *germinal cells* are arranged in several layers about the periphery of the tubule. The spermatogonia are next to the basement membrane, and the other forms, primary spermatocytes, secondary spermatocytes, spermatids, and spermatozoa, follow in orderly sequence

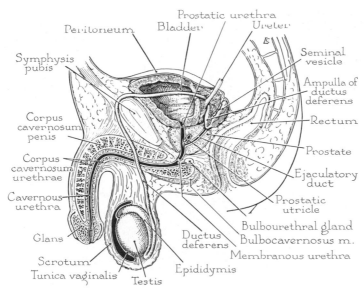

Figure 20.8 Diagrammatic sagittal section of the male pelvis, showing the genital organs and their relation to the bladder and urethra. (After Turner: General Endocrinology.)

toward the center. The mature spermatozoa become detached from their moorings on the sustentacular cells and are forced out into the lumen of the tubule and finally reach the efferent ducts of the gland. The interstitial tissue of the testes, which is made up of epithelioid cells within a stroma of connective tissue, lies between the seminiferous tubules.

TESTICULAR HORMONES. The male hormones are called androgens. Androgens are produced primarily by the testes but also are produced by the adrenal glands and in small amounts by the ovaries. The most important androgen is *testosterone*. This steroid hormone is secreted by the *Leydig cells* of the interstitial tissue of the testis.

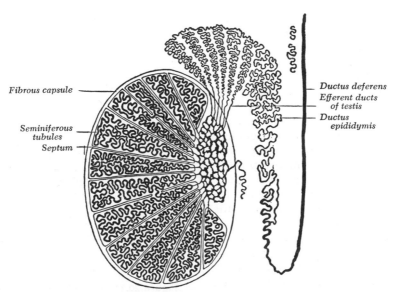

Figure 20.9 Arrangement of the seminiferous tubules and the excretory ducts in the testis and epididymis. (From Bloom and Fawcett.)

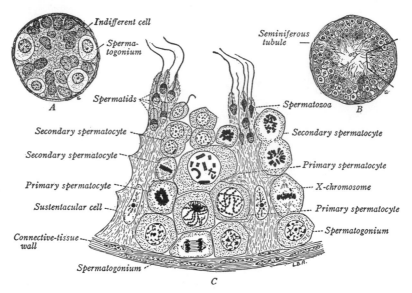

Figure 20.10 Human seminiferous tubules in transverse section. *A*, Newborn (× 400). *B*, Adult (× 155). *C*, Detail of the area outlined in *B* (× 900). (Arey.)

The control of androgen production is vested in the adenohypophysis. ICSH is a necessary stimulant to the Leydig cells. The mechanism is basically the same "negative feedback" principle described for other endocrine glands. A decrease in testosterone results in a decrease in gonadotrophin secretion, and castration results in increased pituitary gonadotrophic activity.

The primary sexual characteristics are the production of mature sperm and the capability of erection and ejaculation. Secondary sexual characteristics are the full growth of the penis, the "stepwise" development of the hair pattern of the male body (pubic hair first, and then axillary, facial, thoracic, scapular, pinnal, and nasal hair in order), the enlargement of the larynx, which accounts for the lower pitch of the male voice, and the psychosexual male behavior pattern. These characteristics, except for the last one, are entirely dependent upon androgens for development and maintenance.

The reproductive passageways and accessory male reproductive organs are greatly influenced by androgens. Testosterone also has a general effect on the body metabolism in that it promotes protein anabolism and a positive nitrogen balance. The influence of androgens is one of the underlying mechanisms for the distinguishing pattern of muscular development in the adolescent male.

Reproductive Passageways. The structures forming the efferent ducts consist of the epididymides, the deferent ducts, the ejaculatory ducts, and the urethra. All these structures are paired except the urethra (Figs. 17.6, 20.8, 20.11).

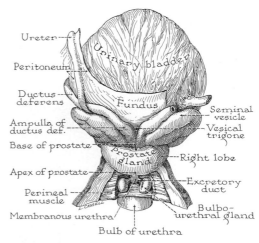

Figure 20.11 Posterior view of bladder in male, showing seminal vesicles, ductus deferens, and prostate gland. (Modified after Spalteholz.)

EPIDIDYMIS. The epididymis is an elongated body lying along the upper and posterior parts of the testis. It has a large upper portion, or head, and narrower body and tail. The efferent ducts of the testis fuse to form the single ductus epididymis, which is a highly convoluted canal 4 to 6 meters in length. Near the lower pole of the organ the duct straightens out and connects with the ductus deferens.

DUCTUS DEFERENS. The ductus deferens is a thick-walled tube about 45 cm. long, extending from the epididymis to the ejaculatory duct. It ascends in the scrotum and passes through the inguinal canal to enter the abdominal cavity. Under cover of the peritoneum it crosses the brim of the pelvis and passes to the inferior surface of the bladder, where it ends by uniting with the duct of the seminal vesicle to form the ejaculatory duct. The ductus deferens, the spermatic artery, vein, and nerves, together with the surrounding membranes, form the spermatic cord. The *spermatic cord* extends from the testis and epididymis through the inguinal canal to the internal inguinal ring on the inner wall of the abdomen.

EJACULATORY DUCT. The ejaculatory duct arises from the union of the ductus deferens and the duct of the seminal vesicle. It is a short, straight tube that pierces the prostate gland to open into the floor of the urethra at the side of the urethral crest.

URETHRA. The urethra, which in the male belongs to both the urinary and the reproductive system, is discussed on page 325. It is divided into three parts by the pelvic wall: the first portion is above the pelvic floor and is surrounded by the prostate gland; the second, or membranous, portion pierces the pelvic wall; the third portion traverses the penis (see Fig. 17.6, p. 326).

Auxiliary Structures

SEMINAL VESICLES. (Fig. 20.8) The seminal vesicles are two tortuous pouches developed as evaginations from the ductus deferens. They are placed between the bladder and the rectum. They elaborate a thick, alkaline, globulin-containing secretion that is added to the spermatozoa during ejaculation.

PROSTATE GLAND. (Figs. 20.8, 20.11) The prostate gland lies beneath the bladder and surrounds the first portion of the urethra. It is pyramidal in shape, with its base above in contact with the inferior surface of the bladder and its apex directed downward. The prostate gland is an aggregate of about forty tubuloalveolar glands widely separated from each other by smooth muscular and dense fibrous tissue, so that the organ is one-half glandular, one-quarter smooth muscle and one-quarter fibrous tissue. Around the urethra the smooth muscle fibers form a ring that is called the internal sphincter of the bladder. The ducts of the glands open into the urethra.

BULBOURETHRAL GLANDS. (Fig. 20.11) These are two small glands that lie on either side of the membranous urethra. They open into the cavernous urethra near its origin. The secretion, which is slimy and viscid, lubricates the urethra.

PENIS. (Fig. 20.8). The penis is composed of three cylinders of cavernous tissue, called the *corpora cavernosa*. Two of them, the corpora cavernosa penis, form the dorsal and upper part of the organ, the third, the corpus cavernosum urethrae, lies in a groove below the other two. The two *corpora cavernosa penis* separate posteriorly to be attached, one on either side, to the descending ramus of the pubis. The *corpus cavernosum urethrae* begins at the pelvic floor with the urethral bulb and is traversed throughout its length by the urethra. It ends in a cone-shaped expansion, the *glans penis*. The *bulbocavernous muscle* surrounds the urethral bulb. The circular fold of skin reflected over the glans is called the foreskin or *prepuce*. The tissue of the cavernous bodies of the penis is the erectile tissue. It is spongelike, with large vascular spaces interposed between arteries and veins.

Composition and Course of Semen.

The semen contains spermatozoa and seminal fluid, made up of the secretions of the epididymides, the ductili deferentia, the prostate, the seminal vesicles, and bulbourethral glands. The latter three contribute the most important part of the secretion from both a qualitative and a quantitative point of view. The seminal fluid is responsible for providing nutrition and a means of transport for the spermatozoa.

Semen is a thick, whitish fluid of high viscosity. It has a specific gravity of about 1.028 and a pH of about 7.4. It contains buffer systems (phosphate and bicarbonate) that protect the sperm from the acid pH of the vagina. Seminal fluid coagulates within seconds after ejaculation, but is liquefied a few minutes later by its own enzyme systems so that the sperm are freed. The average volume of seminal fluid per ejaculation in the mature male is about 3 ml. Each ejaculation may produce between 250 and 350 million sperm. There is a great deal of individual variation in sperm counts. Spermatozoa counts as low as 20 million per ml. have resulted in fertilization; a count below 60 million, however, is considered as possibly infertile.

The spermatozoa, which are formed in the testes, pass slowly through the epididymis and may remain in the tail of the epididymis for several months. Here they are nourished and reach maturity. The ductus deferens serves for rapid transport of the sperm. The wavelike contractions of its muscular walls, together with the action of the bulbocavernous muscle and muscular tissue of the prostate gland, produce discharge of the semen through the urethra, the process of ejaculation. Seminal vesicles, prostate gland, and bulbourethral glands add their secretions at the proper time.

Sperm usually move (a "swimming" type of movement) at about 3 mm. per minute. Two hours after ejaculation normal sperm can still travel at a rate of about 0.5 mm. per minute, and they retain some motility even after 24 hours.

Reproductive Physiology. Early adolescence, which includes puberty, is the period during which both primary and secondary sex characteristics are developed. Puberty ends with the maturing of the reproductive organs and male germ cells. After loss of testicular hormones as a result of accident, surgery, or disease these sex characteristics are lost in varying degree and the reproductive system reverts to a preadolescent state. However, the psychosexual pattern of behavior, including the desire and ability to copulate, often may persist. The mechanism and capability of erection and ejaculation survive castration, even though the penis is reduced in size. Spermatogenesis, however, does not survive in such cases.

MECHANISM OF ERECTION. Erection is the stiffening of a flaccid penis. It is basically a cardiovascular event that is controlled by the central nervous system. It is brought about by neuromuscular events that simultaneously increase the amount of blood entering the organ and decrease the rate at which blood is allowed to leave it. The increased arterial flow is accomplished by active dilatation of the arterioles. The decreased venous drainage is a passive event that results from a compression of the sinuses by the expanding cavernous bodies, and from the deformation of the funnel-shaped valves in the venules. The entire process is reversed by the sudden constriction of the arterioles that accompanies ejaculation.

Erection may be produced reflexly by tactile stimulation of the penis or of the erogenous zone that surrounds it. Reflex erection may be produced in animals, including man, that have undergone complete spinal cord section (see p. 83). In man, erection is most often evoked by stimuli of psychic origin.

MECHANISM OF EJACULATION. Ejaculation is actually two events. The first, properly called emission, is the contraction of the smooth muscle of the internal reproductive organs, which moves the semen into the prostatic urethra. The second event, ejaculation *per se*, is brought about by the contraction of the bulbocavernous muscle, which propels the semen into and through the distal segments of the urethra and out of the penis through the external urethra orifice at its end.

Ejaculation is a reflex event that may be inhibited by higher centers. The afferent limb of the reflex arises in sensory receptors located mainly in the glans penis. The nerve impulses reach the spinal cord by way of the internal pudendal nerves. The efferent limb of the reflex originates in ventral horn cells in the lumbar cord. The efferent pathway is through the lumbar sympathetic trunk (hypogastric plexus) and the hypogastric nerves, and terminates in the smooth muscle of the seminal vesicles and vasa deferentia, and in the bulbocavernous muscle. This musculature is activated in an orderly sequence to produce first emission and then ejaculation.

Ejaculation is accompanied by a great deal of sensory and neuromuscular activity. The combination of sensory and motor events is called *orgasm*. It is accompanied by an increase in heart rate, in arterial pressure, and in pulmonary ventilation. The neuromuscular mechanisms that control erection, emission, and ejaculation become refractory for a variable period of time following orgasm.

QUESTIONS FOR DISCUSSION

1. Explain the time relations of ovulation and menstruation.

2. Trace the cyclic changes in the endometrium from the first to the twenty-eighth day. Correlate these changes with the action of ovarian and pituitary hormones.

3. What hormone interactions are responsible for proper development of the female reproductive system?

4. Distinguish between puberty, menstruation, climacteric, and menopause.

5. Trace the course of the spermatozoa from their origin in the testes to their discharge in ejaculation. Refer to Figures 17.6 and 20.8.

6. What glands add secretions to the spermatozoa, and what is the function of each secretion?

7. What hormone interaction is responsible for proper development of the male reproductive system?

8. Between what two points do the urinary system and the reproductive system occupy a common pathway in the male? In the female?

9. List three causes of infertility in the male.

DEVELOPMENT OF THE HUMAN BODY

**CHAPTER
TWENTY-ONE**

CHARACTERISTICS OF DEVELOPMENT

The development of the human body involves an orderly sequence of changes that progressively increase the complexity of cellular organization and function. The pattern begins with differentiation of cells which are in a dynamic equilibrium in terms of a nuclear system, a cytoplasmic system, and an environmental system. The destiny of a particular cell is determined chemically *(chemodifferentiation)* before visible changes occur. The observable changes *(cytodifferentiation)* are followed by the aggregation of various cell types into tissues *(histodifferentiation)*. Various nucleocytoplasmic relationships, cytoplasmic feedback loops, and gene combinations become operative during mitosis. The daughter cells may be presented with different amounts of changing *microenvironments*. The microenvironment includes the position of an individual cell and its contacts with adjacent cells and matrix containing active micromolecules and macromolecules.

The properties of a particular cell depend largely upon the kinetics of production of its group of macromolecules (Fig. 21.1). There may be thousands of macromolecules in a cell. The primary protein nature of the macromolecule is determined by the sequence of amino acids in its structure. The secondary protein nature of these macromolecules refers to the electrochemical interaction of peptide linkages with the formation of helices and side chains (Fig. 3.2). The tertiary characteristics of the macromolecules appear with the total disposition of the polypeptide chain in the formation of collagen (p. 49) or globular proteins. Finally the

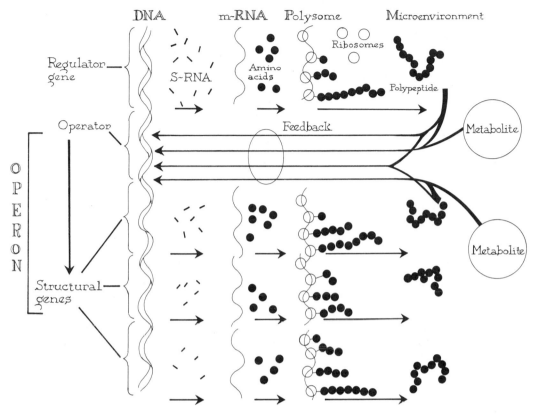

Figure 21.1 Kinetics of protein synthesis.

macromolecules may be associated with nonprotein groups such as heme in hemoglobin (p. 258). Protein synthesis occurs in cytoplasm in relation to the *polysomes* or *polyribosomes*. A long strand of DNA-like RNA (m-RNA) with collections of itinerant ribosomes "read" the information necessary to synthesize a polypeptide chain. The protein of a DNA molecule of the chromosome in the nucleus which specifies a single polypeptide chain is called a *structural gene*. A short initiating segment of the chromosome is an *operator*. If a protein contains several polypeptide chains

the operator and structural genes requisite to its formation are designated as an *operon*. *Regulator genes* enhance or depress the nearby structural genes. Figure 21.1 illustrates the kinetics of protein synthesis.

Interaction of some of the features in differentiation may be indicated as shown at the bottom of the page.

Development also involves the growth of groups of cells. This change of the cellular aggregate may result from mitosis and the increase in the number of cells. Growth may also occur by increases in the

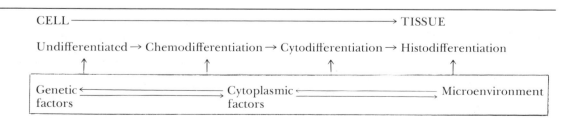

size of the cells and in the quantity of intercellular material. All of these features of growth depend upon a synthesis of protoplasm that results in a permanent enlargement of the total cell mass. Growth is regulated in several ways. The genetic constitution governs synthesis of macromolecules as shown in Figure 21.1. An adequate nutrient supply is necessary to provide the raw materials for growth. As the organism grows its volume increases faster than its surface area so that an optimal ratio of surface to volume is established for the continuation of growth. Cytogenetic errors in protein formation (p. 405), limitations on the supply of nutrition, and wildly growing masses of tumor cells may have adverse effects upon growth and development.

It appears that some system exists that informs the cell about the state of the total mass or growth product of an organ. If part of a kidney or liver has been removed, circulating molecules from the remaining tissue effect an increase in the size of the intact liver or kidney cells. A circulating growth factor has been identified in the salivary glands that will increase the size of the sensory and sympathetic ganglia under experimental conditions.

Morphogenesis is the assumption of a new shape or the generation of form. The changes which result in the development of an organ, the embryonic body, or the fetus require movements of cells, differential growth, and selective cell death. The specific cell contains those genetically determined macromolecules that characterize it as unique in its participation in the process of morphogenesis. Remodeling and reshaping of form of parts of the body occur throughout life. Details of prenatal morphogenesis are given in the next section of this chapter.

PRENATAL DEVELOPMENT

The account of development here followed is that generally held to be true of man. Many conclusions are based upon studies of prenatal processes in avian and amphibian forms.

Gametogenesis. The development of the human body is initiated by the union of two *haploid* sex cells, the egg and the sperm (Fig. 21.2). These specialized cells are the result of maturation (p. 37) of the *diploid* generative cells or gametes contained in the male and female gonads (Figs. 20.10, 20.2). In development the gonad is bisexually organized into a cen-

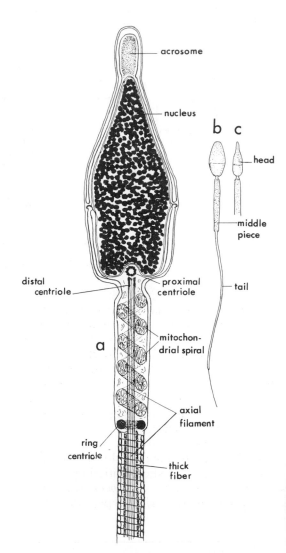

Figure 21.2 A mammalian spermatozoon. *a*, Semidiagrammatic drawing (redrawn after an electron micrograph by Burgos and Fawcett: J. Biophys. & Biochem. Cytol., 1955.) *b, c,* The same, as seen in the light microscope; the head is seen from the flattened side in *b* and from the narrow side in *c*. (From Balinsky: Introduction to Embryology. 2nd ed., 1965.)

tral medulla and peripheral cortex. Primordial germinal cells migrate from the yolk sac (Fig. 21.6) into the gonad early in embryonic development. In the male the medullary tissue persists in the seminiferous tubules of the testes as the site of *spermatogenesis*. In the female the cortical tissue predominates and *oogenesis* occurs in the ovarian follicles. The transformation of embryonic gonads into physiologically mature ovaries or testes is believed to depend initially upon estrogens and androgens respectively. The maintenance of gametogenesis utilizes particularly the pituitary-gonadal interactions previously described in Chapter 20.

Fertilization and Sex Determination. Fertilization involves the penetration of the ovum by the spermatozoon and the union of the nucleus of the spermatozoon with the nucleus of the ovum. The human ovum has twenty-three chromosomes, and the spermatozoon has the same number; thus, at fertilization the chromosome number, which is forty-six, is restored. Fertilization takes place in the outer third of the uterine tube. The ovum escapes from the surface of the ovary and enters the uterine tube. Spermatozoa deposited in the vaginal tract of the female make their way through the cavity of the uterus and out into the tubes. The acrosome of the sperm produces lysins or enzymatic substances that dissolve the surface coverings of the ovum. An acrosomal filament aids the spermatozoon in penetrating the ovum. The head, middle piece, and tail of the spermatozoon enter the ovum. A change occurs in the surface of the cytoplasm following penetration of the ovum, which prevents the entry of additional spermatozoa. Ribosomes become very active and new types of macromolecules appear in the cytoplasm of the *zygote*.

The head soon undergoes development into a typical nucleus called the *male pronucleus*. It looks very much like the egg nucleus, which is now called the *female pronucleus*. As soon as the female and male pronuclei are formed, they come together and fuse to form a single nucleus called the *segmentation nucleus*. The chromatin granules of the segmentation nucleus form chromonemata, and the chromonemata

separate into forty-six chromosomes. The nuclear membrane disappears and the chromosomes lie free in the cytoplasm. While these changes are occurring a spindle has formed between the centrosomes, and the chromosomes of the segmentation nucleus mingle in the equatorial plane. This brings the fertilization of the zygote to an end. In maturation of the gametes the chromosome number is halved so that the ovum and polar bodies contain 22 + X (haploid number). Maturation of one spermatogonium results in two haploid spermatozoa with a chromosome number of 22 + X and two haploid spermatozoa with a chromosome number of 22 + Y. When a spermatozoon with a haploid number of 22 + X fertilizes an ovum with a haploid number of 22 + X, the restored diploid number is 44 + XX and the individual is a female (Fig. 21.3, *A*); if, on the other hand, a spermatozoon with a haploid number of 22 + Y fertilizes an ovum, 22 + X, the diploid number becomes 44 + XY and a male is the result (Fig. 21.3, *B*).

Cytogenetics. The characteristics of individuals can be described in terms of their chromosomal composition, i.e., the *karyotype* (Fig. 21.3). The karyotype represents the cell, the individual, and the species. The *genotype* describes the genetic composition of all the genes of the karyotype. The outward manifestation of the hereditary constitution of the individual is referred to as the *phenotype*.

In an earlier section we learned that there are 46 chromosomes in man (p. 35) and that the gene which transmits hereditary characteristics is a subdivision or segment of a DNA molecule. Techniques for separating and spreading out chromosomes for study are now available. Twenty-three pairs (46 ÷ 2 = 23) of linked homologous chromosomes have been numbered according to shape and size (Fig. 21.3). Twenty-two of the pairs are *autosomes*, that is, somatic chromosomes, not sex chromosomes. The other pair, XX in the female and XY in the male, are sex chromosomes. One homologue of each pair comes from each parent. Many different genes are located on each chromosome. The genes in each chromosome also exist in pairs;

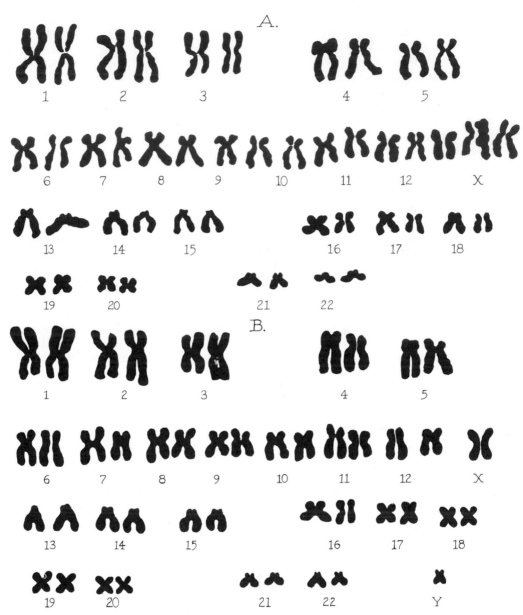

Figure 21.3 Karyotypes. *A*, female; *B*, male.

these are called *allelic pairs*, each member being an *allele*. Genes that lie on different chromosomes are distributed independently. Mendel's law of segregation states that a pair of genes can be separated during the reduction division of meiosis, so that a gamete contains only one gene of a pair, the other going to another gamete. This law of segregation or separation states that one gene of a pair can be trans-

mitted without contamination or mixing with the other genes. Later it was demonstrated by Morgan that linkage occurs forming combinations of two or more allelic pairs on the same chromosome and that there is separation of the linked genes, with one linkage going to one gamete and the other to another. Linked genes, however, do not always remain together. Sometimes paired chromosomes may exchange segments as they lie side by side during the reduction division, since chromosomes may break at almost any point. The resulting fragments of a chromosome may then join with fragments from its homologue if the homologue has broken in the same place or places; such exchange is known as *crossover*.

To summarize the means by which genes are inherited, we have shown that (1) single genes on different chromosomes can be inherited in accordance with the principle of segregation or separation during meiosis; (2) genes that are linked together are inherited together unless (3) the chromosome breaks into segments which allows for exchange of separated links and new combinations of inherited characteristics.

INHERITED CHARACTERISTICS. The genes for inherited traits may be carried by sex chromosomes or by somatic chromosomes. They determine visual expression of parental characteristics such as color of the eyes, skin, and stature as well as the genotype of the individual.

Knowing that a gene is a segment or subdivision of DNA helps us to understand the molecular basis of genetics. Since DNA serves as a template for RNA, which in turn is involved in synthesis of specific proteins including enzymes, a highly effective mechanism exists for continuity of inheritance of traits from one generation to another (Fig. 21.1).

MUTATIONS AND ABERRATIONS. Undesirable changes in genetic composition may occur and these may even be fatal. Since many of these changes are associated with recessive characteristics, frequently with the female gamete, they are the exception rather than the rule; a condition transmitted by an X chromosome would be likely to appear only when an X chromosome of a male carried the other homologous allele.

Anomalies of the X and Y chromosomes may result in aberrations in the gametes. If a pair of chromosomes fail to separate during the reduction division of a female gamete, the mature ovum may carry two X chromosomes while another ovum has none. Thus in fertilization a sperm carrying an X chromosome may join with an XX

ovum so that the zygote, i.e., the fertilized ovum, will contain three X chromosomes; if the sperm carries a Y chromosome, an XXY zygote results. If the sperm carrying an X chromosome joins with an ovum without an X chromosome, the zygote is XO; if the sperm carries a Y, the zygote is YO, which is a lethal combination. These aberrations result in clinical manifestations, which are described as clinical syndromes.

Turner's syndrome results from the XO zygote. The individual is female in appearance (since no Y chromosome is present) but the female sexual organs and secondary sexual characteristics are rudimentary or fail to develop. If the fertilization results in XXY, the person appears to be a nearly normal male, but the seminiferous tubules fail to develop and spermatogenesis does not occur. This is known as Klinefelter's syndrome. Other aberrations may occur, such as XXX, XXXY (48 chromosomes) and XXXXY (49 chromosomes). These combinations are frequently associated with impaired intelligence or with mongolism.

The sex chromosomes carry genes that are not involved in sex determination. These genes may be responsible for such conditions as hemophilia, color blindness, night blindness, retinitis, optic atrophy, cleft palate, harelip, and sickle cell anemia.

Certain conditions have been associated with anomalies of the autosomes. For example, the presence of three chromosomes (trisomy) in chromosome "pair" number 21 is associated with Down's syndrome, i.e., mongolism. Anomalies affecting pair numbers 16 to 18 are associated with skull deformation and malformation of the external ear.

Chromosomal aberrations may also result from loss of a whole chromosome or a piece of a chromosome. This is called disintegration. Alterations in the chemical structure of a nucleoprotein may be responsible for mutations. Other inherited characteristics develop only in the presence of a sex hormone; these are called sex limited characteristics.

When mutations or aberrations are associated with gametes these conditions are inherited. When aberrations occur in somatic cells, the aberrations are present in all cells derived from mitotic division of such somatic cells.

Pre-embryonic Phase. Segmentation or *cleavage* of the fertilized zygote by rapid mitoses yields two, four, eight, sixteen, thirty-two celled aggregates and finally a *morula*, or mass of small cells (Fig. 21.4). With ensuing mitoses the morula is transformed into a *blastocyst* of loosely packed adherent cells in the shape of a hollow sphere. Cells of the blastocyst are high in DNA content. There is a rapid increase in the cellular surfaces, and the regional differences of the cytoplasm of the fertilized zygote become parcellated to groups of cells. Individual cells of the blastocyst manifest pulsatile activity and movement. New ribosomes and macromolecules are being formed. The microenvironment is changing as new cellular associations are bringing about further differentiation. Within fourteen days the primary germ layers and presumptive organ rudiments appear (Figs. 21.5, 21.6). Differentiation of the blastocyst produces a *presomite embryo* and *extraembryonic membranes* as shown in (Fig. 21.6, *c, d, e*).

During the development of the morula, the mass gradually moves down the uterine tube toward the uterus. The first change appearing in the morula is its differentiation into an outer layer and an inner mass. The outer layer is the *trophoblast*, which plays an important part in the nutrition of the embryo. The *inner cell mass* soon separates into three portions, the ectoderm, entoderm, and primary mesoderm. During the period of growth of the primary mesoderm, *cavities* appear in the ectoderm and entoderm segments, converting them into hollow vesicles. These changes are shown in Figure 21.5. The ectoderm vesicle is the amniotic cavity. The entodermal vesicle is the yolk sac. Primary

mesoderm fills in between the trophoblast and the ectoderm and entoderm. The cellular area of contact between the amniotic cavity and the yolk sac is called the embryonic area or disc. The primary mesoderm is reduced to a thin layer that lines the trophoblast and covers the outer surfaces of the walls of the amniotic cavity and yolk sac. The cavity formed is called the extraembryonic coelom.

PRESOMITE EMBRYO. The embryonic area is a flat plate that is circular in outline when first seen, but later changes to an oval form as growth continues (Fig. 21.6, *c*). It is composed essentially of epithelial layers of ectoderm and entoderm. The posterior end of the oval is marked by a line, the primitive streak. The *primitive streak* is a thickened ridge of cells that grows outward from the ectoderm and projects against the entoderm. Immediately after the formation of the primitive streak, a groove and two folds or ridges appear in the anterior part of the disc. These structures mark the beginnings of the nervous system and are called the *neural groove* and *neural folds*, respectively. They are formed by an infolding of the ectoderm layer; gradually the edges of the folds come together, and the loop of ectodermal cells is pinched off and comes to lie below the surface. This tube or cylinder of cells is called the *neural tube*; the anterior end develops into the brain, the posterior portion into the spinal cord.

Two important structures that develop from the primitive streak are the notochord and the secondary mesoderm (Fig. 21.6, *d*). The *notochord* develops by a proliferation of cells from the anterior end of the primitive streak. It serves as a primitive body axis about which the vertebral column is later constructed. The *secondary mesoderm* is the embryonic mesoderm,

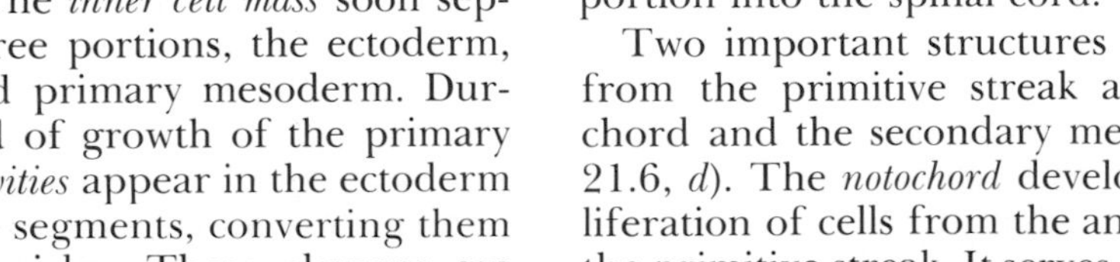

a   b   c   d

Figure 21.4 Segmentation of the blastocyst. *a*, Ovum in pronuclear stage. *b*, Two-cell stage. *c*, Four-cell stage. *d*, Solid sphere of cells, the morula mass.

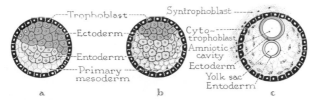

Figure 21.5 Diagram of the early differentiation of the blastocyst. Here *a* and *b* show the inner cell mass separated into ectoderm and primary mesoderm. In *c*, cavities have formed in the ectoderm and entoderm.

which enters into the formation of the body of the embryo. The secondary mesoderm develops by a proliferation of the cells of the primitive streak, which move out between the ectoderm and entoderm layers to form a continuous sheet of cells in the embryonic disc on either side of the median plane (Fig. 21.6, *e*).

Embryonic Phase. With differentiation of the mesoderm (Figs. 21.7, 21.8) into somites, intermediate mesoderm, and lateral mesoderm, development enters the embryonic phase. The somites continue to develop into segmentally arranged cartilage and bone, skeletal muscles, and dermis of the skin. Intermediate mesoderm contributes to the formation of the urogenital and vascular structures. The somite stage extends from the twentieth to thirtieth day of development and the embryo measures about 5 mm. from crown to rump at the termination of the somite stage. During the second month the embryo assumes the characteristics of human form (Fig. 21.9).

Numerous tissue interactions occur during *organogenesis* as the embryo develops. There does not appear to be any single inductive agent responsible for the myriad of changes in morphogenesis.

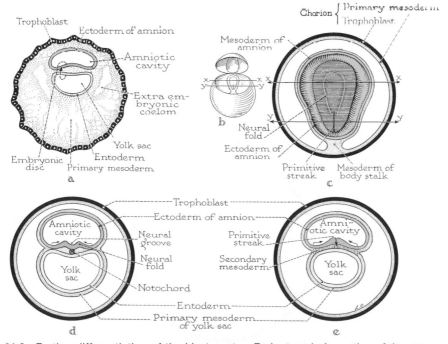

Figure 21.6 Further differentiation of the blastocyst. *a*, Early stage in formation of the extra-embryonic celom. *b*, Indicates how cut is made through blastocyst to obtain view shown in *c. c*, Diagram of dorsal surface of embryonic area after removal of part of the chorion and part of the amnion. *d*, Shows plan of the blastocyst cut through *yy* in the region of the primitive streak.

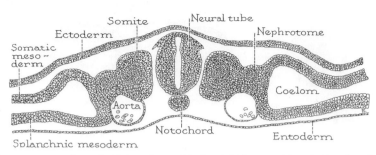

Figure 21.7 Transverse section of chick embryo at forty-eight hours of incubation (semi-diagrammatic).

Certain areas of entodermal and ectodermal epithelium require the presence of mesenchyme, i.e., formation of the kidney, pancreas, thyroid, salivary gland, thymus, and skin is the result of interaction of the epithelium and mesenchyme. The induction of these changes may work in one direction only, i.e., the epithelium may not influence the mesenchyme. Such one way induction occurs in the development of the pancreas by evagination of duodenal entoderm in the presence of mesenchyme from any part of the embryo. However, only precardiac mesoderm is believed to be responsible for the symmetrical development of the heart. The continued development of motor neurons of the spinal cord requires the presence of skeletal muscle at the periphery. In the formation of body structures such as the eye and the limb buds reciprocal tissue induction produces the final form. The lens of the eye is developed in the ectoderm of the optic placode (Fig. 21.9) as a result of contact with the optic vesicles of the forebrain. The corneal epithelium is produced by the interaction of ectoderm and lens.

Remodeling and replacing of tissues occurs throughout life and it is particularly striking during development. The kidney begins as a pronephros and a wolffian duct in intermediate mesoderm. The pronephros is replaced by the mesonephros. In final form the kidney develops from the metanephros and a ureteric bud. The wolffian duct is incorporated into the male excretory ducts as part of the epididymis, ductus deferens, and ejaculatory duct. Cellular death is also necessary for portions of morphogenesis. Such a process is conspicuous in the formation of extremities, particularly the digits, from the limb buds (Fig. 21.9). Selective growth is occurring during embryonic development so that parts of certain structures mature more rapidly than others. The external

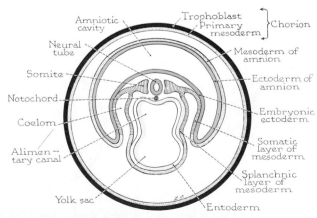

Figure 21.8 Transverse section of blastocyst, showing differentiation of mesoderm and extension of amnion.

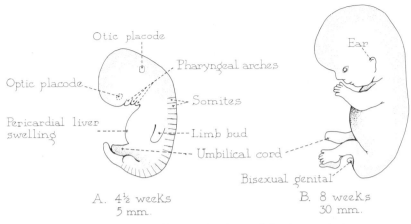

Figure 21.9 Embryonic phase of development.

remodeling of the face, which reflects tissue interaction and replacement, cellular death, and selective growth, is illustrated in Figure 21.10.

Fetal Phase. This phase of development extends from the beginning of the third month of intrauterine life to birth. Differentiation of tissues is of minor significance. Rapid growth of the established organs occurs. During the third month the face assumes a more human look (Fig. 21.10). The eyes shift from a lateral to a medial position and the ears assume their final location at the side of the face. Arms and legs reach their relative length as compared to the body. Sex of the fetus can be distinguished as compared to the bisexual primordia (Fig. 21.9). In the fourth and fifth months the length of the fetus develops rapidly and bodily movements begin. During the remaining four months of the fetal period the body weight increases. Subcutaneous fat is deposited, and the sebaceous glands secrete the thick white vernix caseosa that covers the body. Basic neuronal reflexes are present at

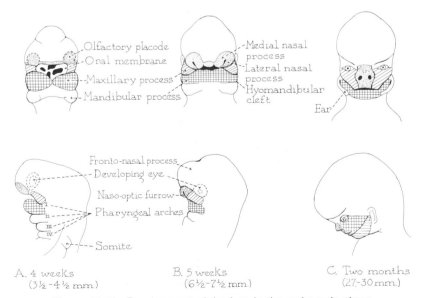

Figure 21.10 Development of the face in the embryonic phase.

seven months and survival is possible with premature birth. However, lung development is incomplete, temperature regulation poor, and reserves of fat, calcium, potassium, and iron are low; therefore, survival is difficult. By the ninth month the fetus measures close to 50 cm. and weighs about 3200 Gm. The testes have descended into the scrotum, and the umbilical cord is attached near the center of the abdominal wall.

Protection and Nourishment of the Embryo and Fetus. The embryo is protected and nourished during development (Figs. 21.8, 21.11). It grows in a bag of watery *amniotic fluid*. The *amniotic wall* of the bag is composed of an inner layer of ectoderm and an outer layer of mesoderm. Covering the amnion, the *chorion* is formed by the trophoblast and primary mesoderm. Chorionic *villi* containing blood vessels develop in the chorion. As the embryonic mass grows, it moves downward in the uterine tube and at the end of eight to ten days reaches the uterus. The uterine mucosa is in the premenstrual condition induced by progesterone of the

corpus luteum. The trophoblast first attaches to the uterine epithelium and then through the secretion of a cytolytic enzyme proceeds to destroy it. The trophoblast sinks into the uterine wall and becomes embedded in the mucosa, which grows over it. This process is called *implantation*. The mucosa of the pregnant uterus is named the *decidua*. Three regions of this thickened membrane can be recognized at an early stage. They are the decidua parietalis, or general lining of the uterus, exclusive of the embryonic area; decidua basalis, the region between the chorionic sac and the muscular wall of the uterus; and decidua capsularis, a portion that covers the embedded embryo. Figure 21.11 shows a section of the uterus in early pregnancy.

The young embryo is connected with the inner surface of the chorion by the body stalk. The chorionic villi in this area enlarge, penetrating deeply into the uterine wall and establishing intimate connections with blood spaces. Villi on other parts of the chorion soon disappear. The structures composing the decidua basalis and the chorionic villi embedded in it con-

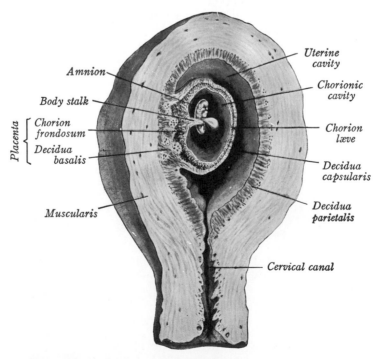

Figure 21.11 Section of uterus in early pregnancy. (From Arey.)

stitute the *placenta* or nutritive organ of the embryo. The body stalk of the young embryo becomes narrowed down and elongated to form the umbilical cord. In it run the blood vessels that connect the embryo with the chorionic villi. Through the walls of the villi interchanges of food and waste between mother and embryo are effected (see p. 291). There is, however, no actual mingling of the blood of the embryo with the blood of the mother; all interchanges take place through the walls of the villi by means of such physiochemical processes as filtration, diffusion, osmosis, and active transport mechanisms.

The placenta produces the *chorionic gonadotrophin* (CG) hormone and steroids with estrogenic and progesteronic activity. Chorionic gonadotrophin is secreted by the inner layer of the chorion, or cytotrophoblast (Fig. 21.5), while estrogens and progesterone are secreted by the syntrophoblast (Fig. 21.5), or outer layer of the chorion of the placenta. A peak secretion of CG is reached about twenty days after implantation of the embryo in the uterus. This is maintained for about a week and then declines to a lower, constant level for the remainder of pregnancy. Corpus luteum persists under the stimulation of CG. The placenta and corpus luteum augment the effects of one another through the synergistic action of the estrogens and progesterones, which they both produce to promote the changes necessary in the reproductive structures for the protection and nutrition of the embryo. Detection of CG in urine forms the basis of certain pregnancy tests. Late in pregnancy the estrogens sensitize the uterus to the action of oxytocins from the pituitary gland.

PARTURITION

Delivery of the baby occurs approximately two hundred seventy days following fertilization. The cause of the onset of labor is obscure. Placental estrogen and progesterone levels decline antecedent to parturition. The myometrium has been sensitized to oxytocin stimulation for con-

traction. When contractions of the uterus begin, genital tract stimulation causes a reflex secretion of oxytocin and delivery proceeds by means of spinal reflexes reinforced by voluntary contraction of abdominal muscles.

Onset of labor:

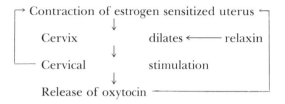

Continuation of labor:

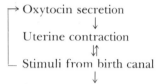

Reflex and voluntary abdominal contraction.

POSTNATAL GROWTH

At birth the skull possesses fontanels that have permitted molding of the fetal head in parturition (p. 164). Facial and mastoid areas are underdeveloped. The tongue is thick and flat, and the cheeks are lined with fat pads or "sucking pads." The thymus, heart, adrenal glands, and liver are proportionally large. The lungs are small and alveolar development is incomplete. The urinary bladder is located in the abdomen rather than in the pelvic cavity. The special sensory organs are functional at birth although hearing is dull until amniotic fluid drains from the middle ear. The important sensory and association pathways of the nervous system are myelinated, and reflex mechanisms, except superficial ones, are operant. The long pyramidal motor pathways myelinate between ten and fifteen months after birth. The reflex mechanisms of the newborn emphasize stimulation of the perioral area and trigeminal and facial nerves involved in rooting and sucking. Grasp, startle, and plantar reflexes are well established at birth. Sequential motor activity occurs with progressive maturation of the nervous system, such as sitting with support at four months and walking alone at fifteen months. Morphogenesis from birth through adolescence modifies the "immaturity" of the neonatal structures to an adult form and function, the study of which has been the essential focus of this book.

QUESTIONS FOR DISCUSSION

1. On the basis of study of the entire body, what factors do you think are most important in regulating the development of the human body? Why?

2. Explain the role played in development by the following hormones: androgens, chorionic gonadotrophin, oxytocin, estrogens, progesterone.

3. Review fetal circulation. Discuss the significance of the placenta in terms of an endocrine and vascular structure.

4. Describe the details of organogenesis of one or more of the following: eye, kidney, palate, heart, pancreas, ear, diaphragm, spinal cord, lung, adrenal gland.

What are some congenital defects in relation to these structures?

5. What factors determine maleness? Femaleness?

6. Discuss one or more of these cytogenetic abnormalities: Turner's syndrome, Down's syndrome, Klinefelter's syndrome, phenylketonuria.

7. What might be some of the problems of survival of a premature infant?

INDEX